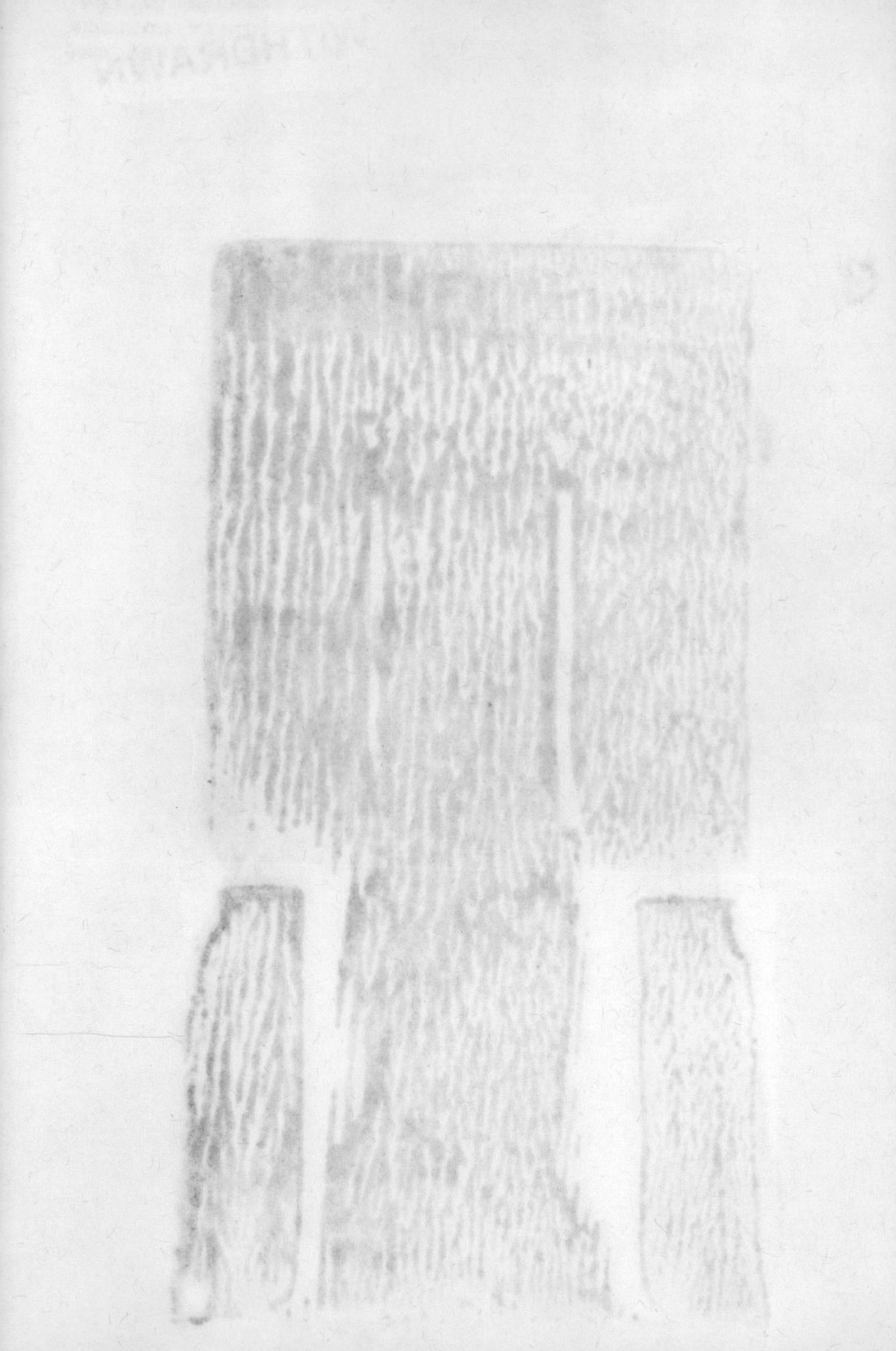

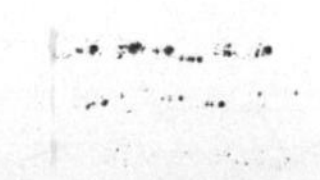

ANATOMY OF THE CAT

BY

JACOB REIGHARD

Professor Emeritus of Zoölogy in the University of Michigan

AND

H. S. JENNINGS

Henry Walters Professor of Zoölogy in the Johns Hopkins University

WITH

ONE HUNDRED AND SEVENTY-THREE
ORIGINAL FIGURES

DRAWN BY

LOUISE BURRIDGE JENNINGS

THIRD AND ENLARGED EDITION
WITH FOUR NEW FIGURES

BY

RUSH ELLIOTT, PH.D.

Professor of Anatomy, Department of Zoology,
and Dean, College of Arts and Sciences, Ohio University

HOLT, RINEHART AND WINSTON
New York · Chicago · San Francisco
Toronto · London

OCTOBER. 1966

(27394-0115)

PRINTED IN THE
UNITED STATES OF AMERICA

PREFACE TO THE THIRD EDITION.

DURING thirty-three years of increasing use of this book the authors have received occasional suggestions from teachers that it be revised so as to include recent additions to our knowledge of cat anatomy. They have been fortunate in persuading Dr. Rush Elliott to undertake this labor which has long lain outside their own special fields of interest. He has brought to it a knowledge of both human and mammalian anatomy and of neurology, together with ten years of abundant and recent experience in intensive use of the book with laboratory classes. The senior author has coöperated with him in the undertaking.

Dr. Elliott's search of the literature has shown that only a few minor changes are necessary in the text; except in the section on the sympathetic nervous system. This has been re-written to embody the results of work of Ranson and Billingsley [1] on the cat and to bring it into line with our increasing knowledge in this field. To make the account of the sympathetic system clear the book departs from its original plan of omitting minute structure and follows current texts on human anatomy by including briefly the minute structure of that system. The original figures are retained without alteration and to them have been added four diagrammatic figures (92a, 92b, 163a, 164a) to illustrate the relations of the viscera to the pleural, pericardial and peritoneal cavities and the gross and minute structure of the sympathetic system.

The original "practical directions" for the preparation of material and for dissection have been retained with minor changes. These are directions for dissection by systems of organs and are adapted to the use of those teachers who prefer

[1] *Journal of Comparative Neurology*, Vol. XXIX, no. 4, August, 1918.

to emphasize the comparative viewpoint. But they require the use of two or more cats, while by the regional plan of dissection in common use in medical schools a single cat may be made to serve for the entire course. Expense is thus saved to the student who must pay for the material he uses, and he gains experience in the sort of procedure he will encounter in the medical dissecting room. Dr. Elliott has therefore devised a set of directions which requires the use of but one specimen and this has been added to the book. He has also added a series of tables which summarize our knowledge of certain systems of organs or system parts. These should be useful for review and for reference. Among them is a summary of the innervation of the muscles, a topic not included in the chapter on the muscles.

The original plan of including the descriptive anatomy of the cat and the directions for dissection in a single volume has been retained. It is preferred by some teachers and has the advantage of cheapness. But since very frequent reference must be made from part to part of the book there is an annoying waste of time. Much of this is saved when the **Anatomy** and the **Dissection** are in separate volumes, so that each may lie open at the pages in use. To meet the wishes of some teachers, the **Dissection** is now offered separately, as well as in combination with the **Anatomy.**

Regional dissection involves the study of all the structures of a region at one time and before the student is familiar with the systems of organs of which they are parts. Thus the particular muscles, blood vessels and nerves of a region must be dissected and studied together before their relations to other parts of the muscular, vascular and nervous systems are understood. This is apt to be difficult and confusing. To lessen the difficulty Dr. Elliott has so planned his directions that, so far as practicable, structures are traced from their origin to their peripheral distribution rather than in the reverse direction. Thus, by beginning with dissection of the back, nerves are traced peripherally from the central nervous system and arteries outward from the trunk vessels. So the unity of the structures of each organ-system becomes, to some extent, apparent. This plan has the further advantage of enabling the student to follow the text descriptions more readily, for these, particularly in the case of nerves and blood vessels, present the structures in the conventional way from origin to periphery.

The authors continue to believe that, at least for students not grounded in comparative anatomy, dissection of the cat by systems affords a better general preparation for the anatomical work of the medical school, because it sends the student to the dissecting room with a clearer understanding of the relations of the parts within each system. The regional relations of the parts of different systems are then more readily grasped. When, for instance, the student encounters the internal mammary artery regionally he can more easily "think it back" through the subclavian and the aorta to the heart if he is familiar with the circulatory system as a whole. The regional plan, on the other hand, may provide a better *technical* preparation for the premedical student versed in comparative anatomy, for it presents the structures to him in the order and in the relations in which he will probably encounter them in the dissecting room. Although the point may be debatable, both plans are now made available.

We are indebted to Professor Ranson for reading the section on the sympathetic system and for examining figures 163a and 164a.

J. R.

September 1934.

PREFACE TO THE FIRST EDITION.

ALTHOUGH the cat has long been in common use for the practical study of mammalian anatomy, a clear, correct, not too voluminous account of its structure, such as should be in the hands of students in the laboratory, has remained a desideratum. A number of works have been published on the cat, some of them of much value, yet there is none which fulfils exactly the conditions mentioned. The books which have appeared on this subject are the following:

1. Strauss-Durckheim, H. *Anatomie descriptive et comparative du Chat.* 2 vols. Paris, 1845.

2. Mivart, St. George. *The Cat:* an Introduction to the Study of Back-boned Animals, Especially Mammals. New York, 1881.

3. Wilder, Burt G., and Gage, Simon H. *Anatomical Technology as Applied to the Domestic Cat.* New York, 1882.

4. Gorham, F. P., and Tower, R. W. *A Laboratory Guide for the Dissection of the Cat.* New York, 1895.

5. Jayne, H. *Mammalian Anatomy.* Vol. I. Philadelphia, 1898.

The first of these works treats only of the muscles and bones, and is not available for American students. Its excellent plates (or Williams's outline reproductions of the same) should be in every laboratory.

The second book named is written in such general terms that its descriptions are not readily applicable to the actual structures found in the dissection of the cat, and experience has shown that it is not fitted for a laboratory handbook. It contains, in addition to a general account of the anatomy of the cat, also a discussion of its embryology, psychology, palæontology, and classification.

The book by Wilder and Gage professedly uses the cat as a means of illustrating technical methods and a special system of nomenclature. While of much value in many ways, it does not undertake to give a complete account of the anatomy of the animal.

The fourth work is a brief laboratory guide.

The elaborate treatise by Jayne, now in course of publication, is a monumental work, which will be invaluable for reference, but is too voluminous to place in the hands of students At present only the volume on the bones has been published.

As appears from the above brief characterization, none of these books gives a complete description of the anatomy of the cat in moderate volume and without extraneous matter. This is what the present work aims to do.

In the year 1891–92, Professor Reighard prepared a partial account of the anatomy of the cat, which has since been in use, in typewritten form, in University of Michigan classes. It has been used also at the Universities of Illinois, Nebraska, and West Virginia, and in Dartmouth College, and has proven so useful for college work in Mammalian Anatomy that it was decided to complete it and prepare it for publication. This has been done by Dr. Jennings.

The figures, which are throughout original, are direct reproductions of ink drawings, made under the direction of Dr. Jennings by Mrs. Jennings.

The book is limited to a description of the normal anatomy of the cat. The direct linear action of each muscle taken alone has been given in the description of muscles; other matters belonging to the realm of physiology, as well as all histological matter, have been excluded. It was felt that the monumental work of Jayne on the anatomy of the cat, now in course of publication, forms the best repository for a description of variations and abnormalities, so that these have been mentioned in the present volume only when they are so frequent as to be of much practical importance.

Except where the contrary is stated, the descriptions are based throughout on our own dissections and observations and are in no sense a compilation. For this reason we have not thought it necessary to collect the scattered references to the anatomy of the cat that may occur in the literature. A collection of such references may be found in Wilder and Gage's *Anatomical Technology.* In addition to the works already referred to, we have of course made use of the standard works on human and veterinary anatomy. Among these should be mentioned as especially useful the *Anatomie des Hundes* by Ellenberger and Baum. Other publications which have been of service in the preparation of the work are Windle and Parson's paper *On the Myology of the Terrestrial Carnivora,* in the Proceedings of the Zoological Society of London for 1897 and 1898, T. B. Stowell's papers on the nervous system of the cat in the Proceedings of the American Philosophical Society (1881, 1886, 1888) and in the Journal of Comparative Neurology (vol. I.), and F. Clasen's *Die Muskeln und Nerven des proximalen Abschnitts der vorderen Extremität der Katze,* in Nova Acta der Ksl. Leop-Carol. Deutschen Akademie der Naturforscher, Bd. 64.

Nomenclature.—The question of nomenclature has been one of difficulty. What is desired is a *uniform* set of anatomical names,—a system that shall be generally used by anatomists. At present the greatest diversity prevails as to the names to be applied to the different structures of the body. The only set of terms which at the present time seems to have any chance of general acceptance is that proposed by the German Anatomical Society at their meeting in Basel in 1895, and generally designated by the abbreviation BNA. This system has therefore been adopted, in its main features, for use in the present work. It seems impossible at the present time, however, to impose any one set of terms absolutely upon anatomists of all nations, and we have felt it necessary to use for certain familiar structures, in place of the BNA terms, names that have come to have a fixed place in English anatomy, and may almost be considered component parts of the English language. The German anatomists have expressly recognized the fact that this would be to a greater or less degree necessary among anatomists of different nations, and have characterized their list as for the present tentative, and capable of farther development. The only purpose of a name is that it shall furnish a key to a common understanding; where the BNA name does not furnish such a key to English readers, and where there is a term in established English usage that does serve this purpose and seems unlikely to be supplanted, we have used the latter. But we have endeavored to make the number of these exceptions as small as possible, and in such cases we have usually cited at the same time the term proposed by the German society, followed by the abbreviation BNA. When, on the other hand, we have adopted a BNA term for which there is also a commonly used English equivalent, the latter has likewise usually been cited in parenthesis.

In deciding whether or not to use in a given case the BNA term many difficult cases arose. Will the common English name *innominate* bone (os innominatum) be replaced by the BNA term *os coxæ* or *coxal bone?* We have held this to be highly improbable, and have therefore used the term *innominate bone*, merely citing *os coxæ* (BNA) as a synonym. In the same way we have used *centrum* as a designation of a part of a vertebra, in place of *corpus* (BNA); *premaxillary* bone or *premaxilla* in place of *os incisivum* (BNA); *malar* bone in place of *os zygomaticum* (BNA); *trapezoid* as a name of one of the bones of the carpus, in place of *os multangulum minus* (BNA), etc. In other cases where it has seemed probable that the BNA term would come into common use, though now unfamiliar, this and the more common English expression are both used or used alternatively; such has been the case, for example, with the Gasserian ganglion or semilunar ganglion (BNA). In naming the cerebral sulci and gyri the system in use for man is not well fitted for bringing out the plan of those in the brain of the cat, so that it was necessary to reject the BNA names for these structures.

As to the use of the Latin terms and their equivalents in English form, we have made a practice of employing in the text sometimes one, sometimes the other; this has the advantage of giving variety, and of impressing the interchangeability of the Latin and English forms on the mind of the student. Where a given structure is called by two equally well-known names, we have used both, holding that the student should become familiar with each and recognize their identity of meaning.

In general we have maintained the principle that the primary purpose of such a work as the present is not to illustrate or defend any particular system of nomenclature, but to aid in obtaining a knowledge of the structures themselves. With this end in view, we have used such terms as would in our judgment best subserve this purpose, making the BNA system, as the one most likely to prevail, our basis. In applying the system we have had to keep in mind a number of sometimes conflicting principles. In some cases the judgment of other anatomists will doubtless differ from our own; but this we feel to be inevitable. The matter of an absolutely uniform nomenclature is not ripe for settlement at the present time.

Some further explanation is needed in regard to the topographical terms, or terms of direction, used in the present work. We have adopted the BNA terms in this matter also. The terms *superior*, *inferior*, *anterior*, and *posterior* have been avoided, as these terms do not convey the same meaning in the case of the cat as they do in man, owing to the difference in the posture of the body. In place of these terms are used *dorsal* and *ventral*, *cranial* and *caudal*. As terms of direction these, of course, must have an absolutely fixed meaning, signifying always the same *direction* without necessary reference to any given structure. For example, *cranial* means not merely toward the *cranium*, but refers to the *direction* which is indicated by movement along a line from the middle of the body, toward the cranium; after the head or cranium is reached, the term still continues in force for structures even beyond the cranium. Thus the tip of the nose is considered to be *craniad* of the cranium itself. *Lateral* signifies away from the middle plane; *medial* toward it. *Inner* and *outer* or *internal* and *external* are used only with reference to the structure of separate organs, not with reference to the median plane of the body.

In describing the limbs the *convexity* of the joint (the elbow or knee) is considered as *dorsal*, the concavity being therefore ventral. *Medial* refers to that side of the limb which in the normal position is toward the middle of the body; *lateral* to the outer side. Terms of direction which are derived only from the structure of the limb itself are in some cases more convenient than the usual ones. In the fore limbs the terms *radial* (referring to the side on which the radius lies) and *ulnar* (referring to the side on which the ulna lies) are used; in the hind limbs the terms *tibial* and *fibular* are used in a similar manner. *Distal* means toward the free end of a limb or other projecting structure; *proximal*, toward the attached end.

For all these terms an adverbial form ending in *-ad* has been employed. Experience has shown this to be very useful in practice, and while not expressly recommended by the BNA, it is not condemned. Terms ending in *-al* are therefore adjectives; those ending in *-ad* are adverbs.

In compounding these terms of direction, the hyphen has been omitted in accordance with the usage recommended by the Standard Dictionary. Thus *dorsoventral* is written in place of *dorso-ventral*, etc. The student will perhaps be assisted in understanding these compounds if he notes that the first component always ends in *-o*, so that the letter *o* practically serves the purpose of a hyphen in determining how the word is to be divided.

In one particular the BNA nomenclature is not entirely consistent. While recommending or at least permitting the use of the general terms *dorsal* and *ventral* in place of the human *posterior* and *anterior*, and *cranial* and *caudal* in place of *superior* and *inferior*, it retains the words *anterior*, *posterior*, *superior*, and *inferior* as parts of the names of definite organs. For example, we have the muscle *serratus anterior* in place of *serratus ventralis; serratus posterior inferior* in place of *serratus dorsalis caudalis*. This is very unfortunate, from a comparative standpoint, but we have felt it necessary to retain the BNA terms in order that the structures of the cat may receive the same names as the corresponding structures of man.

In the matter of orthography we have endeavored to follow the best English anatomical usage, as exemplified in Gray's

Human Anatomy,—therefore writing *peroneus* in place of *peronæus*, *pyriformis* in place of *piriformis*, etc.

The book is designed for use in the laboratory, to accompany the dissection and study of the structures themselves. Anatomy cannot be learned from a book alone, and no one should attempt to use the present work without at the same time carefully dissecting the cat. On the other hand, anatomy can scarcely be learned without descriptions and figures of the structures laid bare in dissection, so that this or some similar work should be in the hands of any one attempting to gain a knowledge of anatomy through the dissection of the cat.

The figures have all been drawn from actual dissections, and have been carefully selected with a view to furnishing the most direct assistance to the dissector. It is hoped that no figures are lacking that are required for giving the students the necessary points of departure for an intelligent dissection of any part of the body. The fore limb is illustrated somewhat more fully than the hind limb, because it was thought that the fore limb would usually be dissected first; the hind limb will be easily dissected, with the aid of the figures given, after the experience gained in dissecting the fore limb.

As the book is designed to accompany the dissection of the specimen in the laboratory, it was deemed best to give succinct specific directions for the dissection of the different systems of organs, together with suggestions as to methods of preserving and handling the material. These are included in an appendix.

CONTENTS.

Part I: Descriptive Anatomy of the Cat.

LIST OF ILLUSTRATIONS.

PART I.

DESCRIPTIVE ANATOMY OF THE CAT.

THE SKELETON OF THE CAT.

THE skeleton of the cat consists of 230 to 247 bones exclusive of the sesamoid bones (44) and the chevron bones (8). These are divided as follows: head 35–40, vertebral column 52–53, ribs 26, sternum 1–8, pelvis 2–8, upper extremities 62, lower extremities 54–56. The number of bones varies with the age of the individual, being fewer in the old than in the young animal, owing to the fact that in an old animal some bones that were originally separate have united.

I. THE VERTEBRAL COLUMN. COLUMNA VERTEBRALIS.

The vertebral column, spinal column, or back-bone, consists of a varying number of separate bones, the vertebræ. At its cranial end are seven vertebræ (**cervical,** Fig. 1, *c*) which are without ribs and support the head; caudad of these are thirteen rib-bearing vertebræ (**thoracic,** Fig. 1, *m*); caudad of these are seven that are again without ribs (**lumbar,** Fig. 1, *o*); these are followed by three vertebræ (**sacral,** Fig. 1, *x*) which are united into a single bone, the **sacrum,** which supports the pelvic arch. Following the sacral vertebræ are twenty-two or twenty-three small ribless vertebræ which support the tail (**caudal,** Fig. 1, *y*).

Thoracic Vertebræ. Vertebræ thoracales (Fig. 4).—The **thoracic vertebræ** are most typical, and the fourth one of these may therefore be first described (Figs. 2 and 3). It forms an oval ring which has numerous processes and surrounds an opening which is the vertebral foramen (*a*). The ventral one-

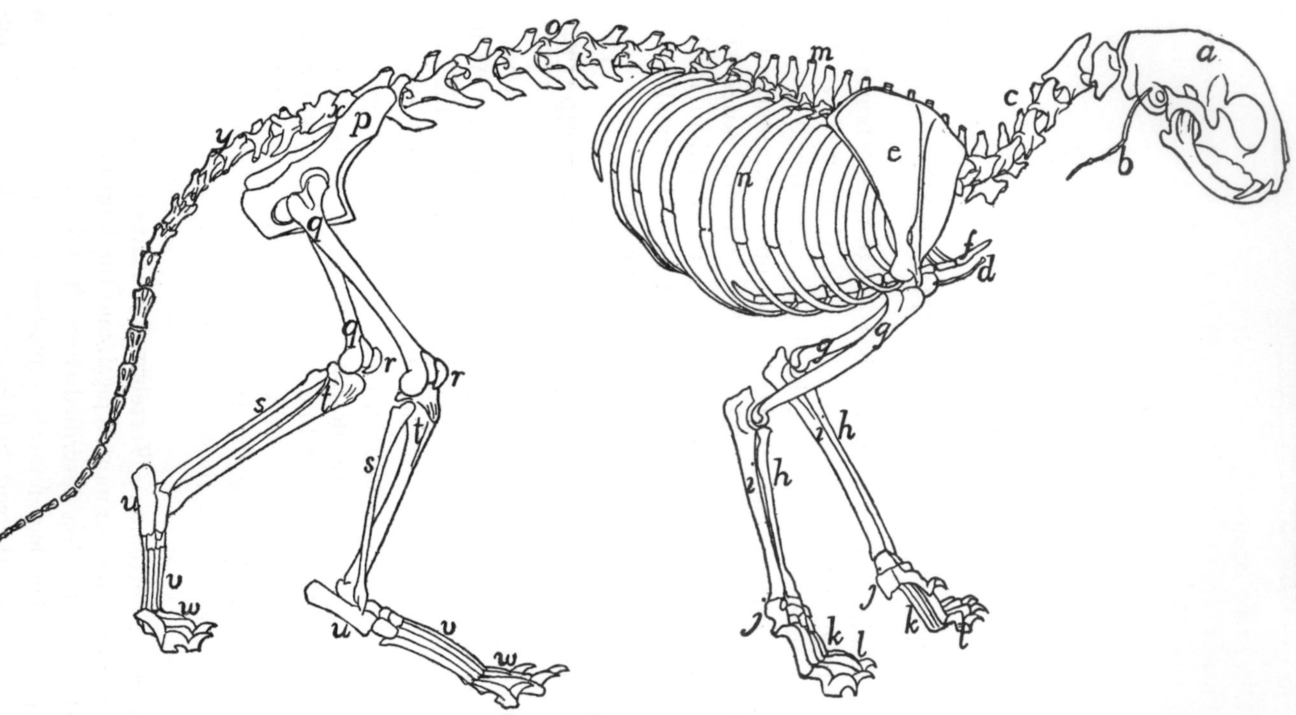

Fig. 1.—Skeleton of Cat.

a, skull; *b*, hyoid; *c*, cervical vertebræ; *d*, clavicle; *e*, scapula; *f*, sternum; *g*, humerus; *h*, radius; *i*, ulna; *j*, carpus; *k*, metacarpus; *l*, phalanges; *m*, thoracic vertebræ; *n*, ribs; *o*, lumbar vertebræ, *p*, innominate bones; *q*, femur; *r*, patella; *s*, fibula; *t*, tibia; *u*, tarsus; *v*, metatarsus; *w*, phalanges; *x*, sacrum; *y*, caudal vertebræ.

third of this ring is much thickened and forms the **centrum** or body (**corpus**) (*b*) of the vertebra. The centrum is a semicylinder, the plane face of which bounds the vertebral canal, while the curved surface is concave longitudinally and is directed ventrad. The dorsal plane surface of the centrum is marked by a median longitudinal ridge on either side of which

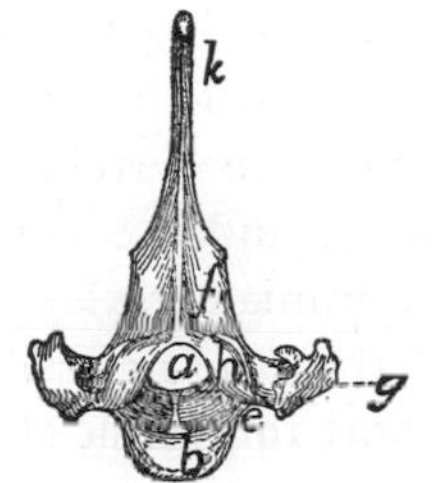

FIG. 2.—FOURTH THORACIC VERTEBRA, CRANIAL END.

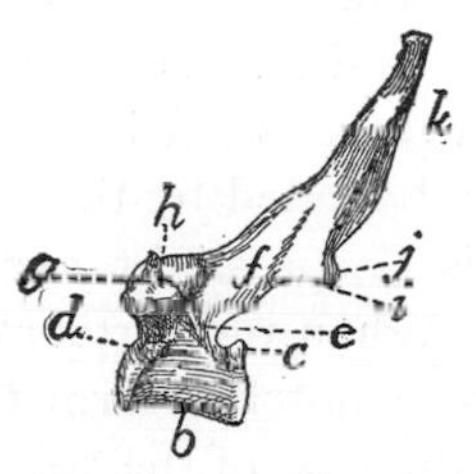

FIG. 3.—FOURTH THORACIC VERTEBRA, SIDE VIEW.

a, vertebral foramen; *b*, centrum; *c*, caudal, and *d*, cranial, costal demifacets; *e*, radix or pedicle; *f*, lamina; *g*, transverse process; *h*, cranial articular facet; *i*, caudal articular facet; *j*, caudal articular process; *k*, spinous process.

is an opening (nutrient foramen) for a blood-vessel. The ends are nearly plane, the caudal being slightly concave; they are harder and smoother than the other surfaces. They may be easily separated in a young specimen as thin plates of bone known as **epiphyses.**

At the caudal end of the centrum, at its dorsolateral angle, is a smooth area on each side continuous with the surface of the epiphysis and bounded dorsolaterally by a sharp ridge of bone (*c*). It is a **costal demifacet.** In corresponding positions at the cranial end of the centrum are two demifacets not limited by bony ridges (*d*). When the centra of two contiguous thoracic vertebræ are placed together in the natural position the cranial costal demifacets of one together with the caudal demifacets of the other form two **costal** facets (Fig. 4, *e*), one on each side, and each receives the head of a rib.

The dorsal two-thirds of the vertebral ring forms the **vertebral arch** which is continued dorsally into the long, bluntly pointed **spinous process** (Figs. 2 and 3, *k*) for attachment of muscles.

The vertebral arch (each half of which is sometimes called a **neurapophysis**) rises on each side from the cranial two-thirds of the dorsolateral angle of the centrum, as a thickened portion, the radix or pedicle (Figs. 2 and 3, *e*), which forms the ventral half of the lateral boundary of the vertebral canal. From the dorsal end of each radix a flat plate of bone, the **lamina** (*f*), extends caudomediad to join its fellow of the opposite side and form the vertebral arch. Owing to the fact that the radix rises from only the cranial two-thirds of the centrum there is left in the caudal border of the vertebral arch a notch bounded by the radix, the lamina, and the centrum. There is also a slight excavation of the cranial border of the radix. When the vertebræ are articulated in the natural position, these notches form the **intervertebral foramina** (Fig. 4, *d*), for the exit of the spinal nerves.

At the junction of radix and lamina the arch is produced craniolaterad into a short process, the **transverse process** (*g*), knobbed at the end. On the ventral face of its free end the transverse process bears a smooth facet, the transverse costal facet or tubercular facet (Fig. 4, *c*), for articulation with the tubercle of a rib.

On the dorsal face of each lamina at its cranial border is a smooth oval area, the **cranial articular facet** (superior articular facet of human anatomy) (Figs. 2 and 3, *h*). Its long axis is oblique and it looks dorsolaterad. The slight projections of the cranial edge of the laminæ on which the facets are situated are the inconspicuous **cranial articular processes** (prezygapophyses).

On the ventral surface of each lamina at the caudal border, near the middle line is a similar area, the **caudal articular facet** (inferior articular facet of human anatomy) (*i*); these occupy the ventral surfaces of two projections which form the **caudal** (inferior) **articular processes** (postzygapophyses) (*j*). These are separated by a median notch. When the vertebræ are in their natural position the caudal articular facets lie dorsad of the cranial facets and fit against them. They thus strengthen the joint between contiguous vertebræ, while permitting slight rotary motion.

Differential Characters of the Thoracic Vertebræ (Fig. 4).—Following the thoracic vertebræ caudad there is to be seen a gradual increase in the size of the centra brought about by an increase in their craniocaudal and transverse measurements.

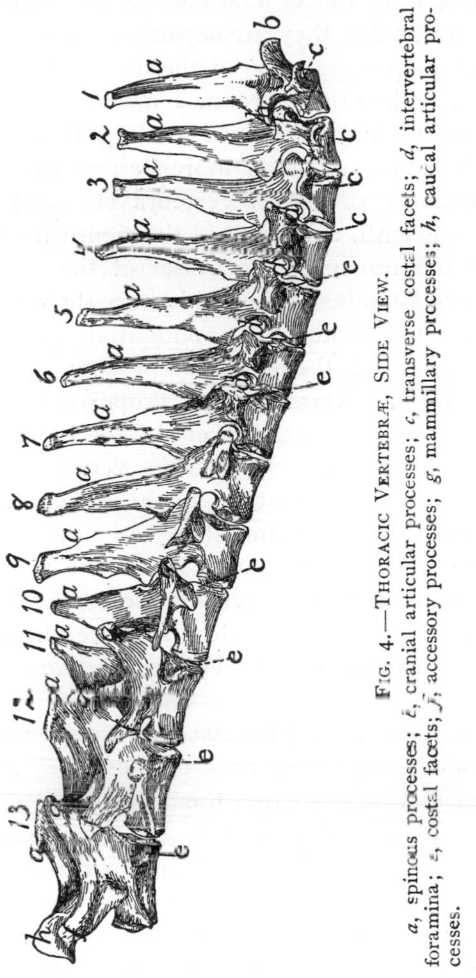

FIG. 4.—THORACIC VERTEBRÆ, SIDE VIEW.

a, spinous processes; *b*, cranial articular processes; *c*, transverse costal facets; *d*, intervertebral foramina; *e*, costal facets; *f*, accessory processes; *g*, mammillary processes; *h*, caudal articular processes.

The dorsoventral measurements remain nearly the same. The costal facets (Fig. 4, *e*) shift caudad so that on the eleventh, twelfth, and thirteenth thoracic vertebræ each lies entirely on the cranial end of its centrum, while the caudal end of the centrum immediately preceding is not marked by any part of it. In the eleventh thoracic vertebra each costal facet is usually still confluent with the smooth cranial end of the centrum. In the twelfth vertebra the facets are separated by smooth ridges from the cranial end of the vertebra, while in the thirteenth vertebra they are separated by rough ridges.

The spinous processes (*a*) of the first four are of about the same length. They then decrease in length to the twelfth, while the twelfth and thirteenth are slightly longer than the eleventh. The first ten slope more or less caudad, while the spinous process of the tenth vertebra is nearly vertical and those of the eleventh, twelfth, and thirteenth point craniad.

Each of the transverse processes of the seventh thoracic vertebra shows a tendency to divide into three tubercles; one of these is directed craniad, the mammillary process (or metapophysis), one caudad, the accessory process (or anapophysis), while the third (transverse process proper) looks ventrad and bears the transverse costal facet. This division becomes more prominent in the succeeding vertebræ, being most marked in the ninth and tenth. In the eleventh, twelfth, and thirteenth vertebræ the mammillary (*g*) and accessory (*f*) processes are very pronounced, while the transverse costal facet and that part of the transverse process which bears it have disappeared. The ribs of the eleventh, twelfth, and thirteenth vertebræ are thus attached to their respective centra by their heads alone.

The cranial articular processes (*b*) are prominent on the first two thoracic vertebræ; back of these they are very small as far as the eleventh, so that the articular facets seem to be borne merely upon the dorsal surface of the cranial edge of the laminæ. In the eleventh, twelfth, and thirteenth the cranial articular processes are large, bearing the articular facets on their medial surfaces, while the mammillary processes appear as tubercles on the lateral surfaces of the articular processes. The caudal articular processes (*h*) are prominent in the first thoracic, then smaller until the tenth is reached; in the tenth, eleventh, twelfth, and thirteenth they are large and their facets are borne laterally, so as to face the corresponding cranial facets. Thus from the tenth to the thirteenth thoracic vertebra rotary motion is very limited, owing to the interlocking of the articular processes.

The Lumbar Vertebræ. Vertebræ lumbales (Fig. 5).—The last thoracic vertebræ form the transition to the typical lumbar vertebræ. These are larger than the thoracic vertebræ.

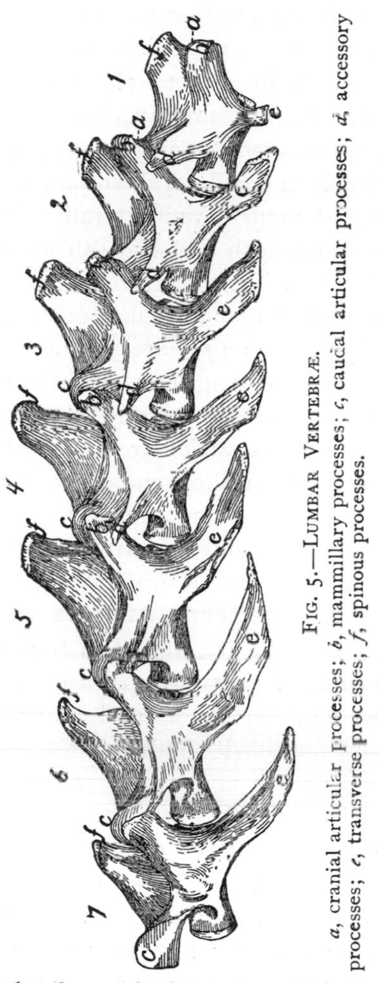

Fig. 5.—Lumbar Vertebræ.
a, cranial articular processes; *b*, mammillary processes; *c*, caudal articular processes; *d*, accessory processes; *e*, transverse processes; *f*, spinous processes.

The centra are of the form of the centra of the thoracic vertebræ, and increase in length to the sixth, but the seventh is about the length of the first. They increase in breadth to the last.

The cranial articular processes (Fig. 5, *a*) are prominent and directed craniodorsad; they have the facets on their medial surfaces, while their dorsolateral surfaces bear the mammillary processes (*b*) as prominent tubercles. The caudal articular processes (*c*) are likewise large; their facets look laterad. When the vertebræ are articulated they are received between the medially directed cranial processes.

The accessory processes (*d*) are well developed on the first vertebra, diminish in size to the fifth or sixth, and are absent on the seventh and sometimes on the sixth.

The transverse processes (more properly pseudo-transverse processes) (*e*) arise from the lateral surface of the centra; are flat and are directed ventrocraniolaterad. The first is small, and they increase in length and breadth from the first to the sixth, those of the last being slightly smaller than in the sixth. The free ends of the last four are curved craniad.

The spinous processes (*f*) are flat and directed craniodorsad. They increase in length to the fifth and then decrease. The first five are knobbed at the end. In a dorsal view the spinous process and cranial articular processes of each vertebra are seen to interlock with the caudal articular processes and accessory processes of the preceding vertebra in such a way as to prevent rotary motion, and this arrangement may be traced craniad as far as the eleventh thoracic vertebra.

Sacral Vertebræ. Vertebræ sacrales (Figs. 6 and 7).—The three sacral vertebræ are united in the adult into a single bone, the **os sacrum,** or **sacrum.** In a kitten the three vertebræ are separate, while in an animal almost mature the first two are united and the third is still separate. The sacrum lies between the last lumbar and the first caudal vertebræ and articulates laterally with the two innominate bones. It is pyramidal, with the base of the pyramid directed craniad, and is perforated by a depressed longitudinal canal, the **sacral canal,** which is a continuation of the vertebral canal, and by four large foramina dorsally and four ventrally. It may be described as having a cranial end or base and a caudal end or apex, a dorsal, a ventral, and two lateral surfaces.

The **base** is slightly oblique and presents a smooth transversely oval articular facet (the cranial end of the centrum of the first sacral vertebra), for articulation with the centrum of the last lumbar vertebra. Dorsad of this is the sacral canal, more depressed than the vertebral arch craniad of it. It supports a spinous process (Fig. 6, *a*) which is directed dorsad. At the junction of its lamina and radix is seen the prominent

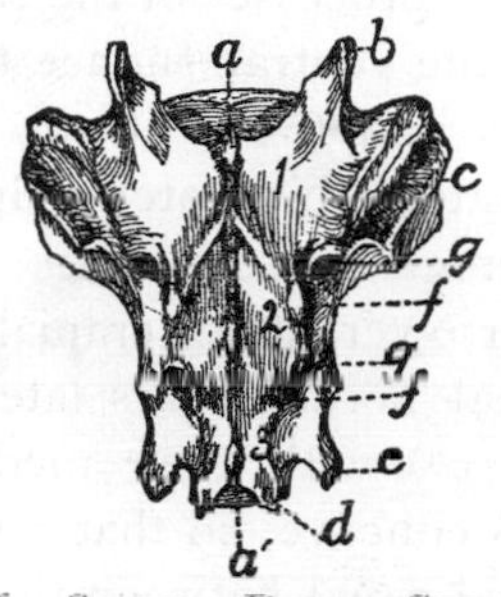

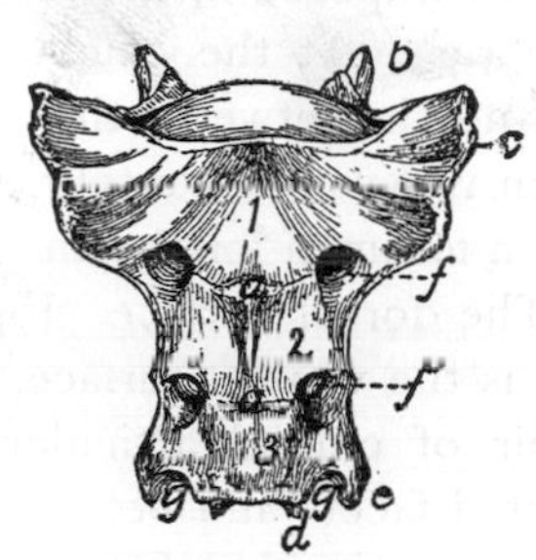

FIG. 6.—SACRUM, DORSAL SURFACE. FIG. 7.—SACRUM, VENTRAL SURFACE.

Fig. 6.—1, 2, 3, the three sacral vertebræ. *a*, *a'*, spinous processes; *b*, cranial articular process of first sacral vertebra; *c*, expanded transverse process of first sacral vetebra; *d*, caudal articular processes of third sacral vertebra; *e*, transverse processes of third sacral vertebra; *f*, tubercles formed by fused articular processes of the vertebræ; *g*, dorsal (or posterior) sacral foramina.

Fig. 7.—1, 2, 3, the three sacral vertebræ. *a*, the transverse ridges formed by the union of the centra; *b*, cranial articular processes of first vertebra; *c*, transverse process of first vertebra; *d*, caudal articular processes of third vertebra; *e*, transverse processes of third sacral vertebra; *f*, *f'*, ventral (or anterior) sacral foramina; *g*, notch which helps to form third ventral sacral foramen.

cranial articular process (*b*) with sometimes slight indications of a mammillary process on its lateral surface. Laterad of the articular facet is seen the cranial face of the expanded "pseudo-transverse process" (*c*) of the first sacral vertebra. The ventral border of the base is concave ventrad, forming an arc of about 120 degrees. The **apex** shows the caudal end of the last sacral centrum. Dorsad of this are the vertebral arch with a very short spinous process (*a'*), and the caudal articular processes (*d*). Laterad of the centrum appears the laterally directed thin transverse process (*e*).

The ventral or pelvic surface (Fig. 7) is smooth, concave craniad, convex caudad, and crossed by two transverse ridges (*a*) along which are seen the ossified remains of the intervertebral fibro-cartilages. At the ends of the first ridge is a pair of nearly circular **ventral** (or anterior) **sacral foramina** (*f*) for the passage of sacral nerves. At the end of the second ridge is a pair of ventral sacral foramina (*f′*), smaller than the first pair and continued laterocaudad into shallow grooves for the ventral rami of the sacral nerves. That portion of the bone lying laterad of a line joining the medial borders of these two pairs of foramina is known as the **lateral mass** of the sacrum and is composed of the fused transverse processes of the sacral vertebræ. At the caudal margin of the ventral surface there is a notch between the lateral mass and the centrum (*g*). When the caudal vertebræ are articulated, this notch helps to form a foramen for the third sacral nerve.

The dorsal surface (Fig. 6) is narrower at its cranial end than is the ventral surface. Its cranial border bears laterally a pair of cranial articular processes (*b*) with their medially directed facets and between them it is concave, so that a large dorsal opening is left into the vertebral canal between the last lumbar vertebra and the sacrum. Caudad of the articular processes are two pairs of tubercles (*f*). These are the fused cranial and caudal articular processes of the sacral vertebræ. Caudad of them are the caudal articular processes of the last sacral vertebra (*d*). Craniolaterad of the middle and cranial tubercles are **dorsal** (posterior) **sacral foramina** (*g*) for the transmission of the dorsal rami of the sacral nerves. Three spinous processes (*a*) appear between these rows of tubercles. They decrease in height caudad. That part of the surface included between the spinous process and the tubercles is made up of the fused laminæ of the sacral vertebræ. That part between the tubercles and a line joining the lateral margins of the dorsal (posterior) sacral foramina is formed by the fused radices of the sacral vertebræ.

The lateral surface may be divided into two parts. Craniad is a large rough triangular area with equal sides and with one of its angles directed ventrocraniad. It is the lateral face of the pseudo-transverse process of the first sacral vertebra (Fig. 6, *c*). A smooth curved surface (the auricular facet) along its ventral edge articulates with the ilium, while the dorsal portion is rough for attachment of ligaments. Caudad is the narrow longitudinal triangular area of the lateral faces of the fused transverse processes of the second and third sacral vertebræ.

Caudal Vertebræ. Vertebræ caudales (Fig. 1, *y*, and Figs. 8 and 9).—The caudal vertebræ (21–23 in number) decrease gradually in size to the last one. Caudad they become longer and more slender and lose the character of vertebræ. They become finally reduced to mere centra,—slender rods of bone knobbed or enlarged at their two ends (Fig. 8). The last one is more pointed than the others and bears at its caudal end a small separate conical piece, the rudiment of an additional vertebra.

FIG. 8. FIG. 9.

Fig. 8.—Caudal Vertebra, from near the caudal end of the tail.

Fig. 9.—Fourth Caudal Vertebra, ventral view. *a*, transverse processes; *b*, cranial articular processes; *c*, hæmal processes; *d*, chevron bone.

The parts of a typical vertebra—vertebral arch, transverse processes, cranial and caudal articular processes—may be recognized in the vertebræ as far back as the eighth or ninth. The transverse processes (Fig. 9, *a*) are directed caudad and decrease rapidly in length. They are very small on the ninth vertebra, but may be recognized for a considerable distance back of this. The spinous process disappears at about the fourth caudal vertebra, and the vertebral canal becomes gradually smaller caudad, until on the eighth or ninth vertebra it becomes merely a groove open dorsad.

Caudad of the third vertebra for a considerable distance, each centrum bears on each lateral face at its cranial end a short **anterior transverse** process, and on its ventral face at its cranial end a pair of rounded tubercles, **hæmal processes** (*c*), which articulate with a small pyramidal **chevron** bone (*d*) so as to enclose a canal. These structures disappear caudad.

Cervical Vertebræ. Vertebræ cervicales (Fig. 10).—The cervical vertebræ number seven. The first two of these are so peculiar as to require a separate description, so that the last five may be first considered.

Passing craniad from the fourth thoracic vertebra to the third cervical there is a gradual transition. The centra of the cervical vertebræ are broader and thinner than those of the thoracic vertebræ, while the vertebral arches and vertebral canal are larger (Fig. 11). The caudal end of each centrum is concave and looks dorsocaudad when the centrum is held with its long axis horizontal. The cranial end of the centrum is convex and looks ventrocraniad when the centrum is horizontal. These peculiarities are more marked in the third vertebra than in the seventh. The spinous processes grow

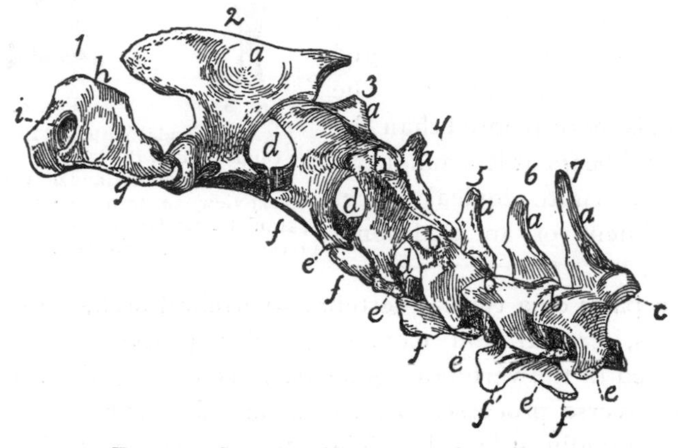

FIG. 10.—CERVICAL VERTEBRÆ, SIDE VIEW.

a, spinous processes; *b*, cranial articular processes; *c*, caudal articular facet; *d*, intervertebral foramina; *e*, transverse process proper; *f*, processus costarius; *g*, wing of the atlas; *h*, dorsal arch of the atlas; *i*, atlantal foramen.

rapidly shorter as we pass craniad; the fifth, sixth, and seventh are directed dorsocraniad, the third and fourth dorsad.

The caudal articular processes are situated at the junction of the radices and laminæ; their facets (Fig. 10, *c*) look ventrocaudolaterad. The cranial articular processes also become more prominent than is the rule in the thoracic vertebræ; they are borne at the junction of radix and lamina and have their facets (Fig. 11, *b*) directed dorsomediad. The cranial and caudal articular processes of each side are joined by a prominent ridge which is most pronounced in the third, fourth, and fifth vertebræ.

The characteristic feature of the cervical vertebræ is their transverse process, so called. In each of them it arises by two roots, one from the centrum and one from the arch.

These two roots, which are broad and thin, converge and unite so as to enclose a canal or foramen, the **foramen transversarium** (Fig. 11, *g*), for the vertebral artery. Laterad of the foramen the two parts of the process are, in the third cervical, almost completely united, the dorsal part being, however, distinguishable as a tubercle at the caudolateral angle of the thin plate formed by the process as a whole. This dorsal component is the **transverse process proper** (Figs. 10 and 11, *e*), while the ventral portion represents a rib, and is hence known as the **processus costarius** (*f*). The expanded plate formed by the union of these two processes is directed nearly ventrad and somewhat craniad in the third, fourth, and fifth vertebræ. The two components of the process gradually separate as we

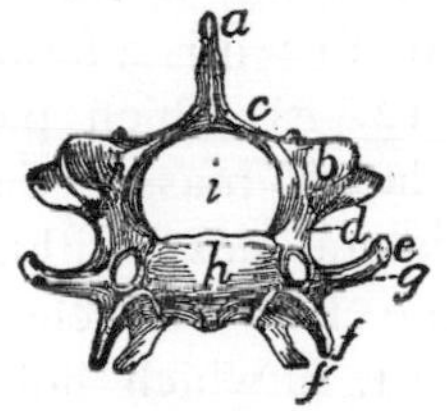

FIG. 11.—SIXTH CERVICAL VERTEBRA, CRANIAL END.

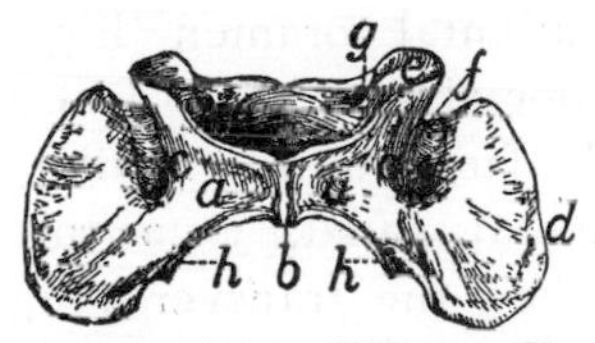

FIG. 12.—ATLAS, VENTRAL VIEW.

Fig. 11.—*a*, spinous process; *b*, cranial articular facet; *c*, lamina; *d*, radix or pedicle; *e*, transverse process proper; *f*, *f'*, processus costarius; *g*, foramen transversarium; *h*, centrum; *i*, vertebral canal.

Fig. 12.—*a*, ventral arch; *b*, tuberculum anterius; *c*, lateral masses; *d*, transverse processes; *e*, cranial articular facets; *f*, groove connecting the foramen transversarium with the atlantal foramen; *g*, atlantal foramen; *h*, caudal articular facets.

pass caudad; in the fourth and fifth vertebræ the part which represents the transverse process proper forms a very prominent tubercle at the caudolateral angle of the plate formed by the processus costarius. In the sixth (Fig. 11) the two parts are almost completely separated; the dorsal part forms (*e*) a slender knobbed process, while the processus costarius is divided into two portions (*f* and *f'*) by a broad lateral notch. In the seventh the ventral part (processus costarius) is usually quite lacking, though sometimes represented by a slender spicule of bone. In the former case the foramen transversarium is of course likewise lacking.

The Atlas (Fig. 10, 1; Fig. 12).—The first cervical vertebra or atlas has somewhat the form of a seal ring. The centrum is absent; it has united with the second vertebra to form the odontoid process or dens. Its place is taken in the atlas by a narrow flat arch of bone, narrower at the ends than in the middle, the **ventral arch** (Fig. 12, *a*) of the atlas. This connects the lateral, thicker portions of the ring ventrally and bears on its caudal margin a blunt tubercle (**tuberculum anterius,** Fig. 12, *b*). Laterally the ring is thickened, forming thus the **lateral masses** (*c*) which are continued into the broad thin transverse processes (Fig. 10, *g*; Fig. 12, *d*). Each lateral mass bears at its cranial end on its medial surface a concave, pear-shaped facet, cranial (or superior) articular facet, (Fig. 12, *e*) for articulation with the condyles of the skull. These facets look craniomediad. Dorsad of each is a foramen, the atlantal foramen (Fig. 10, *i*; Fig. 12, *g*), which pierces the dorsal arch at its junction with the lateral mass. Caudal to the facet, on the medial face of each lateral mass, within the vertebral canal, is a tubercle. To the two tubercles are attached the transverse ligament (Fig. 14, *b*) which holds in place the odontoid process (dens) of the axis.

That part of the lateral mass which bears the articular facet projects craniad of the dorsal arch and is separated by a deep triangular notch from the transverse process. Along the bottom of this notch runs a groove (Fig. 12, *f*), convex craniad, which connects the cranial end of the foramen transversarium and the atlantal foramen. The vertebral artery passes along it. The foramen transversarium is circular. It is bounded laterally by the lateral masses, and dorsally by the dorsal arch.

The dorsal arch (Fig. 10, *h*) is two to three times as broad as the ventral, has a thick convex cranial border with a median notch, and a thin concave caudal border.

The caudal articular facets (Fig. 12, *h*) are borne by the caudal ends of the lateral masses. They are slightly concave, triangular, and look caudomediad, so that their dorsal borders form with the caudal border of the dorsal arch nearly a semicircle. The transverse processes are flat and directed laterad.

The attached margin of each is about two-thirds the length of the thinner free margin. The somewhat thicker caudal end of the transverse process projects further caudad than any other part of the vertebra and is separated by a slight notch from the caudal articular facet. From the bottom of this notch the foramen transversarium extends craniad and opens at the middle of the ventral face of the transverse process.

Epistropheus or **Axis** (Fig. 10, 2; Fig. 13).—The second cervical vertebra (epistropheus or axis) is not so wide as the atlas but is much longer. Craniad the centrum is continued into a slender conical, toothlike projection, the **dens or odontoid process** (Fig. 13, *a*) which represents the centrum of the atlas. The dens is smooth below for articulation with the ventral arch of the atlas. It is rougher above. Laterad of the dens the centrum bears a pair of large cranial articular facets (*b*) which look craniolaterad. These have each the form of a right-angled triangle with rounded angles, one side of the triangle being nearly horizontal. Each is separated from the articular face of the dens by a roughened groove. The spinous process (*c*) runs the length of the vertebral arch. It extends craniad of the vertebral arch nearly as far as the dens, as a flat rounded projection. Caudad of the vertebral arch it projects for a short distance as a stout triangular spine. The caudal articular facets (*d*) are borne on thickenings of the caudolateral portions of the arch; they face almost directly ventrad. The transverse process (*e*) is slender and triangular and directed nearly caudad. Its apex reaches no farther than the caudal or articular face of the centrum. Its base is traversed by the foramen transversarium (*f*).

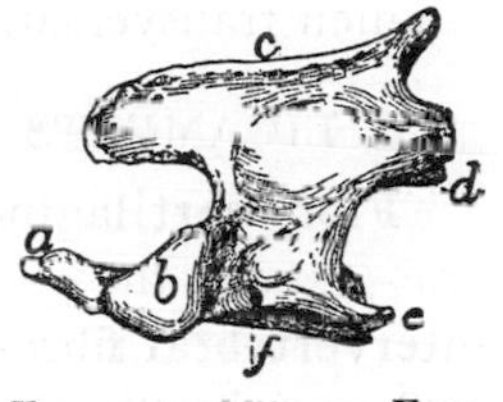

FIG. 13.—AXIS OR EPISTROPHEUS, SIDE VIEW.

a, odontoid process or dens; *b*, cranial articular facets; *c*, spinous process; *d*, caudal articular facet; *e*, transverse process; *f*, foramen transversarium.

Differential Characters of the Cervical Vertebræ.—It is possible to identify each of the cervical vertebræ:

The first by the absence of the centrum.

The second by the dens or odontoid process.

The third by the small spinous process and slightly marked

tubercle of the transverse process, and by a median tubercle on the cranial border of the vertebral arch.

The fourth by the spinous process directed dorsad, and the short thick tubercle of the transverse process not trifid.

The fifth by the spinous process directed craniad, and the more slender spine-like tubercle of the transverse process not trifid.

The sixth by the trifid transverse process.

The seventh by the long spinous process and the slender simple transverse process, and by the usual absence of the foramen transversarium.

LIGAMENTS OF THE VERTEBRAL COLUMN.

Fibro-cartilagines intervertebrales.—The separate vertebræ (except the atlas and axis) are united by the disk-shaped **intervertebral fibro-cartilages,** which are situated between the centra of the vertebræ. Each consists of a central pulpy portion and a fibrous outer portion, covered by strong intercrossing tendinous fibers which unite with the periosteum of the vertebræ.

Ligamentum longitudinale anterius. — On the ventral face of the centra of the vertebræ, from the atlas to the sacrum, lies a longitudinal ligament, the **anterior longitudinal ligament.** It is very small, almost rudimentary, in the cervical region: large and strong in the thoracic and lumbar regions.

Ligamentum longitudinale posterius (Fig. 14, *a*). — A corresponding ligament (**posterior longitudinal ligament**) lies on the dorsal surface of the centra (therefore within the vertebral canal). It is enlarged between each pair of vertebræ and closely united to the intervertebral fibro-cartilages.

Ligamentum supraspinale. — Between the tips of the spinous processes of the thoracic and lumbar vertebræ extend ligamentous fibers. They are not united to form a distinct band, and can hardly be distinguished from the numerous tendinous fibers of the supraspinous muscles. Together they represent the **supraspinous ligament.** From the tip of the spinous process of the first thoracic vertebra to the caudal end of the spine of the axis extends a slender strand representing the **ligamentum nuchæ** or **cervical supraspinous ligament.** It is imbedded in the superficial muscles of this region, some of which take origin from it.

Ligamentous fibers are also present between the spinous processes of the vertebræ (**ligamenta interspinalia**): between the transverse processes (**ligamenta intertransversaria**), and between the vertebral arches (**ligamenta flava**).

Capsulæ articulares.—The joints between the articular processes are furnished with **articular capsules** attached about the edges of the articular surfaces. These are larger and looser in the cervical region.

Atlanto-occipital Articulation.—The joint between the atlas and the occipital condyles has a single articular capsule, which is attached about the borders of the articular surfaces of the two bones. This capsule is of course widest laterally, forming indeed two partially separated sacs, which are, however, continuous by a narrow portion across the ventral middle line. This capsule communicates with that which covers the articular surface of the dens, and through this with the capsule between the atlas and axis. That portion of the capsule which covers the space between the ventral arch of the atlas and the occipital bone represents the **anterior atlanto-occipital membrane**; it is strengthened by a slender median ligamentous strand. The **posterior atlanto-occipital** membrane covers in the same way the space between the dorsal arch of the atlas and the dorsal edge of the foramen magnum. In it a number of different sets of fibers, with regard to direction and to degree of development, may be distinguished; these have sometimes been considered separate ligaments.

The **lateral ligaments** of the atlas begin at the lateral angle of the cranial margin of the atlas, at about the junction of its dorsal and ventral arches, and pass cranioventrad to the jugular processes.

Articulation between the Axis and Atlas.—The **articular capsule** is large and loose, being attached to dorsal and ventral borders of the atlas, about the articular surfaces of the axis, and to the cranial projection of the spine of the atlas. It also passes craniad along the ventral side of the dens and communicates here with the capsule of the atlanto-occipital articulation. In the dorsal part of the capsule a short strong ligamentous strand is developed, connecting the caudal border of the dorsal arch of the atlas with the tip of the cranial projection of the spinous process of the axis.

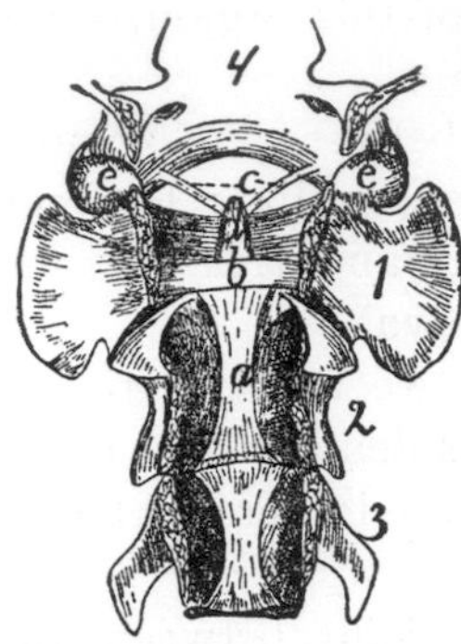

FIG. 14.—LIGAMENTS OF THE ODONTOID PROCESS OR DENS.

First three cervical vertebræ and base of the skull, with dorsal surface removed. *a*, ligamentum longitudinale posterius; *b*, transverse ligament of the atlas; *c*, ligamenta alaria; *d*, odontoid process; *e*, occipital condyles; 1, 2, 3, the first three cervical vertebræ; 4, basal portion of the occipital bone.

The dens or odontoid process is held in place by the **transverse ligament** (Fig. 14, *b*) of the atlas, which passes across the process as it lies within the vertebral canal of the atlas. The transverse ligament is attached at its two ends to the medial surface of the sides of the atlas at about the region where the dorsal and ventral arches of the atlas unite.

From the cranial end of the odontoid process the two **ligamenta alaria** (Fig. 14, *c*) diverge craniolaterad to the rough ventromedial angle of the condyles of the occipital bone.

II. RIBS. COSTÆ. (Figs. 1 and 15.)

The cat has thirteen pairs of ribs. One of the fifth pair (Fig. 15) may be taken as typical. It is a curved flattened rod of bone attached at its dorsal end to the vertebral column, and at its ventral end to a cartilage (**costal cartilage,** Fig. 15, *f*) which serves to unite it to the sternum.

The most convex portion of the bone is known as the **angle** (*e*). Each rib presents a convex lateral and a concave medial surface, a cranial and a caudal border. The borders are broad dorsad and narrow ventrad, while the surfaces are narrow dorsad and broad ventrad. The rib has thus the appearance of having been twisted.

The rib ends dorsad in a globular head or **capitulum** (*a*), by which it articulates with the costal demifacets of two contiguous thoracic vertebræ. Between the capitulum and angle on the lateral surface is an elevated area, the **tubercle,** marked by the smooth tubercular facet (*c*) for articulation with the transverse process of a vertebra. The constricted portion between the head and tubercle is known as the **neck (collum)** (*d*). The angle is marked by a projecting process (*e*) (**angular process**) on its lateral border, for attachment of a ligament.

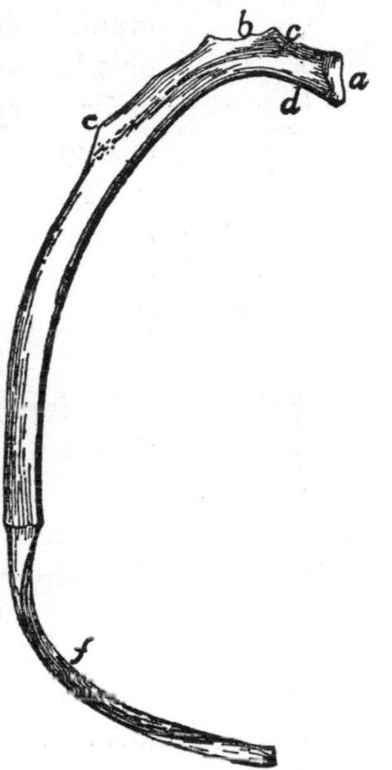

Fig. 15.—Fifth Rib of Left Side, Cranial View.

a, head; *b*, tubercle; *c*, tubercular facet; *d*, neck; *e*, angle, with angular process; *f*, cartilage.

The ribs increase in length to the ninth (the ninth and tenth are of the same length) and then decrease to the last. They decrease in breadth behind the fifth. The first is nearly in a dorsoventral plane, while the others have their dorsal ends inclined slightly craniad.

The tubercles become less prominent as we pass caudad and are absent on the last two or three ribs, which do not articulate with the transverse process.

The first nine ribs (**true ribs** or **costæ veræ**) are attached separately to the sternum by their costal cartilages. The last four (false ribs or costæ spuriæ) are not attached separately to the sternum. The costal cartilages of the tenth, eleventh, and twelfth are united to one another at their sternal ends. They may be united also to the ninth costal cartilage or to the sternum by a common cartilage of insertion, or they may be quite free from the sternum. The thirteenth costal cartilages are free (floating ribs).

Ligaments of the Ribs.—The articular surfaces between the head of the rib and the centra, and between the tubercle and the transverse process of the vertebra, have each an articular capsule. There are also a number of small ligamentous bands from the tuberosity and the neck of the rib to the transverse process of the vertebra.

III. STERNUM. (Fig. 16.)

The sternum consists of three portions, a cranial piece or **manubrium** (*a*), a caudal piece or **xiphoid** process (*c*), and a middle portion or **body (corpus)**, which is divided into a number of segments (*b*).

To the sternum are united the ventral ends of the first nine ribs. It thus forms the median ventral boundary of the thorax. Since the thorax decreases in dorsoventral measurement craniad, the long axis of the sternum is inclined from its caudal end dorsocraniad, and if continued would strike the vertebral column in the region of the first cervical vertebra.

The manubrium (*a*) makes up about one-fifth the whole length of the sternum and projects craniad of the first rib. It has the form of a dagger and presents a dorsal surface and two lateral surfaces, the latter uniting ventrad to form a sharp angle. In the middle of the lateral surface near the dorsal margin is an oval articular surface (*d*) borne on a triangular projection. It looks caudodorsad and is for the first costal cartilage.

The caudal end articulates with the body by a synchondrosis and presents a slightly marked oval facet on each side for the second costal cartilage.

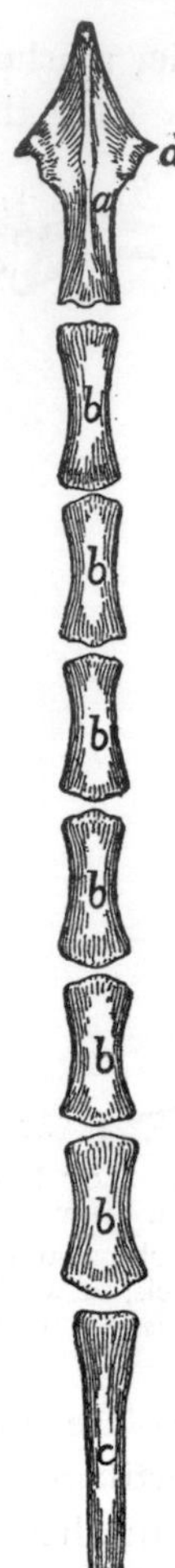

FIG. 16.—STERNUM, VENTRAL VIEW.

a, manubrium; *b*, the separate pieces forming the body; *c*, bony part of the xiphoid process (the expanded cartilaginous portion not being shown); *d*, facet for attachment of first rib.

The body consists of six cylindrical pieces (*b*) enlarged at their ends and movably united by synchondroses. They increase in breadth from the first, and decrease slightly in length and thickness. At the caudal end of each near its ventral border there is a pair of facets looking caudolaterad. They are for the costal cartilages.

The xiphoid process (*c*) is a broad thin plate of cartilage at its caudal end; bony and cylindrical at its cranial end. It is attached by its base to the last segment of the body by a considerable cartilaginous interval, while the opposite end is free and directed caudo-ventrad.

The cartilage of the ninth rib is attached to the lateral face of the cartilage between the xiphoid and the body, and just caudad of this the common cartilage of insertion of the tenth, eleventh, and twelfth costal cartilages is attached, if present.

IV. THE SKULL.

The bones of the head consist of the **skull proper** together with a number of separate bones forming part of the **visceral skeleton**; these are the lower jaw, the hyoid, and the ear-bones.

The skull proper is considered as divided into **cranial** and **facial** portions. The former includes all the bones which take part in bounding the cranial cavity or cavity of the brain; the latter includes the bones which support the face.

The cranial portion of the skull includes all that part enclosing the large cavity which contains the brain. For convenience this portion may be considered as made up of three segments, each of which forms a ring surrounding a part of the cranial cavity. The first or caudal segment or ring consists of the occipital bone (with the interparietal) surrounding the foramen magnum. The second segment consists of the sphenoid ventrad, the parietals laterad and dorsad. Between the first and second segments are intercalated laterally the temporal bones containing the auditory organ. The third segment or ring consists of the presphenoid ventrad, of the frontals laterad and dorsad. The cranial opening of this ring is closed by the lamina cribrosa of the ethmoid.

The cranial portion of the skull therefore contains eleven separate bones: one occipital, one interparietal, two temporals, one sphenoid, two parietals, one presphenoid, two frontals, and one ethmoid.

The facial portion of the skull is much smaller than the

cranial, and lies craniad of the latter; it encloses the nasal cavity. It contains the following thirteen bones: two palatines, one vomer, two maxillaries, two lachrymals, two premaxillaries, two nasals, two malar or zygomatic bones. The two halves of the mandible or lower jaw are frequently included in the facial portion of the skull, making in all fifteen separate bones in this part of the skull.

In the following the bones of the skull are first described separately, then an account is given of the skull as a whole.

Occipital Bone. Os occipitale (Figs. 17 and 18).—The occipital bone forms the most caudal portion of the cranium, entering into the formation of its caudal wall and of its base. It connects the cranium with the vertebral column and surrounds a large opening, the **foramen magnum** (*d*), by means of which the cranial cavity communicates with the vertebral canal.

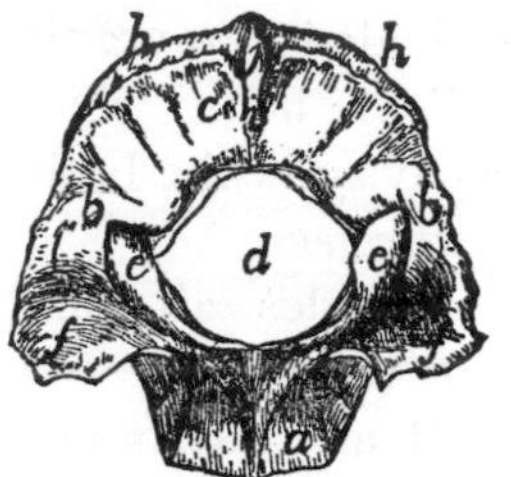

FIG. 17.—OCCIPITAL BONE, CAUDAL OR OUTER SURFACE.

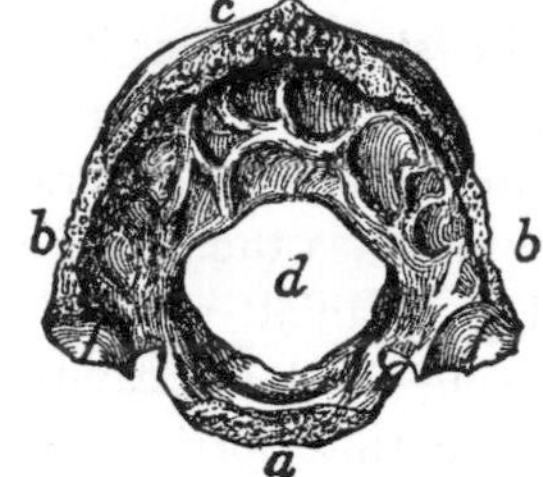

FIG. 18.—OCCIPITAL BONE, INNER SURFACE.

a, basilar portion; *b*, lateral portions; *c*, squamous portion; *d*, foramen magnum; *e*, occipital condyles; *f*, jugular processes; *g*, jugular notch; *h*, lambdoidal ridge; *i*, external occipital crest; *j*, external occipital protuberance.

In young kittens four portions may be distinguished in this bone. These are, a basal portion (the **basioccipital bone**), two lateral portions (the **exoccipital bones**), and a dorsal portion (the **supraoccipital bone**). These four bones remain separate through life in many lower vertebrates. In the adult cat they are completely united into a single bone, but it is convenient to describe this bone as made up of four parts: a basal portion (*a*) (**pars basilare**), corresponding to the basioccipital, two lateral portions (*b*) (**partes laterales**), corresponding to the exoccipitals, and a squamous portion (*c*) **squama occipitalis**) corresponding to the supraoccipital.

The basilar portion (*a*) as seen from the dorsal or ventral surface is oblong and flattened. It is broadest at the junction of its middle and last thirds, and tapers toward both ends. It presents a cranial end and a caudal end, a dorsal, a ventral, and two lateral surfaces. Its caudal end, which helps to form the ventral boundary of the foramen magnum, is concave from side to side. The cranial end is transversely elongate, about five times as broad as high, pointed laterally and roughened for attachment to the caudal end of the body of the sphenoid, which has a corresponding form. The joint is a synchondrosis.

The dorsal surface is concave from side to side, forming a longitudinal groove in which rest the pons and medulla. The concavity is more pronounced caudad, where the bone is thinner at its middle.

The ventral surface is marked by three parallel longitudinal ridges. One of them is median and expands caudad into a smooth triangular elevated area which extends to the foramen magnum. The other two ridges run near the lateral edges of the bone. Between them and the median ridge the surface is smooth and is depressed caudad. Laterad of each lateral ridge is a rough triangular surface overlaid in the natural state by the medial edge of the tympanic bulla.

The lateral surfaces are smooth and sharp and abut against the petrous portion of the temporal bone. They pass into the lateral portions of the occipital caudad.

The **lateral portions** (*b*) of the occipital arise from the caudal margin of the basilar portion in the transverse plane; a short distance laterad of the line of junction they turn dorsad at an angle of nearly ninety degrees. They form the lateral boundaries of the foramen magnum and pass dorsally into the squamous portion.

The external surface of each presents an elongated elevated spirally curved surface, the **occipital condyle** (*e*), for articulation with the atlas. A small part of each condyle is formed from the basal portion. The two condyles are separated from one another ventrally by a narrow notch, and each extends (laterad) along the border of the foramen magnum to a point slightly dorsad of the transverse diameter of the latter.

Laterad of each condyle the bone is elevated into a blunt triangular projection, the **jugular process** (*f*), which covers the caudal end of the tympanic bulla. Between the jugular process and the condyle is a deep depression.

The internal surface (Fig. 18) is concave dorsoventrally, following the outline of the foramen magnum. It is convex from side to side. It is smooth except at its outer margin, which is rough for articulation with the mastoid portion of the temporal bone. The cranial face of the jugular process (*f*) shows a rough concavity for the reception of the bulla tympani. Mediad of the jugular process is a notch (**jugular notch**) (*g*) which when the bones are articulated forms part of the boundary of the jugular foramen. Mediad of this notch is a foramen which forms one end of the **hypoglossal canal.** It passes dorsocaudad into the cranial cavity and transmits the hypoglossal nerve. Dorsad of the hypoglossal canal is the cranial opening of the **condyloid canal,** which passes caudad and opens just craniad of the dorsal end of the condyle. It transmits a vein. The outer border of this portion is rough for articulation with the petrous and mastoid portions of the temporal.

The **squamous portion** (*c*) has the form of a sector of a circle whose arc is a little more than ninety degrees. The central angle of the sector is truncated and bounds the foramen magnum dorsally. The arc of the sector forms the dorsal margin of the bone, while along the radii it passes into the lateral portions. Its dorsal portion is thick and porous; its ventral portion near the foramen magnum is thin and compact.

The external surface (Fig. 17) is marked by a prominent ridge, the **lambdoidal ridge** (*h*), parallel with the dorsal border and near to it. The narrow portion of the outer surface that lies dorsad of the ridge forms an angle of about ninety degrees with the remainder of the surface.

A median crest (*i*) extends ventrad from the middle of the lambdoidal ridge toward the foramen magnum; this is the **external occipital crest.** At its junction with the lambdoidal ridge it is elevated into a tubercle, the **external occipital protuberance** (*j*).

The inner surface (Fig. 18) presents depressions for the convolutions of the cerebellum.

The dorsal border is thick and rough for articulation with the parietals and interparietal. The ventral border abuts on the foramen magnum and is thin and smooth.

Interparietal Bone. Os interparietale (Fig. 19).—This is a small triangular bone lying between the parietals, with its apex directed craniad, and its base in contact with the squamous portion of the occipital.

Its dorsal surface is arrow-shaped and has its posterior border notched. It is marked by a median crest (part of the **sagittal crest**) which is continued craniad from the middle of the lambdoidal crest.

The ventral surface is irregularly triangular, smooth, and concave. The three borders are rough for articulation with the parietals and occipital.

FIG. 19.—INTERPARIETAL BONE, OUTER SURFACE.

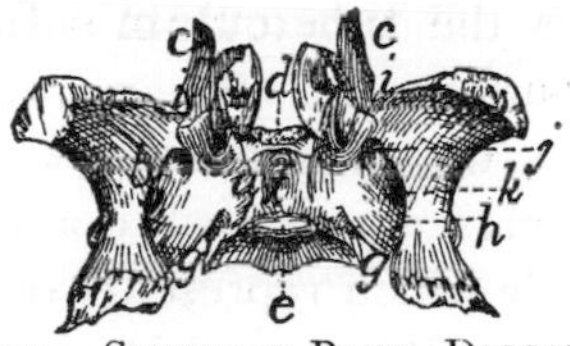

FIG. 20.—SPHENOID BONE, DORSAL OR INTERNAL SURFACE.

Fig. 19, showing the sagittal crest running craniocaudad across its middle.

Fig. 20.—*a*, body; *b*, wings; *c*, pterygoid process; *d*, tuberculum sellæ; *e*, dorsum sellæ; *f*, sella turcica; *g*, notch which aids in forming the foramen lacerum; *h*, longitudinal groove of alisphenoid; *i*, notch which aids in forming the orbital fissure; *j*, foramen rotundum; *k*, foramen ovale.

Sphenoid Bone. Os sphenoidale (Fig. 20).—The sphenoid bone of man is represented in the cat by two entirely distinct bones,—one cranial, the other caudal. The cranial portion may be designated as the **presphenoid** (Fig. 21); the caudal part will be described as the **sphenoid** (proper) (Fig. 20).

The sphenoid bone in the kitten is in three parts: a central portion, the **basisphenoid,** and two lateral portions, the **alisphenoids.** In many lower vertebrates these three bones are permanently distinct, but in the adult cat they are united to form the sphenoid bone. To these there is added a fourth element, separate in many vertebrates as the **pterygoid** bone.

The sphenoid may thus be described as composed of a central portion, the body (*a*) (basisphenoid), and of two thin expanded wings (*b*) (alisphenoids, alæ magnæ of the human sphenoid); each of which has arising from it a thin curved process, the **pterygoid process** (*c*), directed craniad and largely made up of the pterygoid bone.

The body of the sphenoid (*a*) lies in the middle line of the base of the skull. It is wedge-shaped, with the converging sides of the wedge directed laterad and its apex pointed craniad.

It has six surfaces, of which the dorsal and a part of the laterals look into the cranial cavity. The cranial end articulates with the body of the presphenoid, and the caudal with the body of the occipital.

The dorsal surface is triangular, with one apex of the triangle truncated, elevated, and directed craniad. This elevation is the **tuberculum sellæ** (*d*). Just caudad of the middle the surface presents a rectangular elevation with rounded angles, the **dorsum sellæ** (*e*). The cranial end of the dorsum sellæ presents at each dorsolateral angle a very small smooth tubercle which represents one of the posterior clinoid processes of man. Between this elevation and the elevated cranial end of this surface there is a deep excavation, the **sella turcica** (*f*), in which in the natural state is lodged the hypophysis. Near the cranial end of the sella is a small foramen, probably nutrient. At the caudal end of the body a slight notch (*g*) separates it from the wing: this notch forms a part of the **foramen lacerum.** Against this notch fits the apex of the petrous bone, and from it a groove (**carotid groove**) is continued mediocraniad to the sella turcica.

The ventral surface (Fig. 41, 3) is triangular, smooth, and nearly flat; it is marked by a median ridge which is the continuation craniad of the ridge on the ventral face of the basilar portion of the occipital.

Its caudal angles are separated from the rest of the bone by sharp triangular elevations, laterad of which are rough triangular areas, overlaid when the bones are articulated by a triangular spine from the tympanic bulla.

Its lateral surfaces are mostly covered by the wings. They appear at the sides of the elevated cranial end of the dorsal surface as triangular areas.

The caudal end is concave, rough, and has the form of the cranial end of the basilar part of the occipital.

The cranial end is nearly square and rough for articulation with the body of the presphenoid.

The Wing (**alisphenoid ;** ala magna of the human sphenoid) (Fig. 20, *b*).—This is a thin quadrilateral plate of bone attached by its medial border to nearly the whole of the lateral surface of the body. Its middle portion lies nearly in the same plane as the body, but its ends are curved dorsad so that its internal surface is concave and its external surface is convex. The curvature is most pronounced near the long lateral border, so that this border forms nearly a semicircle.

The internal surface supports the occipital lobe of the cerebrum. It is marked by a rounded groove (*h*) which is parallel with the lateral surface of the body. The dorsal margin of the groove projects mediad in the form of a sharp ridge which is broadest caudad, where it often reaches nearly to the posterior clinoid process. The groove passes craniad into three foramina. The first (cranial) of these, the **orbital fissure** (*i*), is large and lies between the wing, the body, and the pterygoid process. It is incomplete, but is completed by the presphenoid. The second foramen is small and rounded; it is the **foramen rotundum** (*j*). The third, **foramen ovale** (*k*), is larger and oval and penetrates the wing through about the middle of its longitudinal axis. Another minute foramen penetrates the sphenoid between the wing and the body of the bone, just laterad of the tuberculum sellæ. This foramen is continuous craniad with a groove on the dorsal surface of the pterygoid process; the groove and foramen constitute the **pterygoid canal.** It transmits a nerve.

The external surface shows the orbital fissure, the foramen rotundum and the foramen ovale, bounded ventrally by a sharp ridge, which is continued onto the pterygoid process. Between this ridge and the body the surface is longitudinally grooved for the tuba auditiva or Eustachian tube.

The semicircular margin of the bone articulates with the squamous portion of the temporal. At the junction of its caudal and middle third there is sometimes a toothlike projection which underlies the root of the zygoma.

The whole of the cranial margin, except the lateral end, articulates with the wing of the presphenoid. At this end the angle formed by the junction of lateral and cranial borders is produced into a flat process, which passes dorsocaudad between the squamous portion of the temporal and the frontal, and articulates by the roughened internal surface of its free end with a similar process from the parietal.

The caudal margin laterad of the groove is bevelled and roughened at the expense of the dorsal surface and is overlaid by the ventral end of the tentorium. Mediad of the groove it projects caudad as a slender point, the **lingula** of the sphenoid. This is received into a narrow cleft between the apex of the petrous bone and the bulla tympani.

The pterygoid process (*c*) is a nearly square, thin plate of bone. The medial surface is smooth and concave, the lateral face is convex and marked by two parallel ridges. The medial one of these is continued craniad from the bony septum which separates the orbital fissure from the foramen rotundum, and the lateral one from the septum which separates the foramen rotundum from the foramen ovale. A sharp triangular spine projects laterad from near the caudal end of the lateral ridge.

The two ridges and that part of the lateral surface of the bone included between them form a part of the sphenoid bone known as the pterygoid process of the sphenoid bone, in those cases where the pterygoid is a separate bone.

The remainder of the process is equivalent to the pterygoid bone of other vertebrates.

Between the caudal margin of this bone and the lateral of the two ridges, i.e., between the pterygoid bone and the pterygoid process of the sphenoid, is a long deep fossa, the **internal pterygoid fossa** (Fig. 40, *s*). The laterocaudal margin of the pterygoid process projects caudad, as a curved triangular spine, the **hamulus** or **hamular process** (Fig. 40, *t*; Fig. 43, *i*).

The **Presphenoid Bone. Os presphenoidale** (Fig. 21).—In a young cat this bone is in three pieces, a basal portion (**presphenoid**) and two wings (**orbitosphenoid bones**). These bones remain distinct throughout life in many lower vertebrates, but in the adult cat they fuse to form a single bone. We may nevertheless conveniently describe this bone as made up of a body (*a*) (the basisphenoid), and two wings (*b*), the orbitosphenoids (the alæ parvæ of the human sphenoid).

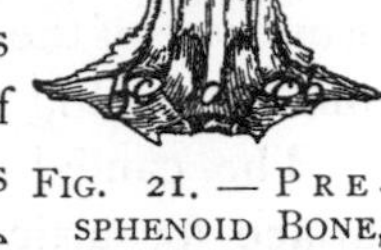

FIG. 21.—PRESPHENOID BONE, VENTRAL VIEW. *a*, body; *b*, wings; *c*, optic foramina.

The body (*a*) lies in the base of the skull in the median line, craniad of the basisphenoid. It has the form of a rectangular prism about twice as long as broad. It is hollow, and the cavity is divided by a median longitudinal partition into two cavities (**sphenoidal sinuses**, Fig. 43, *l*). The sphenoidal sinuses are continued craniad into the cavities of the ethmoid. The body has six surfaces:

The dorsal or internal surface (Fig. 42, *n*) looks into the cranial cavity and is continuous with the dorsal surface of the wings. The caudal end of the body is depressed, and when united to the basisphenoid aids in forming the cranial wall of the sella turcica. At each caudolateral angle is a short spine, the **anterior clinoid process.** At about one-third the length of the bone from the caudal end is a transverse groove (**chiasmatic groove,** Fig. 42, *m*) for the optic chiasma. Its ends lead into two round foramina (**the optic foramina,** Fig. 42, *l*; Fig. 21, *c*) which pass craniolaterad between the body and the wings of the presphenoid and transmit the optic nerve and the ophthalmic artery.

The ventral surface (Fig. 21) is hour-glass-shaped and marked by a smooth median ridge, continuous with the ridge on the basisphenoid and overlaid at its cranial end by the vomer. The caudal end presents a rough triangular area on each side, for articulation with the pterygoid process of the sphenoid bone, while the cranial end has similar areas overlaid by the nasal portion of the palatine bones.

The lateral surface looks towards the orbitotemporal fossa. It is notched near the caudal end by the ventral border of the optic foramen (*c*). Caudad of this foramen the surface presents an oblique groove which forms in the natural condition the medial boundary of the orbital fissure.

Craniad of the optic foramen the surface is smooth and marked near its ventral border by a longitudinal ridge which forms part of the dorsal boundary of a fossa, the **external pterygoid fossa** (Fig. 40, *p*).

The caudal end presents ventrally a quadrangular rough surface for articulation with the body of the sphenoid. The cranial end presents the two sphenoidal sinuses separated by a median partition.

The median partition articulates by its free border with the lamina perpendicularis of the ethmoid. At its ventral end is the abruptly truncate end of the median ridge of the ventral surface, which is continuous with the ventral cartilaginous portion of the lamina perpendicularis. The lateral walls of the sphenoidal sinuses are continued craniad of the dorsal and ventral walls and of the median partition, and articulate ventrally with the nasal portion of the palatine bones, and dorsally with the orbital plate of the frontal. Between them is received the caudal ends of the labyrinths of the ethmoid in the middle, while between their dorsal edges is received the caudal end of the cribriform plate, and between their ventral edges the expanded end of the vomer.

The **wings** (*b*) arise each from nearly the whole of the dorsolateral angle of the body. They form prominent nearly horizontal triangular projections over the optic foramina.

The dorsal and ventral surfaces are smooth and continuous respectively with the dorsal and lateral surfaces of the body. The dorsal surface looks into the cranial cavity, while the ventral looks into the orbitotemporal fossa.

Craniad of the apex of the wing its border articulates with the ventral edge of the orbital portion of the frontal bone. Caudad of the apex the border articulates with the cranial border of the wing of the sphenoid.

Temporal Bone. Os temporale (Figs. 22 and 23).—This forms a part of the lateral wall of the cranium, filling the gap between the occipital and the sphenoidal segments. It is made up of three portions which are distinct in kittens but somewhat firmly united in adult cats. In lower vertebrates these portions are distinct bones called the **Squamous,** the **Petrous,** and the **Tympanic** bones. In the cat they may be described as the squamous (*a*), petrous (*b*), and tympanic (*c*) portions of the temporal bone.

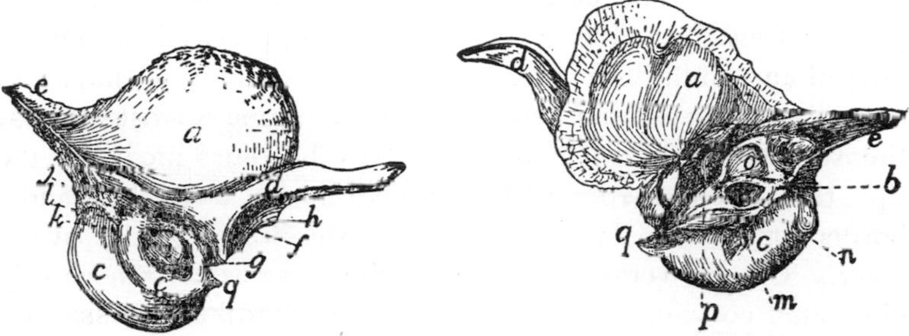

FIG. 22.—TEMPORAL BONE, EXTERNAL SURFACE. FIG. 23.—TEMPORAL BONE, INTERNAL SURFACE.

a, squamous portion; *b*, petrous portion; *c*, *c'*, tympanic portion (*c*, entotympanic; *c'*, ectotympanic); *d*, zygomatic process; *e*, mastoid portion of the petrous; *f*, mandibular fossa; *g*, postmandibular process; *h*, tuberculum articulare; *i*, external auditory meatus; *j*, stylomastoid foramen; *k*, pit for tympanohyal bone; *l*, mastoid process; *m*, grooves bounding the jugular foramen; *n*, internal auditory meatus; *o*, appendicular fossa; *p*, hiatus facialis; *q*, styliform process of tympanic bulla.

The **squamous portion** (*a*) **(squama temporalis)** is thin and oval or has the form of an equilateral triangle with rounded angles, with a curved process, the **zygomatic process** (*d*), arising from its ventral border. Its outer surface (Fig. 22) is convex and smooth and gives origin to part of the temporal muscle. Its inner surface (Fig. 23) is concave and smooth except near the margins, where it is bevelled and rough. The roughened border is broader dorsad and caudad. The ventral margin of the bone is turned mediad at its cranial end so that the lateral face of the inverted portion looks ventrad. By this portion of its lateral face the squamous rests upon the tympanic bulla, and its edge articulates with the tentorium and the wing of the sphenoid. The remaining (caudal) portion of the ventral border overlies the mastoid portion (*e*) of the petrous. By the remainder of its border the bone articulates with the parietal dorsad and with the wing of the sphenoid craniad. The roughened portion of its inner surface overlies the margins of both these bones.

The zygomatic process (*d*) is formed by the confluence of two roots. One of these starts from the ventral end of the lambdoidal ridge and passes along the ventral margin of the squama dorsad of the external auditory meatus. The other arises abruptly from the cranioventral angle of the bone. The process thus formed is at first broad and passes horizontally laterad and slightly craniad. It soon grows more slender and turns gradually craniad, while at the same time it twists so that the surface which is dorsal at the base becomes medial at the tip; the posterior root which is continuous with the caudal border at the base is continuous with the dorsal border at the apex. On the ventral surface of the base is a transversely elongated concave articular surface, the **mandibular fossa** (*f*), for the condyloid process of the lower jaw. Caudad of this is a sharp transverse ridge, the **postmandibular** or **postglenoid process** (*g*), and craniad of the lateral end of the fossa a slight tubercle, the **tuberculum articulare** (*h*). Near its apex the zygomatic process is more slender and its ventral border is bevelled for articulation with the malar or zygomatic bone.

The **tympanic** (Figs. 22 and 23, *c*; Fig. 24) is expanded into a large hollow olive-shaped bone which is known as the **auditory bulla** and encloses the tympanic cavity. Its substance is very compact. Unlike the tympanic of most other mammals it is developed from two bones, known as the **ectotympanic** (Fig. 22, *c'*) and **entotympanic** (*c*). These are strongly marked in young kittens, and can usually be easily distinguished in adult cats. The entotympanic (Figs. 22 and 23, *c*) forms the larger part of the bulla, constituting its ventral and medial surfaces; it is thin, smooth, and transparent. The ectotympanic (Fig. 22, *c'*) surrounds the external auditory meatus: it is thicker and more opaque than the entotympanic. The bulla lies ventrad of the squamous, and in an external view conceals a large part of the petrous.

On its lateral surface it presents near the dorsal border an irregular oval opening, that of the **external auditory meatus** (Fig. 22, *i*), which leads into the tympanic cavity. Caudad of the external auditory meatus is a nearly dorsoventral groove, which, when the bone is articulated, forms a part of the boundary of the stylomastoid foramen (Fig. 22, *j*); just ventrad of this groove is a pit (*k*) which lodges the tip of the tympanohyal bone.

Craniad the bone is produced into a short spine, the **styliform** process (*q*), which lies in a horizontal groove in the ventral surface of the basisphenoid. Laterad of this spine is a groove for the tuba auditiva or Eustachian tube.

The medial surface (Fig. 24) presents in the middle near its ventral margin a short triangular spine which lies in the natural state against the ventral surface of the basilar portion of the occipital.

Caudad of this spine the surface is marked by two or three vertical parallel grooves (Fig. 23, *m*). They indicate the portion of the bone which bounds the jugular foramen, and are possibly impressions of the ninth, tenth, and eleventh nerves.

FIG. 24. — TYMPANIC BULLA, ISOLATED, MEDIAL SURFACE.
a, inner end of auditory meatus; *b*, partition dividing tympanic cavity; *c*, styliform process.

The dorsal two-thirds of the medial surface is lacking in the disarticulated bulla (Fig. 24), so that the cavity of the bone is exposed. This opening is in the natural state closed by the petrous bone. The caudal end is rough where it is overlaid by the jugular process.

On the inner surface of the tympanic bulla is seen the thickened margin of the inner end of the auditory meatus (Fig. 24, *a*). To it is attached the membrana tympana. In the median dorsal line this margin is notched for the reception of the incus and head of the malleus. From the lateral wall of the cavity at the line of junction of the ectotympanic and entotympanic a thin bony partition (*b*) rises. It runs almost directly mediad; is concave dorsally and divides the tympanic cavity into two chambers.

The Petrous Portion (Fig. 23, *b*, and Fig. 25).—This consists of two parts, a very dense part (the petrous portion proper, Fig. 25), which has the form of a triangular pyramid and encloses the auditory labyrinth, and a less dense part, the

mastoid portion (Figs. 22 and 23, *e*), which is flattened and triangular and is attached by its base to the base of the pyramid.

The petrous portion may be described as having a base and three sides, lateral, dorsal, and medial. It completes the medial wall of the tympanic bulla, so that it is not possible to see it from the exterior of a skull except through the auditory meatus (Fig. 22, *i*). When the bones of the skull are articulated its dorsal surface is covered by the tentorium and alisphenoid. Its lateral face looks into the tympanic cavity, while the medial face looks into the cranial cavity.

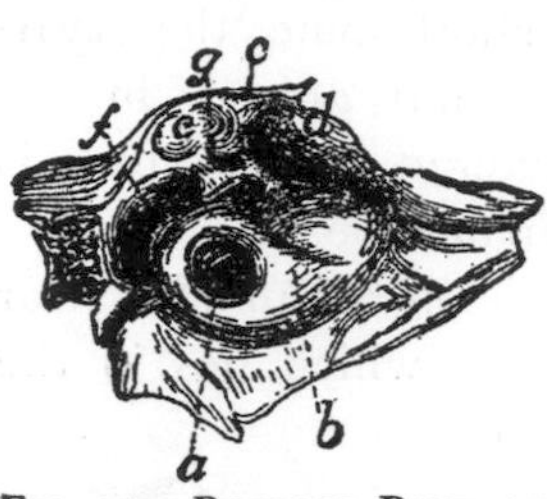

FIG. 25.—PETROUS BONE OF RIGHT SIDE, LATERAL SURFACE, ENLARGED.

a, fenestra cochleæ; *b*, promontory; *c*, fenestra vestibuli; *d*, fossa for the tensor tympani muscle; *e*, fossa for incus and malleus; *f*, fossa continuous with stylomastoid foramen; *g*, foramen leading to facial canal.

Its lateral face (Fig. 25) (medial wall of the tympanic cavity) presents just ventrad of the middle of its base a large circular foramen, the **fenestra cochleæ** (*a*) (or fenestra rotunda), which looks caudolaterad; it leads into the cochlea. The fenestra cochleæ lies at the summit of a nipple-like elevation, the **promontory** (*b*), which is continued toward the apex of the bone as a gradually diminishing semicylindrical ridge, due to the presence within it of the bony cochlea. Dorsad of the fenestra cochleæ is the much smaller **fenestra vestibuli** (*c*) (or ovalis) which leads into the vestibule. It is occupied in the natural condition by the base of the stapes.

Dorsocraniad of the fenestra vestibuli is a large fossa (*d*) which contains the tensor tympani muscle. Dorsocaudad of this, partly bounded by the squamous portion of the temporal, is another large fossa (*e*), the cranial end of which is occupied by the incus, while its caudal end is occupied by the head of the malleus.

Nearly caudad of this fossa and separated from it by an oblique bony septum is a third fossa (*f*) which is narrow and curved. It is continuous with a notch in the mastoid portion of the bone. When the tympanic is articulated the notch is converted into a foramen (**stylomastoid foramen,** Fig. 22, *j*) for the exit of the seventh nerve. The fossa gives passage to the seventh nerve and also lodges the stapedius muscle. A groove may be traced from the stylomastoid foramen to the caudal border of the fossa for the tensor tympani muscle, where it passes into a canal (*g*). The groove and canal are parts of the **canalis facialis** or **facial canal** (aqueductus Fallopii) for the passage of the seventh nerve through the petrous bone.

The medial surface (Fig. 23, *b*) of the petrous portion shows near its middle a fossa, the **internal auditory meatus** (*n*). This is divided by a partition of bone into a dorsal and ventral part. The dorsal portion is the beginning of the facial canal (aqueductus Fallopii) by which the seventh nerve passes through the petrous bone to emerge at the stylomastoid foramen. The ventral portion shows at its bottom several small foramina for the auditory nerve.

Dorsocaudad of the internal auditory meatus is a deep fossa (*o*) for a small lobe, the so-called appendicular lobe, of the cerebellum. This may be called the appendicular fossa.

The dorsal surface is triangular and presents near its apex a foramen—the **hiatus facialis** (*p*), the opening of a canal which joins the canalis facialis and transmits the superficial petrosal branch of the nerve of the pterygoid canal (Vidian nerve). That part of the dorsal surface which lies caudad of the hiatus facialis is known as the **tegmen tympani.**

The base of the petrous is attached to the mastoid portion (Fig. 23, *e*).

(For an account of the structures within the petrous bone and the tympanic cavity, see the description of the internal and middle ear.)

The **mastoid portion** (Figs. 22 and 23, *e*) is attached by its base to the pyramidal petrous portion, with which it forms an angle of about 120 degrees. It appears in the lateral wall of the skull between the parietal bone and the occipital (Fig. 40, *d*). The lambdoidal ridge is continued on its outer surface to the caudal border of the external auditory meatus. Caudad of the stylomastoid foramen it forms a slight nipple-like eminence, the **mastoid process** (Fig. 22, *l*). Its inner face looks into the cranial cavity.

Parietal Bone. Os parietale (Figs. 39, 40, and 43, 3).—The parietal bones form the larger part of the lateral and dorsal boundary of the cranial cavity. Each is a thin rectangular bone, compact and curved and with a deeply notched shelf of bone, the **tentorium** (Fig. 42, *e*, and Fig. 43, *f*), projecting inward from near the caudal margin.

The outer surface is smooth and convex. The highest part of the convexity, a little caudad of the middle of the bone, is known as the **parietal tubercle** or **eminence** (Fig. 39, *d*); it marks the point of beginning ossification. An obscure curved ridge (Fig. 39, *e*), running from the caudodorsal angle or a point craniad of it craniolaterad, indicates the boundary of the origin of the temporal muscle. Near the ventral border the surface is roughened and is covered in the natural state by a part of the squamous portion of the temporal bone.

The inner surface (Fig. 43, 3 and 3′) is smooth and marked by ridges and grooves for the convolutions of the cerebrum. Near the medial border is a ridge which, when the bone is articulated with that of the opposite side, forms a shallow groove for the **superior sagittal sinus.** Beginning near the middle of the ventral margin and passing dorsad is a groove for the middle meningeal artery. The **tentorium** (Fig. 43, *f*) arises from the inner surface near its caudal margin and projects mediad as a thin curved or notched shelf of bone which separates the cerebellar fossa (Fig. 43, *I*) of the cranium from the cerebral fossa (Fig. 43, *II*). When the parietals are articulated there is left between the tentoria a large foramen by means of which the two fossæ communicate. The foramen is bounded laterally and dorsally by the free margins of the tentoria, while the ventral end of each tentorium articulates with the alisphenoid, and its dorsal end with the opposite tentorium.

The medial border is straight and is united by suture to the opposite bone.

The cranial border is bevelled at the expense of the inner surface and articulates with the frontal. Just ventrad of the middle of the border projects a sharp spine which fits into a corresponding notch in the caudal border of the frontal.

The ventral border is concave, sharp, and bevelled at the expense of the outer surface, for articulation with the squamous portion of the temporal, except near the cranial end, where it articulates with the wing of the sphenoid.

The caudal border is thick and porous medially, but thin laterally, and bevelled at the expense of the inner surface for articulation with the interparietal and mastoid portion of the temporal.

Frontal Bone. Os frontale (Figs. 39, 40, and 41, 5; Fig. 43, 8; Fig. 26).—The frontal bones meet one another in the median dorsal line so as to form the roof of the skull between the parietal and nasal bones. A part extends also ventrad, forming a large part of the medial wall of the orbit and a part of the temporal fossa.

The bone may be divided into two portions, a plate forming the cranial portion of the roof of the skull and a part of the roof of the nasal cavity, the **frontal plate** (Fig. 40, 5), and a part descending into the orbit, the **orbital plate** (Fig. 40, 5′).

The frontal plate (Fig. 40, 5) is a right-angled triangle with the hypothenuse lateral. Its dorsal surface is convex and smooth. The cranial two-thirds of its lateral border is separated from the orbital fossa by a ridge, the **supraorbital arch** or margin (Fig. 39, *i*; Fig. 40, *o*); the caudal third passes gradually into the temporal fossa. At its cranial angle is a triangular projection, the **frontal spine** or nasal spine (Fig. 26, *a*), which fits into a space between the nasal and maxillary bones.

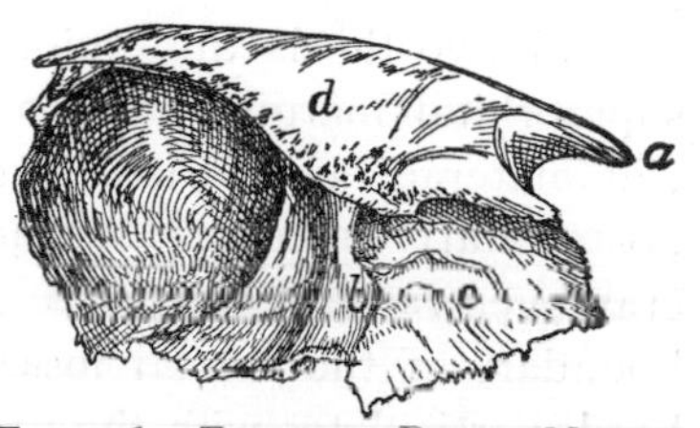

FIG. 26.—FRONTAL BONE, MEDIAL SURFACE.

a, frontal spine; *b*, transverse ridge; *c*, surface applied to the ethmoid; *d*, vertical plate of medial border.

The ventral surface is concave and smooth over its caudal one-half and helps to form the cranial part of the brain-case. It presents slight ridges and depressions for convolutions of the cerebrum. At its narrowed middle region the ventral surface is marked by a thick transverse ridge (Fig. 26, *b*). Caudally the ridge descends by a gentle slope to the level of the ventral surface of the bone. The cranial end of the ridge is pierced by an oval foramen through which the frontal sinus (Fig. 43, *m*, *m'*), which lies within the ridge, communicates with the spaces in the ethmoid bone (nasal cavity). Craniad of the ridge the surface (Fig. 26, *c*) is rough and, together with the raised medial border of the bone and the orbital plate, encloses a rectangular space which in the natural state receives a portion of the labyrinth of the ethmoid. The ventral surface is marked at its medial edge by a thin longitudinal ridge which, when the bones are articulated, is continuous with one of the vertical lamellæ of the ethmoid.

The medial border forms a vertical plate (*d*), broadest craniad and roughened for articulation with its fellow of the opposite side except at its cranial end, where it articulates with the border of the nasal bone.

The caudal border is roughened, bevelled at the expense of the outer surface, and articulated with the parietal bone except at its ventral end, where it articulates with the alisphenoid.

The lateral border is smooth, and it is here that the orbital plate is joined to the frontal plate at right angles. Along its cranial two-thirds this union is marked by a sharp ridge, the supraorbital margin (Fig. 40, *o*) or arch. This ridge extends caudolaterad as a triangular projection, the **zygomatic** (or postorbital) **process** (Fig. 40, *n*), which is flattened on its cranioventral face near its extremity and forms part of the boundary of the orbital fossa. At its cranial end the lateral border articulates with the nasal and maxillary bones.

The orbital plate (Fig. 40, 5') arises from the ventral surface of the lateral border of the frontal plate. It is directed ventrad, is smooth and concave on its outer surface, and forms the dorsal portion of the medial wall of the orbital fossa. Near its ventral border it bears the small **ethmoidal foramen,** for the artery and nerve (page 370) of the same name.

On the caudal one-half of its inner surface (Fig. 26) it assists the caudal part of the dorsal plate in forming the brain-case. The cranial one-half of its inner surface is marked off from the remainder of the surface by a sharp irregular ridge which is for articulation with the cribriform plate of the ethmoid. Craniad of this the surface is marked by ridges and looks into the nasal cavity.

The cranial margin is produced dorsally in the form of a blunt triangular spine. Mediad of this spine the bone articulates with the lachrymal bone.

The ventral border articulates by its cranial one-third with the orbital plate of the palatine, and by its caudal two-thirds with the body and wing of the presphenoid.

Maxillary Bone. Maxilla (Figs. 27 and 28). — The maxillary bone forms the cranial and lateral portions of the roof of the mouth. The bones of opposite sides meet craniad, but diverge caudad to enclose the palatal plates of the palatine bones. Each consists of a thick prismatic ventral portion or

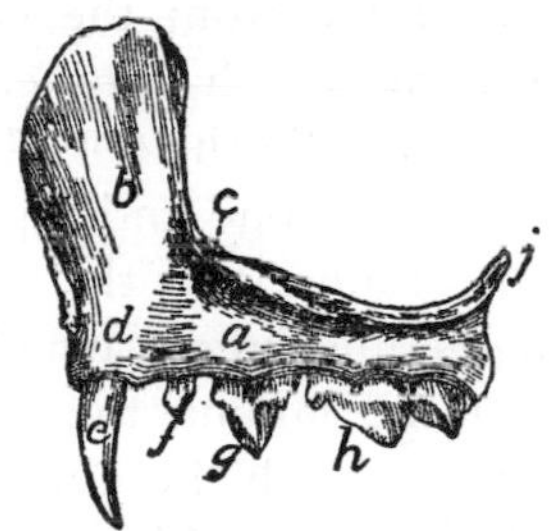

FIG. 27.—MAXILLARY BONE, LATERAL SURFACE.

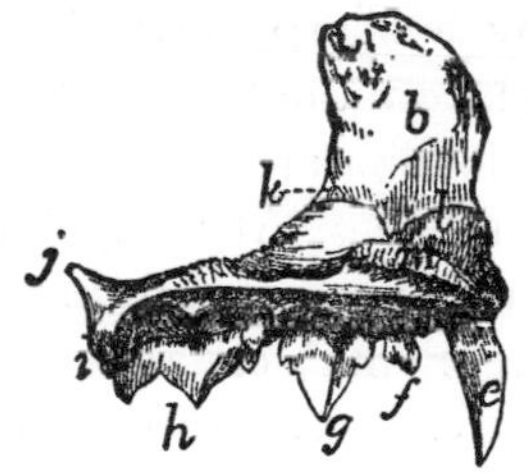

FIG. 28.—MAXILLARY BONE, MEDIAL SURFACE.

a, body; *b*, frontal process; *c*, infraorbital foramen; *d*, elevation for root of canine tooth; *e*, canine tooth; *f*, first premolar; *g*, second premolar; *h*, third premolar; *i*, molar tooth; *j*, zygomatic process; *k*, beginning of lachrymal canal; *l*, ridge to which the ventral nasal concha is attached; *m*, nasal crest of palatine process.

body (*a*) and a thin flat plate, the **frontal process** (*b*), extending dorsad from the cranial part of the bone.

The body (*a*) has the form of a triangular prism whose broader dorsal face looks into the nasal cavity and orbit, while the ventral face looks into the mouth, and the lateral face toward the cheek. From the junction of the dorsal and lateral surfaces at the cranial end the large flat curved frontal process (*b*) passes dorsad, while the teeth are implanted along the border, **alveolar border** or process, formed by the junction of the ventral and lateral surfaces.

The lateral surface is continuous with the lateral surface of the frontal process and shows at the base of the frontal process on its caudal border the large **infraorbital** foramen (Fig. 27, *c*), for the vessels and nerves of the same name. Near the medial end of the surface is a cylindrical elevation (*d*) for the root of the canine tooth (*e*).

The ventral surface is smooth and looks into the roof of the mouth.

On the dorsal surface caudal and cranial halves may be distinguished. The caudal one-half enters into the floor of the orbit. The lateral edge of this portion is divided into two laminæ, between which is received the end of the malar bone. Caudad this edge is prolonged into the short dorsally directed **zygomatic process** (*j*). The cranial half of the dorsal surface looks into the nasal cavity and is separated from the caudal half by a sharp vertical lamina of bone which runs caudomediad from the base of the nasal process. To the dorsal edge of this lamina are articulated the lachrymal bone and a part of the palatine. At the point where the lamina joins the base of the nasal process a foramen is seen leading into a canal, the **nasolachrymal canal** (*k*). Craniad of the lamina the surface is concave. Where it becomes continuous with the inner edge of the frontal process there is attached to it a thin bone, the **ventral nasal concha** (or maxilloturbinal), which is rolled into an irregular spiral. The nasolachrymal canal opens ventrad of its cranial end.

The cranial third of this part of the bone projects further mediad than does the rest of the medial border, forming thus the broad **palatine process.** This is rough on its medial edge for articulation with the premaxillary and the palatine process of the opposite bone. This medial edge rises also dorsally into a low ridge, the **nasal crest** (*m*), which is roughened for articulation with the vomer. The caudal two-thirds of the medial edge articulates with the palatine bone.

The cranial end of the bone articulates with the premaxilla.

The caudal end is smooth.

The frontal process (*b*) presents on its inner surface, which looks into the nasal cavity, certain transverse ridges which are in relation with the ethmoid bone. Its outer surface is smooth. By its cranial border it articulates with the nasal bone dorsally and with the premaxillary bone ventrally.

Its dorsal end articulates medially with the nasal spine of the frontal bone, and caudally with the orbital plate of the same bone.

Premaxillary Bone. (Os incisivum BNA.) Premaxilla (Fig. 29).—The premaxillary bones bear the incisor teeth and form the cranial portion of the roof of the mouth.

Each consists of an irregular, horizontal **palatal portion** (*b*) and of a perpendicular **nasal process** (*c*) which forms part of the lateral boundary of the nares and enters into the formation of the lateral wall of the nasal cavity.

The palatal portion has in its caudal border a deep notch for the foramen incisivum or anterior palatine canal, which lies between it and the maxillary and transmits blood-vessels and nerves. It articulates with the maxillary bone by this border.

FIG. 29. — PREMAXILLARY BONE, OBLIQUELY CRANIOLATERAL ASPECT.
a, the three incisor teeth; *b*, palatal portion of the bone; *c*, nasal process.

The medial border is raised into a thin crest of bone which, besides forming the medial wall of the foramen incisivum or anterior palatine canal, articulates by its medial border with the bone of the opposite side, forming a sort of median trough (**sulcus palatinus**) which projects dorsad into the nasal cavity and receives the ventral border of the nasal septum. The caudal end of this border articulates laterad with the maxilla, dorsad with the vomer.

Its craniolateral border bears the incisor teeth (*a*).

The nasal process (*c*) presents three surfaces, all elongated and triangular; one, the medial surface, is smooth and concave and looks into the nasal cavity. Its dorsal border is rough for articulation with the nasal bone dorsad, and smooth ventrad where it aids in forming the nares.

The lateral surface is smooth.

The caudal surface is rough for articulation with the maxillary bone.

Nasal Bone. Os nasale (Fig. 30).—The nasal bones fill the space between the nasal process of the premaxillary, the frontal process of the maxillary, and the nasal spine of the frontal bone (Fig. 39, 7). They thus form part of the dorsal wall of the nasal cavity near the middle line.

Fig. 30. Nasal Bone, Dorsal View.

Each may be described as consisting of two elongated triangular lamellæ, one vertical, the other horizontal. The vertical lamella is curved slightly ventrad and has its apex directed craniad. It is applied by its medial surface against the vertical lamella of the opposite bone, the two thus forming a median vertical partition, the **nasal crest** (Fig. 43, 12), which extends ventrad into the nasal cavity and, by joining the dorsal edge of the lamina perpendicularis, helps to form the internasal septum.

The horizontal lamella is attached to the dorsal margin of the vertical lamella in such a way that its apex lies opposite the base of the vertical lamella. It helps to roof in the nasal cavity, and by its base forms a part of the dorsal boundary of the narial opening. By its lateral margin it articulates with the nasal spine of the frontal at its caudal end, with the frontal process of the maxillary at its middle, and with the nasal process of the premaxilla at its cranial end. The lateral angle of its base projects in a curved line which forms the dorsal part of the lateral boundary of the narial opening.

From the lateral border of the horizontal lamella a bony plate curves ventrad and mediad, enclosing a narrow fossa which receives a part of the ethmoid. This is the **concha nasalis superior** (nasoturbinal bone).

Ethmoid Bone. Os ethmoidale (Figs. 31 and 32).—The ethmoid bone closes in the cranial cavity at its cranial end and extends forward into the nasal cavity, which it largely fills.

It consists of a median vertical portion, the **lamina perpendicularis** (Fig. 43, *n*; Fig. 42, *p*), forming a part of the nasal septum, of two lateral portions made of thin sheets of bone variously folded and united—the **labyrinths** (or ethmoturbinals), which fill the greater part of the nasal cavity; and of a transverse perforated plate, the **cribriform plate** (lamina cribrosa), attached to the caudal end of the lamina perpendicularis and the labyrinths.

The lamina perpendicularis (Fig. 43, *n*; Fig. 42, *p*) is a flat four-sided bone. By its caudal margin it is continuous with the cribriform plate; by its ventral margin it is enclosed by the halves of the vomer; by its dorsal margin it unites with the crest formed by the vertical portion of the nasal bone craniad and with the vertical lamina of the medial margin of the frontal caudad, while its cranial margin is continued into the septal cartilage of the nose. Its lateral faces are smooth and free.

The lamina cribrosa or cribriform plate (Fig. 42, *o*) is elongated heart-shaped, with the apex of the heart ventrad. Its caudal face is concave and looks into the cranial cavity. It presents three irregular longitudinal rows of holes, one median and two lateral, for the passage of the olfactory fibres from the cranial cavity into the nasal cavity. Its cranial face is continuous along the medial line with the lamina perpendicularis, and at the sides with the labyrinths.

The notch in the heart is directed dorsad and receives the vertical lamina of the medial border of the frontal bone. The

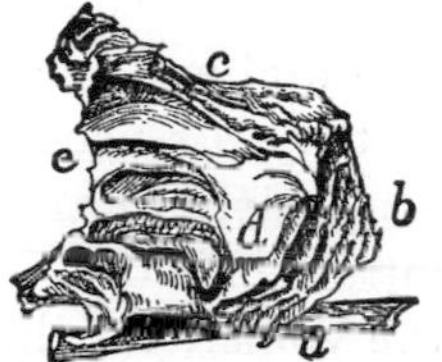

FIG. 31.—ETHMOID AND VOMER, SIDE VIEW.

FIG. 32.—ETHMOID AND VOMER, VENTRAL VIEW.

a, vomer; *b*, vertical cells of the labyrinth of the ethmoid; *c*, horizontal cell of the same; *d*, part of the ethmoid that forms the lamina papyracea; *e*, edge of cribriform plate.

apex of the heart articulates with the cranial end of the dorsal surface of the presphenoid. Its lateral margins are articulated with the ethmoidal ridges on the medial surface of the frontal bone.

The labyrinths (Figs. 31 and 32) are attached to the cranial face of the lamina cribrosa, one on each side of the lamina perpendicularis. Each is made of thin bony plates irregularly folded so as to enclose spaces, the **ethmoid cells.** In each may be distinguished a cranial portion (*b*), in which the cells are nearly vertical, and a caudal portion (*c*), in which the cells are nearly horizontal.

The medial surfaces are separated by a space from the lamina perpendicularis. This space is broadest along the junction of the horizontal and vertical portions of the labyrinth. There are thus formed two passageways which correspond to the superior meati of human anatomy.

The lateral surfaces come into contact with the frontal process of the maxillary and the orbital plate of the frontal bone. On the lateral surface of each labyrinth there is a thin irregular lamina of bone lying in a dorsoventral longitudinal plane and closing in some of the ethmoid cells laterally (*d*). A small part of this lamina, situated near the caudoventral angle of the bone, appears in the orbital fossa on the external surface of the skull between the presphenoid, palatine, and frontal bones or between the lachrymal, palatine, and frontal bones. Sometimes in the entire skull two such pieces may be seen, one in each of these positions. This corresponds to the **lamina papyracea** of human anatomy.

The dorsocaudal angle of each bone is received into the space between the orbital plate of the frontal and the vertical lamina of the medial border of the frontal. Its ventrocaudal angle is received between the cranial extensions of the lateral walls of the presphenoid, while its ventral surface is overlaid caudally by the expanded portion of the vomer, to which it is attached at its caudolateral angles.

Vomer (Figs. 31 and 32, *a*).—The vomer consists of two thin laminæ of bone which ensheath the ventral margin of the lamina perpendicularis (or the cartilaginous plate which continues ventrad from this margin) and unite ventrad of it; the two thus form a trough open dorsad.

Each becomes horizontal near its caudal end and at the same time expands. The expanded portion lies ventrad of the labyrinth of the ethmoid, closing in some of its cells: its lateral angles are united with the labyrinths.

At its caudal end the bone articulates with the body of the

presphenoid, and each half of it is produced caudad near the middle line into a triangular spine which lies ventrad of the body of the presphenoid. The horizontal portion of the bone helps to separate the olfactory and respiratory passages of the nasal chamber, while its vertical portion contributes to the formation of the nasal septum.

The ventral margin formed by the junction of the two halves of the bone is smooth and free caudad, but at its cranial end is broad and rough for articulation with the palatal processes of the maxillæ.

Palatine Bone. Os palatinum (Fig. 33).—The palate bone or palatine bone consists of two portions, a **horizontal** or **palatal** portion (*a*) and a **perpendicular** or **nasal** portion (*b*), uniting at an angle of about forty-five degrees.

The horizontal portions (*a*) of the two bones are received between the maxillary bones and form the caudal and medial part of the roof of the mouth. Each is irregularly quadrilateral in form, with the caudolateral angle produced caudad into a long process which is continuous with the perpendicular portion of the bone. The lateral margin of the horizontal portion articulates over its cranial half with the maxillary bone. At about its middle a short thick **maxillary spine** (*c*) projects caudolaterad. The remainder of the lateral margin is directly continuous with the perpendicular plate of the bone. The medial margin is rough for articulation with the corresponding margin of the opposite palatine; the caudal angle of this margin projects caudad as the short **posterior nasal spine** (*d*). The caudal margin forms a free edge which bounds the choanæ; it passes laterally into the perpendicular portion.

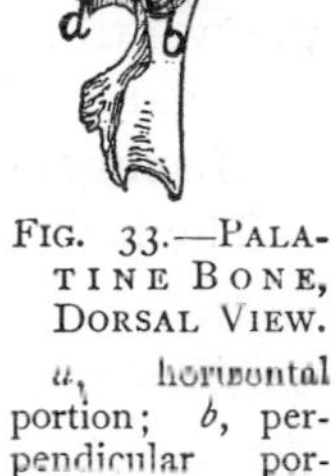

FIG. 33.—PALATINE BONE, DORSAL VIEW. *a*, horizontal portion; *b*, perpendicular portion; *c*, maxillary spine; *d*, posterior nasal spine; *e*, sphenopalatine foramen; *f*, caudal opening of posterior palatine canal.

The ventral surface (Fig. 41, 8) looks into the mouth. Near the middle of its craniolateral margin are two or more small foramina (Fig. 41, *q*) which form the cranial temination of the posterior palatine canal. The dorsal surface is smooth and looks into the nasal cavity.

The perpendicular or nasal portion (Fig. 33, *b*) of the palatine is thin and irregularly quadrilateral in form. It is attached by its cranial two-thirds to the dorsal surface of the horizontal portion. The outer surface is concave and looks into the orbital fossa. The inner surface is convex and looks into the nasal cavity.

The perpendicular portion is marked by two formaina just craniad of the middle. The larger dorsal oval foramen is the **sphenopalatine** foramen (*e*). The smaller ventral foramen is the caudal opening of the posterior palatine canal (*f*). From this opening the canal passes craniomediad, lying in the substance of the palatine bone; it opens on the ventral surface of the horizontal portion at the small openings previously described (Fig. 41, *q*).

By its cranial margin it articulates with the lachrymal bone. By its dorsal margin it articulates craniad with the orbital plate of the frontal: with the lamina papyracea at its middle, and with the body of the presphenoid caudad. The caudal half of the dorsal margin is partially divided into two lamellæ with a rough surface between them: this rough surface lies against the ventral surface of the presphenoid. The caudal margin articulates with the pterygoid portion of the sphenoid.

Lachrymal Bone. Os lachrymale (Fig. 34; Fig. 39, 10). —The lachrymal bone is a thin pentagonal scale of bone filling

FIG. 34.—LACHRYMAL BONE OF LEFT SIDE, EXTERNAL SURFACE.

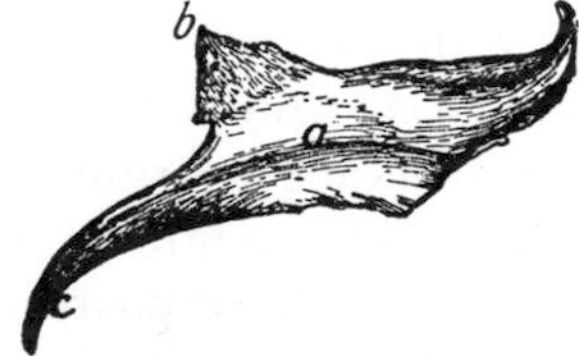

FIG. 35.—MALAR BONE OF RIGHT SIDE, LATERAL SURFACE.

Fig. 34.—*a*, notch forming the beginning of the lachrymal canal.
Fig. 35.—*a*, ridge for origin of the masseter muscle; *b*, frontal process; *c*, zygomatic process.

the interval between the horizontal plate of the palatine, the maxillary, and the orbital plate of the frontal. Its outer surface looks into the orbit, its inner surface into the nasal cavity.

Near the middle of its cranial border it is notched obliquely by a foramen (*a*), the beginning of the nasolachrymal canal.

Malar Bone. Jugal Bone. Os zygomaticum (Fig. 35).—The malar or zygomatic bone is a flat curved plate of bone which forms the lateral wall of the orbit and together with the zygomatic process of the temporal forms the zygomatic arch. Its outer surface is smooth and marked by a longitudinal ridge (*a*) for attachment of the masseter muscle.

At its caudal end the bone is continued into two processes: one, the **frontal** process or **orbital** process (*b*), is a triangular spine of bone directed caudomediad; when the bones are articulated it lies opposite the zygomatic process of the frontal to which it is joined by a ligament (orbital ligament). The other, **zygomatic** process (*c*) of the malar bone, extends ventrocaudad and articulates with a similar process from the temporal to form the zygomatic arch above mentioned.

Its inner surface is smooth and looks into the orbit, except that of the zygomatic process, which looks into the temporal fossa.

Its cranial border is roughened at the expense of both surfaces and articulates with the maxillary bone. Its other borders are smooth except the dorsal border of the zygomatic process, which is roughened for attachment to the zygomatic process of the temporal.

The Mandible. Mandibula (Figs. 36 and 37).—The mandible (or inferior maxillary bone) is composed of two halves which come together at the cranial end and form the lower jaw. At its caudal end each half articulates with the temporal bone at the mandibular fossa, and at its cranial end it joins the opposite bone, the suture being known as the **symphysis** of the jaw (**symphysis menti**) (Fig. 37, *a*).

Each half consists of a horizontal portion, the **body** (*b*), bearing teeth on one of its borders (the **alveolar border**), and of a vertical portion, the **ramus** (*c*).

The body (*b*) has the form of a flattened cylinder and has two surfaces and two borders. The lateral surface (Fig. 36) is smooth and presents near its cranial end one or two **mental foramina** (*d*) which form the cranial end of the mandibular canal and give exit to the mental arteries and nerves. At its caudal end is a deep fossa continuing on to the ramus, the **coronoid fossa,** or **masseteric fossa** (*e*).

The medial surface (Fig. 37) is smooth and has near its caudal end the **mandibular foramen** (*f*) for the entrance of the

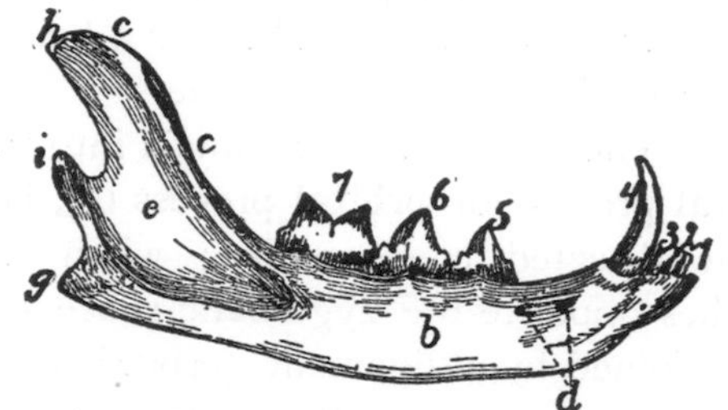

FIG. 36.—MANDIBLE, LATERAL SURFACE.

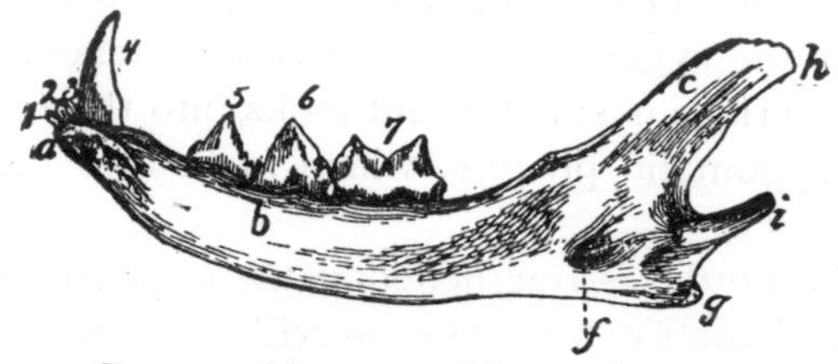

FIG. 37.—MANDIBLE, MEDIAL SURFACE.

a, symphysis; *b*, body; *c*, ramus; *d*, mental foramina; *e*, coronoid fossa; *f*, mandibular foramen; *g*, angular process; *h*, coronoid process; *i*, condyloid process; 1, 2, 3, the three incisor teeth; 4, the canine tooth; 5, 6, the premolars; 7, the molar tooth.

inferior alveolar artery and nerve, which pass through the mandibular canal to the mental foramen. The cranial end is roughened for attachment to the bone of the opposite side.

The ventral border is smooth and rounded; it ends caudally in a blunt point, the **angular process** (*g*). The dorsal (alveolar) border is slightly curved and bears the sockets (**alveoli**) for the teeth. It is continuous with the cranial margin of the coronoid process.

The ramus is divided into two portions, the **coronoid** process (*h*) and the **condyloid** process (*i*). The coronoid process (*h*) extends dorsocaudad as a thin plate of bone with smooth surfaces and borders. Its outer surface is partly occupied by the **coronoid fossa** (*e*). The condyloid process (*i*) has the form of a semicylindrical transverse piece of bone attached to the caudal margin of the coronoid process. It articulates with the mandibular fossa of the temporal bone.

Hyoid Bone. Os hyoideum (Fig. 38 and Fig. 104).—The hyoid bone forms the support for the tongue and gives origin to muscles passing to the tongue and larynx. It also supports the thyroid cartilage (Fig. 104, 1).

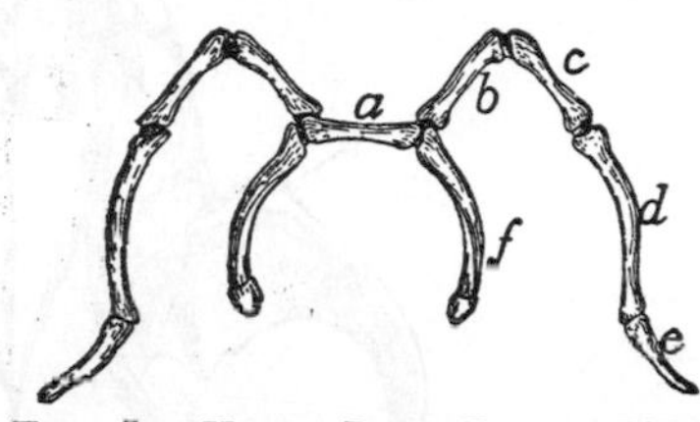

Fig. 38.—Hyoid Bone, Dorsal View. *a*, body; *b*, *c*, *d*, *e*, cranial cornu; *f*, caudal cornu; *b*, ceratohyal; *c*, epihyal; *d*, stylohyal; *e*, tympanohyal; *f*, thyrohyal.

It consists of a transverse bony bar, the **body** (Fig. 38, *a*) and of two **cornua** or horns attached to each end of the body.

The cranial cornu (lesser cornu of human anatomy) is the longer (Fig. 38, *b–e*). Each arises from the cranial face of the body at its lateral end, curves laterad, and then caudodorsad. It consists of four bony pieces movably united by cartilage.

The terminal piece is the **tympanohyal** (*e*); it is imbedded in the tympanic bulla just ventrad of the stylomastoid foramen. It is not therefore seen attached to the cornu after the latter has been separated from the skull. The other pieces become successively shorter toward the body, and are called **stylohyal** (*d*), **epihyal** (*c*), and **ceratohyal** (*b*).

The caudal cornua (*f*) (greater cornua of human anatomy) arise from the ends of the body. Each consists of a single piece of bone, the **thyrohyal** (*f*), which passes caudolaterad; its free end is united to a process of the thyroid cartilage (Fig. 104, 1).

The Skull as a Whole.—In the following description of the skull as a whole the mandible, hyoid, and ear-bones are not included.

The skull forms a bony box which contains the brain and is produced craniad into the **facial** portion which encloses the nasal cavity and forms the framework of the face.

In **dorsal view** (Fig. 39) the skull presents a smooth convex surface, broadest caudad, with the two **zygomatic arches** (*g*) curving out some distance laterally. The following bones are visible in dorsal view: the occipital (1), interparietal (2), parietals (3), temporals (4), frontals (5), malar or zygomatic

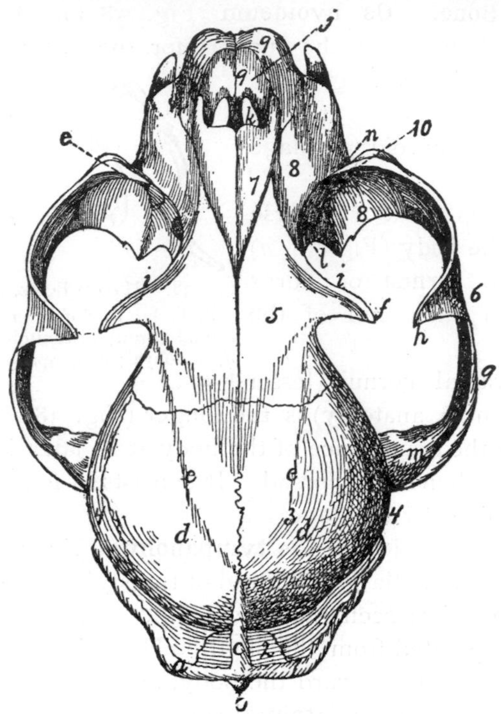

FIG. 39.—SKULL, DORSAL SURFACE.

1, occipital bone; 2, interparietal bone; 3, parietal bones; 4, temporal; 5, frontal; 6, malar; 7, nasal; 8, maxillary; 9, premaxillary; 10, lachrymal. *a*, lambdoidal ridge; *b*, external occipital tubercle; *c*, sagittal crest; *d*, parietal eminence; *e*, line which forms the dorsal boundary of the temporal fossa; *f*, zygomatic process of the frontal; *g*, zygomatic arch; *h*, frontal process of the malar; *i*, supraorbital arch; *j*, nares; *k*, foramen incisivum or anterior palatine foramen; *l*, sphenopalatine foramen; *m*, zygomatic process of the temporal; *n*, infraorbital foramen; *o*, opening of lachrymal duct.

bones (6), nasals (7), maxillaries (8), premaxillaries (9), and lachrymals (10).

The caudal boundary of the dorsal surface is marked by the prominent **lambdoidal ridge** (*a*) which passes from the middle cranioventrad along each side to the root of the zygomatic arch: it is borne by the occipital and temporal bones. From the middle of the lambdoidal ridge a second ridge, the **sagittal**

crest (*c*), passes craniad in the middle line across the interparietal bone: it varies greatly in extent, reaching in a very old and muscular cat to the cranial border of the parietals, while in kittens it does not exist. The most prominent portions of the skull in this region, just craniad of the middle of the parietal bones, are known as the parietal tubercles or eminences (*d*). A faint curved line (*e*) runs from the cranial end of the sagittal crest craniolaterad to the base of the zygomatic process of the frontal: it marks the dorsal boundary of the origin of the temporal muscle, and may therefore be considered the dorsal boundary of the temporal fossa. This fossa extends from its dorsal boundary as far laterad and caudad as the lambdoidal ridge (*a*), and as far craniad as a line connecting the tip of the zygomatic process of the frontal (*f*) with the frontal process of the malar (*h*). The temporal muscle takes origin from its surface.

The middle portion of the dorsal surface is formed by the frontals (5). Each frontal presents laterally a prominent **zygomatic process** (*f*), extending ventrolaterad toward a corresponding (frontal) process (*h*) of the malar bone. These two processes mark the boundary between the orbital fossa (craniad) and the temporal fossa (caudad). Craniad of the zygomatic process of the frontal a sharp margin separates the dorsal surface of the skull from the wall of the orbital fossa: this is the **supraorbital arch** or margin (*i*).

The cranial portion of the dorsal surface is formed by the maxillary (8), nasal (7), and premaxillary bones (9). Just craniad of the nasals, bounded ventrad and craniad by the premaxillaries, appears the large opening of the nares (*j*), leading into the nasal cavity.

The **zygomatic arch** (*g*) is formed by the zygomatic process of the temporal (*m*) and the malar or zygomatic bone (6). Each presents near its middle a prominent dorsocaudally directed process, the frontal process (*h*) of the malar bone. The zygomatic arch forms the lateral boundary of the temporal and orbital fossæ, which are separated by a line connecting the frontal process of the malar (*h*) and the zygomatic process of the frontal (*f*).

A portion of the floor of the orbit and the opening of the lachrymal canal (*o*) may also be seen in dorsal view; they are described in connection with the lateral surface.

The **caudal surface** of the skull is formed largely by the occipital bone (Fig. 17), surrounding the foramen magnum (Fig. 17, *d*). At the sides of the foramen magnum are the two prominent curved occipital condyles (*e*) for articulation with the atlas. Craniolaterad of the condyles, separated from them by a deep notch, are the jugular processes (*f*) of the occipital, closely applied to the caudal ends of the tympanic bullæ.

Dorsad of the foramen magnum are faint indications of a median ridge running dorsad, the **external occipital crest** (Fig. 17, *i*); this rises at its junction with the lambdoidal ridge to form the prominent **external occipital tubercle** (Fig. 39, *b*). The dorsal and dorsolateral boundaries of the posterior surface are formed by the lambdoidal ridge (Fig. 17, *h*; Fig. 39, *a*).

The **lateral surface** of the skull (Fig. 40) is much more complicated than the dorsal and posterior surfaces. Caudally the occipital condyles (*a*) and external occipital crest (*b*) are visible; dorsocaudad the sagittal crest (*c*).

Extending from the caudal end of the sagittal crest the lambdoidal ridge (*d*) is seen passing ventrocraniad to the tympanic bulla, thence craniad to the root of the zygomatic arch. In the ventral part of the caudal region the tympanic bulla (*e*) is visible with the jugular process (*f*) of the occipital pressed close against its caudal end. Just craniad of the jugular process the mastoid process (*g*) of the temporal rests against the side of the bulla. Beneath the cranial edge of this process is the opening of the stylomastoid foramen (*h*) for the seventh nerve, while just ventrad of the foramen is the small pit (*i*) in the tympanic bulla for the reception of the tympanohyal bone. Craniad of the stylomastoid foramen is the large opening of the external auditory meatus (*j*), leading into the middle ear.

Immediately dorsocraniad of the external auditory meatus the zygomatic arch begins as the zygomatic process (*k*) of the temporal bone. On the cranial surface of the base of this process is the deep mandibular fossa (*l*) for the condyle of the mandible. This fossa is bounded caudally by the prominent postmandibular process (*m*).

All that portion of the lateral surface of the skull which lies craniodorsad of the lambdoidal ridge may be divided (excluding the zygomatic arch) into three main parts, the **temporal fossa,** the **orbital fossa,** and the **face.** The boundaries of the temporal fossa have been given. The orbital fossa is bounded

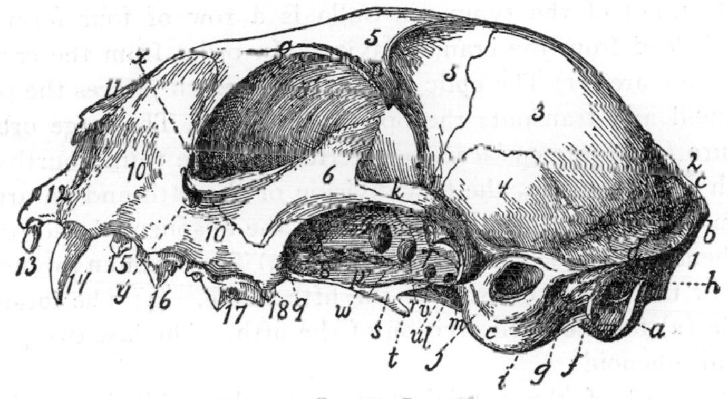

FIG. 40.—SKULL, SIDE VIEW.

1, occipital bone; 2, interparietal; 3, parietal; 4, temporal; 5, 5′, frontal; 6, malar; 7, sphenoid; 8, palatine; 9, presphenoid; 10, maxillary; 11, nasal; 12, premaxillary; 13, incisor teeth; 14, canine; 15, 16, 17, premolars; 18, molar. *a*, occipital condyle; *b*, external occipital crest; *c*, sagittal crest; *d*, lambdoidal ridge; *e*, tympanic bulla; *f*, jugular process; *g*, mastoid process; *h*, stylo-mastoid foramen; *i*, pit for tympanohyal bone; *j*, external auditory meatus; *k*, zygomatic process of temporal bone; *l*, mandibular fossa; *m*, postmandibular process; *n*, zygomatic process of the frontal; *o*, supraorbital margin; *p*, external pterygoid fossa; *q*, sphenopalatine foramen; *r*, orbital fissure; *s*, internal pterygoid fossa; *t*, hamulus; *u*, foramen ovale; *v*, foramen rotundum; *w*, optic foramen; *x*, opening of lachrymal canal; *y*, infraorbital foramen.

externally by a prominent semicircular ridge formed chiefly by the zygomatic arch, the zygomatic process of the frontal (*n*), and the supraorbital arch (*o*) of the frontal, which may be traced to the cranial root of the zygomatic arch. The orbital fossa may be considered to end caudally and ventrally at the level of the optic foramen (*w*); ventrad of it are certain smaller fossæ. Immediately ventrad is the long **external pterygoid fossa** (*p*), from which arises part of the external pterygoid muscle. This fossa begins at the sphenopalatine foramen (*q*) and extends caudad to the orbital fissure (*r*); it is separated by a ridge from the orbital fossa. Caudoventrad of the external pterygoid fossa and separated from it by a sharp ridge is the small narrow **internal pterygoid fossa** (*s*), which extends ventrad without interruption onto the surface of the hamulus (*t*) and caudad to within two or three millimeters of the tympanic bulla. From it the internal pterygoid muscle takes origin. The hamulus (*t*) projects caudoventrad in this region, forming a prominent feature in a lateral view.

Craniad of the tympanic bulla is a row of four foramina which lead from the cranial cavity. In order from the cranial end they are: (1) The **optic foramen** (*w*) which pierces the presphenoid and transmits the optic nerve. (2) The large **orbital fissure** (*r*), (foramen lacerum anterius), for the third, fourth and sixth cranial nerves, the first division of the fifth and an artery from the carotid plexus, lies between the alisphenoid and orbitosphenoid, ventrocaudad of the first. (3) The **foramen rotundum** (*v*) for the second division of the fifth nerve. (4) The **foramen ovale** (*u*) for the third division of the fifth. The last two pierce the alisphenoid.

Ventrad of the cranial portion of the orbit is the large **sphenopalatine foramen** (*q*), for the nerves and arteries of the same name and the posterior nasal nerve. Just craniad of this is the small caudal opening of the **posterior palatine canal** for the greater palatine nerve and descending palatine artery. It traverses the palatine bone and opens on its ventral surface near its cranial margin. Just dorsad of the cranial root of the zygomatic arch is the opening of the **lachrymal canal** (*x*), while the root of the arch is pierced by the large **infraorbital foramen** (*y*), which transmits the **infraorbital** nerves and artery from the orbit.

The teeth (13–18), implanted along the alveolar border of the maxillary and premaxillary, are prominent in a lateral view: they are described in the account of the alimentary canal.

The **ventral surface** of the skull (Fig. 41) is very complex. It consists of broad cranial and caudal portions and of a narrow median trough-like part which unites them. Laterad of this trough-like part are seen parts of the orbits and of the zygomatic arches. These do not properly belong to the ventral surface and have been already described.

Caudally there appear in the ventral view the foramen magnum (*a*), occipital condyles (*b*), and jugular processes (*c*). In front of the jugular processes the two tympanic bullæ (*d*) form prominent features, with the mastoid process (*e*), the stylomastoid foramen (*f*), and the external auditory meatus

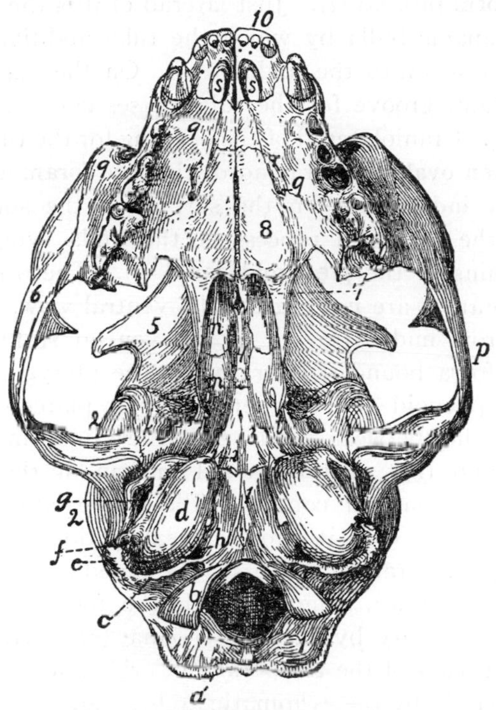

FIG. 41.—SKULL, VENTRAL VIEW.

1, occipital bone; 2, temporal; 3, sphenoid; 4, presphenoid; 5, frontal; 6, malar; 7, vomer; 8, palatine; 9, maxillary; 10, premaxillary. *a*, foramen magnum; *b*, occipital condyles; *c*, jugular process; *d*, tympanic bulla; *e*, mastoid process; *f*, stylomastoid foramen; *g*, external auditory meatus; *h*, jugular foramen; *i*, styliform process; *j*, groove for Eustachian tube; *k*, foramen ovale; *l*, foramen rotundum; *m*, pterygoid process of sphenoid; *n*, perpendicular plate of palatine; *o*, choanæ or posterior nares; *p*, zygomatic arch; *q*, cranial end of posterior palatine canal; *r*, palatine grooves; *s*, foramina incisiva or anterior palatine foramina; *t*, opening of pterygoid canal.

(*g*) on their lateral surfaces. All these structures have been described. The tympanic bullæ (*d*) are placed with long axes directed craniomediad, so that they converge toward their cranial ends. At the caudomedial angle of each bulla is the large **jugular foramen** (*h*), for the ninth, tenth, and eleventh nerves and the inferior cerebral vein (page 325). Opening into the mediocaudal margin of the jugular foramen is the smaller **hypoglossal** foramen, for the twelfth nerve.

The craniomedial end of the tympanic bulla projects craniad as the **styliform** process (*i*). Just laterad of it is the opening (*j*) into the tympanic bulla by which the tuba auditiva or Eustachian tube passes into the middle ear. On the surface of the sphenoid a faint groove for the tube passes craniomediad from this opening. Craniolaterad of the opening for the tuba auditiva is the **foramen ovale** (*k*); craniad of this the **foramen rotundum** (*l*) is faintly indicated. On the surface of the sphenoid just craniad of the styliform process of the bulla tympani is the minute opening of the **pterygoid canal** (*t*). The orbital fissure and optic foramen are not seen in the ventral view.

The narrow middle region of the ventral surface forms a trough-like fossa bounded laterally by the pterygoid processes (*m*) of the sphenoid and the perpendicular plates of the palatines (*n*). It lies between the level of the caudal margin of the last molar and that of the cranial margin of the zygomatic process. In the natural condition the soft palate lies ventrad of the fossa and converts it into the nasal portion of the pharynx or nasopharynx. Craniad the fossa is bounded by the free caudal edges of the palatines, beneath which the fossa communicates with the nasal cavity by the two choanæ (*o*). Laterad of the median fossa parts of the temporal and orbital fossæ are visible, bounded laterally by the zygomatic arches (*p*).

The cranial part of the ventral surface is a somewhat triangular plane area formed by the palatal portions of the palatines (8), maxillaries (9), and premaxillaries (10), which together constitute the hard palate (**palatum durum**). Laterad and craniad this area is bounded by the alveolar borders of the maxillaries and premaxillaries bearing the teeth. The hard palate is marked near the cranial border of the palatine bones with two or more foramina which form the cranial termination of the posterior palatine canal (*q*). Two faint grooves pass from these foramina a short distance craniad, gradually converging; these are known as the **palatine grooves** (*r*) (**sulci**

palatini). Near the cranial end of the hard palate are two large openings close together near the middle line: these are the **foramina incisiva** (or **anterior palatine foramina**) (*s*).

Cavities of the Skull (Figs. 42 and 43).—The bones of the cranial portion of the skull enclose the **cranial cavity** for

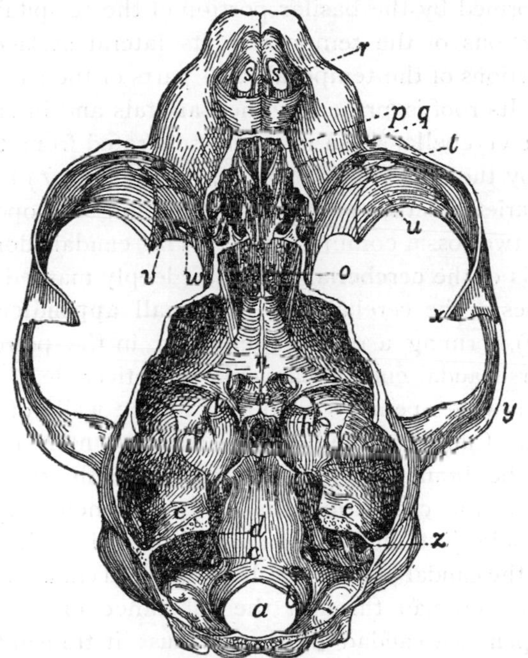

FIG. 42.—SKULL, WITH DORSAL SURFACE REMOVED, SHOWING THE CRANIAL AND NASAL CAVITIES.

a, foramen magnum; *b*, caudal end of hypoglossal canal; *c*, jugular foramen; *d*, internal auditory meatus; *e*, tentorium, forming the cranial boundary of the cerebellar fossa; *f*, dorsum sellæ; *g*, sella turcica; *h*, anterior clinoid processes; *i*, foramen ovale; *j*, foramen rotundum; *k*, orbital fissure; *l*, optic foramen; *m*, chiasmatic groove; *n*, presphenoid bone; *o*, cribriform plate; *p*, lamina perpendicularis of ethmoid; *q*, labyrinths of ethmoid; *r*, nares; *s*, foramina incisiva or anterior palatine foramina; *t*, infraorbital foramen; *u*, opening of the lachrymal canal; *v*, caudal opening of posterior palatine canal; *w*, sphenopalatine foramen; *x*, frontal process of the malar; *y*, zygomatic process of the temporal; *z*, appendicular fossa, in the petrous bone.

the brain; the facial bones enclose the **nasal cavity**, for the olfactory organ.

The **cranial** cavity is divisible into three principal fossæ: the **cerebellar** fossa (Fig. 43, *I*) caudad, for the cerebellum;

the **cerebral** fossa (*II*) in the middle, for the cerebrum; the small **olfactory** fossa (*III*) at the cranial end for the olfactory bulb of the brain.

The **cerebellar** fossa (*I*) is bounded caudally by the occipital bone enclosing the foramen magnum (Fig. 42, *a*). Its ventral surface is formed by the basilar portion of the occipital and the petrous portions of the temporals; its lateral surface by the mastoid portions of the temporals and parts of the parietals and occipital. Its roof is formed by the parietals and interparietal. Craniad the cerebellar fossa is partly separated from the cerebral fossa by the tentorium (Fig. 42, *e*; Fig. 43, *f*) formed by the two parietals: this encloses a quadrangular opening by which the two fossæ communicate. The caudal, dorsal, and lateral walls of the cerebellar fossa are deeply marked by fossæ for the lobes of the cerebellum; the small **appendicular** fossa (Fig. 43, *e*), forming a deep indentation in the petrous bone near its dorsocaudal end, is particularly noticeable.

The following openings are found in the walls of the cerebellar fossa. Caudad is the large foramen magnum (Fig. 42, *a*) by which the brain-cavity communicates with the vertebral canal. Near the caudal margin of the foramen magnum, on its lateral side, just mediad of the dorsal end of the occipital condyle, is the caudal opening of the condyloid canal (Fig. 43, *a*) which passes craniad through the substance of the occipital bone to open just caudad of the petrous: it transmits a vein. The condyloid canal varies greatly in size in different specimens. A few millimeters craniad of the edge of the foramen magnum on the floor of the fossa is the small opening of the hypoglossal canal (Figs. 42 and 43, *b*), for the twelfth nerve. Just craniad of this, at the caudomedial border of the petrous, is the large jugular foramen (*c*). On the petrous itself, near the middle, is the internal auditory meatus (*d*) divided into the dorsal **facial canal** for the seventh nerve, and a ventral passage for the eighth nerve. At the cranial end of the cerebellar fossa is the large opening bounded by the free edges of the tentorium.

The **cerebral** fossa forms much the largest part of the cranial cavity. It is bounded by the parietals (Fig. 43, 3'), squamous portions of the temporals (4), frontals (8), the sphenoid (5), and presphenoid (6). A slight rounded ridge on its lateral wall at about the position of the suture between the frontals and parietals separates a smaller cranial portion sometimes called the **anterior** fossa, from a larger caudal portion sometimes known as the **middle** fossa of the cranial cavity. The walls of the cerebral cavity are marked with numerous ridges and shallow furrows for the cerebral convolutions.

The floor of the cerebral cavity is bounded caudad by the prominent dorsum sellæ (Fig. 42, *f*; Fig. 43, *g*), just craniad of which is a rounded depression, the sella turcica (Fig. 42, *g*; Fig. 43, *h*), for the hypophysis. A number of foramina pierce the floor of the cavity in this region. Just ventrad of the cranial tip of the petrous portion of the temporal is the small **foramen lacerum** (medius) for the internal carotid artery (page 285). Craniad and laterad of this row is a row of four foramina: the caudal one is the foramen ovale (Fig. 42, *i*); then come in order the foramen rotundum (*j*), the orbital fissure (*k*), and the optic foramen (Fig. 42, *l*; Fig. 43, *k*). The two optic foramina are connected by the shallow transverse **chiasmatic groove** (Fig. 42, *m*), for the optic chiasma. Another small foramen continues caudad from a groove on the floor of the orbital fissure; this opens on the ventral surface of the sphenoid, between the wing and the body of the bone. The groove and foramen constitute the **pterygoid canal,** which transmits a nerve,—the **nerve of the pterygoid canal,** or Vidian nerve.

At its cranial end the cranial cavity narrows and forms the small **olfactory** fossa (Fig. 43, *III*) which is continuous caudally with the cerebral fossa but bounded elsewhere by the frontals and lamina cribrosa (Fig. 42, *o*) of the ethmoid. Numerous openings in the lamina cribrosa connect the olfactory fossa and nasal cavity and transmit olfactory fibres. The roof of the fossa is marked by a prominent median crest from the united edges of the frontals.

The **nasal** cavity is almost completely filled by the ethmoid and vomer and the conchæ nasales. Its roof is formed by the nasal bones and portions of the frontals; its sides by the frontals, lachrymals, maxillaries, premaxillaries, and palatine bones; its floor by the horizontal plates of the palatines, maxillaries, and premaxillaries.

The nasal cavity opens craniad by the large **nares** (Fig. 39, *j*; Fig. 42, *r*), which are bounded by the premaxillary and

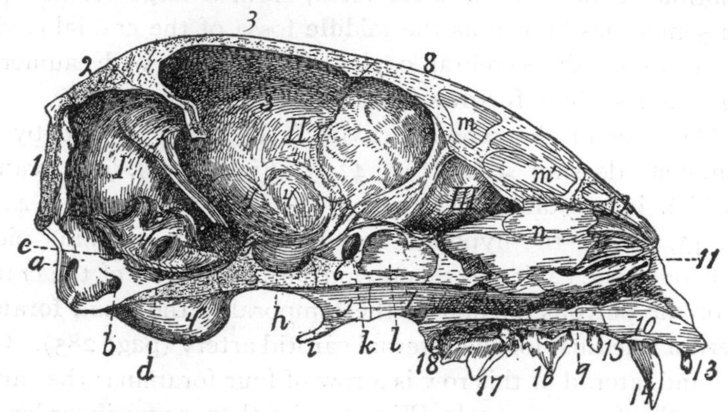

FIG. 43.—SKULL, MEDIAN LONGITUDINAL SECTION, SHOWING THE CAVITIES.

I, cerebellar fossa; *II*, cerebral fossa; *III*, olfactory fossa. 1, occipital bone; 2, interparietal; 3, 3′, parietal; 4, temporal (4, squamous portion; 4′, petrous portion; 4″, tympanic portion); 5, sphenoid; 6, presphenoid; 7, palatine; 8, frontal; 9, maxillary; 10, premaxillary; 11, ethmoid; 12, nasal; 13, incisor teeth; 14, canine; 15, 16, 17, premolars; 18, molar. *a*, condyloid canal; *b*, hypoglossal canal; *c*, jugular foramen; *d*, internal auditory meatus; *e*, appendicular fossa; *f*, tentorium; *g*, dorsum sellæ; *h*, sella turcica; *i*, hamular process; *j*, pterygoid process of sphenoid; *k*, optic foramen; *l*, presphenoid sinus; *m*, *m*′, frontal sinus; *n*, lamina perpendicularis of the ethmoid (broken at cranial edge).

nasal bones. In the natural condition this opening is divided by a median cartilage which is continuous with the lamina perpendicularis (Fig. 43, *n*) of the ethmoid, thus forming a partition which divides the nasal cavity into two separate halves. From the floor of the cranial part of the cavity rises a ridge formed of the nasal crests of the maxillaries and premaxillaries, and the cranial portion of the vomer. Farther caudad the vomer spreads out in a horizontal plane and separates from the floor of the cavity, so that the nasal cavity is thereby divided by a horizontal partition into dorsal and ventral portions. The ventral portion is small, forming the inferior meatus of the nose; it ends caudally at the **choanæ** (posterior nares, Fig. 41, *o*) which lead into the nasopharynx. That portion of the nasal cavity lying dorsad of the vomer is almost completely filled by the ethmoid and the conchæ nasales, superior and inferior. It is bounded caudally by the lamina cribrosa of the ethmoid (Fig. 42, *o*). The nasal cavity communicates with the cranial cavity by the foramina for the olfactory fibres in the lamina cribrosa; with the nasopharynx by the choanæ; with the exterior by the nares; with the mouth-cavity by the foramina incisiva or anterior palatine foramina (Fig. 42, *s*); with the orbit by the sphenopalatine foramen and the nasolachrymal canal. It communicates directly also with the frontal sinuses (Fig. 43, *m*, *m'*), the sphenoidal sinuses (Fig. 43, *l*), and with the cells of the labyrinths of the ethmoid.

JOINTS AND LIGAMENTS OF THE SKULL.

Sutures of the Skull.—The bones of the skull join each other by means of immovable articulations known as sutures. These sutures are designated by combining the names of the bones between which they are situated: as, **sphenofrontal** suture (**sutura sphenofrontalis**), between the sphenoid and frontal; **nasomaxillary** suture (**sutura nasomaxillaris**), between the nasal and maxillary bones. When a suture joins the two corresponding bones of opposite sides the prefix **inter** is used, as the **intermaxillary** suture (**sutura intermaxillaris**) between the maxillaries. But the suture separating the two frontals is known as the **frontal** suture, not as interfrontal. The sutures bounding the parietals have, moreover, received special names not derived in the above manner. The suture caudad of the parietals, separating them from the occipital and interparietal, is known as the **lambdoidal** suture: that between the two parietals is the **sagittal** suture: that separating the parietals and squamous portions of the temporals is the **squamous** suture: that between the parietals and frontals is the **coronal** suture.

Articulations of the Mandible.—In man the two halves of the mandible are united craniad, so as to form a single bone. In the cat the two halves are separate, but articulate closely at the **symphysis menti** by a thin interarticular cartilage.

The articulation of the mandible at the mandibular fossa of the temporal is of the hinge or ginglymus type and is covered by a close **articular capsule.** The mandibular fossa is lined with cartilage. A slender ligament passes from the angular process of the mandible caudad to the external auditory meatus, and is attached to the latter about 8 millimeters from its medial end. This is the **stylomandibular ligament.**

V. BONES OF THE THORACIC EXTREMITIES.

Scapula (Figs. 44 and 45). — The scapula may be described as a flat triangular bone with one surface convex. It lies

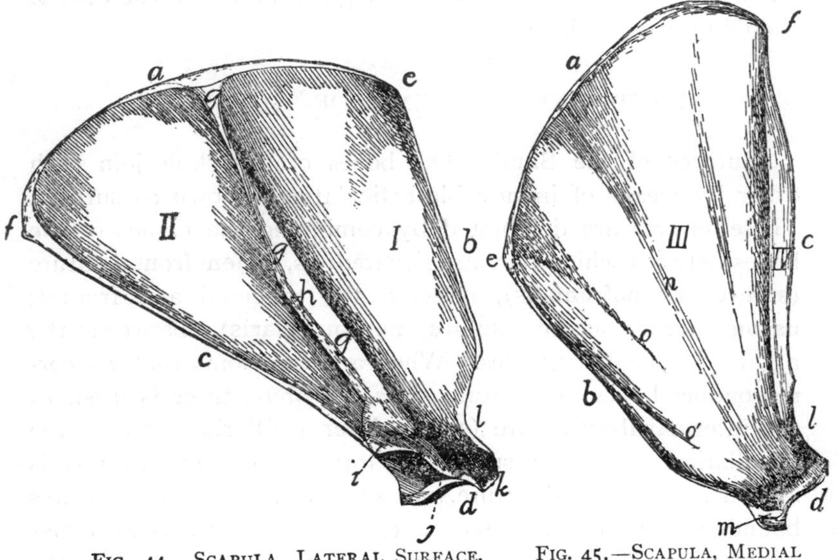

FIG. 44.—SCAPULA, LATERAL SURFACE. FIG. 45.—SCAPULA, MEDIAL SURFACE.

I, fossa supraspinata; *II*, fossa infraspinata; *III*, fossa subscapularis; *IV*, fossa for teres major. *a*, vertebral border; *b*, coracoid border; *c*, glenoid border; *d*, glenoid angle and fossa; *e*, coracovertebral angle; *f*, glenovertebral angle; *g*, spine; *h*, tuberosity of the spine; *i*, metacromion; *j*, acromion; *k*, supraglenoidal tubercle; *l*, incisura scapulæ; *m*, coracoid process; *n*, groove indicating portion of spine; *o*, *o'*, ridges for attachment of muscle-fibres.

beneath the muscles on the lateral face of the thorax near its cranial end. From its lateral surface there projects a flat ridge (Fig. 44, *g*), the **spine** of the scapula. The ventral end of the ridge is free as a curved process, the **acromion** process (Fig. 44, *j*).

The ventral angle of the scapula (*d*). the **glenoid** angle (lateral angle of human anatomy), is much heavier than the others and bears a concave, pear-shaped articular facet, the **glenoid fossa,** for articulation with the humerus. The border with which this angle is more nearly continuous may be called the **glenoid** border (*c*) (axillary border of human anatomy).

Near the narrower cranial end of the glenoid fossa is a small curved projection of the bone, the **coracoid** process (Fig. 45, *m*). The border upon which it lies is the **coracoid border** (*b*) (superior border of human anatomy). The third border is turned toward the vertebral column and is the **vertebral border** (*a*).

The angle between the glenoid and vertebral borders is the **glenovertebral** angle (*f*) (inferior angle of human anatomy), and that between the coracoid and vertebral borders the **coracovertebral** angle (*e*) (medial angle of human anatomy).

The medial or costal surface (Fig. 45) is smooth and nearly flat. A shallow furrow (*n*) marks the position of the spine of the scapula. Between the furrow and the coracoid border are two oblique parallel ridges (*o* and *o'*) for the insertion of muscle-fibres. Near the glenoid border is a well-marked ridge separating the subscapular fossa (*III*), comprising the greater part of the medial surface of the scapula, from the fossa in which the teres major muscle has origin (*IV*). The surface presents several nutrient foramina usually directed toward the glenoid angle.

The lateral surface (dorsal surface of human anatomy) (Fig. 44) is divided by the spine (*g*) into two portions. The portion of the scapula craniad of the spine and the cranial surface of the spine bound the **supraspinous** fossa (**fossa supraspinata**) (*I*), while the surface caudad of the spine and the caudal portion of the spine bound the **infraspinous** fossa (**fossa infraspinata**) (*II*).

The spine (*g*) begins as a triangular elevated area in the middle of the vertebral margin and runs toward the glenoid angle. It rises gradually for about two-fifths of its length and then the margin becomes broader and the spine remains of the same height to its glenoid end. There is a rough thickening, the **tuberosity** (*h*) of the spine, situated on its free border about midway between the tip of the acromion and the vertebral end of the spine. The spine is inclined toward the glenoid margin so as to form an angle of about 60 degrees with the caudal half of the lateral surface.

At the base of the acromion process (*j*) the margin of the spine presents a flat triangular projection, the **metacromion** (*i*), directed toward the glenoid border.

The acromion (*j*) continues in the direction of the spine. It is thicker than the spine, smooth and rounded on both its surfaces and both its borders, and its apex is connected by fibrous tissue to the clavicle.

The coracoid border (*b*) presents a slight rounded notch, the **incisura scapulæ** or suprascapular notch (*l*), just dorsad of the glenoid angle, and at its ventral end bears the coracoid process (*m*) which is directed ventromediad.

The glenoid angle (*d*) is the only one requiring special mention. Between the root of the coracoid process and the glenoid cavity it presents a tubercle, the **supraglenoidal** or bicipital tubercle (*k*), for the tendon of origin of the biceps muscle. The glenoid angle is separated by a contracted neck from the rest of the bone. Between this angle and the inner margin of the acromion there is left a deep notch, the **great scapular notch.**

Clavicle. Clavicula (Fig. 46).—The clavicle in the cat is greatly reduced. It is a slender curved rod of bone imbedded in the muscles of the shoulder and connected by fibrous tissue to the apex of the acromion process. The lateral end (*b*) is slightly enlarged.

b *a*

FIG. 46.—CLAVICLE. *a*, medial end; *b*, lateral end.

Humerus (Figs. 47 and 48).—The humerus forms the support of the upper arm and articulates by its proximal end with the scapula at the glenoid cavity, and by its distal end with the radius and ulna, the bones of the lower arm. It is a nearly cylindrical bone with enlarged ends, and is so curved that its dorsal and ventral borders are hooked at the opposite ends so that it has the form of an Italic *f*.

The proximal end of the bone bears on its dorsomedial portion a thickening, the **head** of the humerus (*a*), which bears a smooth ovoid articular facet by which the bone articulates with the glenoid cavity of the scapula. The head is not separated from the body by a distinct anatomical **neck** as in the human humerus.

Along the lateral border of the proximal end of the shaft is a high rough ridge semicircular in side view, the **great tuberosity** (*b*). It gives attachment to muscles and is marked

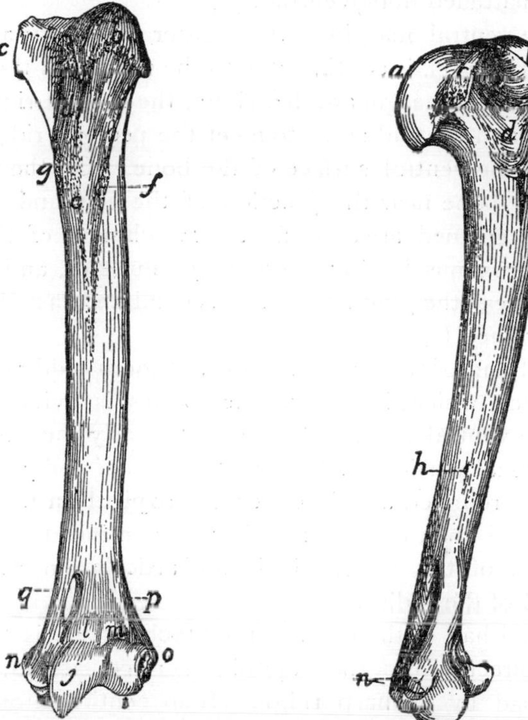

FIG. 47.—HUMERUS, VENTRAL SIDE. FIG. 48.—HUMERUS, MEDIAL SIDE.
a, head; *b*, greater tuberosity; *c*, lesser tuberosity; *d*, bicipital groove; *e*, pectoral ridge; *f*, deltoid ridge; *g*, rough area for insertion of latissimus dorsi and teres major; *h*, nutrient foramen; *i*, capitulum; *j*, trochlea; *l*, coronoid fossa; *m*, radial fossa; *n*, medial epicondyle; *o*, lateral epicondyle; *q*, supracondyloid foramen.

on its dorsal border by a deep depression for the tendon of the infraspinatus muscle. On the medial margin of the proximal end closely associated with the head is a smaller elevation, the **lesser tuberosity** (*c*), also for muscular attachment.

Between the greater and lesser tuberosities on the ventral

surface is seen a broad groove, the **sulcus intertubercularis** or **bicipital groove** (*d*), which passes distad onto the surface of the shaft. In the natural state it is converted into a canal by overlying tendons and lodges the tendon of the biceps muscle.

The shaft is nearly cylindrical at its middle, but its dorsoventral diameter is slightly greater than its mediolateral diameter. Its proximal end is flattened mediolaterad, while its distal end is flattened dorsoventrad.

From the ventral margin of the greater tuberosity a ridge, the **pectoral** ridge (*e*), is continued onto the surface of the shaft, and from the dorsal margin another ridge, the **deltoid** ridge (*f*), passes distad and ventrad so as to meet the pectoral ridge near the middle of the ventral surface of the bone. On the medial margin of the bone near the junction of the first and second fourths is a roughened area (*g*) for the attachment of the tendons of the latissimus dorsi and teres major muscles, and on the same surface near the junction of the second and last thirds is a nutrient foramen (*h*).

The distal end of the bone presents a smooth saddle-shaped articular surface, which, in well-marked bones, is divided, when seen from the ventral surface, by a slight nearly median ridge into two unequal portions, lateral and medial (*i* and *j*). The lateral half is rounded and is called the **capitulum** (*i*). It is broader ventrad than dorsad, and is not continued onto the dorsal surface of the bone. It is for articulation with the proximal end of the radius.

The medial half of the surface, the **trochlea** (*j*), is concave and passes directly into the capitular surface laterad, but is limited mediad by a sharp ridge. It is continued onto the dorsal surface of the bone, where it is limited also laterad by a ridge. It articulates with the semilunar notch of the ulna.

Proximad of the trochlea the dorsal surface presents a deep fossa, the **olecranon fossa,** which receives the olecranon of the ulna when the arm is straightened. On the ventral surface (Fig. 47) are two shallower fossæ separated by a longitudinal ridge. The one over the trochlea receives the coronoid process of the ulna when the arm is bent, and is called thence the **coronoid fossa** (*l*). The one over the capitulum, the **radial**

fossa (*m*), receives a triangular facet on the proximal end of the radius at the same time. Between the radial and coronoid fossæ on one side and the olecranon fossa on the other is only a thin plate of bone. On the medial surface of the distal end is a considerable roughened elevation, the **medial epicondyle** (*n*) (epitrochlea). It gives origin to flexor muscles and to the ulnar collateral ligaments of the elbow-joint. Opposite the medial epicondyle over the capitulum is the **lateral epicondyle** (*o*) for the origin of extensor muscles of the forearm and of the radial collateral ligaments of the elbow-joint. From the lateral epicondyle a ridge, the lateral **supracondyloid ridge** (*p*), continues proximad, curving onto the dorsal surface of the bone and ending about opposite the junction of the deltoid and pectoral ridges.

Proximad of the medial epicondyle the bone is pierced near its medial margin by an oblique oval foramen, the **supracondyloid foramen** (*q*).

Radius (*I*, Figs. 49 and 50).—In the usual position the radius lies with its proximal end on the lateral side of the arm, articulating with the capitulum of the humerus. The proximal end is thus laterad of the proximal end of the ulna. Its distal end, however, lies on the medial side of the distal end of the ulna, so that the radius in the natural position crosses ventrad of the ulna.

The radius is a curved bone slightly flattened dorsoventrally, with enlarged ends. It may be described as consisting of a shaft and of a proximal and a distal end. Its proximal end presents on the ventral surface a tuberosity, the **bicipital tuberosity** (*c*), for the insertion of the tendon of the biceps muscle. Proximad of this the bone is contracted to form a **neck** (*b*) which is surmounted by a **head** (*a*). The head has on its proximal surface a depressed oval facet by which it articulates with the capitulum, and on its ulnar border a long narrow facet, the **articular circumference** (*d*), for articulation with the radial notch of the ulna; also a triangular facet (*e*), which fits into the radial fossa of the humerus.

The shaft is convex dorsad and concave ventrad. The distal end is somewhat pyramidal. From its medial or radial side a wedge-shaped process, the **styloid** process (*f*), extends distad. The distal surface of the end together with the lateral surface of the styloid process form a concave articular cavity (*g*) which fits against the scapholunar bone.

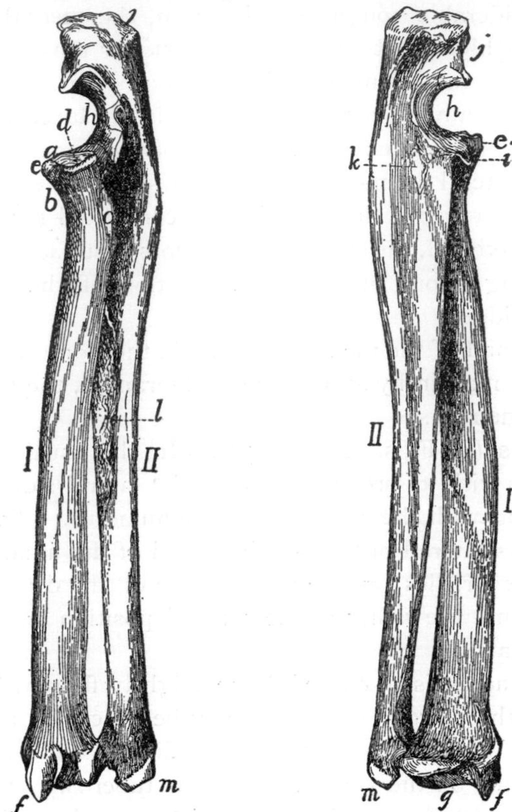

FIG. 49.—RADIUS AND ULNA, DORSO-LATERAL VIEW. FIG. 50.—RADIUS AND ULNA, VENTRO-MEDIAL VIEW.

I, radius; *II*, ulna. *a*, head of radius; *b*, neck; *c*, bicipital tuberosity; *d*, articular circumference; *e*, facet for radial fossa of humerus; *f*, styloid process of radius; *g*, facet for articulation of scapholunar bone; *h*, semilunar (or great sigmoid) notch of ulna; *i*, coronoid process; *j*, olecranon; *k*, area for insertion of brachialis and clavobrachial muscles; *l*, rough area for attachment of interosseous membrane; *m*, styloid process of ulna.

The dorsal surface of the distal end is marked by longitudinal grooves for tendons, and its lateral or ulnar surface bears a concave facet for articulation with the ulna.

Ulna (*II*, Figs. 49 and 50).—The ulna is a long slender bone, flattened mediolaterad. It is enlarged at its proximal end and becomes gradually smaller toward the distal end.

The proximal end is marked ventrally by a deep excavation, the **semilunar notch,** or **great sigmoid cavity** (*h*). By the saddle-shaped articular surface of the semilunar notch it articulates with the trochlea. This articular surface is divided into two parts by a transverse non-articular area. The distal boundary of the semilunar notch is a blunt process, the **coronoid** process (*i*), which bears on its lateral surface a concave facet, the **radial notch,** for the head of the radius.

The portion of the bone proximad of the semilunar notch is called the **olecranon** (*j*). It fits into the olecranon fossa of the humerus when the arm is straightened, and is rough at its end for the insertion of tendons.

The body of the ulna becomes triangular distad. The distal end is slightly larger than the shaft just proximad of it, and bears on its radioventral side a hemispherical head for articulation with the radius. Distad of the head the bone continues as the flattened **styloid** process (*m*), which projects distad from its dorsolateral side and is smooth on the medial side of its apex, for articulation with the cuneiform bone of the wrist.

Carpus (Fig. 51).—The carpus (wrist) consists of seven bones arranged in two rows, three in the proximal row and four in the distal row. Beginning on the medial side of the hand (thumb or radial side), the first bone in the proximal row is the **scapholunar** (*a*) (equal to the scaphoid or navicular and lunar of the human hand). It articulates with the radius. The next is the **cuneiform** (*b*), articulating with the styloid process of the ulna, and the next, which is attached to the cuneiform and projects freely ventrad, is the **pisiform** (*c*).

In the distal row the bone on the radial side is the **trapezium** (*d*); the next is the trapezoid (*e*), the next the os magnum (*f*), and the last the unciform (*g*). The distal row articulates with the metacarpals or bones of the palm of the hand (1–5).

In the kitten the scapholunar is represented by three bones, the **scaphoid** or navicular, on the radial side, the **lunare**, between the scaphoid and the cuneiform, and a **centrale**, which lies distad of the other two.

Scapholunar Bone. Os scapholunaris (Fig. 51, *a*).—The scapholunar is a quadrangular bone with the ventroradial angle produced into a blunt process. Its proximal surface is smooth and articulates with the distal end of the radius. The distal end is marked by oblique ridges and articulates with the unciform, os magnum, trapezoid, and trapezium. The ulnar surface articulates with the cuneiform, and the dorsal surface of the ventroradial process with the radial sesamoid.

Cuneiform Bone. (*Os triquetrum BNA*) (Fig. 51, *b*).—The cuneiform bone has the form of a flattened pyramid. Its base articulates with the unciform, its proximoulnar surface with the pisiform except at its dorsal margin, where it articulates with the styloid process of the ulna. On its proximoradial surface is a smooth facet for articulation with the scapholunar.

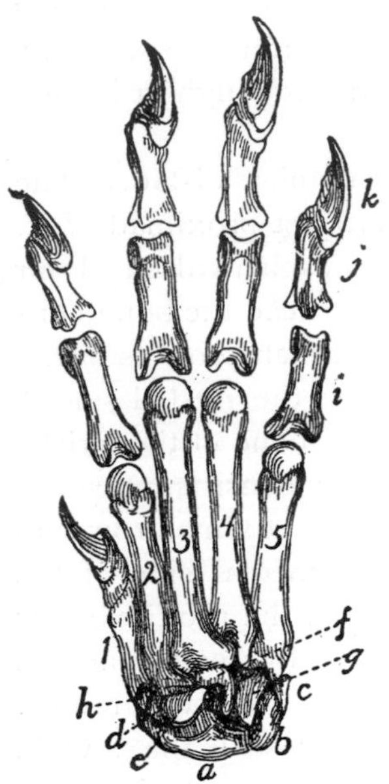

FIG. 51. — CARPUS, METACARPUS, AND PHALANGES, DORSAL SURFACE.

a, scapholunar bone; *b*, cuneiform; *c*, pisiform; *d*, trapezium; *e*, trapezoid; *f*, os magnum; *g*, unciform; *h*, radial sesamoid; *i*, proximal phalanges; *j*, second phalanges; *k*, distal phalanges; 1, 2, 3, 4, 5, metacarpals in order from the radial side.

Pisiform Bone. Os pisiforme (Fig. 51, *c*).—The pisiform bone is about twice as long as broad, with enlarged ends. Its dorsal end articulates with the cuneiform, and on its proximal surface, separated from the above by a smooth ridge, is a smooth facet for articulation with the styloid process of the ulna.

Unciform Bone. (*Os hamatum BNA*) (Fig. 51, *g*).—The unciform is a wedge-shaped bone with the apex of the wedge directed proximad, and smooth for articulation with the scapholunar. By a part of its ulnar surface it articulates with the cuneiform, and by its radial surface with the os magnum. Its distal end articulates with the fourth and fifth metacarpals.

Os magnum. (*Os capitatum BNA*) (Fig. 51, *f*).—The os magnum may be described as an oblong plate bearing on its proximal surface a semicircular ridge which crosses it diagonally. The proximal end of the bone articulates with the scapholunar. Its distal end articulates with the third metacarpal except near its ventroulnar angle, where it articulates with the fourth metacarpal. Its ulnar surface articulates with the unciform. Its radial border articulates with the trapezoid, the third metacarpal, and, by two facets, with the second metacarpal.

Trapezoid. (*Os multangulum minus BNA*) (Fig. 51, *e*).—The trapezoid is somewhat wedge-shaped, with the apex of the wedge pointing ventrad. Its proximal side articulates with the scapholunar, its distal side with the second metacarpal, its ulnar side with the os magnum, and its radial side with the trapezium.

Trapezium. (*Os multangulum majus BNA.*) (Fig. 51, *d*).—The trapezium has the form of a triangular prism curved into a semicircle. The convex face looks proximad and articulates by its ventral half with the scapholunar. The ulnar surface articulates with the second metacarpal dorsally, and ventrally with the trapezoid. Its radial surface articulates with the first metacarpal.

Bones of the Hand or Manus (Fig. 51, 1-5).—The *Metacarpals. Metacarpus.*—The metacarpals are the five bones of the palm of the hand; they are numbered from one to five, beginning with the thumb. They are cylindical elongated bones with enlarged ends. The distal end is called the head, and the proximal end the base. Each head bears a hemispherical articular facet which is marked over its ventral half by a prominent smooth ridge. The surface dorsad of the ridge articulates with the proximal head of a phalanx. The ridge and the surface at its sides are for a pair of sesamoid bones.

The first metacarpal (1) is the shortest. Its head is oblique, and it articulates by the ulnar half of its proximal surface with the trapezium (*d*); by the radial half with the radial sesamoid (*h*).

The second metacarpal (2) is marked on the proximal part of its dorsal surface by an oblique groove passing from the radial side distad to the ulnar side. The base articulates with the trapezoid (*e*). The ulnar surface of the proximal end articulates with the os magnum (*f*) and third metacarpal, while the radial surface articulates with the trapezium (*d*).

The third metacarpal (3) is the longest, and its base is rhomboidal with a projecting dorsoradial angle separated by a groove from the rhomboid surface. The proximal end articulates with the os magnum (*f*) and second metacarpal; the radial surface of the proximal end with the second, and the ulnar surface with the fourth, metacarpal.

The fourth metacarpal (4) has a base similar in form to that of the third, and when placed in position with the fifth the two form a hemispherical facet which articulates with the unciform (*g*) and os magnum (*f*). The fourth metacarpal articulates by its radial side with the third, and by its ulnar side with the fifth.

The fifth metacarpal (5) articulates by its proximal end with the unciform (*g*), and by the radial side of its proximal end with the fourth metacarpal.

Digits (Fig. 51).—The first digit of the hand is called the **pollex** (thumb), the second the **index,** the third the **medius,** the fourth the **annularis,** the fifth the **minimus.**

The first digit has two phalanges, each of the others three phalanges.

Phalanges (Fig. 51, *i*, *j*, *k*).—The phalanges of the proximal row (*i*) are elongated, flattened dorsoventrally and curved so as to be longitudinally convex dorsad. All have thickened ends. The proximal end is notched, and its proximal surface looks dorsad and is concave for the head of the metacarpal. The distal end is pulley-shaped, and the pulley surface extends farther on to the ventral than on to the dorsal surface, and serves for articulation with the middle phalanx.

The phalanges of the middle row (*j*) are like those of the proximal row, but shorter. The proximal surface is triangular and marked by a median facetted ridge. The whole surface is smooth and adapted to the distal end of the phalanx of the first row. The distal end is transversely elongated, so as to be cylindrical, and projects more toward the ulnar than toward the radial side. The distal phalanx (*k*) articulates with this cylinder so that when it is fully extended it lies on the ulnar side of the middle phalanx.

The distal phalanx (*k*) has the form of a quadrangular prism. It is excavated on its proximal surface for articulation with the middle phalanx. Its distal surface presents dorsad a deep excavation from the bottom of which arises a compressed plate of bone having the form of a bird's beak. The depression receives the base of a claw, and the beak-like projection supports the claw.

Sesamoid Bones of the Hand. Ossa sesamoidea.—The hand contains, in addition to those already described, eleven small bones that are developed in tendons.

One of these, the **radial** sesamoid (Fig. 51, *h*), is closely applied to the radial end of the scapholunar bone. It is developed in the tendon of the extensor brevis pollicis muscle.

The other ten occur in pairs as small flattened curved bones on the ventral side of the joint between each metacarpal and the phalanx with which it articulates.

JOINTS AND LIGAMENTS OF THE THORACIC LIMBS.

The **shoulder-joint** is an enarthrodial or ball-and-socket joint. The bones entering into its formation are the scapula and the humerus.

The **capsular ligament** or **articular capsule** is very ample and allows for extended movement of the humerus. It is attached to the edge of the glenoid fossa of the scapula and passing distad covers the head of the humerus and is inserted at the line of junction of the shaft and the epiphysis which forms the head of the bone. On the lateral side of the ventral surface of the humerus the attachment continues distad about two centimeters along the lateral edge of the bicipital groove. On the medial side the insertion passes over the proximal end of the lesser tuberosity. A strong transverse band passes from the greater tuberosity to the lesser tuberosity and bridges the bicipital groove, converting it into a canal. The lateral and medial parts of the capsule are strengthened by thicker bands of fibres, the more prominent medial one of which passes from the coracoid process of the scapula to the lesser tuberosity. To the capsule are closely united parts of the supraspinatus infraspinatus, coracobrachialis, and subscapularis muscles. A synovial membrane lines the capsule within and forms a sheath around the biceps tendon, so that the latter does not actually enter the synovial capsule.

The **elbow-joint** (Figs. 52 and 53) is a ginglymus or hinge-joint. The bones which enter into it are the humerus, radius, and ulna.

The capsule of the joint forms a sac, with the following attachments to the bones: (1) To the humerus it is attached at the proximal edge of the coronoid and radial fossæ; to the sides of the capitulum and trochlea distad of the two epicondyles, and to the distal edge of the olecranon fossa. (2) To the ulna it is attached at the edges of the radial and semilunar

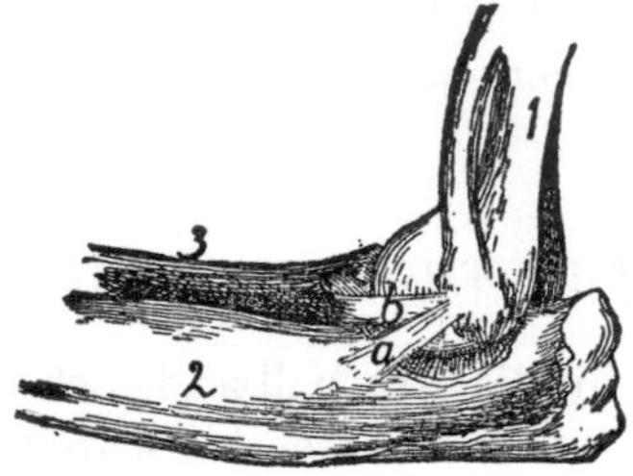

FIG. 52.—LIGAMENTS OF ELBOW-JOINT, MEDIAL SIDE.

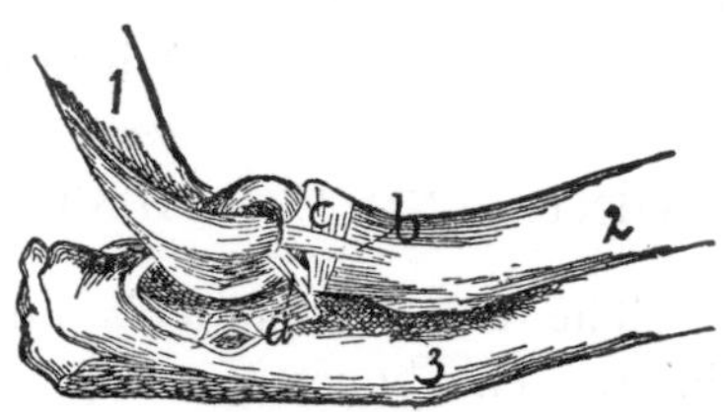

FIG. 53.—ELBOW-JOINT, LATERAL VIEW.

Fig. 52.—1, humerus; 2, ulna; 3, radius. *a* and *b*, the two medial collateral ligaments.

Fig. 53.—1, humerus; 2, radius; 3, ulna. *a*, dorsal collateral ligament; *b*, ventral collateral ligament; *c*, annular ligament.

notches; (3) to the radius around the articular facet, two or three centimeters distad of the border. Many of the muscles of this region are closely attached to the capsule.

Closely connected with the capsule of the joint are the **collateral ligaments.** The two **medial** collateral ligaments (Fig. 52) arise from the medial epicondyle. One (*b*) passes distad and laterad to the interval between the radius and ulna; here it divides, one branch going to the head of the radius, while the other is attached to the lateral surface of the ulna at the edge of the semilunar notch. The second medial ligament (*a*) lies dorsad of the first; it passes to the medial surface of the ulna, at the distal edge of the semilunar notch.

The two collateral ligaments on the **lateral** side (Fig. 53) arise from the lateral epicondyle. The ventral one (*b*) passes almost directly distad and is inserted into the lateral surface of the proximal end of the radius about one centimeter from the articular surface; its inner surface is partly united to the annular ligament (*c*) of the radius. The dorsal one (*a*) is attached to the lateral border of the semilunar notch of the ulna.

Articulations of Radius and Ulna.—The **proximal radio-ulnar articulation** (Fig. 53) is by a pivot-joint or trochoid. The two bones are held in place by the **annular** ligament (Fig. 53, *c*). This is attached on the lateral side to the dorsal border of the radial notch of the ulna, passes around the head of the radius, receiving some ligamentous fibres which come from the lateral epicondyle, and is attached to the coronoid process of the ulna. The annular ligament is closely united with the capsule of the joint.

The radius and ulna are united for about their middle third by the thin **interosseous membrane,** which fills the interosseous space between their adjacent edges.

The Wrist.—At the wrist or carpus there are in reality three joints, the first between the radius and ulna proximad and the first row of carpals distad, the second between the two rows of carpal bones, the third between the distal row of carpals and the metacarpals. The first two are movable joints; the third is not. Each of these three joints has a capsule, and the bones entering into the joints are interconnected by numerous ligaments. These ligaments are named by combining the names of the two bones which they interconnect. Ligaments which interconnect bones of the same row in the carpus are sometimes distinguished as **interosseous** ligaments, as contrasted with **intercarpal** ligaments, which connect together bones of different rows. According to their position the ligaments may also be distinguished as dorsal, ventral, and lateral. Detailed descriptions and figures of all these ligaments are given by Strauss-Durckheim.

Metacarpals.—The joint between the carpals and metacarpals has been described. At the distal end of the metacarpals the articulations with the phalanges have each a capsule. The joint is further strengthened by a double lateral ligament on each side. The two sesamoid bones at each joint are interconnected by a strong transverse ligament, and each is connected with the head of the metacarpal and the base of the first phalanx by a lateral ligament.

Phalanges.—Between the phalanges the joints possess capsules, and each has a radial and an ulnar lateral ligament.

VI. BONES OF THE PELVIC EXTREMITIES.

Innominate Bones. Ossa innominata. (**Os coxæ BNA**) (Figs. 54 and 55).—The two innominate bones articulate with the sacrum and extend thence caudoventrad and finally turn mediad and unite in the middle line, forming the **symphysis pubis.** They thus form an arch, the **pelvic arch, pelvic girdle** or **pelvis,** which is closed dorsad by the sacrum.

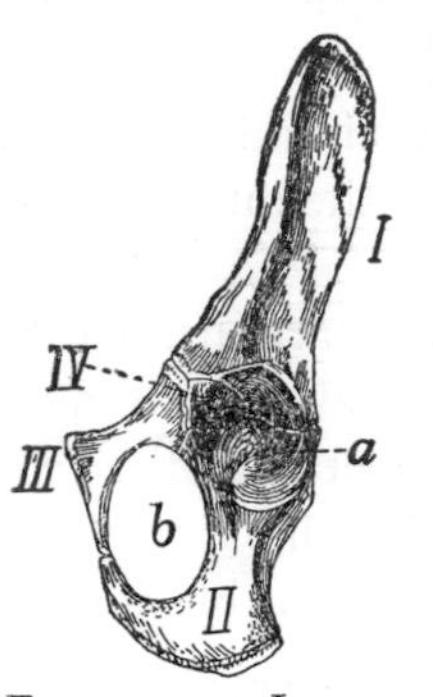

Fig. 54. — Innominate Bone of Kitten, Ventrolateral View.

I, ilium; *II*, ischium; *III*, pubis; *IV*, acetabular bone. *a*, acetabulum; *b*, obturator foramen.

In the middle of the lateral surface of each bone is a hemispherical depression, the **acetabulum** (Fig. 55, *d*), which receives the head of the femur.

In the kitten each innominate bone is composed of three principal parts united by sutures (Fig. 54). From the sacrum to the acetabulum is a single bar, the **ilium** (*I*). Caudad of the acetabulum are two bars. The dorsal one of these is the **ischium** (*II*), and the ventral one is the **pubis** (*III*). The ischium enters into the formation of the acetabulum (*a*), but the pubis does not. The two bones, however, are in contact at the ventral edge of the acetabulum. From this point they diverge, but unite with one another again near the middle line and thus enclose an oval foramen, the **obturator foramen** (*b*). Wedged between the ilium, ischium, and pubis at their point of junction and helping to form the acetabulum is a small irregular bone, the **acetabular bone** (*IV*). In the adult cat these four parts are united into a single bone which is nevertheless usually described, ignoring the acetabular piece, as made up of ilium (Fig. 55, *I*), ischium (*II*), and pubis (*III*).

The **ilium** (*I*) is somewhat contracted at the middle and broader at its ends. One end enters into the acetabulum (Fig. 55, *d*) and forms about one-fifth the articular surface. This end is also the thickest part of the bone. The lateral surface of the ilium is concave for the attachment of muscles. The medial surface is smooth over its acetabular half and rough over its sacral half. The rough portion is marked at its junction with the smooth portion by the ear-shaped **auricular impression** by which the bone articulates directly with the sacrum. The caudal half of that part of the medial surface craniad of the auricular impression gives attachment to the ilio-sacral ligaments which bind the ilium to the sacrum. The dorsal border is straight at its cranial end and concave and rounded at its caudal end. Between the two portions and at the dorsal edge of the auricular surface is a protuberance corresponding to the **posterior inferior spine** (Fig. 55, *b*) of the human ilium. The concavity of the dorsal border (*c*) corresponds to the great sciatic notch of the human ilium. At its caudal end is the short **spine of the ischium** (*e*), which is not a part of the ilium. The ventral border of the ilium is broad caudad, becoming narrower craniad. The lateral margin of the ventral border is continued to a tuberosity at the edge of the acetabulum; its medial margin is called the

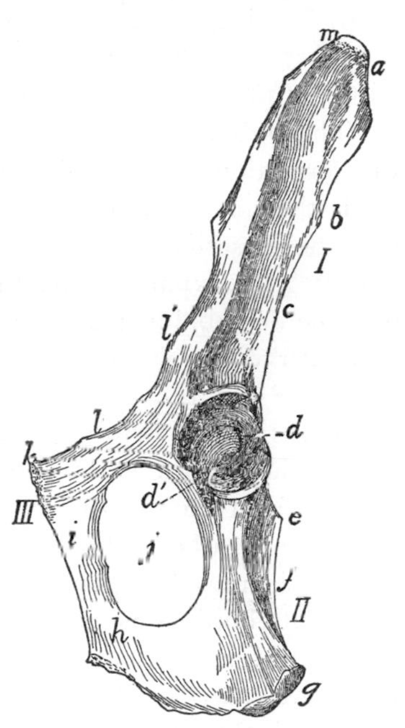

FIG. 55.—INNOMINATE BONE OF ADULT CAT, VENTROLATERAL VIEW.

I, ilium; *II*, ischium; *III*, pubis. *a*, crest of the ilium; *b*, posterior inferior spine; *c*, great sciatic notch; *d*, acetabulum; *d'*, incisura acetabuli; *e*, spine of the ischium; *f*, lesser sciatic notch; *g*, tuberosity of the ischium; *h*, ramus of the ischium; *i*, ramus of the pubis; *j*, obturator foramen; *k*, pubic tubercle; *l*, iliopectineal line; *l'*, ilio-pectineal eminence; *m*, anterior superior process.

iliopectineal line (*l*) and extends on the pubis to the symphysis. An eminence, the **iliopectineal eminence** (*l'*), on the iliopectineal line, lies opposite to the acetabulum at about the junction of the ilium and pubis. The cranial end of the bone is thickened, forming the **crest** (*a*) of the ilium. At the junction of the crest with the ventral border is a projection, the **anterior superior process** (*m*) of human anatomy.

The **pubis** (*III*) (including the acetabular bone) enters into the formation of the acetabulum (*d*) constituting about one-sixth the circumference, but less than one-sixth its area. It may be described as a flat, curved bone, contracted at the middle and expanded at the ends. The dorsal end enters into the acetabulum; the ventral end unites with the opposite bone at the symphysis pubis and sends caudad a projection, the **ramus** (*i*) of the pubis, which unites with the ramus of the opposite bone to form about two-thirds of the entire symphysis. At the sides of the symphysis a slightly marked angle projects craniad from each of the pubic bones; these two together constitute the **pubic tubercle** (*k*), for the origin of the rectus abdominis muscle. The surfaces of the ramus are smooth. One of its borders is concave and enters into the formation of the obturator foramen (*j*). Another of its borders is the iliopectineal line (*l*). Its third border is rough for the symphysis.

The **ischium** (*II*) has the form of a triangular prism contracted at the middle. Its cranial end forms nearly two-thirds of the acetabulum. Its caudal end bears dorsad a rough thickening, the **tuberosity** of the ischium (*g*). From the caudal half of the ventral border of the bone a sickle-shaped process, the **ramus** (*h*) of the ischium, curves medioventrad and then craniad and joins the ramus of the pubis. Its medial border is rough and enters into the symphysis, forming the caudal one-third. The lateral angle of the bone is rounded. Its dorsal angle is marked near the cranial end by the **spine** (*e*) of the ischium. The concavity between this spine and the tuberosity corresponds to the **lesser sciatic notch** (*f*) of human anatomy.

The acetabulum (*d*) is cup-shaped. The ventral one-sixth of its border is deficient and a broad groove extends from the deficiency to the bottom of the cup. The deficiency, **incisura acetabuli,** or **acetabular notch** (*d'*), is closed naturally by a ligament, and the groove gives origin to the ligament (ligamentum teres) which attaches the head of the femur.

Femur (Fig. 56).—The femur is the proximal bone of the posterior extremity. It consists of enlarged proximal and distal ends connected by a nearly cylindrical shaft. The proximal end presents on its medial side a hemispherical **head** (*a*) which fits into the acetabulum. It is supported by a **neck** (*b*) which is contracted near the head and expanded dorsoventrally where it joins the remainder of the bone. The medial surface of the head presents near its ventral border a depression (*c*) for the insertion of the round ligament of the femur. Ventrad the articular surface of the head extends as an acute projection onto the shaft, so that the whole articular surface appears somewhat pear-shaped. On the lateral side of the proximal end opposite the head is a projecting mass, the **great trochanter** (*d*), forming the end of the shaft. On the medial side of the great trochanter at its junction with the neck is a deep fossa, the **trochanteric** fossa or **digital** fossa (*e*) for the insertion of muscles. From the ventral surface of the great trochanter a ridge, the **intertrochanteric** line (*f*), is continued distad, ending in a pyramidal projection, the **lesser trochanter** (*g*), which serves for the insertion of muscles. A second ridge is continued to the lesser trochanter from the neck. A slight but well-marked ridge, the **spiral** ridge or line, runs round two sides of the neck parallel to the second ridge.

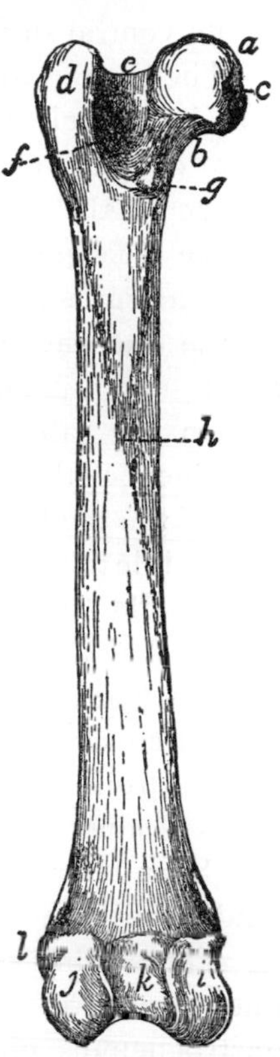

Fig. 56. Left Femur, Ventral Side.

a, head; *b*, neck; *c*, depression for round ligament; *d*, great trochanter; *e*, trochanteric fossa; *f*, intertrochanteric line; *g*, lesser trochanter; *h*, linea aspera; *i*, medial condyle; *j*, lateral condyle; *k*, intercondyloid fossa; *l*, lateral epicondyle.

The shaft is nearly straight and cylindrical. A rough line is continued along its ventral surface from the lesser trochanter, and a similar line along its lateral surface from the greater trochanter; these unite ventrad to form the **linea aspera** (*h*). On its ventral surface is a nutrient foramen, directed proximad.

The shaft gradually widens distad and ends in two **condyles** (*i* and *j*) which are continuous dorsad but separated ventrad by a deep notch, the **intercondyloid fossa** (*k*). The distal surface of the shaft and condyles is articular. This articular surface is larger on the lateral condyle (*j*). The part of the articular surface on the end of the shaft (**patellar surface**) is for the patella; that part of it on the condyles and separated by the notch is for the tibia.

On the lateral surface of the lateral condyle is a slight prominence, the lateral epicondyle (*l*), and on the medial surface of the medial condyle is another prominence, the medial epicondyle; both are for the attachment of ligaments.

Patella (Fig. 1, *r*).—The patella is a small flat bone with a pear-shaped outline, having its apex distad. It lies against the articular surface at the lower end of the shaft of the femur. It thus covers the knee-joint. The inner surface is smooth and convex from side to side, but concave in a proximodistal line. It fits against the lower end of the femur. Its outer surface is rough and concave. It is a sesamoid bone inserted in the tendon of the quadriceps femoris muscle.

Three other sesamoid bones are found in the region of the knee (see Fig. 61, p. 89). Two are in the tendons of the gastrocnemius muscle, proximad of the two condyles of the femur. The third is in the tendon of the popliteus muscle, just laterad of the lateral condyle of the femur.

Tibia (*I*, Fig. 57).—The tibia is the longer of the two bones of the leg between the knee and the ankle, and is the longest bone of the body. It has a triangular shaft and enlarged proximal and distal ends.

The proximal end is curved ventrad and projects into two prominences, the **tuberosities,** on either side. Each tuberosity bears on its proximal end an articular facet for the condyles of the femur; these are known respectively as the **lateral** and

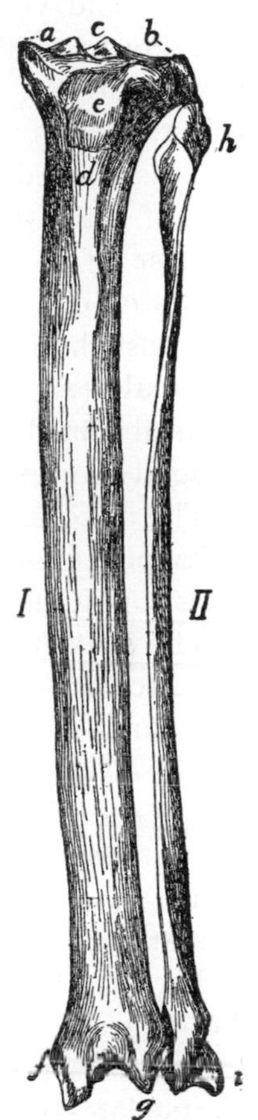

FIG. 57.—TIBIA AND FIBULA OF LEFT LEG, DORSAL VIEW.

I, tibia; *II*, fibula. *a*, medial condyle of the tibia; *b*, lateral condyle; *c*, spine of the tibia; *d*, crest of the tibia; *e*, tubercle for attachment of the patellar ligament; *f*, medial malleolus; *g*, projection of dorsal surface of the tibia; *h*, head of fibula; *i*, lateral malleolus.

medial condyles (*a* and *b*) of the tibia. The condyles are oval, convex dorsoventrad, and concave from side to side. The two condyles are separated at the middle of their contiguous margins by a bicuspid projection, the **spine** of the tibia (*c*). They are continuous dorsad, but separated ventrad by a deep notch between the tuberosities, the **popliteal** notch. On the distal side of the lateral condyle is an elongated facet for the proximal end of the fibula.

The shaft is triangular, smallest at about its middle and enlarged at both ends. It presents dorsal, medial, and lateral borders, and medial, lateral, and ventral surfaces. The lateral surface is concave proximad. The medial surface is convex. The two are continuous at the distal end. At their proximal ends the border separating them is raised into a prominent ridge, the **crest** (*d*) of the tibia, the proximal end of which contributes to increase the proximal surface of the bone, and presents an oblong tubercle (*e*) for the insertion of the **ligamentum patellæ** (ligament of the quadriceps femoris muscle). The ventral surface is concave proximad where it abuts upon the tuberosities. Its proximal half is crossed by two rough parallel lines, the distal one of which crosses in a spiral course from the lateral to the medial border; near its beginning is a nutrient foramen.

The distal end extends farther distad on its medial side. The extension is the **medial malleolus** (*f*). The malleolus presents two grooves on its medial surface for the tendons of muscles. On the lateral side of the distal end is an oblique triangular facet for the distal end of the fibula. The ventral surface of the distal end presents an oblique border which passes from the apex of the malleolus proximolaterad. The dorsal surface extends into a V-shaped projection (*g*) between the malleolus and the fibular facet. The distal end presents an oblique ridge running from the apex of the V-shaped extension of the dorsal surface to near the base of the medial malleolus. The ridge and the concavities on either side of it, the medial one of which is deeper, fit against the proximal trochlear surface of the astragalus.

Fibula (*II*, Fig. 57).—The fibula lies at the lateral side of the tibia in the shank. It is a slender triangular bone with enlarged proximal and distal ends.

The proximal end or head (*h*) is flattened. It bears a facet on its proximomedial surface for articulation with the tibia, and is longitudinally grooved on the outer surface.

The shaft has a very sharp medial border. This border is turned toward the tibia and gives attachment to the interosseous membrane, which runs between the tibia and fibula.

The distal end is expanded to form the **lateral malleolus** (*i*). This bears a facet on the proximal portion of its medial surface near its dorsal margin, for the tibia, and distad of this is a second facet for the astragalus. The ventral and lateral surfaces are grooved for tendons.

Tarsus (Fig. 58).—The tarsus consists of seven bones. The longest of these, lying on the lateral side of the foot and forming the support of the heel, is the **calcaneus** or **os calcis** (*a*). It articulates distad with a bone, the **cuboid** (*c*), which bears the fourth and fifth metatarsals. Lying between the calcaneus and the tibia is the **astragalus** or **talus** (*b*), the distal end of which articulates with the boat-shaped **navicular** or **scaphoid** (*d*). The scaphoid bears on its distal surface the three cuneiform bones, lateral (*e*), medial (*g*), and intermediate, bearing the rudiment of the first metatarsal and the second and third metatarsals.

Astragalus. (*Talus BNA*) (Fig. 58, *b*).—The astragalus may be divided into body, neck, and head. The body is marked on its proximal surface by a deep pulley-like groove for the articulation with the distal end of the tibia, and on its

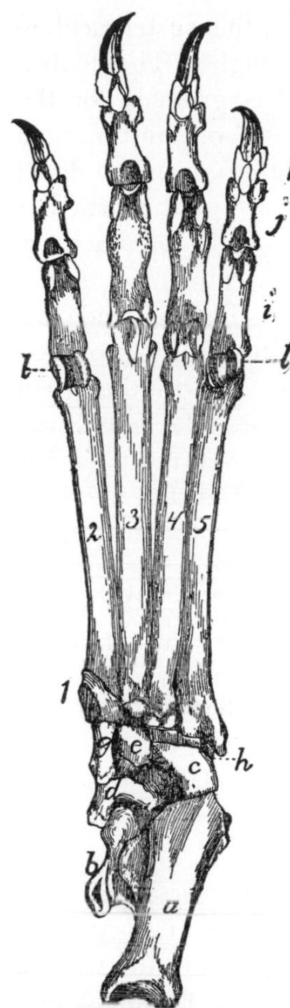

FIG. 58.—TARSUS, METATARSUS, AND PHALANGES OF LEFT FOOT, VENTRAL VIEW.

a, calcaneus; *b*, astragalus; *c*, cuboid; *d*, scaphoid; *e*, lateral cuneiform; *g*, medial cuneiform; *h*, peroneal groove, for the tendon of the peroneus longus muscle; *i*, proximal phalanges; *j*, second row of phalanges; *k*, distal phalanges; *l*, sesamoid bones. 1, rudimentary first (medial) metatarsal; 2, 3, 4, 5, the other metatarsals.

lateral and medial surfaces by curved facets for articulation with the malleoli of the tibia and fibula. This entire surface for articulation with the bones of the leg is known as the trochlea. The lower surface is marked by two facets separated by a groove; these are for articulation with corresponding facets on the calcaneus. Distally the bone contracts to form the **neck** and enlarges at the end, forming the **head,** which is smooth on its distal surface for articulation with the navicular or scaphoid.

Calcaneus (Fig. 58, *a*, and Fig. 59).—The calcaneus (os calcis) is the largest bone of the foot and forms the heel. It is two or three times as long as broad and has six surfaces: dorsal, ventral, medial, lateral, proximal, and distal. The proximal one-half of the dorsal surface (Fig. 59) is smooth, while the distal half is broadened and bears two facets which are separated by a groove. These articulate with the corresponding facets on the astragalus. The medial

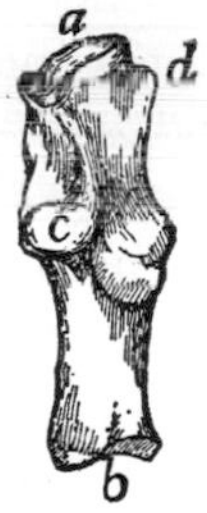

FIG. 59.—CALCANEUS OF RIGHT FOOT, DORSAL VIEW.

a, distal facet for cuboid; *b*, proximal end with groove for tendon of Achilles; *c*, sustentaculum tali; *d*, peroneal tubercle.

facet is borne on a projection of the bone, the sustentaculum tali (*c*). Distad of the facets the surface is rough. The ventral surface is smooth. The proximal end (*b*) is grooved for the tendon of Achilles. The lateral surface is smooth and marked by a grooved tubercle, the **peroneal tubercle** (*d*), near the distal end. The medial surface is marked by part of the articular facet for the astragalus, and also by the grooved sustentaculum tali. The distal end (*a*) articulates with the cuboid.

Cuboid. Os cuboideum (Fig. 58, *c*).—The cuboid has somewhat the form of a cube and articulates by its proximal end with the calcaneus (*a*), and by its distal end with the fourth and fifth metatarsals. Its medial surface articulates with the scaphoid (*d*) and lateral cuneiform (*e*). The ventral surface is marked near its distal end by an oblique ridge, distad of which is a deep groove, the peroneal groove (*h*), for the tendon of the peroneus longus muscle.

Scaphoid. (*Os naviculare pedis BNA*) (Fig. 58, *d*).—The scaphoid is a boat-shaped bone. Its proximal surface is marked by a concave facet for the head of the astragalus (*b*), and its distal surface has three facets for the lateral (*e*), intermediate and medial (*g*) cuneiform bones. At the junction of the ventral with the medial surface is a prominent tubercle. The lateral surface bears two linear facets for articulation with the calcaneus (*a*) and cuboid (*c*).

Lateral Cuneiform. Ectocuneiform. Os cuneiforme tertium BNA (Fig. 58, *e*).—The lateral cuneiform is a wedge-shaped bone with a hooked process extending from the ventral sharp angle of the bone. It articulates by its proximal end with the scaphoid (*d*), and by its distal end with the third metatarsal. The medial surface bears near its distal end two facets for the second metatarsal, and on its proximal end a facet for the intermediate cuneiform. The caudal surface has a facet on its proximal end for the cuboid (*c*).

Intermediate Cuneiform. Mesocuneiform. Os cuneiforme secundum BNA.—The intermediate cuneiform is small and wedge-shaped, with the base of the wedge dorsad. It lies between the lateral cuneiform and the medial cuneiform, articulates by its proximal end with the middle facet of the scaphoid, and bears on its distal end the second metatarsal. It is not visible in ventral view.

Medial Cuneiform. Entocuneiform. Os cuneiforme primum BNA (Fig. 58, *g*).—The medial cuneiform lies on the medial side of the foot. It is a flat triangular bone about twice as long as broad, and broader at its proximal end than at the distal end. It bears on its distal end the rudimentary first metatarsal. The proximal end is oblique and bears a concave facet for the lateral distal facet of the scaphoid (*d*). The lateral surface has a concave facet at its proximal end for the intermediate cuneiform, while the distal portion is applied against the medial surface of the second metatarsal.

Bones of the Foot or Pes (Fig. 58).—*Metatarsals. Metatarsus* (Fig. 58, 1-5).—The metatarsals are five in number. They bear a close resemblance to the metacarpals, but they may be distinguished by their bases.

The *first* metacarpal (1) is rudimentary and conical. Its base has a facet for the distal end of the medial cuneiform (*g*), while the outer surface fits into a depression on the inner surface of the base of the second metatarsal.

The *second* (2). The proximal surface of the base is triangular, corresponding to the distal end of the intermediate cuneiform. The medial surface is marked by two concavities, one along the proximal border for the distal end of the medial cuneiform, and one distad of this for the first metatarsal. The lateral surface bears on the proximal margin an oblique triangular facet dorsad and a similar facet ventrad, both for the lateral cuneiform (*e*). Distad of these facets is a rough ridge.

The *third* (3). The proximal end of its base is a triangular facet with the apex directed ventrad and the sides excavated. It is for the distal end of the lateral cuneiform (*e*). Its medial surface presents a depression which receives the ridge of the second metatarsal. On the lateral surface a short distance distad of the proximal border is a triangular concave facet, and near the proximal border ventrad a second concave facet. Both are for the fourth metatarsal.

The *fourth* (4). The proximal end is convex, notched medially and facetted for the cuboid (*c*). Its medial surface bears dorsad, a short distance from its proximal end, a smooth tubercle, and ventrad a small convex facet. Both articulate with facets on the lateral surface of the third metatarsal. The lateral surface has a sinuous facet along its dorsal border, and ventrad of this a depression. There is a second facet along the ventral border. Both facets are for the fifth metatarsal, and the depression is for ligaments.

The *fifth* (5) has its base flattened and expanded so as to be wedge-shaped, with the apex of the wedge directed proximad. Its dorsal end extends into a tubercle. It thus presents only lateral and medial surfaces. The medial surface shows two tubercles, one distad of the other. The distal tubercle and the distal half of the proximal tubercle are facetted and fit into the sinuous facet on the fourth metatarsal. A narrow facet on the ventral border of the surface articulates with the facet on the ventral border of the lateral surface of the fourth metatarsal. The proximal half of the distal tubercle is facetted for the cuboid (*c*). The lateral surface is smooth, non-articular, and obliquely grooved.

Phalanges (Fig. 58, *i*, *j*, *k*).—There are three phalanges in each of the four digits, and these are almost identical with those described for the manus.

Sesamoid Bones. Ossa sesamoidea (Fig. 58, *l*).—The sesamoid bones are found at the joints between the metatarsals and phalanges, and are in all respects like those of the manus.

JOINTS AND LIGAMENTS OF THE PELVIC LIMBS.

Ligaments of the Pelvis.—The ilium and sacrum are articulated at the auricular facet of the ilium and the corresponding rough surface of the sacrum. The joint is an amphiarthrosis, permitting very little movement. A **capsular ligament** surrounds the articular surface, being attached to the bones about its circumference; it is short and strong. Craniad of the capsule is a thick very short ligament, composed of very strong transverse fibres passing from the rough surface of the sacrum to the corresponding rough surface of the ilium. This forms the **lateral iliosacral ligament,** which is united at its caudal border to the capsule.

A strong, wide ligamentous band passes from the dorsal

border of the ilium to the sides of the sacrum. This is indistinctly subdivided into several bands, which together represent the **long** and **short posterior iliosacral ligaments** of man.

Symphysis pelvis.—The medial borders of the pubis and ilium meet in the middle line ventrad of the pelvis and are here united by cartilage. The joint is strengthened by numerous small bands which pass across the line of junction from one side to the other; these occur on both surfaces.

The Hip-joint.—The hip-joint is an **enarthrosis,** or ball-and socket joint in which more than half the spherical head of the femur is received into the acetabulum. The depth of the acetabulum is increased by a rim of fibrocartilage about its margin, forming the **labrum glenoidale.** This passes across the acetabular notch, forming the **transverse ligament** of the acetabulum; beneath it blood-vessels and nerves pass into the acetabular cavity.

The **capsule of the joint** is large and loose. It is attached about the margin of the acetabulum, and passes over the head of the femur, to be attached to the bone several millimeters distad of the head. It thus encloses both the head and the neck of the femur.

The **ligamentum teres,** or round ligament, is a very strong, short ligament which passes from the depression in the head of the femur to the bottom of the acetabulum.

The Knee-joint (Figs. 60 and 61).—The joint between the femur and the tibia is very complex. The surfaces of the condyles of the femur do not correspond to those of the condyles of the tibia. Between the ends of the two bones are placed two disks of cartilage, the **menisci**, or semilunar cartilages (Fig. 60, *c* and *d*; Fig. 61, *a* and *b*), of such a form that the congruity of articular surfaces is restored. Each meniscus has a proximal surface corresponding to the form of one of the condyles of the femur, and a distal surface corresponding to a condyle of the tibia. The menisci are held in position by ligaments. The knee-joint permits not only backward and forward movement, but also a small amount of rotary motion.

The joint has two **capsules,** one on the dorsal (convex) side, the other on the ventral side. The two communicate only by a small passageway lying within the joint between the ends of the bones. The dorsal one is attached to the femur several millimeters proximad of the patellar surface and some distance on each side of the latter. The patella is imbedded in its outer wall, and it is attached to the tibia on the edges of the articular surface of the latter, from the crest to the tuberosities. The capsule is also attached laterally and medially to the sides of the menisci, and is closely united to the patellar ligaments. Its cavity contains a mass of yellow fat.

The ventral capsule is attached to the borders of the articular surfaces of the femur and tibia on their ventral sides, to the menisci, and to the epicondyles of the femur and the tuberosities of the tibia. Its walls are stronger and its cavity smaller than those of the dorsal capsule.

The ligaments of the knee-joint (Figs. 60 and 61), aside from the capsules, may be classified into: (1) those which are connected with the patella; (2) **collateral** ligaments (Fig. 60, *i* and *j*), which pass from the epicondyles directly distad along the sides of the joint to the tibia or fibula; (3) **crucial** ligaments (Fig. 60, *g* and *h*; Fig. 61, *c* and *d*), which cross within the joint from one side of the femur to the opposite side of the tibia; (4) ligaments which hold the menisci in place (Fig. 60, *e* and *f*; Fig. 61, *e* and *f*).

(1) Ligaments of the Patella.—The patella is imbedded in the dorsal wall of the dorsal capsule of the joint. From its distal end a strong tendon or ligament passes distad to the crest of the tibia. This is known as the **ligamentum patellæ:** it may be considered a part of the tendon of M. quadriceps femoris. On the lateral side the capsule of the joint is strengthened by the transverse fibres of the tendon of M. plantaris, which aid in holding the patella in place.

(2) Collateral Ligaments.—Of these there are two. The **ligamentum collaterale fibulare** (Fig. 60, *j*) is attached to the lateral epicondyle of the femur and passes distad across the tendon of the plantaris muscle to the head of the fibula. Dorsad of the fibular ligament and parallel with it passes the tendon of origin of the extensor longus digitorum. The **ligamentum collaterale tibiale** (Fig. 60, *i*; Fig. 61, *g*) begins on

the medial epicondyle of the femur and passes distad to the lateral tuberosity of the tibia; part of it passes one to one and a half centimeters distad of the tuberosity to be attached to a rough ridge on the side of the tibia.

(3) CRUCIAL LIGAMENTS.—There are two of these also. The **ligamentum cruciatum anterius**, or anterior crucial ligament (Fig. 60, *g*; Fig. 61, *c*), is a thick, strong ligament which begins on the dorsal part of the proximal end of the tibia nearer the medial side (Fig. 60, *g*), and passes ventrad and proxi-

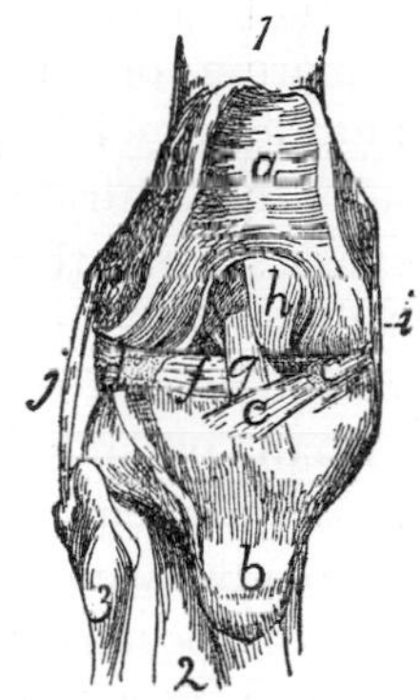

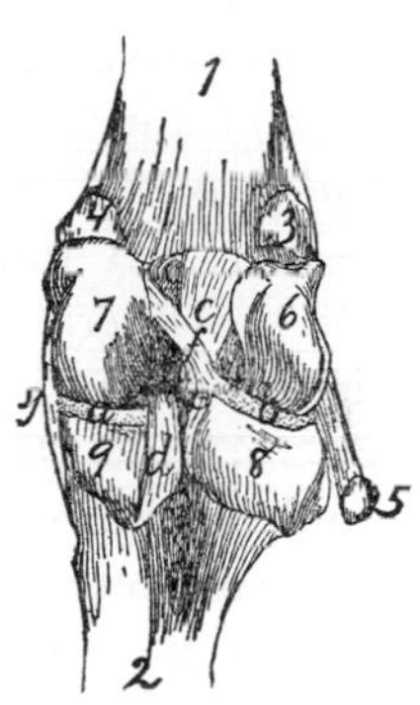

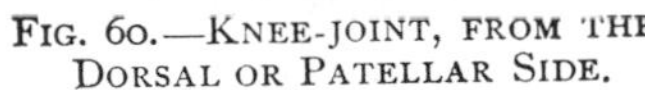

FIG. 60.—KNEE-JOINT, FROM THE DORSAL OR PATELLAR SIDE.

FIG. 61. — KNEE-JOINT, FROM THE VENTRAL OR FLEXOR SIDE.

Fig. 60.—The patella has been removed. 1, femur; 2, tibia; 3, fibula. *a*, patellar surface of femur; *b*, tubercle for attachment of ligamentum patellæ; *c*, medial meniscus; *d*, lateral meniscus; *e*, *f*, ligaments of the menisci; *g*, ligamentum cruciatum anterius; *h*, ligamentum cruciatum posterius; *i*, ligamentum collaterale tibiale; *j*, ligamentum collaterale fibulare.

Fig. 61.—The capsule of the joint has been opened. 1, femur; 2, tibia (fibula not shown); 3, sesamoid bone in lateral head of M. gastrocnemius; 4, sesamoid in medial head of M. gastrocnemius; 5, tendon of M. popliteus, with sesamoid bone; 6, 7, lateral and medial condyles of the femur, with the intercondyloid notch between them; 8, 9, lateral and medial condyles of the tibia, with the popliteal notch between them; *a*, *b*, medial and lateral menisci; *c*, ligamentum cruciatum anterius; *d*, ligamentum cruciatum posterius; *e*, *f*, ligaments of the lateral meniscus; *g*, ligamentum collaterale tibiale.

mad, between the ends of the two bones forming the joint, into the intercondyloid fossa of the femur, and becomes attached to the medial surface of the lateral condyle of the femur (Fig. 61, *c*). It is composed of two partially separated bands, forming a slight angle with one another. It is crossed near its dorsal and ventral ends by two of the ligaments of the menisci. The **ligamentum cruciatum posterius**, or posterior crucial ligament (Fig. 60, *h*; Fig. 61, *d*), begins on the tibia at the edge of the popliteal notch (Fig. 61, *d*), nearer the medial side, and passes dorsad and proximad to be attached to the ventral edge of the patellar surface of the femur, in the intercondyloid fossa (Fig. 60, *h*).

(4) LIGAMENTS OF THE MENISCI.—There are five of these, connecting the menisci with the femur or tibia. One (Fig. 60, *e*) passes from the dorsal edge of the medial meniscus (*c*) transversely across the anterior crucial ligament (*g*) to the proximal end of the tibia nearer the lateral side. A second (Fig. 60, *f*) passes from the dorsal margin of the lateral meniscus (*d*) transversely beneath the anterior crucial ligament (*g*) to the proximal end of the tibia nearer the ventral side and medial border. A third (Fig. 61, *f*) passes from the ventral margin of the lateral meniscus obliquely across the anterior crucial ligament (*c*) to the lateral side of the medial condyle of the femur. The fourth (Fig. 61, *e*) is small, passing from the medial angle of the ventral border of the lateral meniscus distad to the popliteal notch. The fifth passes from the ventral border of the medial meniscus laterad beneath the posterior crucial ligament to the proximal end of the tibia, nearer the ventral and lateral sides.

Articulations between the Tibia and Fibula.—At the proximal end the fibula is as it were suspended from the distal side of the overhanging lateral tuberosity of the tibia by strong ligamentous tissue. The capsule of the joint is formed by an extension of the capsule of the knee-joint which passes between the tibia and fibula on the ventral side. Forming the dorso-lateral wall of this extension is a strong, thick ligament which passes directly from the head of the fibula to the lateral surface of the lateral tuberosity of the tibia. A second more delicate ligament passes from the head of the fibula dorsoproximad to the tubercle laterad of the crest of the tibia, bridging a groove through which passes the tendon of M. extensor longus digitorum.

The tibia and fibula are connected throughout their length by an **interosseus membrane.** This is broad and very thin in its proximal part, narrower and thicker distad.

Distad the two malleoli forming the ends of the fibula and tibia are closely and immovably united. The capsule of the joint is here an extension proximad of the capsule of the articulation with the astragalus. On the dorsal side a short broad band of strong fibres passes from the surface of the tibia obliquely laterodistad to the border of the fibula; this forms the **anterior ligament** of the **lateral malleolus.** On the ventral side a very much weaker set of fibres forms the ventral wall of the articular capsule; it is called the **posterior ligament** of the **lateral malleolus.** Tibia and fibula are also connected on the dorsal side by the **ligamentum transversum cruris,** or transverse ligament of the lower leg (Fig. 91, 5), which spans the tendons of Mm. extensor longus digitorum and tibialis anterior. From the middle of the distal margin of this a slender supporting ligament passes distad and is inserted on the dorsal surface of the tarsus. The grooves in the two malleoli for the passage of the tendons are spanned by ligamentous fibres (retinacula) for holding the tendons in place.

Articulation between the Leg and the Foot.—At the distal end there is formed between the two malleoli a deep irregular fossa, into which is received the trochlea of the astragalus. The joint is covered by a large **articular capsule,** which passes also, as above noted, between the tibia and fibula. In addition to the capsule the following ligaments may be distinguished: (*a*) On the lateral side, (1) a short ligament from the fibula to the astragalus, directed toward the proximal end of the foot; (2) a ligament from the fibula to the calcaneus, attached to the latter proximad of the peroneal tubercle; (3) a stronger ligament from the fibula to the calcaneus, lying beneath the last-mentioned and directed toward the proximal end of the bone. (*b*) On the medial side may be distinguished (1) a strong ligament from the tibia (medial malleolus) to the sustentaculum tali, and passing thence onto the scaphoid; (2) a short ligament from the medial malleolus to the astragalus.

The Tarsus.—The articulations between the separate bones of the tarsus and between the tarsus and metatarsus have a considerable number of variously communicating articular capsules. The separate bones are connected by many ligaments.

The ligaments of the ventral surface (**ligamenta plantaria**) are especially well developed. Here may be noticed particularly a very large **calcaneocuboid** ligament, and a large **calcaneocuneiform** ligament which passes from the sustentaculum tali to the medial cuneiform. Those on the dorsal surface (**ligamenta dorsalia**) are less strong and numerous. Many ligaments, longitudinal, transverse, and oblique, pass also between the separate bones (**ligamenta interossea**). **Ligamenta lateralia,** on the lateral and medial borders of the foot, are also distinguishable. Strauss-Durckheim enumerates ninety-four ligaments of the tarsus; an account of each of these does not form part of the plan of the present work.

The ligaments of the metatarsus and phalanges are of the same general character as in the forelimb. Of these Strauss-Durckheim enumerates thirty-six; they will not be described here.

THE MUSCLES.

I. THE MUSCLES OF THE SKIN. (Fig. 62.)

M. cutaneus maximus (Fig. 62, *b*).—This is a very large, thin muscle which covers almost the whole side of the body. It arises from the outer surface of the latissimus dorsi (Fig. 68, *m*) near its ventral end and from the bicipital arch (Fig. 65, *t'*) in the axilla; from the linea alba for a considerable distance (two or three inches) caudad of the base of the xiphoid process, and from the thorax over a line joining the axilla and the base of the xiphoid. Sometimes a few fibres take origin from the fascia which covers the pectoantibrachialis on the ventral side of the arm.

From their origin the fibres diverge. The cranial ones curve about the base of the forelimb and are inserted into the skin at or near the middle line caudad of the first thoracic vertebra. The most cranial fibres of all are inserted about one to one and a half centimeters from the middorsal line; thence the line of insertion approaches the middorsal line to reach it at about the eighth or ninth thoracic vertebra. The middle fibres run parallel to the middorsal line in the lumbar and sacral regions as far as the root of the tail, a small bundle passing onto the dorsal side of the tail, another onto the ventral side. The fibres of the caudal portion pass onto the thigh, the ventral ones running in the fold of skin which stretches from thigh to abdomen, and are finally lost in the fascia along a line connecting the knee and the root of the tail. A strong fascia connects the adjacent borders of the cutaneus and platysma and lies over the scapular region.

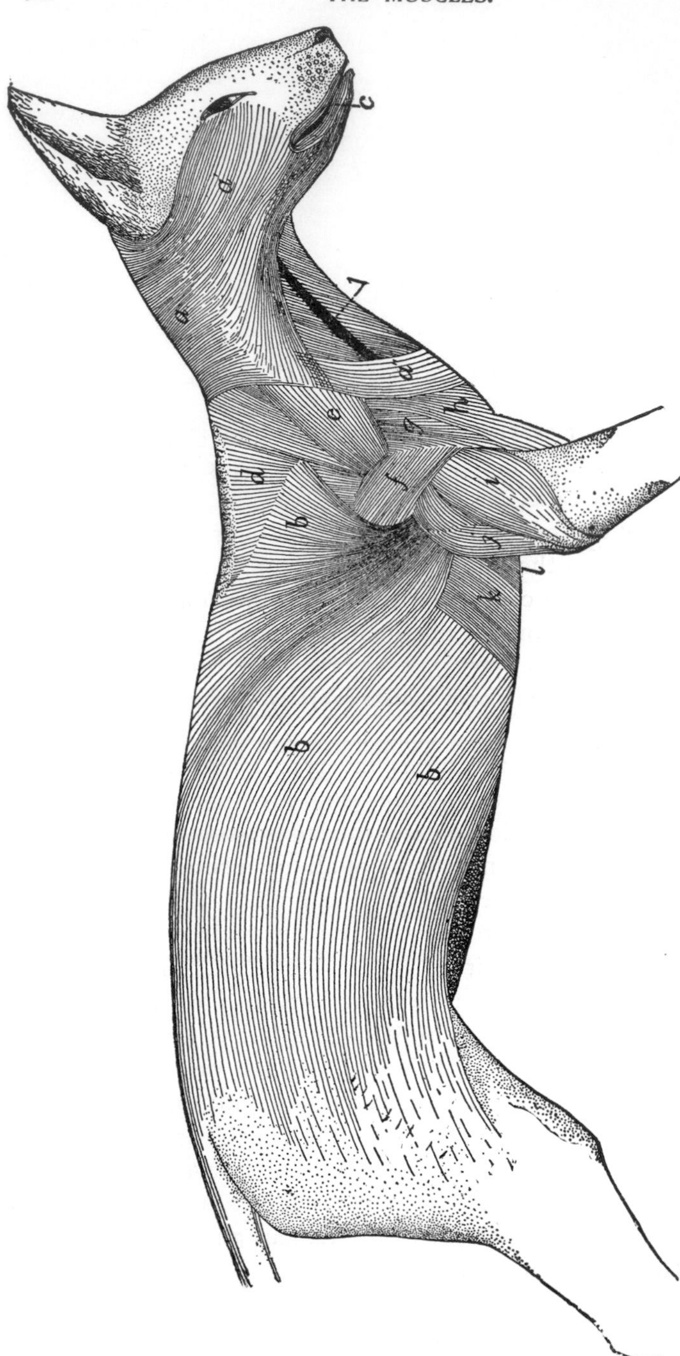

Fig. 62.—Muscles of the Skin.

a, *a′*, *a″*, M. platysma; *b*, M. cutaneus maximus; *c*, M. orbicularis oris. Between the platysma and the cutaneus maximus are seen the following deeper muscles: *d*, M. acromio-trapezius; *e*, M. levator scapulæ ventralis; *f*, M. spino-deltoideus; *g*, M. acromio-deltoideus; *h*, M. clavo-brachialis; *i*, caput laterale of M. triceps brachii; *j*, caput longum of M. triceps brachii; *k*, M. xiphi-humeralis; *l*, M. pectoralis minor. **1**, external jugular vein.

This muscle lies immediately beneath the integument. It covers the first layer of body muscles.

Action.—Moves the skin.

M. platysma (Figs. 62 and 64, *a*, *a'*, *a''*).—This muscle forms a thin layer of fibres covering the sides of the neck and face, in close relation with the integument. Several more or less distinct portions may be distinguished.

(1) Most of the fibres (*a*) arise from the middorsal line, from the occiput to the first thoracic vertebra, in a narrow fascia common to the muscles of the two sides. The most cranial fibres of this region arise as a small bundle from the external occipital crest, beneath the levator auris longus (Fig. 63, *g*, *g'*).

From this origin in the middle line the fibres pass craniolaterad. The most cranial fibres curve about the ventral side of the ear and pass toward the caudal angle of the eye, where they unite with fibres of the zygomaticus (Fig. 64, *d*) or corrugator supercilii lateralis (Fig. 64, *k*), or pass to the lower eyelid. Caudad of these the fibres cover the side of the face and become lost among the facial muscles, some passing to the lower eyelid, some to the fibrous pad which supports the vibrissæ, some to the angle of the mouth, some to the lower lip. The most ventral fibres meet the fibres of the opposite muscle just ventrad of the symphysis of the mandible.

The ventral free border of the platysma is separated on the ventral side of the neck from the border of the opposite muscle by a wedge-shaped area having its point at the symphysis menti.

The fibres of this portion of the muscle are interrupted by an attachment to the skin, along a line passing from the base of the ear to about the middle of the coracoid border of the scapula. The dorsal (*a*) and ventral (*a'*) portions of the muscle, separated by this line of attachment, are sometimes described as separate muscles (the **supercervicocutaneus** and **cervicofacial,** respectively, of Strauss-Durckheim).

(2) A band of fibres one or two centimeters across (*a''*) arises in the fascia of the side of the neck just craniad of the middle of the coracoid border of the scapula, and passes caudo-

ventrad toward the manubrium, its fibres crossing the fibres of the first part of the platysma at right angles. These fibres become lost in the fascia ventrad of the manubrium, or pass across the middle line to intermingle with the corresponding fibres of the opposite side. This portion of the platysma is sometimes absent.

The platysma is everywhere subcutaneous, except at its dorsocranial angle, where a small bundle of fibres is covered by the levator longus auris. It covers the deeper muscles of the neck and head. Closely attached to its inner surface are the submentalis and depressor conchæ, whose fibres bridge over the ventral interval between the borders of the platysmas of opposite sides.

Action.—Moves the skin of the face and neck.

II. THE MUSCLES OF THE HEAD.

A. SUPERFICIAL MUSCLES.—The most superficial layer of muscles on the face and head is formed by differentiation of the fibres of the platysma. The muscles thus formed are not clearly distinct from each other; in this region sets of fibres differing in direction and in origin or insertion receive separate names even though the different sets of fibres are closely interwoven.

In the quadrangle on the dorsal surface of the head enclosed between the two eyes and the two ears, a thin superficial sheet of fibres is found, in which a number of different sets may be distinguished (Fig. 63). These have received the following names.

M. intermedius scutulorum (Fig. 63, *a*).—This consists of a broad thin sheet of transverse fibres between the two external ears. The fibres are attached at either end to the scutiform cartilage (1) of the two ears, and pass without interruption across the middle line. At its cranial edge this muscle is continuous with the corrugator supercilii medialis (*b*); at its lateral edge with the frontoscutularis; at its caudal edge with the levator auris longus (*g*).

Relations.—Outer surface with the integument. Inner surface with the galea aponeurotica (to which the muscle is closely united), the epicranius muscle (*h*) and the temporal muscle (*n*).

Action.—Draws the two ears dorsad, toward the middle line.

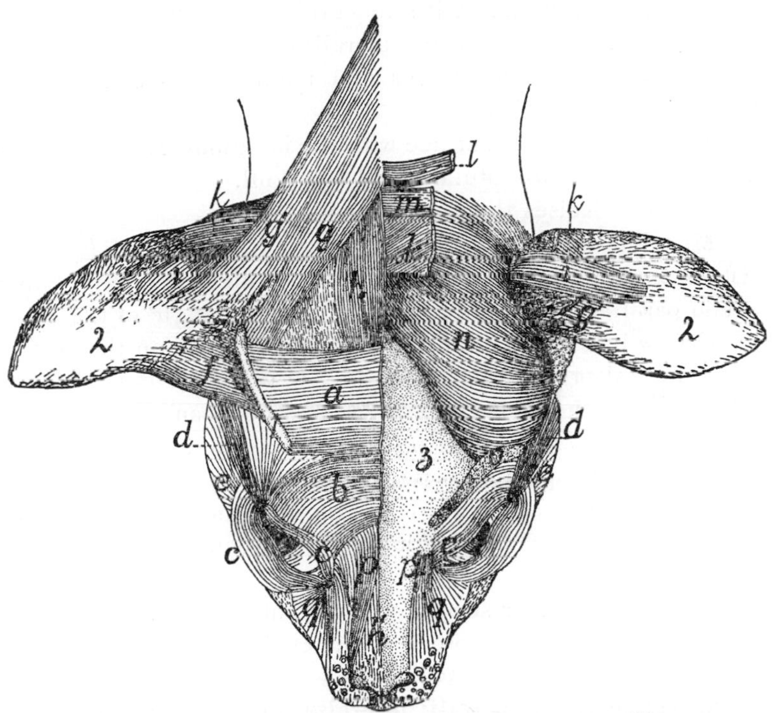

FIG. 63.—MUSCLES ON THE DORSAL SURFACE OF THE HEAD.

On the right side are shown the superficial muscles; on the left side the superficial muscles have mostly been removed, exposing the deeper muscles and the bone. *a*, M. intermedius scutulorum; *b*, M. corrugator supercilii medialis; *c*, M. orbicularis oculi; *d*, M. corrugator supercilii lateralis; *e*, cranial end fibres of M. platysma; *f*, M. adductor auris superior; *g*, *g'*, M. levator auris longus (*g*, cranial portion; *g'*, caudal portion); *h*, *h'*, M. epicranius (*h*, M. occipitalis; *h'* M. frontalis); *i*, M. transversus auriculæ; *k*, M. auricularis superior (cut on the left side); *l*, M. abductor auris brevis; *m*, M. abductor auris longus; *n*, M. temporalis; *o*, cut origin of M. frontoscutularis; *p*, *p'*, M. levator labii superioris alæque nasi (*p'*, the origin from the maxillary bone); *q*, angular head of M. quadratus labii superioris. 1, scutiform cartilage; 2, external ear; 3, bones of the skull.

M. corrugator supercilii medialis (*b*).—This consists of a thin sheet of scattered fibres lying craniad of the last and intermingling with it. The fibres take origin near the middle line, pass laterad, then curve craniad, converging, to be inserted into the whole extent of the upper eyelid, especially near the caudal angle. Here the fibres unite with those of the orbicularis oculi (*c*).

This muscle is continuous caudad with the intermedius scutulorum (*a*), craniad with the orbicularis oculi (*c*); laterad with the corrugator supercilii lateralis (*d*). Toward the medial side the fibres lose themselves in a tendinous sheet that joins the galea aponeurotica.

Relations.—Outer surface with the integument. Inner surface with the frontoscutularis and the skull.

Action.—Raises the upper eyelid.

M. orbicularis oculi (Fig. 63, *c*; Fig. 64, *s*).—This consists of two thin bands of muscle-fibres which lie one in either eyelid parallel to its border and unite at the angle of the eye.

Origin by short tendon-fibres from a tubercle on the surface of the frontal process of the maxillary bone just dorsad of the orbital end of the lachrymal canal and between the two parts of the quadratus labii superioris (Fig. 63, *p* and *q*).

The muscle splits into two parts which pass into the two eyelids. At the outer angle of the eye the two bands unite by the intervention of tendon-fibres between the muscle-fibre bundles of the two.

Relations.—Outer surface with the integument. Inner surface with the inner membrane of the eyelid.

Action.—Closes the eye.

M. corrugator supercilii lateralis (Fig. 63, *d*; Fig. 64, *k*).—This consists of a number of scattered fibres which arise from among the fibres of the frontoscutularis, and from the tendon lying just craniad of the external opening of the ear, to which are united also parts of the zygomaticus (Fig. 64, *d*) and submentalis (Fig. 64, *c*). The fibres pass craniad, converging so as to form a narrow band which is inserted at the caudolateral angle of the eye, where it unites with the orbicularis oculi (Fig. 64, *s*). This muscle is continuous on the medial side with the corrugator supercilii medialis (Fig. 64, *j*) and the frontoauricularis, on the lateral side with the platysma.

Relations.—Outer surface with the integument. Inner surface with the frontal bone and the frontoscutularis.

Action.—Pulls the angle of the eye caudad; at the same time pulls the external ear craniad.

M. frontoauricularis.—A few of the fibres which are attached along the upper eyelid sometimes pass dorsocaudad, mingled with fibres of the corrugatores supercilii medialis and lateralis and the frontoscutularis, to the craniomedial angle of the auricular cartilage, where they unite with the fibres of the adductor auris superior. These fibres are sometimes distinguished as the **frontoauricularis** muscle.

M. levator auris longus (Fig. 63, *g* and *g'*). (Part of the auricularis posterior of man.)—This lies on the caudal half of the dorsal surface of the head, forming a laterocaudal continuation of the intermedius scutulorum (*a*).

Origin from the middle line of the neck dorsad of the atlas, and from the sagittal crest for about one centimeter craniad of the external occipital tubercle. The fibres form a broad thin sheet which passes craniolaterad as far as the caudal end of the scutiform cartilage (1). Here the muscle divides; the major portion is attached to the scutiform cartilage (1), its fibres intermingling with those of the intermedius scutulorum (*a*). The caudal portion of the muscle (*g'*) passes onto the surface of the auricle, extending one or two centimeters distad; here it is inserted on an oblique line which lies directly craniad of the insertion of the transversus auriculæ (*i*).

The caudal portion of this muscle (*g'*) having origin above the atlas and insertion on the auricle, is sometimes considered a separate muscle, the supercervicoauricular or cervicoauricular. The cranial portion (*g*) with origin on the sagittal crest and insertion on the scutiform cartilage might be distinguished as the occipitoscutularis.

The levator auris longus is continuous at its cranial end medially with M. epicranius (*h*); laterally with M. intermedius scutulorum (*a*).

Relations.—Outer surface with the integument. Inner surface with the temporal muscle (*n*), the auricularis superior (*k*), the abductor longus auris (*m*), a narrow strand of the platysma, and the clavotrapezius.

Action.—Pulls the external ear dorsocaudad.

The four following muscles lie partly or entirely beneath those already described; they are doubtless formed as differentiations of the inner layers of the platysma.

M. auricularis superior (or attollens auris) (Fig. 63, *k*).—This muscle forms a band about one centimeter broad lying just beneath the levator longus (*g*).

Origin on the sagittal crest for about one centimeter craniad of the interparietal bone. The muscle passes laterad onto the surface of the auricle and is inserted into the auricular cartilage a little caudad of the middle of its convex surface. At its lateral end the cranial margin is closely united to the under surface of the levator auris longus (*g*).

Relations.—Outer surface at the medial end with the epicranius (*h*), the abductor auris longus (*m*), and levator auris longus (*g*); at the lateral end with the skin. Inner surface with the temporal muscle (*n*) and the auricular cartilage.

Action.—Pulls the external ear dorsad.

M. abductor auris longus (Fig. 63, *m*; Fig. 64, *q*). (Part of the auricularis posterior of man.)

Origin on the sagittal crest dorsad of the interparietal bone, caudad of that of the auricularis superior (*k*), which it partly covers.

The muscle passes laterad as a flat band 8 to 10 millimeters wide over the caudal surface of the concha of the ear, and is inserted (Fig. 64, *q*) on the lateral surface of the eminentia conchæ, caudad of the antitragus.

Relations.—Outer surface with the levator auris longus (*g*) and the integument. Inner surface with the auricularis superior (*k*), the abductor auris brevis (*l*), and the concha.

Action.—Pulls the external ear caudad.

M. abductor auris brevis (Fig. 63, *l*).

Origin by a tendon from the lambdoidal crest for one or two centimeters laterad of the middle.

The muscle passes lateroventrad lying beneath the abductor longus (*m*) as a flat band 6 to 8 millimeters wide which is inserted into the medial surface of the most proximal portion of the concha, just distad of its junction with the cartilaginous auditory meatus.

Relations.—Outer surface with the abductor longus (*m*), a small strand of the platysma and the concha. Inner surface with the temporal muscle (*n*).

Action.—Pulls the concha caudad.

M. epicranius (or occipitofrontalis) (Fig. 63, *h* and *h'*).

Origin on the sagittal crest or suture, just craniad of the origin of the levator longus auris, to the inner surface of which this muscle is closely united. From the origin the fibres pass craniad forming a band (*h*) about 8 or 10 millimeters in width, the two muscles lying close to one another and partly united in the middle line. About two centimeters craniad of their origin the fibres of both muscles end in a tendinous sheet, the **galea aponeurotica,** which covers the surface of the skull in the region between the ears and eyes, and is formed by the inner surface of the intermedius scutulorum (*a*) and other muscles of this region. The galea aponeurotica passes craniad onto the surface of the nose, where it gives origin again to a thin sheet of muscle-fibres (*h'*) which are inserted into the integument near the cranial ends of the nasal bones.

M. epicranius is thus formed of two muscular portions (*h* and *h'*), connected by a long tendinous sheet. The caudal portion is frequently distinguished as the **occipital** muscle (**M. occipitalis,** *h*), the cranial portion, on the nose, as the **frontal** muscle (**M. frontalis,** *h'*).

Relations.—Outer surface of the occipitalis (*h*) with the intermedius scutulorum (*a*), the levator auris longus (*g*), and the integument; inner surface with the auricularis superior (*h*), the abductor auris longus, and the bone. Outer surface of the frontalis (*h'*) with the integument; inner surface with the bones of the skull.

Action.—Moves the integument of the dorsal surface of the head and of the nose.

Ventrad of the external ear the following three differentiated portions of the platysma may be distinguished.

M. zygomaticus (major) (Fig. 64, *d*).—A slender band connecting the angle of the mouth with the scutiform cartilage of the ear.

At the angle of the mouth the fibres arise from among those

of the orbicularis oris (*i*), from both the upper and the lower lip. They pass thence dorsocaudad across the zygomatic arch as a band 8 or 10 millimeters wide which is attached to a

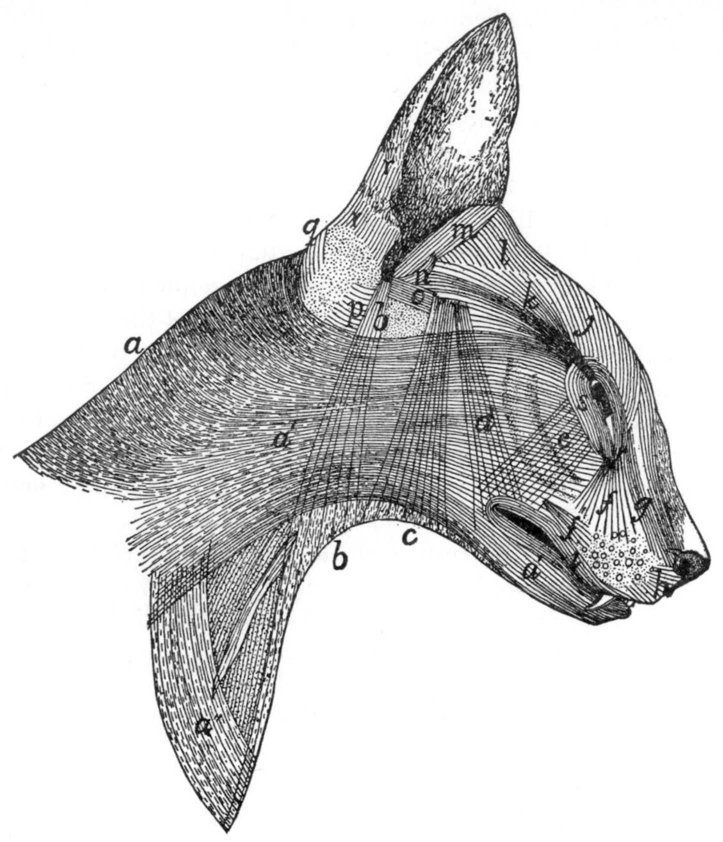

Fig. 64.—Superficial Muscles on the Lateral Surface of the Head and Neck.

a, *a'*, *a''*, M. platysma; *b*, M. depressor conchæ; *c*, M. submentalis; *d*, M. zygomaticus (*b*, *c*, and *d* lie beneath the platysma and are seen through it); *e*, M. zygomaticus minor; *f'*, M. caninus; *f*, *g*, parts of M. quadratus labii superioris (*f*, angular head; *g*, M. levator labii superioris alæque nasi); *h*, M. myrtiformis; *i*, M. orbicularis oris; *j*, M. corrugator supercilii medialis; *k*, M. corrugator supercilii lateralis; *l*, M. adductor auris superior; *m*, M. helicis; *n*, M. antitragicus; *o*, M. adductor auris inferior; *p*, M. conchæus externus; *q*, M. abductor auris longus; *r*, parts of M. auricularis externus; *s*, M. orbicularis oculi.

tendinous aponeurosis lying just craniad of the external opening of the ear. To this aponeurosis are attached also, wholly or partly, the corrugator supercilii lateralis (*k*) and the submentalis (*c*). The aponeurosis is united with the caudoventral angle of the scutiform cartilage and with the ventral edge of the cranial margin of the auricular cartilage.

This muscle is united at its cranial end with the orbicularis oris (*i*); throughout its length more or less with the platysma (*a*, *a'*); at its caudodorsal end with the corrugator supercilii lateralis (*k*) on its medial side, and with the submentalis (*c*) on its lateral side.

Relations.—Outer surface with the integument and the platysma (*a'*). Inner surface with the masseter, temporal, frontoscutularis, and adductor auris inferior (*o*).

Action.—Draws the angle of the mouth dorsocaudad; the external ear ventrocraniad.

M. submentalis (Fig. 64, *c*).—A flat band, similar to the last, and closely connected for some distance to its caudal border.

It arises as scattered fibres near the ventral middle line at about the level of the larynx, the fibres of the opposite muscles crossing the middle line and intermingling. The fibres pass dorsad, converging so as to form a narrower band, which unites dorsad with the zygomaticus (*d*), to be inserted with it into the tendinous aponeurosis above described.

Relations.—Outer surface with the integument and platysma (*a'*). Inner surface with the muscles of the hyoid, the digastricus, the parotid gland, the masseter, the zygomatic arch and the temporal muscle.

Action.—Draws the external ear ventrad.

M. depressor conchæ (Fig. 64, *b*).—A thin band of fibres, caudad of the last and parallel with it. The muscle arises as scattered fibres on the ventral surface of the neck, one or two centimeters craniad of the manubrium, the fibres of the muscles of opposite sides crossing the middle line and interdigitating. They pass dorsad, gathering together to form a narrow band which is inserted into the summit of the antitragus.

Relations.—Outer surface with the skin at the ventral end, and with the platysma (*a'*) further dorsad. Inner surface with the deep muscles of the neck and with the parotid gland.

Action.—Draws the external ear ventrad.

Lying deeper than the muscles thus far described, but closely connected with a number of them, are the following:

M. frontoscutularis.

Origin (Fig. 63, *o*) on the frontal bone, along the supraorbital margin, from the craniomedial angle of the eye caudad to the zygomatic process of the frontal.

The fibres form a large muscle which passes dorsocaudad to the scutiform cartilage and is mostly attached along its ventrolateral border. Some of the outer fibres, however, pass distad of the scutiform cartilage toward the cartilage of the ear, thus joining the adductor auris superior (*f*).

The outer surface of this muscle is closely connected with fibres of the intermedius scutulorum (*a*), the corrugatores supercilii medialis (*b*) and lateralis (*d*), and the frontoauricularis, when this exists. The outer surface is covered near the origin by the orbicularis oculi (*c*), farther dorsad by the muscles just mentioned and the integument. The inner surface is in relation with the frontal bone and the adductor auris inferior (Fig. 64, *o*).

Action.—Pulls the ear craniad.

M. adductor auris inferior. (Fig. 64, *o*.) (Part of the auricularis anterior of man.)—A small muscle lying beneath the frontoscutularis.

Origin on the ligament which connects the zygomatic process of the frontal with the frontal process of the malar. The fibres form a thin band about 7 millimeters wide which passes craniad, closely united to the inner surface of the frontoscutularis. At the caudal edge of the zygomaticus (*d*) the muscle is interrupted by a short tendinous interval; the fibres then continue to their insertion on the tip of the antitragus.

Relations.—Outer surface with the frontoscutularis, the zygomaticus (*d*), and the integument. Inner surface with the temporal muscle and M. antitragicus (*n*).

Action.—Pulls the ear craniodorsad.

The remainder of the muscles of the ear, which, with the exception of the tragicus lateralis, merely interconnect the cartilages of the external ear or parts of these cartilages, are described in connection with the account of the Auditory Organ.

Owing to the presence of the fibrous pad to which the whiskers are attached, the facial muscles between the eye and the mouth differ in the cat in some respects from those of related animals. This fibrous pad interrupts the muscles, frequently breaking muscles which are elsewhere single into two.

M. zygomaticus minor, or malaris (Fig. 64, *e*).—This muscle is not always present; when it exists it forms a very thin flat band of fibres passing from the ventral side of the eye toward the angle of the mouth.

Origin among the fibres of the orbicularis oculi (*s*) in the lower eyelid. The fibres pass ventrad; the insertion varies. In some specimens the insertion is among the fibres of the orbicularis oris (*i*), at the angle of the mouth, beneath the zygomaticus (*d*). In other cases this muscle is said to be inserted into the pad on which the whiskers rest.

Relations.—Outer surface with the integument and near its insertion with the zygomaticus major (*d*). Inner surface with the malar bone and the masseter muscle.

Action.—Pulls the angle of the mouth (or the whiskers) dorsad.

M. orbicularis oris (Fig. 64, *i*).—This forms a very thin layer of subcutaneous concentric fibres which surround the mouth, that of the upper lip being thicker than that of the lower lip. The part of the muscle in the lower lip has its fibres intermingled with those of the platysma (*a'*). In the median line the fibres of the upper lip are interrupted by a raphe, and caudad of this are intermingled with those of the caninus.

M. quadratus labii superioris (Fig. 63, *p* and *q*; Fig. 64, *f* and *g*).—This is a complex of muscle-fibres attached chiefly to the fibrous pad on which the whiskers rest. In it two parts can be distinguished more or less completely.

(1) **M. levator labii superioris alæque nasi** (Fig. 63, *p*; Fig. 64, *g*) on the sides of the nose. This arises (*a*) as a continuation of the frontal portion of the epicranius, and (*b*) in a

small bundle (Fig. 63, *p'*) from near the dorsal end of the frontal process of the maxillary bone, in common with the next. The two slips thus formed unite craniad and are inserted partly into the integument on the outer side of the wing of the nose, partly into the skin of the upper lip, lateroventrad of the nose, and partly into the pad on which the whiskers are located, in connection with the next.

(2) The **angular** head (**caput angulare**), or **levator labii superioris proprius** (Fig. 63, *q*; Fig. 64, *f*) is much larger than the last. It takes origin from a small tubercle at the cranial border of the orbit, close to the origin of the orbicularis oculi. The fibres diverge from their origin to their insertion among the whiskers and in the fibrous pad on which the whiskers rest.

Action.—Erects the whiskers and raises the upper lip.

M. caninus or **levator anguli oris** (Fig. 64, *f'*).

Origin in a depression on the lateral surface of the maxillary bone, just craniad of the last premolar tooth. The fibres pass craniad, diverging, toward the whiskers, and have their insertion into the pad of tissue on which the whiskers rest.

Action.—Retracts the whiskers and raises the upper lip.

M. buccinator.—A thin muscle against the mucous membrane of the upper lip, partly united with the orbicularis oris and lying beneath M. caninus.

Origin on the outer surface of the superior maxillary bone in the depression between the infraorbital foramen and the first premolar tooth. The fibres pass ventrad, diverging, and mingle with those of the deep part of the orbicularis oris.

Relations.—Outer surface with the caninus and with the orbicularis oris. Inner surface with the mucous membrane of the upper lip.

Action.—Raises the upper lip.

M. myrtiformis (probably corresponds to a part of the human M. nasalis) (Fig. 64, *h*).—A thin sheet of muscle-fibres lying craniad of the levator labii superioris alæque nasi and passing from the whiskers to the nose and upper lip. It is distinguishable from the alæque nasi by the direction of the fibres

Origin from the pad upon which the whiskers rest. The fibres diverge and have their

Insertion upon the wing of the nose and into the skin of the upper lip near the median line.

Action.—Dilator of the nares and elevator of the upper lip.

M. "moustachier" (Str.-D.) (probably corresponds to one of the Mm. incisivi).—It lies on the upper lip near the median line.

Origin from the outer surface of the premaxilla near the suture along the ventral border of the narial opening. The fibres diverge and pass caudad into the upper lip within the superficial fibres of the orbicularis oris.

Insertion.—The skin of the upper lip just craniad of the whiskers. Some of the fibres pass into the pad on which the whiskers rest.

Action.—It carries the lip craniad.

M. quadratus labii inferioris.—A thin flat band extending almost the length of the lower lip.

Origin from the alveolar border of the mandible, between the molar tooth and the canine. The fibres pass dorsad into the lower lip, where they intermingle with those of the orbicularis oris. The muscle is perhaps not constant.

Action.—Depressor of the lower lip.

Sometimes a few fibres arising from the cranial portion of the alveolar border of the mandibula pass mediad, seeming to join corresponding fibres from the opposite side. Such fibres would constitute a M. transversus menti.

B. Deep Muscles of the Head.

(*a*) *Muscles of Mastication.*

M. digastricus (Fig. 65, *b*).—The digastric is a thick prismatic muscle lying mediad of the angle of the lower jaw, connecting it with the base of the skull.

Origin by fleshy fibres from the outer surface of the jugular process of the occipital bone, and by a thin tendon from the tip of the mastoid process and from the ridge between the mastoid and the jugular processes. The muscle passes craniad, becoming at the same time broader and more voluminous.

Insertion.—The ventral border of the mandible craniad of the caudal border of the molar tooth. The insertion area extends slightly onto both surfaces of the bone and is triangular, with its apex craniad.

Relations.—Outer (ventral) surface with the following, beginning at the caudal end: the rectus capitis lateralis, the cleidomastoid (*h*), the submaxillary gland (2), the stylohyoid (*d*), a large lymph-gland (3), and the integument. Inner (dorsal) surface with the jugulohyoid, the tympanic bulla, the masseter (*a*), the hyoglossus, and the mylohyoid (*c*).

Action.—Depressor of the lower jaw.

M. masseter (Figs. 65 and 66, *a*).—The masseter forms the projecting mass so prominent in the cat behind and below the eye. Its outer surface is covered by a strong aponeurosis. The muscle is divided into three layers which are distinct as to origin, insertion, and direction of fibres, but which are otherwise not distinct.

The **superficial layer** takes

Origin by the superficial aponeurosis from the ridge which runs lengthwise of the outer surface of the malar bone, and by fleshy fibres from the surface of the malar bone ventrad of this ridge. The fibres pass obliquely caudad to their insertion.

Insertion.—The caudal half of the lateral margin of the ventral border of the mandible, by a sheet of fascia which lies on the inner surface of the muscle. The superficial fibres curve ventrad of the mandible and are inserted into a tendinous intersection between this muscle and the internal pterygoid (Fig. 66, *c*).

The **middle layer** takes

Origin from the ventral border of the malar bone, from opposite the molar tooth to within three millimeters of the mandibular fossa. The fibres pass ventrad and have their

Insertion into the mandible at the ventral border of the external coronoid fossa by means of the aponeurosis which covers the inner surface of the muscle.

The **deep layer** takes

Origin by a strong tendon from the ventral border of the zygoma just craniad of the mandibular fossa. The fibres pass cranioventrad, diverge and have their

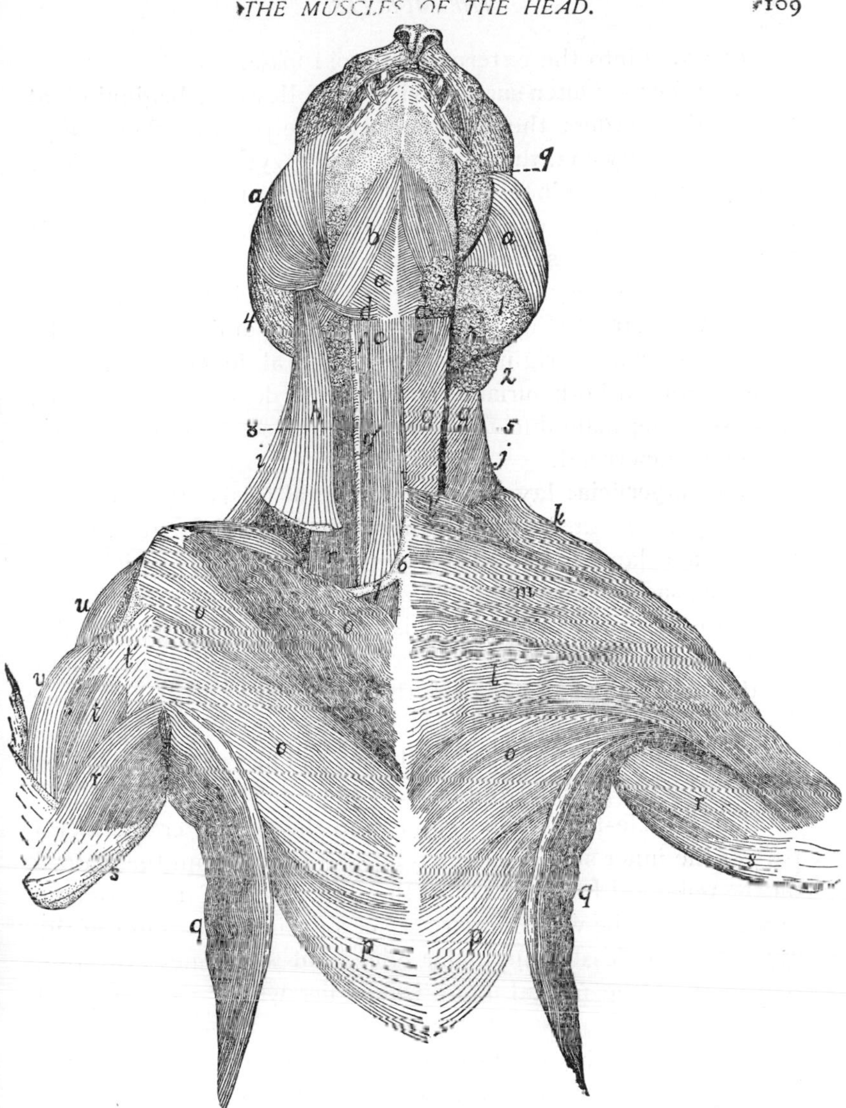

FIG. 65.—MUSCLES ON THE VENTRAL SURFACE OF THE THORAX, NECK AND HEAD.

The left side shows the first layer of muscles beneath the skin and skin-muscles; the right side shows the second layer, except in the head region. *a*, M. masseter; *b*, M. digastricus; *c*, M. mylohyoideus; *d*, M. stylohyoideus; *e*, M. sternohyoideus; *f*, M. thyreohyoideus; *g*, M. sternomastoideus; *g'*, M. sternothyreoideus; *h*, M. cleidomastoideus; *i*, M. levator scapulæ ventralis; *j*, M. clavotrapezius; *k*, M. clavobrachialis; *l*, M. pectoralis major; *m*, M. pectoantibrachialis; *n*, part of M. scalenus; *o*, M. pectoralis minor; *p*, M. xiphihumeralis; *q*, M. latissimus dorsi; *r*, M. epitrochlearis; *s*, caput longum of M. triceps brachii; *t*, M. biceps brachii; *t'*, bicipital arch; *u*, M. acromiodeltoideus; *v*, M. brachialis. 1, parotid gland; 2, submaxillary gland; 3, lymphatic glands; 4, external ear; 5, external jugular vein; 6, manubrium; 7, first rib; 8, common carotid artery; 9, molar gland.

Insertion into the external coronoid fossa.

Relations.—Outer surface with the following, beginning at the caudal border: the external ear, the parotid gland (Fig. 65, 1), the platysma, the submentalis, the zygomaticus (major), the zygomaticus minor. Ventral border with a lymph gland caudad of the angle of the mouth (Fig. 65, 3), and the digastric muscle (*b*). Inner surface with the bones.

Action.—A very powerful elevator of the lower jaw.

M. temporalis (Fig. 63, *n*).—The temporal muscle is the great mass taking origin from the temporal fossa and having its insertion on both surfaces and both borders of the coronoid process of the mandible. It may be divided into two layers, deep and superficial.

The **superficial layer.** The temporal fascia stretches over the temporal fossa, being attached to its borders; that is, to the sagittal and lambdoidal crests, to the curved ridge which connects the sagittal crest with the zygomatic process of the frontal bone, to the caudal border of this process, to the caudal border of the malar bone, to the caudal border of the ligament connecting the malar bone and the zygomatic process of the frontal, and to the dorsal border of the zygomatic process of the temporal bone and its dorsal root. The craniolateral part of this fascia is much stronger than the remainder.

The muscle-fibres take origin from the strong craniolateral part of the inner surface of the temporal fascia, from the groove on the temporal bone dorsad of the dorsal root of its zygomatic process, from the whole inner surface of this process and of the zygomatic process of the malar bone, and sometimes also from that part of the frontal bone which lies within the temporal fossa.

Insertion.—The outer surface of the coronoid process of the mandible dorsad of the coronoid fossa, and both borders of the coronoid process. The cranial fibres may be inserted craniad of the coronoid process onto the aponeurosis covering the deep portion of the muscle. The caudal part of this portion is more or less distinct and is sometimes described as a separate head.

The **deep portion.**

Origin by fleshy fibres from the whole surface of the temporal fossa, except in cases where the cranial part of the fossa is occupied by the superficial portion. The fibres converge toward the coronoid process, and the ventral third of the outer surface is covered by strong fascia.

Insertion.—The whole inner surface of the coronoid process of the mandible.

Relations.—Outer surface with the external ear, the ear-muscles (Fig. 63), the epicranius (Fig. 63, *h*), the corrugatores supercilii lateralis (*d*) and medialis (*b*). Inner surface with the skull, the pterygoideus externus (Fig. 66, *b*), and the structures within the orbit.

Action.—Elevator of the lower jaw.

M. pterygoideus externus (Fig. 66, *b*).—This lies on the medial side of the mandible, ventrad of the ventral portion of the temporal.

Origin.—The external pterygoid fossa (Fig. 40, *p*), which lies on the lateral surface of the perpendicular plate of the palatine bone, and on the surface of the pterygoid process of the sphenoid bone dorsad of the internal pterygoid fossa. The fossa extends from the foramen rotundum to the sphenopalatine foramen. The muscle passes with parallel fibres laterad, ventrad, and caudad and has its

Insertion by a strong flat tendon into the medial surface of the mandible near its ventral border between the opening of the mandibular canal and the base of the angular process.

Relations.—Ventral surface with the masseter (*a*), the digastric, and the soft palate with its muscles. Dorsal surface with the temporal, and near its origin with the muscles of the eye, and other structures in the orbit.

Action.—Elevator of the lower jaw.

M. pterygoideus internus (Fig. 66, *c*).—This lies caudad of the pterygoideus externus, nearly parallel to it, and is connected with it at its lateral end.

Origin from the whole surface of the internal pterygoid fossa (Fig. 40, *s*).

Insertion by fleshy fibres into the ventral surface of the external pterygoid and its tendon, into the medial surface of the angular process of the mandible and caudad of the angular process for about one centimeter into a fascia common to it and the masseter muscle, and into the stylomandibular ligament.

Relations.—Ventral surface with the styloglossus and the

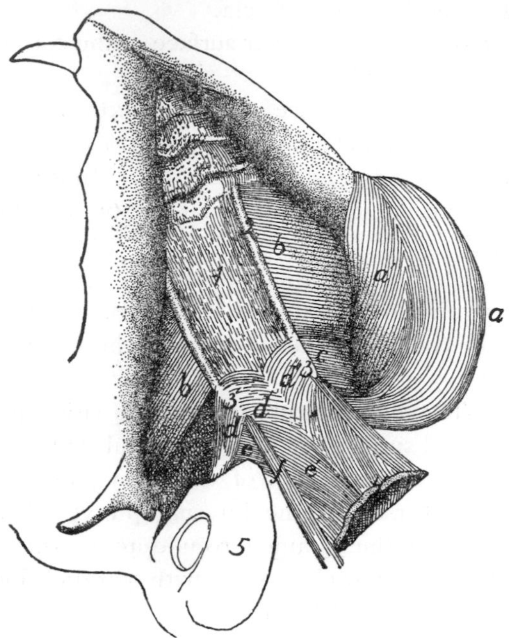

FIG. 66.—OBLIQUELY VENTRAL VIEW OF THE DEEP MUSCLES OF THE LOWER JAW AND PALATE.

The tongue and other structures forming the floor of the mouth have been removed, showing the roof of the mouth. On the right side the masseter and pterygoideus internus have been removed. *a*, *a'*, M. masseter; *b*, M. pterygoideus externus; *c*, M. pterygoideus internus; *d*, *d'*, M. tensor veli palatini; *e*, *e'*, M. levator veli palatini; *f*, M. constrictor pharyngis superior. 1, aponeurosis of the velum palatinum; 2, ridges formed by the palatines and pterygoid portions of the sphenoid; 3, hamular processes; 4, free caudal border of the velum palatinum; 5, bulla tympani.

soft palate. Dorsal surface with the bulla tympani (5) and base of the skull. Cranial surface with the pterygoideus externus (*b*), with which it is partly united.

Action.—Assists the pterygoideus externus.

(*b*) *Muscles of the Hyoid Bone.*

M. stylohyoideus (Fig. 65, *d*).—The stylohyoid is a ribbon-like muscle about three millimeters wide. It lies on the superficial surface of the digastric, caudad and ventrad of the angle of the jaw.

Origin by fleshy fibres from the outer surface of the stylohyal bone near its middle. The muscle curves over the outer surface of the digastric (*b*), and ends about one centimeter from the middle line in a slender flat tendon.

Insertion into the middle of the ventral surface of the body of the hyoid bone. Some of the fibres of the mylohyoid (*c*) are inserted into its tendon.

Relations.—Outer surface with the submaxillary gland (2) and the submentalis muscle. Inner surface with the digastric (*b*), the hyoglossus (Fig. 67, *h*), and the geniohyoid (Fig. 67, *g*).

Action.—Raises the hyoid.

M. geniohyoideus (Fig. 67, *g*).—The geniohyoid is a long slender muscle which lies next to the median line between the symphysis menti and the hyoid bone, closely applied to its fellow of the opposite side and within (dorsad of) the mylohyoid (Fig. 65, *c*).

Origin from the ventral half of the inner surface of the mandibula for about one millimeter from the symphysis.

Insertion by muscle-fibres into the lateral half of the ventral surface of the body of the hyoid bone.

Relations.—Outer (ventral) surface with the stylohyoid (Fig. 65, *d*) and the mylohyoid (Fig. 65, *c*); medial border with the muscle of the opposite side. Lateral border with the hyoglossus (Fig. 67, *h*) and genioglossus (Fig. 67, *f*). Inner (dorsal) surface with the genioglossus.

Action.—Draws the hyoid forward.

M. jugulohyoideus (Fig. 67, *b*).—The jugulohyoid is a small flat quadrangular muscle covering the outer part of the ventral surface of the tympanic bulla.

Origin from the ventral border of the jugular process.

Insertion into the caudal side of the cartilaginous part of the stylohyoid opposite the origin of the styloglossus.

Relations.—Ventral surface with the digastric. Dorsal surface with the tympanic bulla (3).

Action.—Draws the hyoid backward and thus gives a firmer surface of origin for the styloglossus.

M. mylohyoideus (Fig. 65, *c*).—The mylohyoid is a large thin muscle seen after the reflection of the digastric, filling with its fellow of the opposite side the whole angle between the rami of the lower jaw. Its fibres are transverse.

Origin from the middle of the medial surface of the body

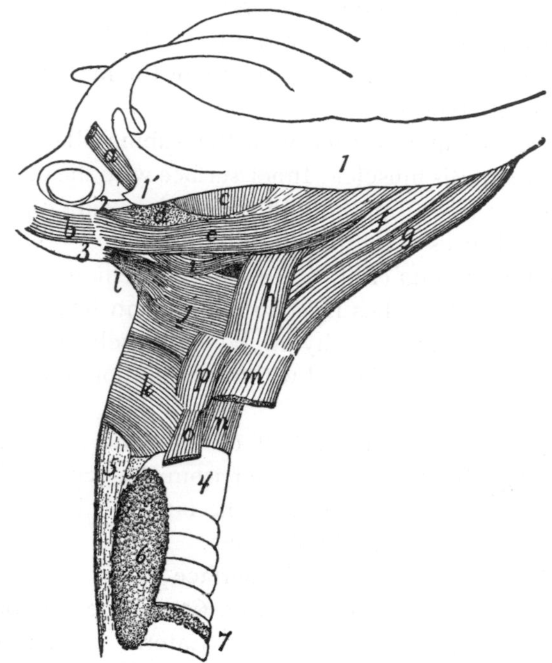

FIG. 67.—MUSCLES OF TONGUE, HYOID BONE, AND PHARYNX.

a, M. tragicus lateralis; *b*, M. jugulohyoideus; *c*, M. pterygoideus externus; *d*, partially cut surface of M. pterygoideus internus; *e*, M. styloglossus; *f*, M. genioglossus; *g*, M. geniohyoideus; *h*, M. hyoglossus; *i*, M. glossopharyngeus; *j*, M. constrictor pharyngis medius; *k*, M. constrictor pharyngis inferior; *l*, M. stylopharyngeus; *m*, M. sternohyoideus (cut); *n*, M. cricothyreoideus; *o*, M. sternothyreoideus (cut); *p*, M. thyreohyoideus. 1, mandible; 1′, angular process of mandible; 2, stylomandibular ligament; 3, bulla tympani; 4, trachea; 5, œsophagus; 6, thyroid gland; 7, isthmus of the thyroid gland.

of the mandible between the caudal opening of the mandibular canal and the symphysis of the jaw.

Insertion with the opposite muscle into a median raphe which extends from the symphysis of the jaw to the hyoid bone and is closely united to the external surface of the geniohyoid. Some of the fibres gain insertion into the body of the hyoid bone through their insertion into the tendon of the stylohyoid (*d*).

Relations.—Outer surface with the submentalis (Fig. 64, *c*) and the digastric (Fig. 65, *b*). Lateral edge with the masseter (*a*), the digastric (*b*), and the mandibula. Caudal border with the stylohyoid (*d*). Inner (dorsal) surface with the geniohyoid (Fig. 67, *g*), the hyoglossus (Fig. 67, *h*), and the genioglossus (Fig. 67, *f*).

Action.—Raises the floor of the mouth and thus brings the hyoid forward.

M. ceratohyoideus.

Origin, the two proximal pieces of the cranial horn of the hyoid. The fibres pass caudad parallel to one another and within the middle constrictor of the pharynx.

Insertion into the whole length of the caudal cornu of the hyoid bone.

Relations.—Outer surface with the middle constrictor of the pharynx. Inner surface with the pharynx.

Action.—Draws craniad the body of the hyoid by bringing its cornua together and bending the joint between the two pieces of the cranial cornua.

The muscles connecting the hyoid and the tongue are described in connection with the description of the tongue.

III. MUSCLES OF THE BODY.

1. Muscles of the Back.

A. MUSCLES OF THE SHOULDER (connecting the forelimb with the back) (Fig. 68).

M. trapezius.—The trapezius muscle is divided in the cat into three portions, the spinotrapezius, the acromiotrapezius, and the clavotrapezius.

M. spinotrapezius, or trapezius inferior (Fig. 68, *j*).—The spinotrapezius (caudal part of the human trapezius) is a flat triangular muscle.

Origin from the tips of the spinous processes of all or nearly all the thoracic vertebræ and from the intervening supraspinous ligament. The origin may extend from a point anywhere between the first and fourth spines to any point between the eleventh and thirteenth.

Insertion along an S-shaped line (Fig. 76, *k–l*) which crosses the tuberosity of the scapular spine and forms an angle with the spine of about forty-five degrees. The line extends on one side onto the fascia covering the supraspinatus muscle, and on the other side onto the fascia covering the infraspinatus, but does not reach the borders of the scapula. The cranial two-thirds of the insertion is by a flat tendon which is broader craniad.

Relations.—Outer surface with the cutaneus maximus, and craniad with the acromiotrapezius (*h*). Inner surface with the latissimus dorsi (*m*) caudad and with the rhomboideus, supraspinatus, and infraspinatus craniad. Caudal border free; cranial border in contact with the acromiotrapezius (*h*).

Action.—Draws the scapula dorsocaudad.

M. acromiotrapezius, or trapezius superior (Fig. 68, *h*).—The acromiotrapezius (middle part of the human trapezius) is a flat four-sided muscle just craniad of the spinotrapezius, from the median dorsal line to the scapular spine.

Origin along the median dorsal line from the spinous process of the axis to a point anywhere between the spinous processes of the first and fourth thoracic vertebræ. Its caudal two-thirds is from a flat tendon which is directly continuous with the muscle of the opposite side and thus bridges the depression between the vertebral borders of the scapulæ. This tendon narrows craniad, and its cranial fourth is attached by a fascia to the spinous processes of the cervical vertebræ. At the cranial border of the muscle the fibres sometimes reach the middle line. The fibres of the muscle run nearly transversely.

Insertion (Fig. 76, *h*).—Into the outer surface of the metacromion, the glenoid border of the scapular spine from the metacromion to the tuberosity, and along a line continued for about one centimeter from the tuberosity onto the surface of the spinotrapezius (*j*) at the junction of its muscular and tendinous portions.

Relations.—Outer surface with the cutaneus maximus, the integument and platysma. Inner surface with a mass of fat partially covering the rhomboideus; with the occipitoscapularis, spinotrapezius, supraspinatus, levator scapulæ, and splenius.

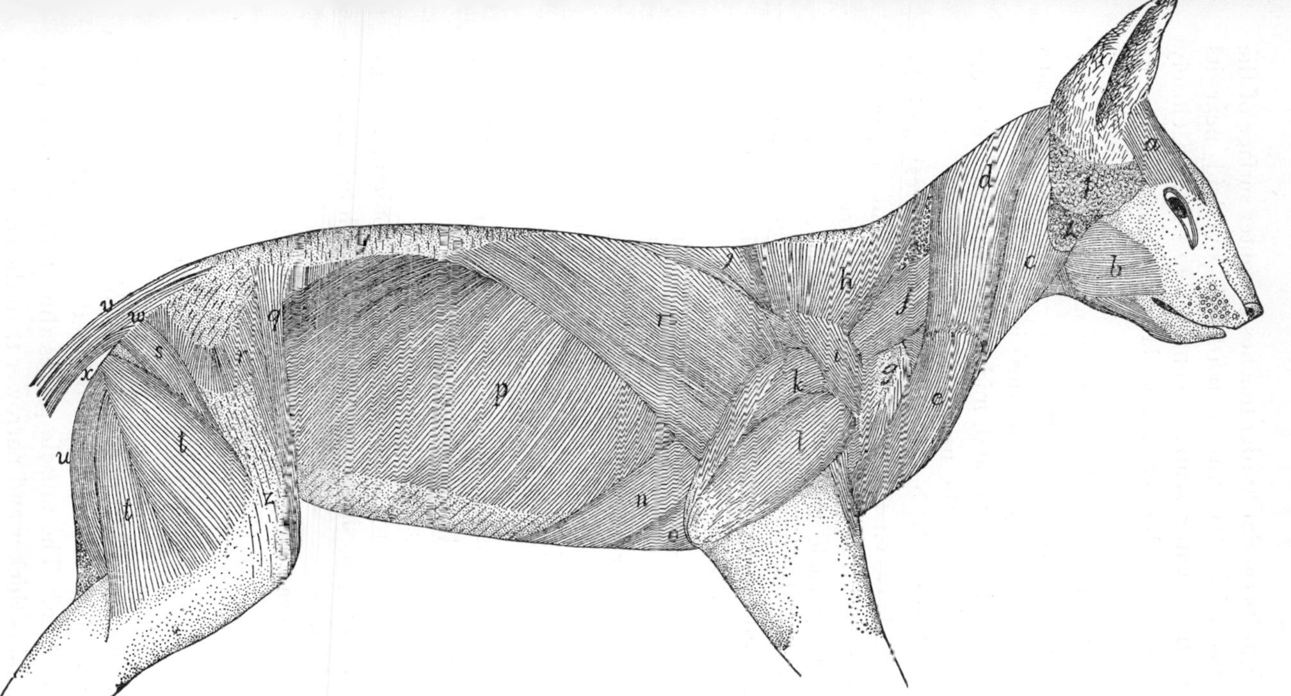

FIG. 38.—FIRST LAYER OF BODY-MUSCLES, BENEATH THE SKIN AND SKIN-MUSCLES.

a, M. frontoscutularis; *b*, M. masseter; *c*, M. sternomastoideus; *d*, M. clavotrapezius; *e*, M. clavobrachialis, *f*, M. levator scapulæ ventralis; *g*, M. acromiodeltoideus; *h*, M. acromiotrapezius; *i*, M. spinodeltoideus; *j*, M. spinotrapezius; *k*, caput longum of M. triceps brachii; *l*, caput laterale of M. triceps brachii; *m*, M. latissimus dorsi; *n*, M. xiphihumeralis; *o*, M. pectoralis minor; *p*, M. obliquus abdominis externus; *q*, M. sartorius, *r*, M. tensor fasciæ latæ; *s*, M. caudofemoralis; *t*, M. biceps femoris; *u*, M. semitendinosus; *v*, M. extensor caudæ lateralis; *w*, M. abductor caudæ externus; *x*, M. flexor caudæ longus; *y*, lumbodorsal fascia, superficial layer; *z*, fascia lata. **1**, parotid gland; **2**, submaxillary gland.

Near its origin its caudal border touches the outer surface of the spinotrapezius (*j*). Its cranial border is overlaid near its insertion by the levator scapulæ ventralis (*f*) and is closely related to the caudal border of the clavotrapezius (*d*) near its origin.

Action.—The two muscles hold the scapulæ together.

M. clavotrapezius (Fig. 68, *d*).—The clavotrapezius (cranial part of the human trapezius) is a flat muscle passing from the lambdoidal crest and middorsal line to the clavicle and covering the side of the neck.

Origin.—The medial half of the lambdoidal crest and the middorsal line between the crest and the caudal end of the spine of the axis. The fibres are parallel and pass caudoventrad so that the muscle covers the ventral surface of the neck caudally and fills the concavity at the front of the shoulder.

Insertion into the clavicle and into a raphe between the clavotrapezius and the clavobrachial (*e*) muscles. This raphe extends along the clavicle and for some distance laterad of it. The muscle is partly continuous with the clavobrachial (*e*).

Relations.—Outer surface with the platysma, and at its craniomedial angle with the levator auris longus. Inner surface with the rhomboideus, splenius, occipitoscapularis, levator scapulæ, cleidomastoid, and supraspinatus. The cranial edge touches the sternomastoid. The caudal border touches the acromiotrapezius near the origin.

Action.—Draws the scapula craniodorsad.

This muscle and the clavobrachial (*e*) are sometimes considered as forming a single muscle, the cephalohumeral, or cephalobrachial.

M. occipitoscapularis (or levator scapulæ dorsalis or rhomboideus capitis) (Fig. 73, *a*).—The occipitoscapularis (equivalent to a part of the human rhomboideus) is a slender flat muscle from the lambdoidal ridge to the coracovertebral angle of the scapula.

Origin, the medial half of the lambdoidal ridge beneath the clavotrapezius (Fig. 68, *d*). The origin does not extend quite to the middle line. The muscle passes almost directly caudad. Its caudal end is thicker and narrower than the cranial end and is wedged between the rhomboideus dorsally and the levator scapulæ ventrally.

Insertion either into the inner surface of the levator scapulæ near its dorsocranial border at its insertion or into the scapula near the coracovertebral angle (Fig. 78, *f*) or into both. Its fibres are very closely related to those of the rhomboideus.

Relations.—By its outer surface with the clavotrapezius (Fig. 68, *d*) and acromiotrapezius (*h*). At its insertion it is often overlaid by either the rhomboideus or the levator scapulæ or both. By its inner surface with the splenius (Fig. 73, *b*). Its caudal third is wedged between the rhomboideus and the levator scapulæ.

Action.—Draws forward and rotates the scapula.

M. rhomboideus (probably equivalent to the human rhomboideus major and rhomboideus minor).—A rather thick trapezoid muscle connecting the vertebral border of the scapula with the spinous processes of the adjacent vertebræ.

Origin from the caudal two or three fifths of the cervical supraspinous ligament and from the sides and tips of the first four thoracic vertebral spines and the interspinous ligaments caudad of these four spines. It passes lateroventrad, and the fibres converge somewhat so that the line of insertion is shorter than the line of origin.

Insertion by a short tendon (1 millimeter long) into the vertebral border of the scapula, the line of insertion passing gradually from the inner (Fig. 78, *e*) to the outer (Fig. 76, *i*) surface; and by fleshy fibres into the outer surface of the glenovertebral angle of the scapula (Fig. 76, *i*) in close connection with the origin of the teres major (*j*). A bundle of fibres at the cranial border may be inserted into the cranial border of the levator scapulæ at its insertion.

Relations.—By its outer surface with the spinotrapezius (Fig. 68, *j*), acromiotrapezius (*h*), latissimus dorsi (*m*), and clavotrapezius (*d*); it is usually partially separated from these muscles by a mass of fat. By its inner surface near its insertion with the serratus anterior (Fig. 73, *i*) and levator scapulæ (Fig. 73, *h*), and craniad with the splenius (Fig. 73, *b*), and the tendon of the serratus posterior superior (Fig. 73, *l*). At its lateral end it touches the occipitoscapularis (Fig. 73, *a*), serratus anterior (*i*), levator scapulæ (*h*), supraspinatus (Fig. 75, *a*), and infraspinatus (Fig. 75, *c*), and the teres major (Fig. 75, *d*).

Action.—Draws the scapula toward the vertebral column.

M. cleidomastoideus (clavicular portion of the human sterno-cleidomastoid) (Fig. 65, *h*).—A narrow flat muscle between the mastoid process and the clavicle.

Origin from the apex and caudal margin of the mastoid process of the temporal bone, by tendon and muscle fibres. The muscle passes caudad, becoming broader and thinner.

Insertion into the lateral four-fifths of the clavicle within the insertion of the clavotrapezius, and into the raphe which continues laterad of the clavicle.

Relations.—Outer or lateral surface at the caudal end with the clavotrapezius (Fig. 65, *j*); further craniad with the depressor conchæ (Fig. 64, *b*), the platysma, and the sterno-mastoid (Fig. 65, *g*). Inner or medial surface with the supra-spinatus (Fig. 75, *a*) caudad, with the mass of fat in the axilla at its middle, with the levator claviculæ ventralis (Fig. 65, *i*) and obliquus capitis superior (Fig. 71, *e*) craniad.

Action.—Pulls the clavicle craniad when the head is fixed. Turns the head and depresses the snout when the clavicle is fixed.

M. levator scapulæ ventralis, or levator claviculæ (Fig. 68, *f*; Fig. 65, *i*; Fig. 72, *c*, *c'*, *c''*) (not usually found in man).

Origin (Fig. 72, *c'*, *c''*) in two parts. (1) By fleshy fibres from the ventral surface of the atlantal transverse process near its caudal border (*c'*). (2) By a small tendon from the ventral surface of the basioccipital opposite the middle of the length of the bulla tympani (*c''*) in common with the longus capitis (*a*). The two heads unite to form a flat band which passes caudo-ventrad and is inserted (Fig. 76, *f*) by a flat short tendon, about eight millimeters broad, into the outer surface of the metacromion along its ventral border, and into the infraspinatus fossa for one or two millimeters distad of that border.

Relations.—Near the insertion the dorsal border overlaps the border of the acromiotrapezius (Fig. 68, *h*), and the ventral border is attached by strong fascia to the border of the clavotrapezius (Fig. 68, *d*). The outer surface is in relation with the longissimus capitis (Fig. 73, *g*), clavotrapezius (Fig. 68, *d*), cleidomastoid (Fig. 73, *d*), platysma, and the skin. The inner surface is in relation caudad with the supraspinatus and with a mass of fat and a lymphatic gland which occupy the hollow of the shoulder. Craniad it is in relation with the cleidomastoid (Fig. 73, *d*), the scalenus (Fig. 73, *f*), the longus capitis (Fig. 73, *e*), and the obliquus superior (Fig. 71, *e*).

Action.—Pulls the scapula craniad.

M. latissimus dorsi (Fig. 68, *m*; Fig. 65, *q*; Fig. 77, *e*). —A large triangular sheet covering rather more than the dorsocranial half of the abdomen and thorax. It arises from the middorsal line, from the pelvis to the fifth thoracic spine, and is inserted into the humerus.

Origin from the tips of the neural spines of the vertebræ from the fourth or fifth thoracic to about the sixth lumbar. As far as the tenth or eleventh thoracic vertebra the origin is directly by muscle-fibres. Caudad of this is a broad triangular tendon which may be so closely united to the tendons of the underlying muscles that it cannot be separated. The muscle passes cranioventrad, the fibres converging to the axilla. In the axilla a part of the cutaneus maximus and the epitrochlearis (Fig. 65, *r*) take origin from the outer surface.

Insertion.—The muscle then ends in a flat tendon, to the cranial surface of which the fibres of the teres major (Fig. 77, *c*) are attached. Five to ten millimeters from the humerus the muscle-fibres of the teres give place to the tendon-fibres, and the conjoined tendon of the teres and latissimus which is thus formed (Fig. 79, *d′*) is inserted into a rough elongated area (Fig. 82, *f*) which lies parallel with the pectoral ridge on the medial surface of the shaft of the humerus (Fig. 48, *g*). The teres tendon forms the proximal part of the conjoined tendon. A part of the tendon of the latissimus may join the pectoralis minor at its distal or caudal border (Fig. 65), and thus it may contribute to the formation of both pillars of the bicipital arch (Fig. 65, *t′*).

Relations.—Its outer surface is covered caudad by the cutaneus maximus, and craniad by the spinotrapezius (Fig. 68, *j*) and the long head of the triceps (Fig. 68, *k*). The cranial border comes into relation with the spinotrapezius (*j*) and teres major (Fig. 77, *c*). The caudal border is in contact at the ventral end with the xiphihumeralis (Fig. 65, *p*) and pectoralis minor (Fig. 65, *o*). The inner surface of the latissimus covers near its cranioventral end parts of the xiphihumeralis (Fig. 68, *n*), pectoralis minor (Fig. 68, *o*), teres major (Fig. 77, *c*), and serratus anterior (Fig. 73, *i*). The caudal border covers a portion of the obliquus externus abdominis (Fig. 68, *p*); the dorsal and middle portions cover parts of the longissimus dorsi (Fig. 69, *f''*), the spinalis dorsi (Fig. 69, *g*), the serratus posterior superior (Fig. 73, *l*), and serratus posterior inferior (Fig. 73, *n*).

Action.—Pulls the arm caudodorsad.

M. serratus anterior and **levator scapulæ** (Fig. 73, *i* and *h*) in the cat are continuous at both origin and insertion, and it is barely possible to separate their contiguous borders without cutting the fibres. The muscle extends from the transverse processes of the last five cervical vertebræ and from the first nine or ten ribs to the medial surface of the scapula near its vertebral margin (Fig. 78, *c* and *d*).

M. serratus anterior (or serratus magnus) (Fig. 73, *i*).

Origin.—From the first nine or ten ribs in as many subdivisions. The first subdivision arises from the whole or nearly the whole of the caudal border of the first rib. The next four or five arise either from the ribs or from the costal cartilages near or at their junction with the ribs. The last four subdivisions arise from the ribs at increasing distances from the cartilages. The fibres converge and the subdivisions join one another.

Insertion (Fig. 78, *c*) into a narrow area on the medial surface of the scapula near the vertebral border. The glenoid half of the insertion is by a short tendon, the remainder by muscle-fibres.

Relations.—Outer (lateral) surface with the latissimus dorsi (Fig. 68, *m*), teres major (Fig. 77, *c*), subscapularis (Fig.

77, *a*), and near the origin with the rectus abdominis (Fig. 73, *k*), the scalenus (Fig. 73, *f–f'''*), and the obliquus externus (Fig. 68, *p*). Inner (medial) surface with the serratus posterior superior (Fig. 73, *l*) and its tendon, and with the intercostales externi (Fig. 73, *m*). At its insertion the muscle touches the rhomboideus. The cranial edge is united to the caudal edge of the levator scapulæ (Fig. 73, *h*).

Action.—Depressor of the scapula.

M. levator scapulæ (Fig. 73, *h*).

Origin.—From the dorsal tubercles of the transverse processes of the last five cervical vertebræ and from the ligaments between the tubercles. A slip sometimes arises from the atlas.

Insertion (Fig. 78, *d*) into a triangular area on the medial surface of the scapula near its vertebral border. It is continuous with the insertion of the serratus anterior.

Relations.—Outer (lateral) surface with a mass of fat separating it from the clavotrapezius (Fig. 68, *d*) and cleidomastoid (Fig. 65, *h*), and with the subscapularis (Fig. 77, *a*). Inner (medial) surface with the splenius (Fig. 73, *b*), the tendon of the serratus posterior superior (Fig. 73, *l*), and the cervical portion of the longissimus dorsi (Fig. 69, *f''*). Near the insertion the muscle touches the occipitoscapularis (Fig. 73, *a*) and rhomboideus. Caudal border united with the serratus anterior (Fig. 73, *i*).

Action.—Draws the scapula cranioventrad.

B. Muscles of the Back (interconnecting parts of the vertebral column) (Fig. 69).—The muscles connected with the vertebral column form a mass which is less markedly differentiated into distinct muscles than is the case in the limbs. A great longitudinal mass of fibres begins in the sacral region and extends along the vertebral column to the head. This mass contains fibres running in various directions and attached at one or both ends to the sacrum, the innominate bones, the spinous, transverse, and articular processes, and to the arches, of the vertebræ; to the ribs and to the head, and having in general the function of moving the vertebræ in various ways, or of moving parts connected with the vertebræ. In some regions, especially the cervical, it is possible to distinguish clearly distinct muscles which have been differentiated from this mass. In the greater part of its extent, however, it is possible to distinguish only more or less closely interconnected bundles,—the more clearly marked of which have received special names.

The great dorsal mass running along each side of the vertebral column, occupying the space between the spinous processes and the transverse processes, receives the general name of **M. extensor dorsi communis**; the separate muscles are to be considered as parts or differentiations of this. The largest part of the mass is in the lumbar region (first portion of the **longissimus dorsi**, Fig. 69, *f*). At the caudal end of the thorax a lateral mass, parts of which become connected with the ribs, is separated off from the main part of the muscle; this extends craniad into the cervical region as **M. iliocostalis** (*h*). The main portion of the longissimus dorsi (*f'*) continues craniad on the medial side of the iliocostal into the neck region. At about the level of the eighth or ninth thoracic vertebra a strip begins to become separated off on the medial side of the longissimus; further forward it becomes clearly distinct, forming the **spinalis dorsi** (*g*). The separate muscles connecting the cervical vertebræ with each other and with the head are differentiations of the extensor dorsi communis.

A still deeper set of fibres, interconnecting the vertebræ, forms the **multifidus spinæ** and a number of other small muscles.

A description of the different bundles of fibres, under the names usually given, follows. Certain general principles are observed in some of the names used. Muscles which interconnect the spinous processes of the vertebræ receive the name **spinalis.** Those interconnecting contiguous spinous processes are called **interspinalis.** Muscles attached at one end to transverse processes, at the other to the spinous processes, receive the name **transversospinalis. Semispinalis** has the same signification as transversospinalis, but is a name usually applied to subdivisions of the transversospinalis group. The **intertransversarii** are muscles interconnecting the transverse processes

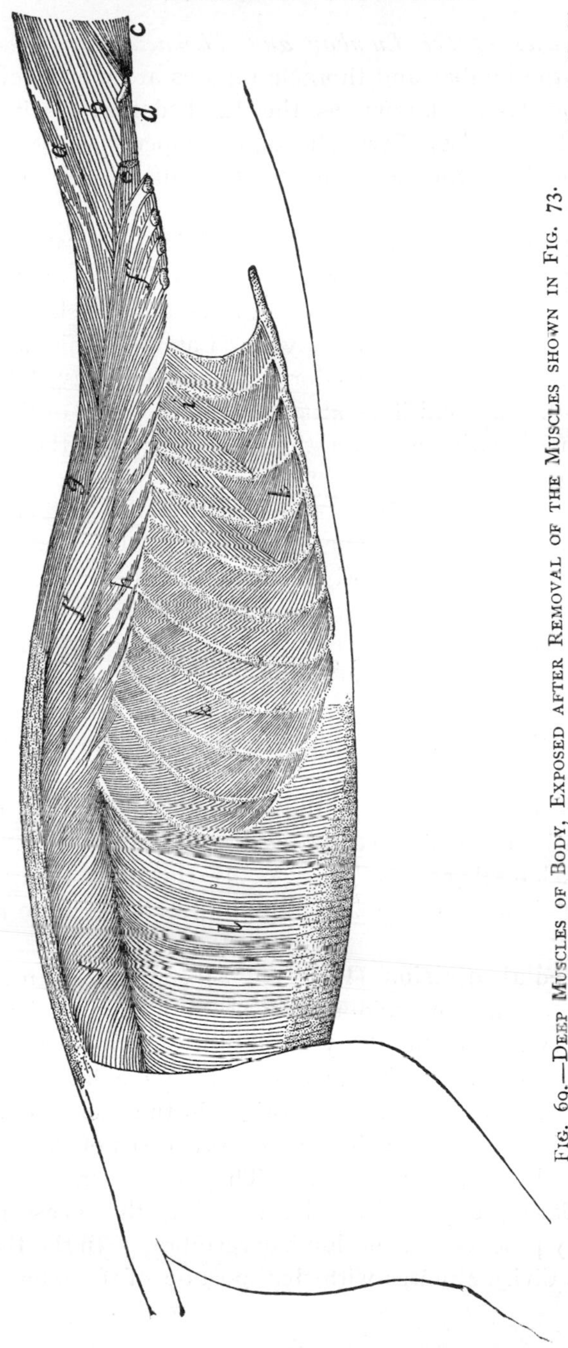

Fig. 69.—Deep Muscles of Body, Exposed after Removal of the Muscles shown in Fig. 73.

a, M. biventer cervicis; *b*, M. complexus; *c*, M. obliquus capitis superior; *d*, M. longus atlantis; *e*, cut end of M. longissimus capitis; *f*, *f′*, *f″*, M. longissimus dorsi; *g*, M. spinalis dorsi; *h*, M. iliocostalis; *i*, Mm. intercostales externi; *k*, Mm. intercostales interni; *l*, M. transversus abdominis.

(*a*) *Muscles of the Lumbar and Thoracic Regions.*—The muscles of the lumbar and thoracic regions are mostly covered by a strong fascia, known as the **lumbodorsal** fascia (Fig. 68, *y*). This consists of two sheets, the superficial sheet being applied directly to the outer surface of the inner sheet, or separated from it by a mass of fat.

The superficial sheet (Fig. 68, *y*) overlies the lumbar region and the caudal half of the thoracic region. On the medial side it is attached to the spinous processes of the vertebræ and is united closely to the deeper layer. Laterally this fascia is continuous with the latissimus dorsi (*m*) and obliquus abdominis externus (*p*). Caudad it is attached to the spine of the ilium and becomes continuous with the fascia covering the gluteus muscles.

The deeper sheet (Fig. 70, *c*) is of a tendinous character, forming the external tendinous layer of the longissimus dorsi, many of whose fibres take origin from its under surface. It is described more fully in the account of this muscle.

M. longissimus dorsi (Fig. 69, *f*, *f'*, *f''*; Fig. 70, *a* and *b*).—A very large muscle, filling most of the region between the spinous processes and transverse processes of the lumbar and thoracic vertebræ, and extending into the cervical region.

The muscle is largest in the lumbar region (Fig. 69, *f*; Fig. 70), where it is divided into a narrow medial (Fig. 70, *a*) and a thick lateral portion (Fig. 70, *b*), the latter being again partially subdivided by the fascia. The two parts unite farther craniad.

The **medial division** (Fig. 70, *a*) consists of muscular bundles connecting the spinous processes of the vertebræ with the accessory and mammillary processes of other vertebræ; it is continuous caudad with the extensor caudæ lateralis (Fig. 70, *f*). The muscle-fibres take origin in the sacral region by small round tendons from the spinous processes of the last two sacral and the caudal vertebræ. They curve cranioventrad, forming a large belly, and are inserted into the accessory and mammillary processes of the lumbar vertebræ. In the thoracic region this division unites with that portion of the lateral division in which the fibres coming from the fascia of origin are inserted into the laminæ and transverse processes of the thoracic vertebræ.

The **lateral division** (Fig. 70, *b*) is much larger than the medial one, forming in the lumbar region a nearly cylindrical mass.

Origin from the crest of the ilium (Fig. 70, 1) and the medial surface of the ilium as far caudad as the auricular impression; also from the deep layer of the lumbodorsal fascia (*c*). This fascia is connected with the crest of the ilium and with the tips of the spinous processes of the vertebræ in the lumbar and thoracic regions, and from it a large proportion of the fibres of the longissimus take origin. In the lumbar region it dips into the muscle as an intermediate longitudinal sheet (*c*), partially dividing it lengthwise into two parts. Fibres taking origin from the lateral surface of this intermediate sheet curve cranioventrad, and are inserted on the transverse processes of the lumbar vertebræ. Fibres taking origin from the medial surface of the sheet pass mediocraniad and are inserted into the accessory processes and the surfaces of the vertebral arches. In the thoracic region (Fig. 69, *f′*)

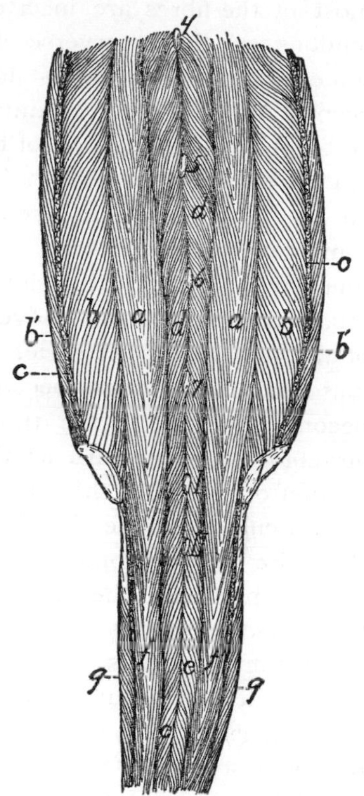

FIG. 70.—MUSCLES ON THE DORSAL SIDE OF THE VERTEBRAL COLUMN IN THE LUMBAR, SACRAL, AND CAUDAL REGIONS.

Both sheets of the lumbodorsal fascia have been removed, the deep layer (*c*) being cut where it passes into the longissimus dorsi. 1, crest of ilium; 4–7, tips of spinous processes of the fourth to seventh lumbar vertebræ. *I*, *II*, tips of spinous processes of first two sacral vertebræ. *a*, *b*, M. longissimi dorsi (*a*, medial portion; *b*, lateral portion; *b′*, portion taking origin from the lumbodorsal fascia); *c*, cut edge of deep layer of lumbodorsal fascia; *d*, M. multifidus spinæ; *e*, M. extensor caudæ medialis; *f*, M. extensor caudæ lateralis. *g*, M. abductor caudæ externus.

most of the fibres are inserted in separate bundles by small tendons on the transverse processes of the vertebræ, while some of the medial fibres unite with tendinous strands which become attached to the laminæ and articular processes of the vertebræ. At the region of the eighth or ninth thoracic vertebra the **spinalis dorsi** (Fig. 69, *g*) begins to be separated off on the medial side, the separation becoming complete only some distance farther craniad; the longissimus dorsi then continues into the cervical region (f''). Bundles of fibres become attached in the manner above described to transverse processes of all the thoracic vertebræ. In the cervical region (f'') the muscle spreads out and becomes thinner, and bundles of fibres become attached to the transverse processes of the cervical vertebræ as far forward as the second. In the more cranial portion of its extent the muscle receives fibres having origin on the articular processes and laminæ of the cervical and a few of the more cranial thoracic vertebræ.

The portion of the muscle which is inserted on the cervical transverse processes (f'') is sometimes distinguished as the **longissimus cervicis;** it is not well separated from the rest of the muscle in the cat. The **longissimus capitis** (Fig. 69, *e*; Fig. 73, *g*) is to be considered a differentiated cranial portion of this muscle.

Relations.—Outer surface with the following, beginning with the caudal end: the sartorius (Fig. 68, *q*), the latissimus dorsi (Fig. 68, *m*), the lumbodorsal fascia (Fig. 68, *y*), the serratus posterior inferior (Fig. 73, *n*) and superior (Fig. 73, *l*), and the levator scapulæ (Fig. 73, *h*). Lateral margin with the abdominal muscles, the iliocostal (Fig. 69, *h*), and the levator scapulæ (Fig. 73, *h*). Medial side with the multifidus spinæ (Fig. 70, *d*), the spinous processes of the thoracic vertebræ, the spinalis dorsi (Fig. 69, *g*), the complexus (Fig. 69, *b*), the biventer cervicis (Fig. 69, *a*), and the longissimus capitis (Fig. 69, *e*).

Action.—Extends the vertebral column.

M. iliocostalis (Fig. 69, *h*).—This is a muscle about 1½ to 2 centimeters wide, lying on the dorsal portion of the ribs, laterad of the longissimus dorsi (f'). It is composed of many partly separated bundles, each with an oblique tendon. The muscle begins at the last or next to the last rib, where it is connected with the longissimus by a rather small bundle of fibres. The rest of the muscle-fibres take origin in bundles from the lateral surface of the ribs, at about the angles, or from thin tendons connecting the angles, of the ribs; they pass obliquely craniad and are inserted, usually by tendons, on the lateral surface of the third or fourth rib craniad of the one on which the given bundle has origin. The insertions on any given rib lie ventrad of the origins on the same rib. In the cat this muscle is confined to the thoracic region.

Relations.—Outer surface with the serratus posterior inferior (Fig. 73, *n*) and superior (Fig. 73, *l*), and the levator scapulæ (Fig. 73, *h*). Inner surface with the dorsal surface of the ribs, the external intercostals (Fig. 69, *i*), and craniad with the levatores costarum. Medial edge in contact with the longissimus dorsi (Fig. 69, *f'*).

Action.—Draws the ribs together.

M. spinalis dorsi (Fig. 69, *g*). A muscle interconnecting the spinous processes of vertebræ some distance apart, in the thoracic and cervical regions. It lies on the medial side of the longissimus dorsi (*f'*).

Origin by strong tendons from the tips of the spinous processes of the tenth to the thirteenth thoracic vertebræ. These tendons represent the cranial portion of the deep layer of the lumbodorsal fascia, and give origin also to many fibres of the longissimus dorsi, so that the two muscles are completely united at the origin of the spinalis. They become separated at about the level of the sixth thoracic vertebra, the spinalis forming a strong separate bundle passing into the neck region close against the sides of the spinous processes. The insertion is by fleshy bundles into the sides of the spinous processes of the first nine or ten thoracic vertebræ and of the cervical vertebræ as far forward as the second. Some of the fibres of this muscle pass craniad into the biventer cervicis (Fig. 69, *a*).

Relations.—Outer surface with the tendons of the serratus posterior inferior (Fig. 73, *n*) and serratus posterior superior (Fig. 73, *l*), and with the splenius (Fig. 73, *b*), biventer cervicis (Fig. 69, *a*), and complexus (Fig. 69, *b*). Lateral and ventral surface with the longissimus dorsi (*f'*); medial surface with the spinous processes and the multifidus spinæ.

Action.—Extensor of the vertebral column.

M. multifidus spinæ.—This consists of bundles of fibres which have origin on the transverse processes or neighboring parts, pass craniodorsad across one or more vertebræ, and are inserted into the spinous processes of vertebræ lying some distance craniad of the origin. They lie deeper than the muscles previously described. The muscle is most strongly developed in the lumbar region (Fig. 70, *d*), where it forms a thick interwoven mass in which it is difficult to distinguish separate bundles. The fibres in this region have origin on the accessory or mammillary processes and usually pass over more than one vertebra between origin and insertion; their insertions reach the dorsal ends of the spinous processes, so that part of the muscle lies immediately beneath the lumbar fascia. In other regions the multifidus is covered by other muscles. In the thoracic region the separate bands are more distinct, and usually pass in their course over but one intervening vertebra. In the cervical region the bands are interconnected, forming a fairly distinct single muscle, which is described separately below as the **semispinalis cervicis** (Fig. 71, *c*). The portion of this muscle attached to the head (**semispinalis capitis**) forms the biventer cervicis (Fig. 69, *a*) and complexus (*b*). Caudad this muscle passes onto the tail as the **extensor caudæ medialis** (Fig. 70, *e*).

Relations.—Outer and lateral surface in the lumbar region with the longissimus dorsi (Fig. 69, *f*) and the lumbodorsal fascia (Fig. 68, *y*); in the thoracic region with the longissimus dorsi (Fig. 69, *f'*) and spinalis dorsi (*g*). Inner surface with the arches, articular processes, and spinous processes of the vertebræ.

Action.—Extends the back when the muscles of both sides work together. Turns the vertebral column obliquely sideways when one set acts alone.

The deepest layer of the multifidus forms what is sometimes

distinguished as the **Mm. rotatores;** no separate layer of this sort is to be made out in the cat.

Mm. interspinales.—Muscle-bundles passing from the spinous process of one vertebra to that of the vertebra immediately craniad or caudad of it. They are best developed in the lumbar region.

Mm. intertransversarii. — Muscle-fibres interconnecting the transverse processes. In the lumbar region the **intertransversarii mediales** connect the accessory and mammillary processes; the **intertransversarii laterales** lying between the transverse processes. In other regions only one set of the intertransversarii is to be distinguished.

(*b*) *Dorsal Muscles of the Cervical Region.*—The clavotrapezius (Fig. 68, *d*) and occipitoscapularis (Fig. 73, *a*) have been described in connection with the muscles of the shoulder. The remaining muscles of this region may be considered as differentiations of the general vertebral musculature (M. extensor dorsi communis).

M. splenius (Fig. 73, *b*.)—A large sheet of muscle covering the dorsal part of the side of the neck, beneath the trapezii.

Origin from the whole cervical ligament and from the fascia covering the deeper muscles along a line which extends from the first thoracic spinous process caudolaterad for about two centimeters.

Insertion by a thin tendon into the whole lambdoidal ridge. Laterad the tendon may be fused with that of the longissimus capitis (Fig. 73, *g*).

Relations. Outer surface with the sternomastoid (Fig. 68, *c*), occipitoscapularis (Fig. 73, *a*), clavotrapezius (Fig. 68, *d*), rhomboideus, tendon of the serratus posterior superior (Fig. 73, *l*), and the levator scapulæ (Fig. 73, *h*). Lateral edge closely united with the longissimus capitis (Fig. 73, *g*). Inner surface with the longissimus capitis, complexus (Fig. 69, *b*), and biventer cervicis (Fig. 69, *a*).

Action.—Lateral flexor of the head. The two together elevate the head.

M. longissimus capitis (trachelomastoideus) (Fig. 73, *g*; Fig. 69, *e*).—This is a slender muscle lying close against the lateral border of the splenius (Fig. 73, *b*), and sometimes fused with the splenius at its craniad end. It is a cranial continuation of the longissimus dorsi (Fig. 69, *f''*).

Origin by five slips which are attached by strong tendons to the anterior articular processes of the last four cervical vertebræ. The tendons are common to this muscle and the complexus. The five slips unite to form a flat belly which has its

Insertion by a strong rounded tendon into the mastoid process of the temporal bone. The tendon may be closely united to that of the splenius.

Relations.—Lateral surface with the sternomastoid (Fig. 68, *c*), the levator scapulæ (Fig. 73, *h*), and longissimus dorsi (Fig. 69, *f''*). Medial surface with the splenius (Fig. 73, *b*) (to which it is partly united), the complexus (Fig. 69, *b*), and the longus atlantis (Fig. 69, *d*).

Action.—Lateral flexor of the head.

M. biventer cervicis (Fig. 69, *a*) (**medial portion of M. semispinalis cervicis et capitis**).—The biventer cervicis is a flat muscle which lies beneath the splenius (Fig. 73, *b*), next the median line of the neck, with its fibres longitudinal.

Origin in three or four slips from the surface of the three or four aponeurotic arches which take origin from the tips of the spinous processes of the last cervical and the first three thoracic vertebræ and pass laterad and caudad to the anterior processes of the second, third, fourth, and fifth thoracic vertebræ. These arches are deviated from their straight course by four aponeurotic bands which pass from them obliquely caudad and dorsad to the sides of the spinous processes of the vertebræ into which the arches are inserted. The arches form the beginning of the sheet of fascia which passes outside of the longitudinal supraspinous muscles, and the anchoring bands form the beginning of a similar sheet which passes within the longitudinal supraspinous muscles. An additional slip may take origin from the cervical ligament between the last cervical and the first thoracic vertebræ. The fibres form a flat band divided by two or three oblique tendinous intersections. It adheres closely to the cervical supraspinous ligament.

Insertion by a strong tendon into the medial part of the lambdoidal crest.

Relations.—Outer surface with the splenius (Fig. 73, *b*) and at the caudal end with the longissimus dorsi (Fig. 69, *f''*). Inner surface with the spinalis dorsi (Fig. 69, *g*), the semispinalis cervicis (Fig. 71, *c*), and the rectus capitis posterior major (Fig. 71, *a*). Medial edge with the muscle of the opposite side; lateral edge with the complexus (Fig. 69, *b*).

Action.—Raises the snout.

M. complexus (Fig. 69, *b*) (**lateral portion of M. semispinalis cervicis et capitis**).—The complexus is closely associated with the biventer cervicis (*a*) and lies on its lateral side beneath the splenius (Fig. 73, *b*).

Origin by tendinous bands from the anterior articular processes of the last five or six cervical and the first one, two, or three thoracic vertebræ. The same bands give origin externally to the fibres of the longissimus capitis (Fig. 69, *e*), and internally to those of deeper muscles of the neck. The six or more muscular slips continued from these tendons unite to form a flat band, the

Insertion of which is by a flat tendon into the medial third of the lambdoidal crest some distance ventrad of the free edge of the crest. Near the insertion the lateral border of the muscle is connected by an aponeurotic band to the lateral border of the transverse process of the atlas.

Relations.—Outer surface at the dorsal border with the biventer cervicis (Fig. 69, *a*); at the middle with the splenius (Fig. 73, *b*); at the ventral border with the longissimus capitis (Fig. 69, *e*) and the longissimus dorsi (Fig. 69, *f''*). Inner surface with the cervical portion of the spinalis dorsi, with the semispinalis cervicis (Fig. 71, *c*), the obliquus capitis inferior (Fig. 71, *b*), the rectus capitis posterior major (Fig. 71, *a*), and the obliquus superior (Fig. 71, *e*).

Action.—Raises the head.

M. spinalis dorsi extends into the cervical region; it has been described.

M. semispinalis cervicis (Fig. 71, *c*).—This represents that portion of the multifidus spinæ which extends into the cervical region. It is not composed of distinct bundles, like the multifidus of the thoracic region, but all the fibres are united into a fairly well-defined muscle.

Origin from the articular processes of the last five cervical vertebræ.

Insertion into the spinous processes of the cervical vertebræ up to the second, the largest part of the muscle being inserted into the caudal end of the spine of the atlas.

Relations.—Outer surface with the spinalis dorsi (Fig. 69, *g*) and the complexus (Fig. 69, *b*). Inner surface with the vertebræ.

Action.—Extends the neck.

M. longissimus dorsi extends into the cervical region, where it is often distinguished as the **longissimus cervicis** (Fig. 69, *f''*). It has been described.

M. longus atlantis (Fig. 71, *f*; Fig. 69, *d*).—This represents a differentiated portion of the longissimus dorsi.

Origin from the transverse process and the side of the vertebral arch of the third cervical vertebra.

Insertion into the caudolateral angle of the wing of the atlas.

Relations.—Dorsal surface with the complexus (Fig. 69, *b*), the longissimus capitis (Fig. 69, *e*), and the obliquus inferior (Fig. 71, *b*). Ventral surface with the scalenus (Fig. 71, *g*), longissimus dorsi (Fig. 69, *f''*), and levator scapulæ (Fig. 71, *h*).

Action.—Extends the neck and turns the head sideways.

M. rectus capitis posterior major (Fig. 71, *a*).

Origin.—The whole length of the spinous process (or crest) of the axis, or its caudal part only. It is united by a raphe to the opposite muscle. The muscle passes craniad and laterad to its

Insertion into an area ventrad of the medial part of the lambdoidal crest beneath the insertion of the complexus (Fig. 69, *b*) and the biventer cervicis (Fig. 69, *a*).

Relations.—Dorsal surface with the biventer cervicis (Fig. 69, *a*). Ventral surface with the rectus capitis posterior medius (Fig. 71, *d*) and the obliquus capitis inferior.

Action.—Raises the snout.

M. rectus capitis posterior medius (Fig. 71, *d*). (This is in man a part of the rectus capitis posterior major.)—It lies beneath the rectus capitis posterior major (Fig. 71, *a*).

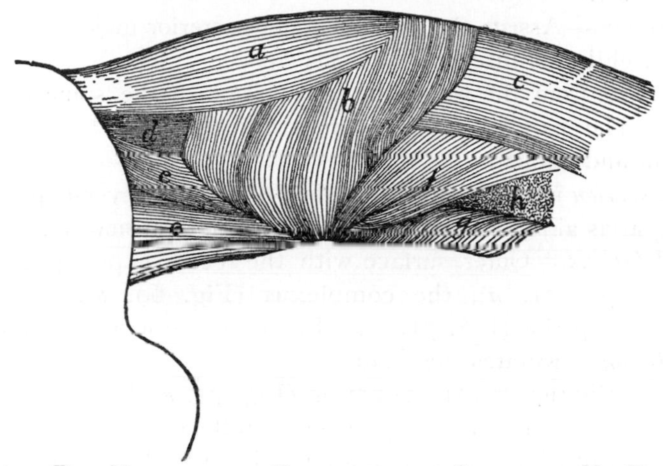

FIG. 71.—DEEP MUSCLES OF THE NECK, AFTER THE REMOVAL OF MM. BIVENTER CERVICIS AND COMPLEXUS.

a, M. rectus capitis posterior major; *b*, M. obliquus capitis inferior; *c*, M. semispinalis cervicis; *d*, M. rectus capitis posterior medius; *e*, M. obliquus capitis superior; *f*, M. longus atlantis; *g*, M. scalenus (part of cervical portion); *h*, cut end of M. levator scapulæ.

Origin from the cranial end of the axial spine. It forms a triangular prismatic mass which passes craniad and has its

Insertion into an elongated area on the occipital bone, ventrad of the median half of the lambdoidal crest.

Relations.—Dorsal surface with the rectus capitis posterior major (Fig. 71, *a*). Ventral surface with the atlas and the rectus capitis posterior minor.

Action.—Assists the rectus capitis posterior major.

M. rectus capitis posterior minor.—A small triangular muscle beneath the rectus capitis posterior medius (Fig. 71, *d*).

Origin by the apex of the triangle from the cranial border of the dorsal arch of the atlas for about two millimeters laterad of the median line. The muscle passes over the ligament which connects the atlas to the occiput and adheres to it.

Insertion into an elongated area on the occipital bone,

ventrad of the insertion of the rectus capitis posterior medius for about five millimeters next to the median line.

Relations.—Dorsal surface with the rectus capitis posterior medius. Ventral surface with the posterior atlanto-occipital membrane.

Action.—Assists the rectus capitis posterior major.

M. obliquus inferior (Fig. 71, *b*).

Origin from the whole lateral surface of the spine of the axis. The parallel fibres form a thick mass which passes laterad and craniad.

Insertion into the dorsal surface of the transverse process of the atlas along a narrow area near its lateral margin.

Relations.—Outer surface with the rectus capitis posterior major (Fig. 71, *a*), the complexus (Fig. 69, *b*), and the obliquus superior (Fig. 71, *e*). Inner surface with the axis.

Action.—Rotates the head.

M. obliquus capitis superior (Fig. 71, *e*; Fig. 72, *e*).—This is a triangular muscle passing from the outer border of the atlas laterad of the recti capitis posteriores to the occiput.

Origin from the lateral border of the transverse process of the atlas on its ventral margin. The fibres pass craniad and diverge.

Insertion into the caudal side of the mastoid process of the temporal bone and into a line parallel with the lambdoidal ridge and ventrad of it, from the mastoid process to within one centimeter of the median line.

Relations.—Outer surface with the splenius (Fig. 73, *b*), complexus (Fig. 69, *b*), and longissimus capitis (Fig. 73, *g*). Inner surface with the obliquus inferior (Fig. 71, *b*), the wing of the atlas, and the rectus lateralis (Fig. 72, *d*). Ventral border with the cleidomastoid (Fig. 73, *d*) and one head of the levator scapulæ ventralis (Fig. 72, *c'*).

Action.—Flexes the head laterally.

Mm. interspinales and **intertransversarii** are found in the neck region also; they are described with the muscles of the back.

C. Muscles of the Tail.—**M. extensor caudæ medialis** (Fig. 70, *e*).—This is a continuation caudad of the multifidus spinæ (Fig. 70, *d*); it lies next to the dorsal median line, the muscles of right and left side touching one another in the middle line.

Origin by numerous fleshy bundles from the spinous processes of the sacral and first caudal vertebræ. The fibres pass caudad and are inserted by tendons into the articular processes and the dorsal surface of the caudal vertebræ.

Action.—Extends (raises) the tail.

M. extensor caudæ lateralis (Fig. 70, *f*).—This is a continuation caudad of the medial portion of the longissimus dorsi (Fig. 70, *a*); it lies just laterad of the extensor caudæ medialis (Fig. 70, *e*).

Origin in many fleshy bundles from the articular processes of the sacral vertebræ, and the transverse processes of the caudal vertebræ. The fibres curve dorsocaudad and are inserted by many long slender tendons on the dorsal surfaces of the caudal vertebræ. The muscle grows continually smaller as it passes caudad.

Action.—Raises the tail.

M. abductor caudæ (coccygis) **externus** (Fig. 68, *w*; Fig. 70, *g*).—A rounded muscle on the lateral surface of the cranial part of the tail.

Origin from the medial side of the dorsal border of the ilium, and from the dorsal surface of the sacrum. The muscle passes caudad, lying just ventrad of the extensor lateralis, and is *inserted* into the transverse processes and lateral surfaces of the caudal vertebræ, as far back as the eighth or ninth.

Action.—Bends the tail sideways.

M. abductor caudæ internus (or M. coccygeus).—A large flat muscle, having origin on the spine of the ischium. The muscle passes dorsomediad, spreading out, and is inserted into the transverse processes of the second to the fourth caudal vertebræ.

Relations.—Lateral surface with the caudofemoralis (Fig. 68, *s*), gluteus maximus, and pyriformis. Medial surface with the iliocaudalis and the flexor caudæ longus (Fig. 68, *x*).

M. iliocaudalis (Str.-D.) (Fig. 162, 11′, page 398).—This represents a portion of the levator ani of man, and in some specimens is united with that muscle (Fig. 162, 11) in the cat.

Origin along the ventral half of the medial surface of the ilium, caudad of the sacrum. The fibres pass caudad and are *inserted* by a flat tendon into the ventral surface of the caudal vertebræ, from the second or third to about the seventh.

Relations.—Lateral surface with the gluteus maximus and abductor caudæ internus (Fig. 68, *w*). Medial surface with the levator ani (Fig. 162, 11), with which this muscle may be partly united.

Action.—The two muscles together flex the tail.

M. flexor caudæ longus (Fig. 162, 12; Fig. 113, *c*, page 270).

Origin on the ventral surface of the last lumbar vertebra, of the sacrum, and of the transverse processes of the caudal vertebræ. Caudad the muscle forms long, strong tendons which are *inserted* on the ventral surface of the tail.

Relations.—Lateral surface with the ilium, the gluteus maximus, the abductor caudæ internus, the iliocaudalis, and the skin of the tail. Dorsally it touches in the caudal region the abductor caudæ externus (Fig. 68, *w*), medially the flexor caudæ brevis (Fig. 162, 13).

Action.—Flexes the tail.

M. flexor caudæ brevis (Fig. 162, 13).

Origin on the ventral surface of the caudal vertebræ, from the first to the seventh or eighth. The principal head comes from the first vertebra. The bundles thus formed pass caudad and are inserted each into the ventral surface of a vertebra some distance caudad of the origin. The muscle extends to about the tenth caudal vertebra, and its most caudal parts are closely interconnected with the flexor caudæ longus.

Relations—Lateral edge with the flexor caudæ longus. Medial edge in the sacral region with the levator ani (Fig. 162, 11) and the iliocaudalis (Fig. 162, 11′); in the caudal region with the muscle of the opposite side.

Action.—Flexes the tail.

2. Muscles on the Ventral Side of the Vertebral Column.

A. Lumbar and Thoracic Regions.—The iliopsoas (Fig.

162, 8) belongs in this group, but since it moves the leg it is described with the muscles of the pelvic limbs.

M. psoas minor (Fig. 162, 9, page 398).—This muscle lies along the ventral surface of the vertebral column, next to the peritoneum, and extends from the thoracic vertebræ to the ilium.

Origin usually by five heads, from the caudal border of the centra of the last two (or one) thoracic and first three (or four) lumbar vertebræ. These heads also serve as origin for a part of the iliopsoas, and are closely united at their origin with the quadratus lumborum. They unite to form an, at first, rather large flat muscle, which rapidly becomes smaller caudad, finally forming a slender tendon which is *inserted* on the iliopectineal line, just craniad of the acetabulum.

Relations.—Dorsolateral surface with the quadratus lumborum and iliopsoas (Fig. 162, 8). Ventral surface with the pleura and diaphragm near the origin; with the peritoneum caudad.

Action.—Flexes the back in the lumbar region.

M. quadratus lumborum.—A flat muscle lying on the ventral surface of the transverse processes of the lumbar vertebræ. Craniad it has origin on the ventral surface of the last two thoracic vertebræ, and by a few fibres from the last rib. The muscle passes caudad, lying on the lateral side of the psoas minor (Fig. 162, 9), and becomes attached to each of the transverse processes of the lumbar vertebræ. Caudad the muscle passes into a strong flat tendon which is inserted into the anterior inferior spine of the ilium.

Relations.—Dorsal surface with the transverse processes and the intertransverse muscles. Ventral and medial surfaces with the psoas minor (Fig. 162, 9) and iliopsoas (Fig. 162, 8).

Action.—Bends the vertebral column sideways.

B. MUSCLES ON THE VENTRAL SIDE OF THE NECK (Fig. 65, page 109).—**M. sternomastoideus** (Fig. 65, *g*; Fig. 68, *c*).—The sternomastoid (sternal portion of the human sternocleidomastoid) is a flat band one to three centimeters wide extending from the cranial end of the manubrium and the midventral line craniad of it to the lambdoidal ridge.

The *origin* extends from the cranial end of the manubrium along the midventral line as far as the caudal border of the cricoid cartilage, and is in two parts. The **caudal** portion arises from the lateral surface of the manubrium along the dorsal half of its cranial end, and from the median raphe for about one centimeter craniad of the manubrium. Its fibres are parallel and tend to diverge into two layers. The **cranial** portion arises by means of fibres which cover the median line and interdigitate with the fibres of the opposite muscle between the cricoid cartilage and a point a few millimeters craniad of the manubrium. Its caudal border is thus overlaid by the caudal portion. Its fibres converge and join those of the caudal portion. The muscle passes dorsocraniad and is

Inserted by means of a flat tendon into the lateral half of the lambdoidal ridge and into a continuation of the ridge onto the mastoid portion of the temporal bone as far as the mastoid process. The thickest part of the tendon is inserted into the mastoid process.

Relations.—Outer surface at the caudal end with the pectoralis major (Fig. 65, *l*); in the middle part with the platysma, the depressor conchæ (Fig. 64, *b*), and with the external jugular vein (Fig. 65, 5), which crosses it obliquely; at the cranial end with the submaxillary (Fig. 65, 2) and parotid (1) glands. Inner surface with the sternohyoid (Fig. 65, *e*), sternothyroid (*g′*), internal jugular vein, longus capitis muscle, the cleidomastoid (*h*), levator scapulæ ventralis (*i*), a large lymphatic gland ventrad of the ear, and the splenius (Fig. 73, *b*).

Action.—One muscle turns the head and depresses the snout. Both together depress the snout.

M. sternohyoideus (Fig. 65, *e*).—A slender muscle on the midventral line of the neck close to the opposite muscle.

Origin from the cranial border of the first costal cartilage. The muscle passes craniad closely united near its caudal end to the sternothyroid (*g′*).

Insertion (Fig. 67, *m*) into the outer half of the ventral surface of the body of the hyoid bone caudad of the origin of the geniohyoid (Fig. 67, *g*).

Relations.—Outer surface with the sternomastoid (Fig.

65, *g*). Inner surface with the thyrohyoid (Fig. 65, *f*; Fig. 67, *p*), the trachea (Fig. 67, 4), and the larynx.

Action.—Draws the hyoid caudad. Raises the ribs and sternum when the hyoid is fixed.

M. sternothyreoideus (Fig. 65, *g'*).—The sternothyroid lies beneath the sternohyoid and is connected with it at its caudal end.

Origin from the first costal cartilage beneath the sternohyoid.

Insertion (Fig. 67, *o*) into the lateral part of the caudal border of the thyroid cartilage of the larynx.

Relations.—Outer surface with the sternohyoid (Fig. 65, *e*) and laterally with the sternomastoid (Fig. 65, *g*). Inner surface with the trachea (Fig. 67, 4), and at the lateral edge with the thyroid gland (Fig. 67, 6).

Action.—Pulls the larynx caudad.

M. scalenus (Fig. 73, *f–f'''*).—This is a large and complex muscle lying on the ventral side of the neck and the lateral surface of the thorax. It might equally well be classified with the muscles of the thorax. It is divisible into a considerable number of interconnected bundles which are sometimes described as separate muscles.

The largest, middle portion (**scalenus medius**) (*f'*) takes origin by thin tendons from the sixth, seventh, eighth, and ninth ribs, just dorsad of their junction with the cartilages; these tendons unite near their origins to form a flat band which becomes fleshy at about the fifth rib, passes craniad, and unites just craniad of the first rib with the other parts of the muscle. The dorsal portion (**scalenus posterior**) (*f''*) has origin by a very slender tendon from about the middle of the outer surface of the third or fourth rib; it extends craniad as a narrow band which passes laterad between the heads of the serratus anterior (*i*) that are attached to the second and third (or third and fourth) ribs, and unites with the other heads. The ventral head (part of **scalenus anterior**) (*f'''*) arises by one or two minute tendons from the cartilages of the second and third ribs; they are partly united with the transversus costarum (*j*). This ventral head passes craniad and unites with the other heads.

These three divisions unite just craniad of the first rib with each other and with the cervical portion of the muscle (*f*) (part of **scalenus anterior**). This consists of a number of small bundles of fibres which arise from the first rib and the transverse processes of the first thoracic and the last six cervical vertebræ.

The *insertion* is onto the transverse processes of all the cervical vertebræ, including the axis and atlas. According to Strauss-Durckheim the fibres from any given transverse process are inserted into the transverse processes of all the vertebræ craniad of it.

The muscle is partly continuous craniad with the longus capitis (*e*). The cervical nerves pass out between the bundles of the cervical portion.

Relations.—Outer (lateral) surface in the thoracic region with the external oblique (Fig. 68, *p*), the pectoralis minor (Fig. 65, *o*), and in part with the serratus anterior (Fig. 73, *i*); in the cervical region with the sternomastoid (Fig. 65, *g*). Inner (medial) surface with the serratus anterior (Fig. 73, *i*), the levator scapulæ (Fig. 73, *h*), the longus atlantis, the transverse processes of the cervical vertebræ, and the longus capitis (Fig. 73, *e*).

Action.—Flexes the neck and draws the ribs craniad.

M. longus capitis (or **rectus capitis anterior major**) (Fig. 72, *a*; Fig. 73, *e*).—This is a long muscle lying on the ventral aspect of the cervical vertebræ. With the muscle of the opposite side and the underlying longus colli (Fig. 72, *g'*) it forms a trough in which lie the œsophagus, pharynx, and trachea.

Origin by five (or six) heads from the ventral margins of the transverse processes of the cervical vertebræ from the second to the sixth inclusive. The heads unite into a common belly, the lateral border of which is united with the levator scapulæ ventralis (Fig. 72, *c''*) near its insertion.

Insertion into the body of the occipital bone between the bulla and the middle line. The insertion extends craniad onto the basisphenoid.

Relations.—Ventral surface with the sternomastoid (Fig. 65, *g*) and the large lymphatic gland ventrad of the external ear. Lateral surface with the scalenus (Fig. 72, *h*) and craniad with the levator scapulæ ventralis (Fig. 72, *c–c''*). Medial surface with the carotid artery, the trachea, œsophagus, and pharynx. Dorsal edge with the vertebræ, the longus colli (Fig. 72, *g'*), and the rectus capitis anterior minor (Fig. 72, *b*).

Action.—Lowers the snout.

M. rectus capitis anterior minor (Fig. 72, *b*). This is a flat band beneath (dorsad of) the longus capitis (*a*).

Origin from the ventral surface of the inferior arch (body) of the atlas (3) for about five millimeters laterad of the middle line.

Insertion into a deep depression on the basioccipital caudad of the insertion of the longus capitis (*a*) and between the caudal end of the bulla (1) and the median line.

Relations.—Ventral surface with the longus capitis (*a*). Dorsal surface with the anterior (ventral) atlanto-occipital membrane (2).

Action. — Depresses the snout.

M. rectus capitis lateralis (Fig. 72, *d*).—This lies ventrad of the obliquus superior (*e*) on the ventral face of the transverse process of the atlas and at first appears to be a part of the obliquus superior.

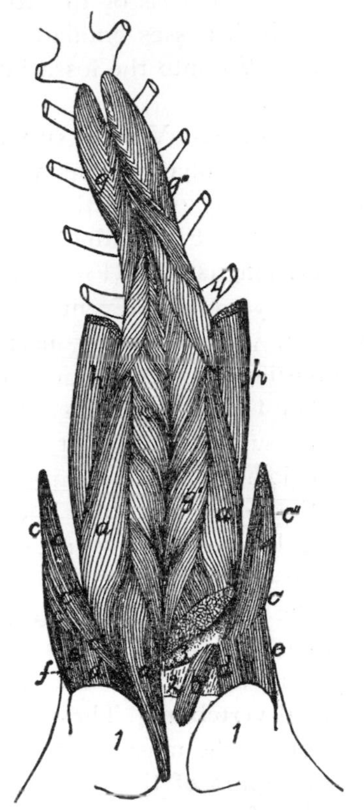

Fig. 72.—Muscles on the Ventral Surface of the Cervical Vertebræ.

On the left side the longus capitis and one head of the levator scapulæ ventralis have been cut, in order to show the rectus capitis anterior minor. *a*, M. longus capitis; *b*, M. rectus capitis anterior minor; *c*, M. levator scapulæ ventralis (*c'*, its atlantal head; *c''*, its occipital head); *d*, M. rectus capitis lateralis; *e*, M. obliquus capitis superior; *f*, M. longissimus capitis; *g*, M. longus colli (*g'*, its cervical portion; *g''*, its thoracic portion); *h*, part of M. scalenus. 1, bulla tympani; 2, ventral atlanto-occipital membrane; 3, ventral arch of atlas; 4, first rib.

Origin from the median half of the ventral surface of the transverse process of the atlas. The fibres form a cylindrical mass which passes craniad and slightly laterad.

Insertion into the fossa laterad of the condyle of the occipital bone.

Relations.—Ventral surface with the digastric (Fig. 65, *b*) and the lymphatic gland ventrad of the ear. Dorsal surface with the wing of the atlas.

Action.—Flexes the head laterally.

M. longus colli (Fig. 65, *g′*, *g″*).—A long, rather slender muscle lying on the ventral surface of the cervical and first six thoracic vertebræ. It consists of many separate bundles, and is divisible into a thoracic and a cervical portion.

The **thoracic portion** (*g″*) has origin by six heads from the ventral surface of the first six thoracic vertebræ. The separate heads join to form a band which passes craniad and is inserted for the most part into the processus costarius of the sixth cervical vertebra; a portion of it joins the cervical division of the muscle.

The **cervical portion** (*g′*) is a continuation craniad of the thoracic portion. It arises in small bundles from the transverse processes and sides of the ventral surfaces of the centra of the cervical vertebræ. These bundles pass craniomediad, so that those from the muscles of opposite sides meet and are inserted on the centra of the vertebræ in the middle line, each pair of bundles forming a V opening caudad. The most cranial insertion is into the tubercle on the middle of the ventral surface of the ventral arch of the atlas (3).

Relations.—Dorsal surface with the centra of the vertebræ. Ventral surface in the thorax with the trachea; in the neck with the œsophagus. Medial edge with the muscle of the opposite side. Lateral margin in the cervical region with the longus capitis (*a*).

Action.—Bends the neck.

3. **Muscles of the Thorax.**—A. BREAST-MUSCLES (connecting the arm and thorax) (Fig. 65, page 109).

The muscles connecting the arm with the sternum, corresponding to the pectoralis muscles of man, fall into a considerable number of not always clearly separated bundles in the cat. We shall distinguish by name four such bundles; these might be, and frequently are, further subdivided.

M. pectoantibrachialis (Fig. 65, *m*).—This is a small flat bundle about one or two centimeters wide, forming the most superficial portion of the pectoralis group.

Origin on the lateral surface of the manubrium. The muscle passes laterad onto the arm and is *inserted* by a flat tendon into the superficial fascia of the dorsal border of the forearm, near the elbow-joint. The tendon is continuous craniad with the border of the clavobrachial (*k*), so that a bundle of fibres may pass from this muscle to be inserted with the clavobrachial, or a bundle from the clavobrachial to be inserted with this. The tendon is continuous caudad with that of the epitrochlearis (*r*). The fascia of insertion may be traced to an attachment into the dorsal border of the ulna. This muscle usually receives near its insertion a slip, sometimes called its caudal division, from the deep layer of the pectoralis major.

Relations.—Outer surface with the integument. Inner surface with both divisions of the pectoralis major (*l*) on its medial two-thirds, and with the biceps (*t*) and bicipital arch (*t'*) in its lateral one-third. The cranial border is closely applied to that of the clavobrachial (*k*), except at the two ends.

Action.—Draws the arm mediad.

M. pectoralis major, or ectopectoralis (Fig. 65, *l*, *l'*).—In this it is usually possible to distinguish a superficial and a deep layer.

The **superficial** (*l'*) layer is a flat band of fibres one or two centimeters wide.

Origin from a raphe in the midventral line, along the cranial half of the manubrium and for five to ten millimeters craniad of it.

Insertion (Fig. 81, *f*).—The pectoral ridge of the middle third of the shaft of the humerus, slightly dorsad of the line of insertion of the deep portion.

Relations.—Outer surface with the clavobrachial (Fig. 65, *k*) and integument, the medial end caudally with the pectoantibrachialis (*m*), and the distal end with the brachialis (*v*). Inner surface with the deep portion (*l*), the fibres of which it crosses obliquely.

The **deep portion** (*l*) is a flat band of parallel fibres about three times as broad as the superficial portion.

Origin.—The ventral surface of the manubrium and of the first three divisions of the sternum, and the median raphe for about one centimeter craniad of the manubrium. It passes directly laterad.

Insertion (Fig. 81, *e*) along a line which begins at the infraspinatus fossa of the great tuberosity, and runs parallel to the deltoid ridge until it reaches the pectoral ridge at the junction of the second and third fourths of the humerus and then continues in the direction of the pectoral ridge as far as the junction of the third and fourth fourths of the humerus. Some of its fibres may pass caudad of the biceps and be inserted with the epitrochlearis. Into the part of the line which is parallel to the deltoid ridge the muscle is inserted by a flat tendon; into the remainder of the line it is usually inserted directly by muscle-fibres, though at its caudal end its insertion may again be tendinous.

Relations.—Outer surface with the cutaneus maximus, the outer layer of the pectoralis major (Fig. 65, *l'*), the pectoantibrachialis (*m*), and the clavobrachial (*k*). Inner surface with the pectoralis minor (*o*), the proximal end of the humerus, the coracobrachialis (Fig. 77, *f*), and the supraspinatus (Fig. 77, *d*) at the insertion of the latter. At the cranial part of its origin it touches the sternomastoid (Fig. 65, *g*) and sternohyoid (Fig. 65, *e*).

Action.—Draws the arm mediad and turns the foot forward.

M. pectoralis minor, or **entopectoralis** (Fig. 65, *o*).—This is a fan-shaped mass of fibres, flat but thicker than the pectoralis major.

Origin from the lateral half of the first six divisions of the body of the sternum and sometimes from the xiphoid process. The fibres are divisible into several bundles which vary in extent and distinctness and are sometimes described as separate muscles. They pass craniolaterad and converge so that the line of insertion is about one-half as long as that of the origin.

Insertion (Fig. 81, *d*) into the humerus along a line which forms the ventral border of the bicipital groove at the proximal end of the bone, passes thence onto the pectoral ridge and continues in the direction of the pectoral ridge nearly as far as the middle of the length of the humerus. The cranial and caudal fibres are inserted by means of a thin tendon; the middle fibres directly. The cranial border of the tendon of insertion is continued as a thin tendon to the coracoid process; it is closely united with the insertion of the supraspinatus.

Relations.—By its outer surface with the pectoralis major (Fig. 65, *l*) over its cranial half; with the cutaneus maximus, latissimus dorsi (Fig. 65, *q*), and integument over its caudal half. By its inner surface with the xiphihumeralis (Fig. 65, *p*), rectus abdominis (Fig. 73, *k*), and a mass of fat in the axilla. The tendon of the xiphihumeralis is also connected with its inner surface near its insertion. Its cranial border is free. Its caudal border is in relation at its medial end with the xiphihumeralis, at its lateral end with the tendon of the latissimus dorsi (Fig. 65, *q*).

Action.—Draws the arm toward the middle line.

M. xiphihumeralis (Fig. 65, *q*).—A long, thin, narrow muscle which may be considered as part of the pectoralis minor.

Origin a median raphe along the xiphoid process or at an angle to the median line on the rectus abdominis muscle. It passes craniad, becoming gradually smaller, and about two centimeters from its insertion ends in a thin tendon.

Insertion.—It ends in a flat tendon which in passing is connected by a strong fascia with the tendon of the latissimus (Fig. 65, *q*). It passes along the inner surface of the pectoralis minor (*o*) to be inserted with its cranial fibres near the ventral border of the bicipital groove.

Relations.—Outer surface with the cutaneus maximus at its medial end, with the pectoralis minor (*o*) at its distal end. Inner surface with the external oblique (Fig. 68, *p*), the rectus abdominis (Fig. 73, *k*), and a mass of fat in the axilla. Borders free. Some of the fibres of the cutaneus maximus are attached to its outer surface.

Action.—Assists the pectoralis minor.

B. Muscles of the Wall of the Thorax.—**M. serratus posterior superior** (Fig. 73, *l*).—A thin sheet of muscle and tendon beneath the serratus anterior (*i*) on the dorsal part of the thorax and neck.

Origin by fleshy slips from the outer surfaces of the first nine ribs just ventrad of their angles. The origin may extend as far as the tenth or eleventh ribs. The first slip is usually delicate. The fibres are directed dorsad and craniad and unite to form a continuous sheet. This ends along a longitudinal line opposite the vertebral transverse processes in the aponeurosis which covers the longissimus dorsi and other muscles in this region. Its insertion is into the median dorsal raphe between the axial spinous process and the tenth thoracic spinous process.

Relations.—Outer surface with the serratus anterior (*i*), the latissimus dorsi (Fig. 68, *m*), and the rhomboideus. Inner surface with the external intercostals (Fig. 73, *m*), the iliocostal (Fig. 69, *h*), the longissimus dorsi (Fig. 69, *f*), the spinalis dorsi (Fig. 69, *g*), and the splenius (Fig. 73, *b*).

Action.—Draws the ribs craniad.

M. serratus posterior inferior (Fig. 73, *n*).—The serratus posterior inferior is a thin muscle lying caudad of the serratus posterior superior (*l*) and sometimes overlying the caudal end of the latter.

Origin by four or five heads from the last four or five ribs. In some specimens only three heads may be present. The separate bundles pass dorsocaudad and unite to form a continuous sheet which ends in a continuation of the aponeurosis of the serratus posterior superior (*l*).

Insertion into the lumbar spinous processes and the intervening interspinous ligaments.

Relations.—Outer surface with the latissimus dorsi (Fig. 68, *p*), and at the origins with the intercostales externi (Fig. 73, *m*). Inner surface with the intercostales interni (Fig. 69, *k*) at the origin and with the intercostales externi (Fig. 69, *i*), iliocostal (Fig. 69, *h*), longissimus dorsi (Fig. 69, *f*), and the caudal end of the spinalis dorsi (Fig. 69, *g*).

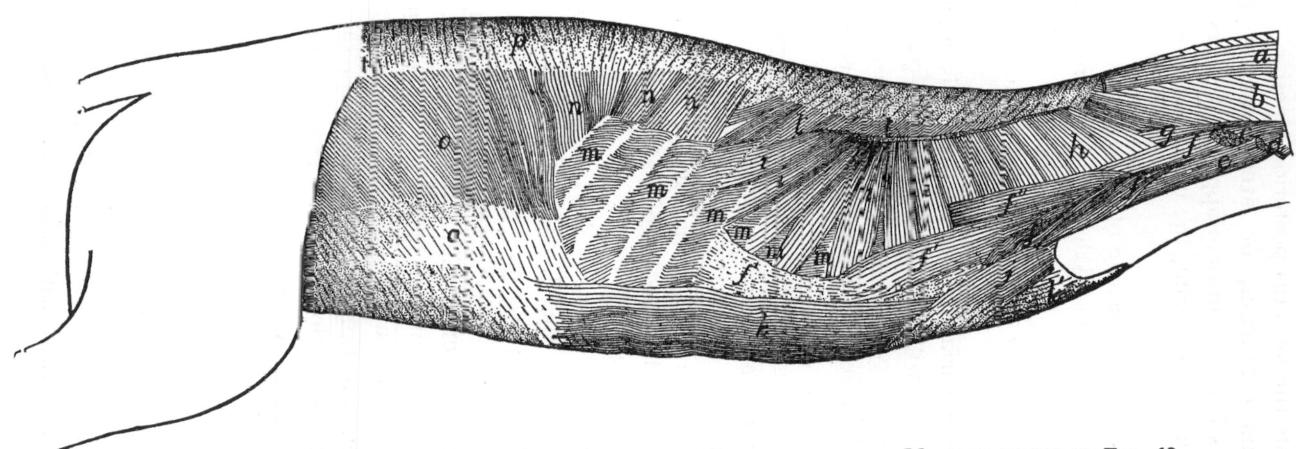

FIG. 73.—BODY MUSCLES EXPOSED AFTER REMOVAL OF THE FORELIMB AND THE MUSCLES SHOWN IN FIG. 68.

a, M. occipitoscapularis (cut); *b*, M. splenius; *c*, M. levator scapulæ ventralis (cut); *d*, M. cleidomastoideus (cut); *e*, M. longus capitis; *f*, M. scalenus (*f*′, middle division; *f*″, dorsal division; *f*‴, ventral division; *f*, cervical portion); *g*, M. longissimus capitis; *h*, M. levator scapulæ (cut); *i*, M. serratus anterior (cut); *j*, M. transversus costarum; *k*, M. rectus abdominis (*k*′, its tendon); *l*, M. serratus posterior superior; *m*, M. intercostales externi; *n*, M. serratus posterior inferior; *o*, M. obliquus abdominis internus; *p*, lumbodorsal fascia.

Action.—Assists the serratus posterior superior.

M. transversus costarum, or **sternocostalis externus** (Fig. 73, *j*).—This is a thin muscle applied to the cranial part of the side of the thorax, covering the cranial end of the rectus abdominis (*k*).

Origin by tendon from the side of the sternum between the attachments of the third and sixth ribs. The muscle passes dorsocraniad to its

Insertion on the first rib and the lateral portion of its costal cartilage.

Relations.—Outer surface with the pectoralis minor (Fig. 65, *o*). Inner surface with the scalenus (Fig. 73, *f'''*), the rectus abdominis (Fig. 73, *k*), and the intercostales externi (Fig. 73, *m*). At its insertion it is united with a portion of the scalenus (Fig. 73, *f'''*).

Action.—Draws the sternum forward.

Mm. levatores costarum.—Small muscles having *origin* on the transverse processes of the thoracic vertebræ, passing caudoventrad, and becoming *inserted* on the angle of the rib lying immediately caudad of the origin. They are continuous with the external intercostals.

Relations.—Outer surface with the longissimus dorsi (Fig. 69, *f*), and craniad with the iliocostal (Fig. 69, *h*). Inner surface with the internal intercostals (Fig. 69, *k*).

Action.—Pull the ribs dorsocraniad.

Mm. intercostales externi (Fig. 73, *m*; Fig. 69, *i*).—The external intercostals are placed in the outer portion of the intercostal spaces. They are composed of bundles of fibres attached by their ends to the adjacent borders of the ribs and having in general the direction of the external oblique muscle, i.e., they pass from their cranial ends caudoventrad. They occupy the intercostal spaces between the true ribs and extend even caudad into the spaces between the false ribs. They are lacking between the ventral ends of the costal cartilages of the first six to eight ribs, so that the internal intercostals (Fig. 69, *k*) are here exposed. The more caudal external intercostals are more nearly craniocaudal in direction.

Relations.—Outer surface with obliquus abdominis externus

(Fig. 68, *p*), latissimus dorsi (Fig. 68, *m*), serratus posterior inferior (Fig. 73, *n*) and superior (Fig. 73, *l*), serratus anterior (Fig. 73, *i*), scalenus (Fig. 73, *f*), and iliocostal (Fig. 69, *h*). Inner surface with the internal intercostals (Fig. 69, *k*).

Action.—Protractors of the ribs.

Mm. intercostales interni (Fig. 69, *k*).—The internal intercostals are similar to the external intercostals, beneath which they lie. Their fibres pass between the ribs at nearly right angles to those of the external intercostals and have nearly the direction of the fibres of the internal oblique. They occupy all the intercostal spaces from the first to the thirteenth ribs.

Relations.—Outer surface with the external intercostals (Fig. 69, *i*), and ventrad with the scalenus (Fig. 73, *f*), transversus costarum (Fig. 73, *j*), and rectus abdominis (Fig. 73, *k*). Inner surface with the pleura and the transversus thoracis.

Action.—Retractors of the ribs.

M. transversus thoracis (triangularis sterni; sternocostalis internus). This represents a thoracic portion of the transversus abdominis. It consists of five or six flat muscular bands lying on the inner surface of the thoracic wall.

Origin on the lateral borders of the dorsal face of the sternum, opposite the attachments of the cartilages of the third to the eighth ribs. The six bands thus formed, each about one centimeter wide, pass laterad and are *inserted* into the cartilages of the ribs near their junction with the ribs, and into the fascia which covers the inner surface of the internal intercostals in this region.

Relations.—Outer surface with the internal intercostals and the cartilages of the ribs. Inner surface with the pleura.

Diaphragma (Fig. 74).—The diaphragm consists of a central so-called **semilunar** tendon (*e*) and of muscular fibres which pass radially from the body wall to the tendon. It forms a complete oblique partition between the abdominal and thoracic cavities. The dorsal end is farther caudad than the ventral.

The central tendon (*e*) is thin and irregularly crescent-shaped, with the convexity ventrad and the horns of the crescent prolonged as two tendinous bands (*e'*) which end in two triangular **membranous** portions (*d*) of the diaphragm, one on each side of the spinal column. It is pierced by an opening for the vena cava (*f*).

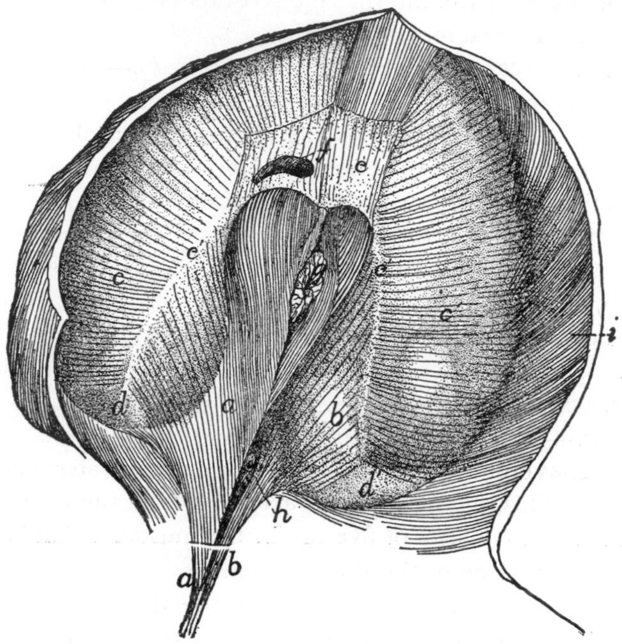

FIG. 74.—DIAPHRAGM, CAUDAL SURFACE SEEN OBLIQUELY FROM THE RIGHT.
a, right crus; *b*, left crus; *c*, *c'*, sternocostal part of diaphragm; *d*, *d'*, membranous portions of the diaphragm; *e*, central tendon; *e'*, prolongations of central tendon; *f*, opening for posterior vena cava; *g*, œsophagus; *h*, aorta; *i*, M. transversus abdominis.

The muscular portion is in two parts: (*a*) The **vertebral** portion (*a*, *b*) arises by a single tendon from the ventral surface of the second, third, and fourth lumbar centra. The tendon diverges into two, the right one (*a*) of which is much stronger, and from each of the two arise muscle-fibres. Each mass of fibres is one of the two **crura** (sing. **crus**) of the diaphragm. The aorta (*h*) enters the abdomen between the crura dorsally. The fibres of each crus diverge to be inserted into the central tendon and the dorsal continuation of its horn. The two sets of fibres unite ventrad of the opening of the aorta. Between this opening and the central tendon is another opening for the œsophagus (*g*); this lies entirely in that part of the diaphragm which arises from the right crus (*a*). The fibres are again united ventrad of the œsophageal opening.

(*b*) The **sternocostal** part (*c*, *c'*) takes origin from the xiphoid process and the last five ribs, by fleshy bundles which interdigitate with those of the transversus abdominis (*i*). The fibres converge to the central tendon (*e*). Between the crus of each side and the most dorsal of the costal fibres is the membranous interval (*d*) mentioned above.

4. **Abdominal Muscles. M. obliquus abdominis externus** (Fig. 68, *p*).—A large, thin sheet of muscle covering the whole abdomen and part of the thorax ventrally.

Origin.—(*a*) From the last nine or ten ribs by means of as many tendons, which are interconnected to form arches that span the slips of the serratus anterior. The muscle-fibres arise from these tendons and from their intervening arches. (*b*) From the lumbodorsal aponeurosis common to it and the internal oblique. The cranial fibres pass nearly ventrad, the caudal fibres caudad, and the intervening fibres take an intermediate course. The fibres end in a thin aponeurosis of insertion along a curved line which passes at first caudad and then laterodorsad. The aponeurosis fibres continue in the direction of the muscle-fibres to the

Insertion into the median raphe ventrad of the sternum from the insertion of the seventh costal cartilage to the xiphoid process, into the linea alba from the sternum to the pubic tubercle, and into the turbercle and the cranial border of the pubis. Caudad of the xiphoid process the aponeurosis is closely united to the superficial layer of the internal oblique, where it forms the outer layer of the sheath of the rectus abdominis. Laterad of the pubic tubercle the tendon is perforated by the inguinal canal. In the cat neither the caudal part of the muscle nor its tendon is attached to the ilium, as it is in man and the dog, so that no Poupart's ligament, or inguinal ligament, is formed.

Relations.—Outer surface with the cutaneus maximus, the integument, and near the origin with the latissimus dorsi (Fig. 68, *m*). Inner surface with the obliquus internus (Fig.

73, *o*), the rectus abdominis (Fig. 73, *k*), the intercostales externi (Fig. 73, *m*), a small part of the serratus posterior inferior (Fig. 73, *n*), and by its dorsal tendon with the longissimus dorsi (Fig. 69, *f*).

Action.—Constrictor of the abdomen.

M. obliquus abdominis internus (Fig. 73, *o*).—A thin sheet similar to the preceding but of less extent. Its fibres cross those of the external oblique nearly at right angles and lie beneath them.

Origin.—(1) Between the fourth and seventh lumbar vertebræ from the lumbar aponeurosis which is common to it and the external oblique. The lumbar aponeurosis takes origin from the lumbar spinous processes and the interspinous ligaments, and is continuous craniad with the aponeurosis of the serratus posterior inferior. Laterad it splits into three sheets, two for the above-named muscles and a third which passes to the vertebral transverse processes and forms the fascia covering the supraspinous muscles of the lumbar region. (2) By a similar aponeurosis from the ventral half of the iliac crest. (3) By fleshy fibres from the three **crural arches**. These are three delicate ligamentous arches which stretch from the crest of the ilium to the pubic spine. The dorsal one gives exit to the iliopsoas muscle, the middle to the femoral vessels, and the ventral to the spermatic cord. In the female the middle and ventral arches may fuse. The pillar between the dorsal and middle arches is attached to the iliopectineal eminence.

Insertion.—The fibres pass cranioventrad and end along a longitudinal line in a thin aponeurosis of insertion, which is united in the linea alba to those of the external oblique and transversus. At the caudal end of the aponeurosis all its fibres pass outside of the rectus abdominis (Fig. 73, *k*). At its cranial end the fibres divide into two sheets or laminæ, one of which passes outside of the rectus and the other inside. The outer lamina unites with the aponeurosis of the external oblique, while the inner lamina unites with that of the transversus. There is thus formed a sheath for the cranial part of the rectus muscle.

Relations.—Outer surface with the obliquus externus (Fig.

68, *p*). Inner surface with the transversus abdominis (Fig. 69, *l*), and by its ventral tendon with the rectus.

Action.—Compressor of the abdomen.

M. transversus abdominis (Fig. 69, *l*).—A thin sheet covering the whole surface of the abdomen and lying beneath the internal oblique. Its fibres are nearly transverse.

Origin.—(1) By fleshy fibres or by a thin aponeurosis from the cartilages of all the false and floating ribs, by interdigitation with the fibres of the diaphragm. (2) From the tips of all the lumbar transverse processes. (3) From the ventral border of the ilium. (4) From the dorsal and middle of the three crural arches, where it may blend partly with the internal oblique. The muscle is continuous craniad with the transversus thoracis muscle. Near the lateral border of the rectus abdominis the muscle ends in a thin aponeurosis of insertion which is continued (its fibres having the direction of the muscle-fibres) to the

Insertion in the linea alba.

Relations.—Outer surface with the internal oblique (Fig. 73, *o*) and the rectus abdominis (Fig. 73, *k*), dorsad also with the longissimis dorsi (Fig. 69, *f*). Inner surface with a thin fascia covering the peritoneum and ventrocaudad with the rectus (Fig. 73, *k*). The dorsal edge of the muscle touches the iliopsoas and longissimus dorsi; the ventral edge touches the muscle of the opposite side.

Action.—Constrictor of the abdomen.

M. rectus abdominis (Fig. 73, *k*).—A rather thick, flat muscle which lies near the median ventral line separated by the linea alba from its fellow of the opposite side and stretching from the pubis to the first costal cartilage. Opposite the first lumbar vertebra it is approximately four centimeters wide. It narrows at both ends.

Origin by a strong tendon from the tubercle of the pubis. The muscle passes craniad at first between the peritoneal fascia and the transversus aponeurosis, then in the sheath formed by the internal and external oblique and the transversus aponeurosis. It emerges from the sheath opposite the xiphoid process and passes ventrad of the costal cartilages. Between the third and fourth costal cartilages it ends in a thin tendon which passes beneath the transversus costarum and is

Inserted into the first costal cartilage near its middle, into the second costal cartilage near its sternal end, and into the sternum between the first and fourth cartilages.

Relations.—Outer surface of the cranial part of the muscle and its tendon with the pectoralis minor (Fig. 68, *o*) and the transversus costarum (Fig. 73, *j*); caudad the muscle is covered by the outer layer of the rectus sheath. Lateral edge with the obliquus externus (Fig. 68, *p*), obliquus internus (Fig. 73, *o*), and transversus abdominis (Fig. 69, *l*). Medial edge with the muscle of the opposite side. Inner surface with the internal intercostals (Fig. 69, *k*) and the rib cartilages; the inner layer of the rectus sheath and the peritoneum.

Action.—Retracts the ribs and sternum and compresses the abdomen.

IV. MUSCLES OF THE THORACIC LIMBS.

The muscles connecting the thoracic limbs with the rest of the body have been described.

1. Muscles of the Shoulder.

A. Muscles on the Lateral Surface of the Shoulder.

M. deltoideus.—The deltoid muscle of the cat is divided into two (or three) portions which are together equivalent to the human deltoid. These are the spinodeltoid, the acromiodeltoid, and possibly the clavobrachial, which is frequently called clavodeltoid.

M. spinodeltoideus (Fig. 75, *e*; Fig. 68, *i*).—A rather thick, flat muscle between the scapular spine and the deltoid ridge of the humerus. It forms a chord of the angle between the glenoid border of the scapula and the humerus.

Origin by short tendon-fibres from the glenoid border of somewhat more than the middle third of the spine of the scapula (Fig. 76, *g*), and from a tendinous raphe between the spinotrapezius (Fig. 68, *j*), acromiotrapezius (Fig. 68, *h*), and infraspinatus (Fig. 75, *c*). The origin may pass toward the vertebral border of the scapula onto the infraspinatus muscle (Fig. 75, *c*).

Insertion (Fig. 81, *h*) by a flat tendon upon the deltoid ridge of the humerus, nearly parallel to that of the pectoralis major.

Relations.—Outer surface with the integument and at the insertion with the acromiodeltoideus (Fig. 75, *f*). Inner surface with the infraspinatus (*c*), teres minor (Fig. 80, *c*), caput laterale (Fig. 75, *h*), and caput longum (Fig. 75, *g*) of the triceps muscle.

Action.—Flexes the humerus and rotates it outward.

M. acromiodeltoideus (Fig. 75, *f*; Fig. 68, *g*).—A flat muscle which overlies the distal end of the spinodeltoideus (Fig. 75, *e*). It connects the acromion with the humerus.

Origin (Fig. 76, *d*).—From the glenoid border of the acromion, and sometimes the adjacent metacromion as far as the tip.

Insertion.—Mostly upon the outer surface of the spinodeltoideus (Fig. 75, *e*). The outer fibres are continued to the bone, especially at the lateral border of the muscle, and are inserted along a line ventrad of the line of insertion of the spinodeltoideus, and extending farther distally (Fig. 81, *g*). Some of the outer fibres pass into the brachialis (Fig. 80, *h*).

Relations.—Outer surface with the integument and the clavobrachial (Fig. 68, *e*). Inner surface with the infraspinatus (Fig. 75, *c*), teres minor (Fig. 80, *c*), spinodeltoid (Fig. 75, *e*), and caput laterale of the triceps (Fig. 75, *h*).

Action.—Like that of the spinodeltoid.

M. clavobrachialis (Fig. 65, *k*; Fig. 68, *e*).—A flat, triangular muscle on the cranial surface of the shoulder, forming a direct continuation of the clavotrapezius (Fig. 68, *d*). These two are frequently described as constituting a single muscle, the cephalohumeral or cephalobrachial. (The clavobrachial is frequently given the name clavodeltoid; as its homology with the human clavodeltoid appears doubtful, it seems well to use the name clavobrachial, as proposed by Clasen.)

Origin.—Its superficial fibres are continuations of the

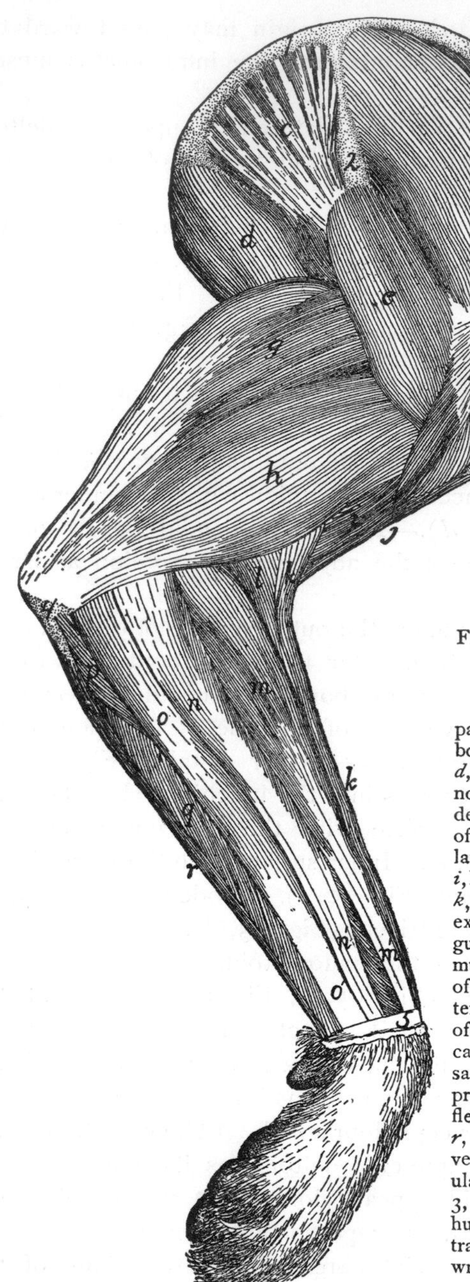

FIG. 75.—MUSCLES ON THE LATERAL SURFACE OF THE ARM.

a, M. supraspinatus; *b*, part of insertion of M. rhomboideus; *c*, M. infraspinatus; *d*, M. teres major; *e*, M. spinodeltoideus; *f*, M. acromiodeltoideus; *g*, caput longum of M. triceps brachii; *h*, caput laterale of M. triceps brachii; *i*, M. brachialis; *j*, M. biceps; *k*, M. brachioradialis; *l*, M. extensor carpi radialis longus; *m*, M. extensor communis digitorum (*m'*, tendon of same); *n*, M. extensor lateralis digitorum; (*n'* tendon of same); *o*, M. extensor carpi ulnaris (*o'*, tendon of same); *p*, M. extensor indicis proprius; *q*, fifth head of M. flexor profundus digitorum; *r*, m. flexor carpi ulnaris. 1, vertebral border of the scapula; 2, spine of the scapula; 3, greater tuberosity of the humerus; 4, olecranon; 5, transverse ligament of the wrist.

clavotrapezius (Fig. 68, *d*); other fibres have origin from the clavicle and from a raphe laterad of the clavicle which is common to this muscle and the clavotrapezius. It passes distad along the cranial surface of the arm, growing narrower as it approaches the convexity of the elbow.

Insertion.—Eight to ten millimeters from the ulna it joins the brachialis muscle (Fig. 79, *i*) to be inserted with it by a flat tendon (Fig. 79, *i*; Fig. 87, *c*) upon a rough area on the medial surface of the ulna just distad of the semilunar notch, and about midway between the dorsal and ventral borders.

Relations.—Outer surface with the integument. Inner surface with the pectoralis major (Fig. 65, *l*), biceps (Fig. 77, *g*), lateral head of the triceps (Fig. 75, *h*), acromiodeltoid (Fig. 75, *f*), and brachialis (Fig. 80, *h*). Medial border with the pectoantibrachialis (Fig. 65, *m*). Lateral border free except near the insertion, where it is in relation with the brachialis.

Action.—Flexor of the antibrachium.

M. supraspinatus (Fig. 75, *a*) occupies the whole of the supraspinatus fossa of the scapula. It is covered by strong fascia which stretches from the free edge of the spine to the coracoid border of the scapula and to the coracoid half of its vertebral border.

Origin (Fig. 76, *b*) by fleshy fibres from the whole surface of the supraspinatus fossa, from the above-mentioned fascia, and from the subscapularis (Fig. 77, *a*) craniad of the coracoid border of the scapula.

Insertion (Fig. 83, *a*).—It passes over the capsule of the shoulder-joint, to which it is closely attached, and is inserted into the free border of the great tuberosity ventrad (or proximad) of the fossa for the infraspinatus (Fig. 83, *c*).

Relations.—Outer surface with the spinotrapezius (Fig. 68, *j*), acromiotrapezius (Fig. 68, *h*), levator scapulæ ventralis (Fig. 68, *f*), clavotrapezius (Fig. 68, *d*), and cleidomastoid (Fig. 65, *h*). Inner surface with the scapula. The distal end of the coracoid border is closely related to the pectoralis minor (Fig. 79, *f*). The glenoid border is related to the origin of the deltoidei.

Action.—Extends the humerus after it has been flexed on the scapula.

M. infraspinatus (Fig. 75, *c*).—This fills the infraspinatus fossa, its fibres converging to the insertion on the great tuberosity of the humerus.

Origin (Fig. 76, *a*).—By fleshy fibres from the whole infraspinatus fossa, and by a raphe between it and the teres major

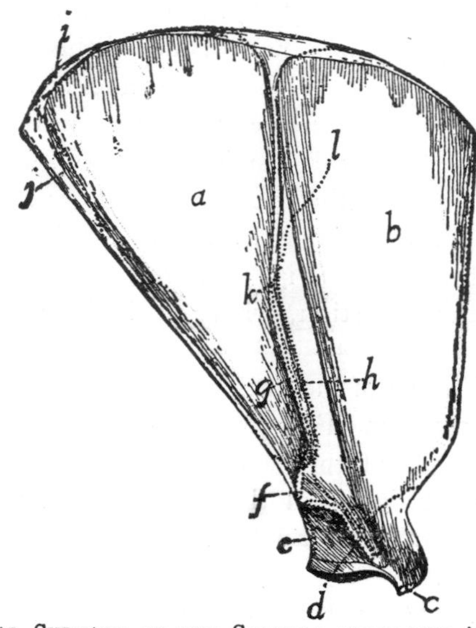

FIG. 76.—LATERAL SURFACE OF THE SCAPULA, WITH THE AREAS OF ATTACHMENT OF MUSCLES.

a, M. infraspinatus; *b*, M. supraspinatus; *c*, origin of M. biceps; *d*, M. acromiodeltoideus; *e*, M. teres minor; *f*, M. levator scapulæ ventralis; *g*, M. spinodeltoideus; *h*, M. acromiotrapezius; *i*, M. rhomboideus; *j*, M. teres major; *k–l*, line of insertion of M. spinotrapezius.

(Fig. 75, *d*), and sometimes by fibres from the teres minor (Fig. 80, *c*), triceps, spinodeltoideus (Fig. 75, *e*), spinotrapezius (Fig. 68, *j*), and subscapularis (Fig. 77, *a*).

Insertion (Fig. 83, *c*).—By a flat tendon which passes over the capsule of the joint, into the ventral half of the infraspinatus fossa on the great tuberosity of the humerus. (The dorsal half of the fossa is covered by a synovial bursa.)

Relations.—Outer surface with the spinotrapezius (Fig. 68, *j*), spinodeltoid (Fig. 68, *i*), acromiodeltoid (Fig. 68, *g*), teres major (Fig. 75, *d*), and levator scapulæ ventralis (Fig.

68, *f*). Inner surface with the scapula. Glenoid border with the teres minor (Fig. 80, *c*), the teres major (Fig. 75, *d*), and the long head of the triceps (Fig. 75, *g*).

Action.—Rotates the humerus outward.

M. teres minor (Fig. 80, *c*).—A small muscle from the glenoid border of the scapula to the proximal end of the humerus.

Origin (Fig. 76, *e*) by a sheet of tendinous fibres from the glenoid border of the scapula beginning about one-fifth the length of the border from the glenoid fossa and extending to its middle. It is often attached to the infraspinatus (Fig. 80, *b*) and the caput longum of the triceps (Fig. 75, *g*).

Insertion (Fig. 83, *d*) by a short tendon into the tubercle just distad of the infraspinatus fossa on the great tuberosity of the humerus.

Relations.—Outer surface with the spinodeltoideus (Fig. 75, *e*), acromiodeltoideus (Fig. 75, *f*), and the infraspinatus (Fig. 80, *b*). Inner surface with the lateral (Fig. 75, *h*) and long (Fig. 75, *g*) heads of the triceps and the capsule of the joint.

Action.—Assists the infraspinatus to rotate the humerus outward.

B. Muscles on the Medial Surface of the Shoulder. (Fig. 77.)

M. subscapularis (Fig. 77, *a*).—A triangular mass from the subscapular fossa to the lesser tuberosity of the humerus.

Origin (Fig. 78, *a*).—From the whole subscapular fossa except along the fusiform area for the attachment of the levator scapulæ and the serratus anterior near the vertebral border, and except over a quadrangular area about one centimeter long near the glenoid angle. The origin is by fleshy fibres directly from the periosteum except along two or three lines marked by oblique ridges. To these lines are attached tendinous fibres. At the glenoid border the area of origin sometimes occupies part or the whole of the surface of the fossa for the origin of the teres major, so that the teres arises from the fascia on the surface of the subscapularis. At the coracoid border some of the fibres may take origin from the adjacent fascia of the supraspinatus (Fig. 77, *d*).

Insertion (Fig. 82, *b*).—The fibres converge to the glenoid border, and the insertion is by a strong, flat tendon into the dorsal border of the lesser tuberosity of the humerus.

Relations. — Lateral surface with the scapula and the capsule of the shoulder-joint. Medial surface with the levator scapulæ (Fig. 73, *h*), serratus anterior (Fig. 73, *i*), part of the scalenus (Fig. 73, *f*), the transversus costarum (Fig. 73, *j*), and the coracobrachialis (Fig. 77, *f*). Cranial border with the supraspinatus (Fig. 77, *d*). Caudal border

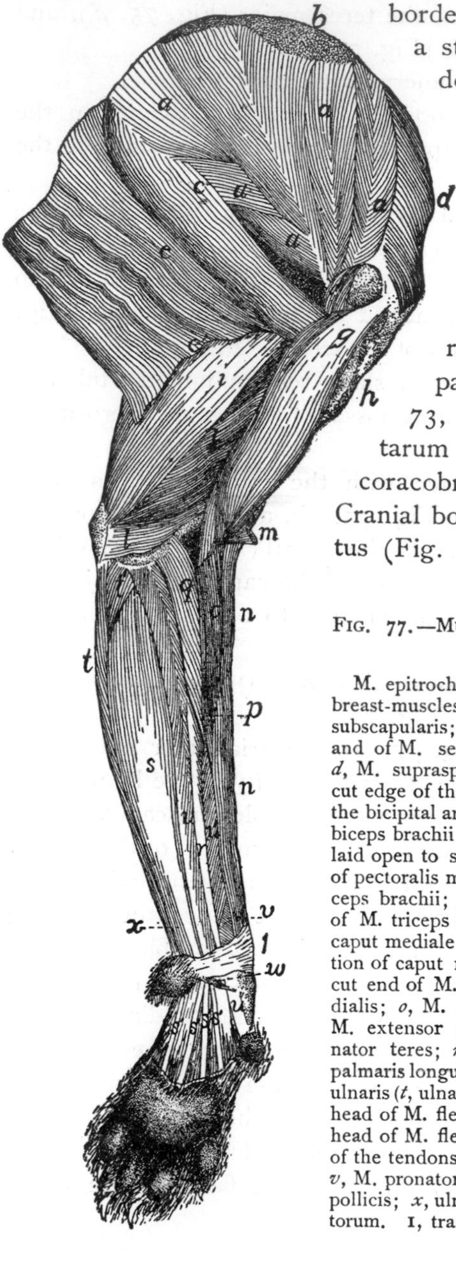

Fig. 77.—Muscles on the Medial Side of the Arm.

M. epitrochlearis, M. clavobrachialis, and the breast-muscles have been removed. *a*, M. subscapularis; *b*, insertion of M. levator scapulæ and of M. serratus anterior; *c*, M. teres major; *d*, M. supraspinatus; *e*, M. latissimus dorsi (*e′*, cut edge of that part which becomes united with the bicipital arch); *f*, M. coracobrachialis; *g*, M. biceps brachii (the capsule of the joint has been laid open to show its tendon); *h*, cut insertions of pectoralis muscles; *i*, caput longum of M. triceps brachii; *j*, long portion of caput mediale of M. triceps brachii; *k*, intermediate portion of caput mediale of M. triceps brachii; *l*, short portion of caput mediale of M. triceps brachii; *m*, cut end of M. clavobrachialis; *n*, M. brachioradialis; *o*, M. extensor carpi radialis longus; *p*, M. extensor carpi radialis brevis; *q*, M. pronator teres; *r*, M. flexor carpi radialis; *s*, M. palmaris longus (*s′*, its tendons); *t*, M. flexor carpi ulnaris (*t*, ulnar head; *t′*, humeral head); *u*, third head of M. flexor profundus digitorum; *u′*, fifth head of M. flexor profundus digitorum; *u″*, one of the tendons of M. flexor profundus digitorum; *v*, M. pronator quadratus; *w*, M. abductor brevis pollicis; *x*, ulnar part of M. flexor sublimis digitorum. 1, transverse ligament of the wrist.

with the teres major (Fig. 77, *c*) and infraspinatus (Fig. 75, *c*).

Action.—Pulls the humerus inward (mediad).

M. teres major (Fig. 75, *d*; Fig. 77, *c*).—A thick muscle, triangular in cross-section, lying parallel with the glenoid border of the scapula.

Origin (Fig. 76, *j*; Fig. 78, *b*) from the vertebral one-third of the glenoid border of the scapula, and from fascia covering the subscapularis (Fig. 77, *a*) and the infraspinatus (Fig. 75, *c*) over a small area near the gleno-vertebral angle of the scapula. It may touch the insertion of the rhomboideus.

Insertion (Fig. 82, *f*) by a tendon common to it and the latissimus dorsi (Fig. 79, *d'*), as already described.

Relations.—Outer surface with the caput longum (Fig. 75, *g*) and the long portion (Fig. 80, *f*) of the caput mediale of the triceps, the latissimus dorsi (Fig. 77, *e*), and the cutaneus maximus. Inner surface with the serratus anterior (Fig. 73, *i*), the scalenus (Fig. 73, *f*), the transversus costarum (Fig. 73, *j*), and the biceps (Fig. 77, *g*). Dorsal border with the subscapularis (Fig. 77, *a*) and infraspinatus (Fig. 75, *c*).

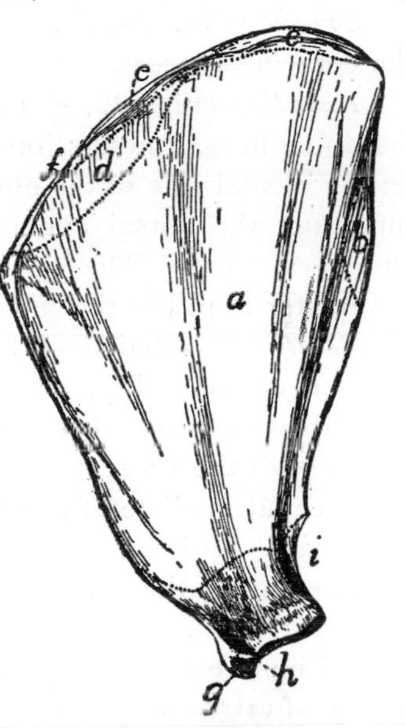

Fig. 78.—Medial Surface of the Scapula with the Areas of Attachment of Muscles.

a, M. subscapularis; *b*, M. teres major; *c*, M. serratus anterior; *d*, M. levator scapulæ; *e*, M. rhomboideus; *f*, M. occipitoscapularis; *g*, M. biceps; *h*, M. coracobrachialis; *i*, caput longum of M. triceps.

Action.—Rotates the humerus inward and flexes it in opposition to the infraspinatus, teres minor, and the deltoidei.

2. Muscles of the Brachium or Upper Arm.

M. clavobrachialis and the pectoralis group (Fig. 65, page 109) lie partly in this region; they have been described.

M. coracobrachialis (Fig. 77, *f*; Fig. 79, *c*).—A very short muscle covering the inner (medial) surface of the capsule of the shoulder-joint. It extends from the coracoid process to the proximal end of the humerus.

Origin (Fig. 78, *h*).—By a round tendon from the tip of the coracoid process.

Insertion (Fig. 82, *e*) usually by fleshy fibres on an area five to eight millimeters long and about half as wide, which lies on the medial side of the humerus parallel with the ridge which runs from the dorsal end of the lesser tuberosity to the shaft and close to it. The proximal end of the area is about one centimeter from the proximal end of the head of the humerus.

Relations.—Medial surface with the biceps (Fig. 77, *g*), pectoralis minor (Fig. 65, *o*), and teres major (Fig. 77, *c*). Lateral surface with the capsule of the shoulder-joint. Dorsal border with the subscapularis (Fig. 77, *a*) and the long portion of the caput mediale of the triceps (Fig. 77, *j*).

Action.—Adducts the humerus.

The part of the coracobrachialis just described is known as the *short* head. A *long* head is sometimes found. It is a conical bundle of fibres of varying size, which arises from the tendon of origin of the short head. It passes distad into a long and extremely slender tendon, the insertion of which varies greatly in different individuals. It is commonly on the humerus in the region of the supracondyloid foramen.

M. epitrochlearis or extensor antibrachii longus (Fig. 65, *r*).—A thin, flat muscle on the inner or medial side of the brachium, from the lateral surface of the latissimus dorsi (Fig. 65, *q*) to the olecranon process of the ulna.

Origin from the lateral or outer surface of the ventral border of the latissimus dorsi (Fig. 65, *q*) near the insertion of the cutaneus maximus. Fibres are often attached to the teres major and the pectoralis minor.

Insertion by a flat tendon which is closely connected with that of the pectoantibrachialis (Fig. 65, *m*) and is continuous with the general antibrachial fascia, into the caudal border of the cutaneous (dorsal) surface of the olecranon process of the ulna.

Relations.—Outer (medial) surface with the integument, the latissimus dorsi (Fig. 65, *q*), and the cutaneus maximus. Inner (lateral) surface with the biceps (Fig. 65, *t*), caput longum (Fig. 65, *s*), and caput mediale (Fig. 77, *j*, *k*) of the triceps.

Action.—Extends the antibrachium and tends to supinate the hand by rotating the ulna.

M. biceps brachii (Fig. 77, *g*; Fig. 65, *t*).—A thick, fusiform muscle lying on the front (ventral) surface of the humerus.

Origin (Fig. 76, *c*) by a strong, round tendon from the bicipital tubercle of the glenoid angle of the scapula, at its coracoid margin. (In man there is a second head—coracoid head—from the coracoid process.) The tendon passes through the capsule of the joint and then along the bicipital groove, which is converted into a canal by a strong ligament.

Insertion by a rounded tendon (Fig. 87, *h*) on the bicipital tuberosity of the radius (Fig. 86, *k*).

Relations.—The tendon of origin passes through the capsule of the joint, which is covered by a part of the pectoralis minor. The muscle is then spanned for the middle part of its course by the bicipital arch (Fig. 65, *t′*), a description of which is given below. Farther distad it is covered by the clavobrachial (Fig. 65, *k*) and epitrochlearis (Fig. 65, *r*). At its distal end (Fig. 79, *l′*) the muscle passes between the pronator teres on the radial side and the conjoined tendon of the brachialis and clavobrachial (Fig. 79, *i′*) on the other. The biceps lies throughout most of its length on the ventral surface of the humerus, and touches along the medial border of its inner surface the coracobrachialis (Fig. 77, *f*), the teres major (Fig. 77, *c*), the intermediate portion of the caput mediale of the triceps (Fig. 77, *k*), and the short portion (Fig. 77, *l*) of the same. Its lateral border touches the pectoralis minor (Fig. 65, *o*) and the brachialis (Fig. 79, *i*).

Action.—Flexes the forearm, and tends to supinate the hand.

The bicipital arch (Fig. 65, *t'*) is a tendinous arch formed over the biceps muscle. Its outer or lateral pillar is formed by the tendon of the pectoralis minor (*o*), to which may be added part of the latissimus (*q*) tendon. Its inner or medial pillar is formed by the conjoined tendon of the teres major and latissimus dorsi (Fig. 79, *d'*), while the xiphihumeralis (Fig. 65, *p*), cutaneus maximus (Fig. 62, *b*), and epitrochlearis (Fig. 65, *r*) are connected with one or the other pillar or with the muscles composing them. The caudal portion of the deep layer of the pectoralis major (Fig. 65, *l*) may be connected with the inner pillar.

M. brachialis (Fig. 79, *i*; Fig. 75, *i*).—From the lateral surface of the humerus to the ulna.

Origin (Fig. 83, *g*, *g'*) from a long V-shaped line two to four millimeters wide on the lateral surface of the humerus. The apex of the V is just distad of the teres minor tubercle (*d*). Its dorsal limb (*g'*) extends along the lateral supracondyloid ridge to a point opposite the proximal margin of the supracondyloid foramen; its ventral limb (*g*) extends in the direction of the deltoid ridge to the middle of the bone. No muscle-fibres take origin between the two limbs. The fibres converge and end in a flat tendon which joins the tendon of the clavobrachial (Fig. 79, *k*).

Insertion (Fig. 87, *c*).—The dorsal portion of the depressed rough area on the lateral surface of the ulna just distad of the semilunar notch.

Relations.—Outer surface with the acromiodeltoid (Fig. 75, *f*), the caput laterale of the triceps (Fig. 75, *h*), the brachioradialis (Fig. 75, *k*), and the proximal end of the extensor carpi radialis longus (Fig. 75, *l*). Inner surface with the humerus. Medial edge with the pectoralis major (Fig 65, *l*) and the biceps (Fig. 77, *g*).

Action.—Flexor of the antibrachium.

M. triceps brachii.—The triceps muscle of the cat, like that of man, is divisible (as its name indicates) into three main portions. These are a lateral portion (caput laterale), an intermediate or long portion (caput longum), and a medial portion (caput mediale). The first two correspond to the similarly named heads in man; the medial portion falls into a number of subdivisions whose homologues are uncertain.

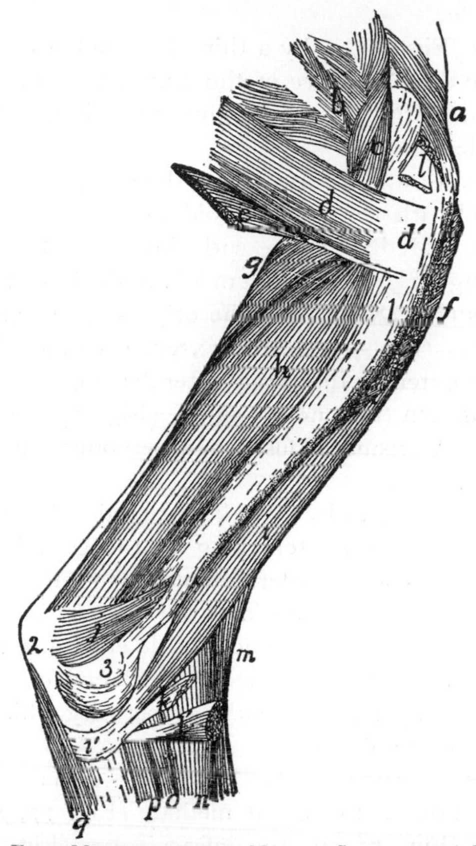

FIG. 79.—DEEP MUSCLES ON THE MEDIAL SIDE OF THE HUMERUS.

a, M. supraspinatus; *b*, M. subscapularis; *c*, M. coracobrachialis; *d*, M. teres major (*d'*, its tendon); *e*, part of M. latissimus dorsi joining the teres major; *f*, cut end of M. pectoralis minor; *g*, long part of caput mediale of M. triceps brachii; *h*, intermediate part of caput mediale of M. triceps; *i*, M. brachialis (*i'*, its tendon); *j*, short part of caput mediale of M. triceps; *k*, cut end of M. clavobrachialis; *l*, *l'*, cut ends of M. biceps; *m*, M. brachioradialis; *n*, M. extensor carpi radialis longus; *o*, M. extensor carpi radialis brevis; *p*, fifth head of M. flexor profundus digitorum; *q*, first head of M. flexor profundus digitorum. 1, humerus; 2, olecranon; 3, medial epicondyle of humerus.

Caput laterale (anconeus lateralis) (Fig. 75, *h*; Fig. 68, *l*). —The lateral portion is a flat muscle (most of it subcutaneous) on the lateral side of the brachium, connecting the proximal end of the humerus with the olecranon process of the ulna

Origin (Fig. 81, *h'*).—By a flat tendon from the proximal portion of the deltoid ridge and the distal border of the teres minor tubercle.

Insertion (Fig. 86, *c*) by a thin, flat tendon into the lateral border of the dorsal surface of the ulna between a point opposite the distal margin of the semilunar notch and the proximal end of the olecranon.

Relations.—Lateral surface with the integument, and at the proximal end with the spinodeltoid and acromiodeltoid (Fig. 75, *e* and *f*). Medial surface with the brachialis (Fig. 75, *i*), the caput longum (*g*), the caput mediale, the brachioradialis (*k*), the anconeus (Fig. 80, *l*), and the origins of the extensor carpi radialis longus (Fig. 75, *l*), the extensor communis digitorum (*m*), and the extensor digitorum lateralis (*n*).

Caput longum (anconeus longus) (Fig. 75, *g*; Fig. 68, *k*; Fig. 77, *i*).—A prismatic, fusiform mass connecting the scapula with the olecranon.

Origin (Fig. 78, *i*) by a thick, flat tendon from a triangular area one or two centimeters long at the glenoid end of the scapula on the glenoid border. The base of the area is about one millimeter from the margin of the glenoid fossa.

Insertion (Fig. 86, *b*).—The muscle ends in a thick tendon which passes over the bifurcated ventral end of the olecranon and is inserted upon the rounded tuberosity which forms the dorsal angle of the olecranon.

Relations.—Lateral surface with the caput laterale (Fig. 75, *h*), a portion of the caput mediale (Fig. 77, *j* and *k*), the spinodeltoid (Fig. 75, *e*), the infraspinatus (Fig. 75, *c*), and the integument. Medial surface with the epitrochlearis (Fig. 65, *r*) and the conjoined portions of the latissimus dorsi and teres major (Fig. 79, *d'*). Ventral border with the caput mediale (Fig. 77, *j* and *k*).

Caput mediale.—The medial head consists of three portions (Fig. 79, *g*, *h*, *j*).

(1) The long portion (anconeus posterior) (Fig. 77, *j*; Fig. 79, *g*; Fig. 80, *f*).

Origin (Fig. 83, *e*) from a triangular area on the dorsal surface of the humeral shaft. The base of the area is against the articular head, and its apex about one-sixth the length of the humerus from the head. It is between the coracobrachialis and the lateral head of the triceps.

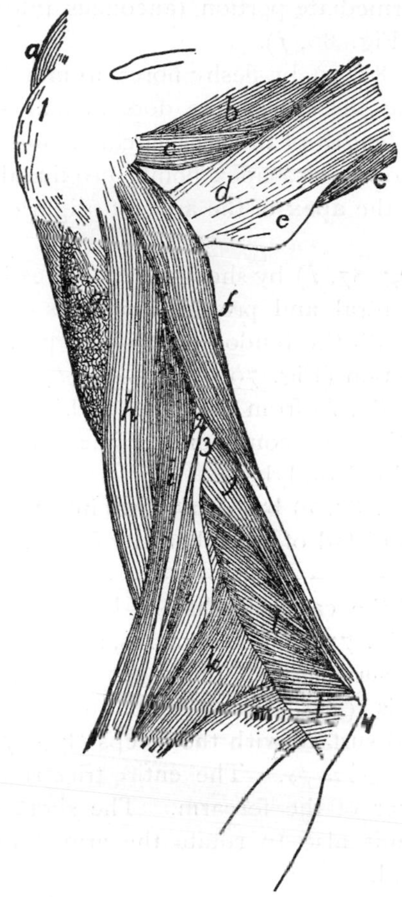

FIG. 80.—DEEP MUSCLES ON THE LATERAL SURFACE OF THE HUMERUS.

a, part of M. supraspinatus; *b*, part of M. infraspinatus; *c*, M. teres minor; *d*, M. teres major; *e*, part of M. latissimus dorsi joining M. teres major; *f*, long part of caput mediale of M. triceps brachii; *g*, cut insertion of M. acromiodeltoideus; *h*, M. brachialis; *i*, M. brachioradialis; *j*, intermediate part of caput mediale of M. triceps brachii; *k*, M. extensor carpi radialis longus; *l*, M. anconeus; *m*, M. extensor communis digitorum. 1, great tuberosity of humerus; 2, 3, superficial radial and dorsal interosseous branches, respectively, of the radial nerve.

Insertion (Fig. 86, *a*).—The muscle ends in a long, slender tendon which passes through the furrow on the ventral angle of the olecranon and is inserted into an oblique ridge which forms the dorsal limit of the furrow. The tendon is separated from the floor of the furrow by a synovial bursa.

(2) The intermediate portion (anconeus internus) (Fig. 77, *k*; Fig. 79, *h*; Fig. 80, *j*).

Origin (Fig. 82, *g*) by fleshy fibres from a triangular area proximad of the middle of the dorsomedial surface of the humerus. The length of the area equals about one-fourth the length of the bone. Its apex points proximad and is almost continuous with the apex of the area of origin of the long portion.

Insertion (Fig. 87, *i*) by short tendon-fibres into the medial border of the ventral and proximal surfaces of the olecranon. It is connected with the tendon of the long portion.

(3) Short portion (Fig. 79, *j*; Fig. 77, *l*).

Origin (Fig. 82, *h*) from the outer surface of the bony bar which encloses the supracondyloid foramen of the humerus, as far as the medial epicondyle.

Insertion (Fig. 87, *e*) by fleshy fibres into the medial border of the olecranon distad of the tuberosity for the insertion of the caput longum.

Relations of the caput mediale.—Lateral surface with the caput laterale (Fig. 75, *h*), the humerus, and the anconeus (Fig. 80, *l*). Dorsal surface with the caput longum (Fig. 77, *i*), the epitrochlearis (Fig. 65, *r*), and the teres major (Fig. 79, *d*). Ventral surface with the biceps (Fig. 77, *g*).

Action of the Triceps.—The entire triceps group forms a powerful extensor of the forearm. The short portion of the medial head tends also to rotate the arm outward, so as to supinate the hand.

M. anconeus (Fig. 80, *l*).—A triangular muscle on the outside of the elbow-joint from the humerus to the ulna.

Origin (Fig. 83, *i*).—An irregularly triangular area at the distal end of the dorsal surface of the humerus. The area of origin is limited laterally by the sharp lateral supracondyloid ridge. It sometimes extends onto the lateral epicondyle.

Insertion (Fig. 86, *d*).—The lateral surface of the ulna from the distal margin of the semilunar notch to the proximal end

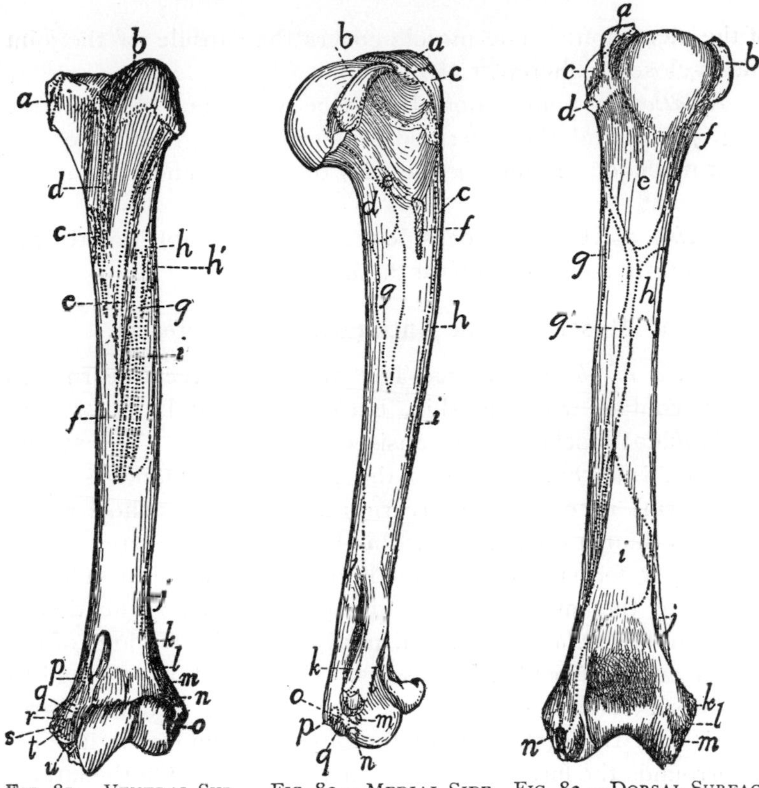

FIG. 81.—VENTRAL SURFACE OF HUMERUS, WITH THE AREAS OF ATTACHMENT OF MUSCLES.

FIG. 82.—MEDIAL SIDE OF HUMERUS, WITH THE AREAS OF ATTACHMENT OF MUSCLES.

FIG. 83.—DORSAL SURFACE OF THE LEFT HUMERUS, WITH THE AREAS OF ATTACHMENT OF MUSCLES.

Fig. 81.—*a*, M. subscapularis; *b*, M. supraspinatus; *c*, Mm. teres major and latissimus dorsi; *d*, M. pectoralis minor; *e*, deep layer of M. pectoralis major; *f*, superficial layer of M. pectoralis major; *g*, M. acromiodeltoideus; *h*, M. spinodeltoideus; *h'*, caput laterale of M. triceps; *i*, M. brachialis; *j*, second portion of M. brachialis; *k*, M. extensor carpi radialis longus; *l*, M. extensor carpi radialis brevis; *m*, M. extensor communis digitorum; *n*, M. extensor lateralis digitorum; *o*, M. extensor carpi ulnaris; *p*, short portion of caput mediale of M. triceps; *q*, M. pronator teres; *r*, M. palmaris longus; *s*, third and fourth parts of M. flexor profundus digitorum; *t*, M. flexor carpi radialis; *u*, second head of M. flexor profundus digitorum.

Fig. 82.—*a*, M. supraspinatus; *b*, M. subscapularis; *c*, M. pectoralis minor; *d*, long portion of caput mediale of M. triceps; *e*, M. coracobrachialis; *f*, Mm. teres major and latissimus dorsi; *g*, intermediate portion of caput mediale of M. triceps; *h*, deep layer of M. pectoralis major; *i*, superficial layer of M. pectoralis major; *j*, M. anconeus; *k*, short portion of caput mediale of M. triceps; *l*, M. pronator teres; *m*, M. flexor carpi radialis; *n*, second head of M. flexor profundus digitorum; *o*, third and fourth heads of M. flexor profundus digitorum; *p*, M. palmaris longus; *q*, M. flexor carpi ulnaris.

Fig. 83.—*a*, M. supraspinatus; *b*, M. subscapularis; *c*, M. infraspinatus; *d*, M. teres minor; *e*, long portion of caput mediale of M triceps; *f*, M. coracobrachialis; *g*, *g'*, M. brachialis; *h*, intermediate portion of caput mediale of M. triceps; *i*, M. anconeus; *j*, short portion of medial head of M. triceps; *k*, M. pronator teres; *l*, second and third heads of M. flexor profundus digitorum; *m*, M. palmaris longus; *n*, M. extensor carpi ulnaris.

of the olecranon. The muscle covers the capsule of the joint and is closely adherent to it.

Relations.—Outer (dorsal) surface with the caput laterale (Fig. 75, *h*) and the intermediate portion (Fig. 80, *j*) of the caput mediale. Inner surface with the bones and the capsule of the joint.

Action.—Keeps the capsule tense and probably rotates the ulna slightly so as to pronate the hand.

3. Muscles of the Antibrachium or Forearm.

Fascia of the Forearm.—The muscles of the forearm are not in contact with the skin, but are covered by the strong **antibrachial fascia.** This consists of two layers. The **superficial** one is a continuation of the general subcutaneous fascia of the arm; it covers the forearm as a continuous sheet which becomes thinner distad, and is finally lost near the wrist. The **deep** layer forms a dense, tendinous sheet which is closely applied to the muscles. It begins partly as a continuation of the general fascia of the arm, partly from the tendons of the triceps and epitrochlearis muscles. The sheet is attached to the dorsal surface of the ulna, between the extensor carpi ulnaris and the first head of the flexor profundus digitorum. It surrounds the forearm as a continuous sheath. On the lateral surface it dips between the extensor muscles, becoming closely attached to them and forming a partial sheath for each; it is attached with special firmness to their tendons. On the medial side of the arm the fascia passes smoothly over the flexors without dipping between them; it is continuous, however, with the border of the pronator teres, and distad of this muscle it is firmly attached to the radius.

At the wrist the fascia becomes attached to the longitudinal ridges on the dorsal surface of the head of the radius, bridging thus the intervening grooves and holding the tendons in place between the ridges. The fascia then continues to form the dorsal fascia of the hand. On the ventral side of the wrist the fascia becomes thickened to form a strong **transverse ligament** (Fig. 77, 1), which is attached at its radial and ulnar ends to the carpus, and which holds in place the tendons of the flexor muscles. Distad of the transverse ligament the fascia spreads out in the palm of the hand, and becomes united with the fibrous pad which is situated here. On the fingers the fascia becomes attached to the phalanges, forming tendinous sheaths, the so-called **vaginal ligaments,** for the flexor muscles. Near the base and the head of the first phalanx strong, narrow, ring-like bands, the **annular ligaments** (Fig. 88, 2), are formed in these sheaths; these surround and bind down the tendons of the flexor muscles.

A. MUSCLES ON THE ULNAR AND DORSAL SIDE OF THE FOREARM (extensors and supinators) (Fig. 75, p. 158).

M. brachioradialis or supinator longus (Fig. 75, *k*; Fig. 77, *n*).—This is a ribbon-like muscle lying on the lateral side of the brachium and the ventrolateral border of the antibrachium just beneath the superficial fascia. It connects the humerus and the radius.

Origin.—By a thin tendon from about the middle fifth of the dorsal border of the humerus, or sometimes proximad of the middle. The muscle curves over the outer surface of the brachialis (Fig. 75, *i*), to which it is closely applied, and runs along the lateral border of the antibrachium to its insertion.

Insertion by a short tendon into the ridge which forms the ventral limit of the groove on the outer surface of the styloid process of the radius and upon the adjacent ligaments.

Relations.—Outer surface with the integument, and at the proximal end with the caput laterale of the triceps (Fig. 75, *h*). Inner surface with the brachialis (*i*), the extensor carpi radialis longus (*l*) and brevis, and the extensor communis digitorum (*m*).

Action.—Supinator of the hand.

M. extensor carpi radialis longus (Fig. 75, *l*; Fig. 77, *o*).—This lies along the radial side of the forearm, and connects the humerus and the second metacarpal.

Origin (Fig. 81, *k*) from the middle portion of the lateral supracondyloid ridge between the origin of the brachialis (*j*) and the anconeus. About the middle of the forearm the muscle ends in a slender tendon (Fig. 84, *e*) which passes through the groove on the radial side of the dorsal surface of the distal end of the radius.

Insertion (Fig. 84, *e*).—The tendon passes across the carpus and is inserted onto the dorsal surface of the base of the second metacarpal on the radial side just distad of the groove for the radial artery.

Relations.—Outer surface at the proximal end with the caput laterale of the triceps (Fig. 75, *h*), farther distad with the integument and the brachioradialis (*k*); the distal tendon with the extensor pollicis brevis (Fig. 84, *d*). Radial surface with the brachialis (Fig. 75, *i*) and the integument. Ulnar surface with the extensor carpi radialis brevis (Fig. 77, *p*), and near the proximal end with the extensor communis digitorum (Fig. 75, *m*).

Action.—Extensor of the hand.

M. extensor carpi radialis brevis (Fig. 77, *p*).—A slender muscle from the humerus to the third metacarpal.

Origin (Fig. 81, *l*) from the distal part of the lateral supracondyloid ridge distad of the extensor longus. Near the carpus the muscle ends in a slender tendon which passes through the groove with the extensor longus tendon. The tendon then diverges from the extensor longus and has its

Insertion (Fig. 84, *f*) into the radial side of the dorsal surface of the base of the third metacarpal.

Relations.—Outer surface with the extensor longus (Fig. 77, *o*), the integument, and distad with the extensor pollicis brevis (Fig. 84, *d*). Radial surface with the extensor longus. Ulnar surface with the extensor communis digitorum (Fig. 75, *m*) and the extensor brevis pollicis. Inner surface with the pronator teres (Fig. 77, *q*), supinator (Fig. 85, *b*), and extensor brevis pollicis (Fig. 85, *a*).

Action.—Extensor of the hand.

M. extensor digitorum communis (Fig. 75, *m*).—A slender muscle from the lateral supracondyloid ridge of the humerus to the phalanges of the second, third, fourth, and fifth digits.

Origin (Fig. 81, *m*).—The distal surface of the lateral supracondyloid ridge dorsad of the origin of the extensor carpi radialis brevis.

At the junction of the middle and distal thirds of the radius the muscle passes into a large, flat tendon (Fig. 75, *m'*) which passes through the groove on the middle of the dorsal surface of the distal end of the radius. The groove is converted into a canal by a strong transverse ligament. The tendon divides near the groove into four portions (Fig. 84, *a*) which diverge and pass to the four ulnar digits.

Insertions.—Each division of the tendon as it passes over the dorsal surface of the first phalanx has its border connected by strong fascia to the dorsal surface of the phalanx. It finally passes through the groove at the distal end of the first phalanx and is inserted mostly into the base of the second phalanx; a portion continues distad to be inserted into the third phalanx.

Relations.—Outer surface with the integument and at the origin with the caput laterale (Fig. 75, *h*) of the triceps. Radial surface with the extensor longus (*l*) and extensor brevis. Ulnar surface with the extensor digitorum lateralis (*n*). Inner surface with the supinator (Fig. 85, *b*) and the extensor pollicis brevis (Fig. 85, *a*).

Action.—Extensor of the four ulnar digits.

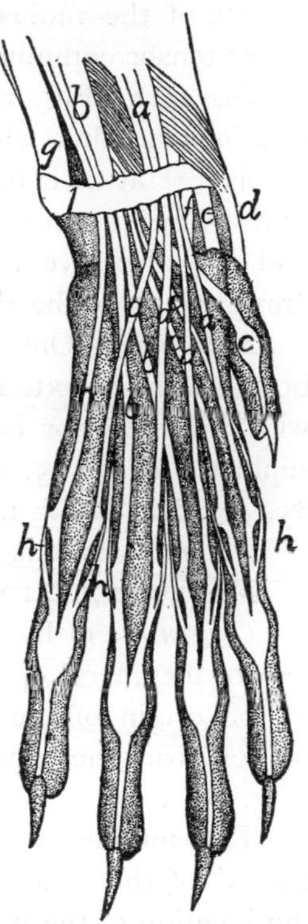

FIG. 84.—ARRANGEMENT OF THE TENDONS ON THE BACK OF THE HAND.

a, M. extensor communis digitorum; *b*, M. extensor lateralis digitorum; *c*, M. extensor indicis; *d*, M. extensor brevis pollicis; *e*, M. extensor carpi radialis longus; *f*, M. extensor carpi radialis brevis; *g*, M. extensor carpi ulnaris; *h*, tendons of the interossei. 1, transverse ligament of the wrist.

M. extensor digitorum lateralis (Fig. 75, *n*). (This corresponds in position to the extensor digiti quinti proprius of man.)

Origin (Fig. 81, *n*) from the lateral supracondyloid ridge of the humerus distad of the origin of the extensor communis.

The muscle passes along the ulnar border and dorsal surface of the forearm between the extensor communis (Fig. 75, *m*) and the extensor carpi ulnaris (*o*). Near the carpus it ends in a tendon (*n'*), which divides immediately into three or four (Fig. 84, *b*). These pass through the groove on the ulnar side of the dorsal surface of the radius and diverge to the digits lying beneath the extensor communis tendon.

Insertion (Fig. 84, *b*).—The three tendons on the ulnar side join the ulnar sides of the tendons of the extensor communis (*a*) at their insertions. The radial of the four tendons (not always present) joins the tendon of the extensor indicis (*c*) and may also give a branch to the radial side of the base of the first phalanx of the third digit.

Relations.—Outer surface with the integument. Radial border with the extensor communis digitorum (*m*); ulnar border with the extensor carpi ulnaris (*o*). Inner surface with the supinator (Fig. 85, *b*) and the extensor brevis pollicis (Fig. 85, *a*); distad with the extensor indicis (Fig. 85, *c*).

Action.—Extensor of the four ulnar digits.

M. extensor carpi ulnaris (Fig. 75, *o*).

Origin.—(1) By a short, broad tendon from the distal portion of the lateral epicondyle of the humerus (Fig. 81, *o*) distad of the origin of the extensor lateralis, and (2) by a smaller tendon from the ulna at the dorsal tip of the semilunar notch (Fig. 86, *e*).

The muscle passes along the ulnar side of the forearm dorsad of the extensor digitorum lateralis (*n*). It ends near the junction of the middle and distal thirds of the forearm in a large, flat tendon (*o'*) which is closely adherent to the ligaments of the wrist and which passes over the distal end of the ulna to its

Insertion into the tubercle on the ulnar side of the base of the fifth metacarpal (Fig. 84, *g*).

Relations.—Outer surface with the integument. Radial (or ventral) border with the extensor digitorum lateralis (Fig. 75, *n*); ulnar (or dorsal) border with the flexor profundus digitorum (*q*). Inner surface with the radius, the extensor indicis Fig. 85, *c*), and the extensor pollicis brevis (Fig. 85, *a*).

Action.—Indicated by its name.

M. extensor indicis (proprius) (Fig. 85, *c*; Fig. 75, *p*) (includes extensor pollicis longus also).

Origin (Fig. 86, *f*) by short, fleshy fibres from the lateral surface of the ulna between the semilunar notch and the junction of the third and fourth (distal) fourths.

The muscle-fibres pass obliquely distad and toward the radial side and join the tendon (Fig. 85, *c'*), which runs nearly the whole length of the radial surface.

Insertion (Fig. 84, *c*).—The tendon passes through the groove on the ulnar side of the dorsal surface of the base of the radius and divides into two. Both of these usually go to the base of the second phalanx of the second digit, but one may pass to the pollex, or there may be three divisions going to the first three digits.

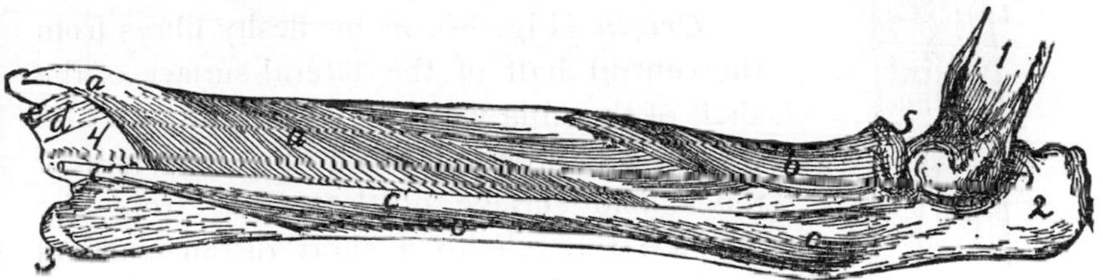

FIG. 85.—DEEP MUSCLES ON THE EXTENSOR SURFACE OF THE RADIUS AND ULNA.

a, M. extensor brevis pollicis (*a'*, its tendon); *b*, M. supinator; *c*, M. extensor indicis (*c'*, its tendon); *d*, tendon of M. extensor carpi radialis brevis; *e*, tendon of M. extensor carpi radialis longus. 1, humerus; 2, olecranon; 3, styloid process of ulna; 4, distal end of radius; 5, head of radius.

Relations.—Outer surface with the integument, the extensor carpi ulnaris (Fig. 75, *o*), and the extensor digitorum lateralis (Fig. 75, *n*). Dorsal border with the flexor profundus digitorum (Fig. 75, *q*). Inner surface with the extensor brevis pollicis (Fig. 85, *a*).

Action as indicated by the name.

M. supinator (Fig. 85, *b*).—A flat muscle wrapped spirally about the proximal end of the radius.

Origin by a short, strong tendon from the lateral side of the annular ligament of the radius and by tendinous fibres from the radial collateral ligament passing from the humerus to the radius. From the tendon of origin the fibres diverge, passing toward the radial side and distad.

Insertion (Fig. 86, *g*).—The dorsal and part of the ventral surface of the proximal two-fifths of the radius to within

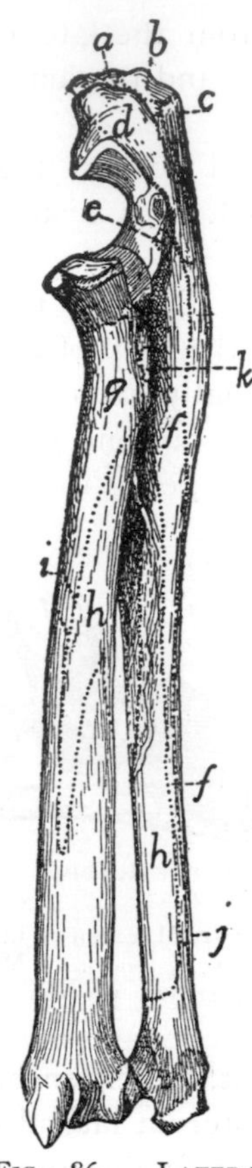

Fig. 86. — Lateral or Extensor Surface of Radius and Ulna, with the Areas of Attachment of Muscles.

a, long portion of caput mediale of M. triceps; *b*, caput longum of M. triceps; *c*, caput laterale of M. triceps; *d*, M. anconeus; *e*, M. extensor carpi ulnaris; *f*, M. extensor indicis; *g*, M. supinator; *h*, M. extensor brevis pollicis; *i*, M. pronator teres; *j*, M. flexor profundus digitorum; *k*, M. biceps.

five millimeters of the articular face of the head.

Relations.—Outer surface with the extensor carpi radialis brevis, extensor communis digitorum (Fig. 75, *m*), and extensor lateralis digitorum (Fig. 75, *n*). Radial border with the pronator teres (Fig. 77, *q*). Inner surface with the radius.

Action.—Supinator of the hand.

M. extensor brevis pollicis or extensor ossis metacarpi pollicis (Fig. 85, *a*) (includes M. abductor longus pollicis of man).

Origin (Fig. 86, *h*) by fleshy fibres from the ventral half of the lateral surface of the shaft of the ulna from the semilunar notch to the styloid process; from the ulnar half of the dorsal surface of the radius from the bicipital tubercle to a short distance distad of the middle of the bone; and from the interosseous membrane between these two areas. The fibres converge to form a strong, flat tendon (Fig. 84, *d*) which passes obliquely over the tendons of the extensor carpi radialis longus (*e*) and brevis (*f*) to its

Insertion into the radial side of the base of the first metacarpal. The radial sesamoid bone of the wrist is imbedded in the tendon at its insertion.

Relations.—Outer surface with the extensor carpi radialis brevis, the extensor communis digitorum (Fig. 75, *m*), extensor lateralis digitorum (Fig. 75, *n*), and extensor indicis (Fig. 85, *c*). Inner surface with the radius and ulna, and distad with the tendons of the two extensores carpi radiales (Fig. 84, *e* and *f*).

Action.—Extends and abducts the pollex.

B. MUSCLES ON THE RADIAL AND VENTRAL SIDE OF THE FOREARM (flexors and pronators).

M. pronator teres (Fig. 77, *q*).

Origin (Fig. 82, *l*) by a short strong tendon from the extremity of the medial epicondyle of the humerus.

Insertion (Fig. 86, *i*) by fleshy fibres and short tendinous fibres along the medial border of the radius, at its middle. The radial edge of the muscle is continuous with the strong deep layer of the antibrachial fascia.

Relations.—Outer surface with the superficial fascia. Radial border with the tendon of the biceps (Fig. 79, *l'*), with the extensor carpi radialis brevis (Fig. 77, *p*), and the supinator (Fig. 85, *b*). Ulnar border with the flexor carpi radialis (Fig. 77, *r*) and part of the flexor profundus digitorum (Fig. 77, *u*).

Action.—Pronates the hand by rotating the radius.

M. flexor carpi radialis (Fig. 77, *r*).—A slender fusiform muscle.

Origin (Fig. 82, *m*) from the tip of the medial epicondyle of the humerus.

Insertion.—The slender tendon passes through a deep groove between the os magnum and the first metacarpal. The groove is converted into a canal by the overlying tendons and muscles. The tendon is finally inserted into the bases of the second and third metacarpals.

Relations.—Outer surface with the pronator teres (Fig. 77, *q*), the superficial fascia, and the third head of the flexor profundus (*u*). Radial border with the pronator teres (*q*). Ulnar border with the third and fourth heads of the flexor profundus. Inner surface with the ulna proximad and the fifth head of the flexor profundus (*u'*) distad.

Action indicated by the name.

M. palmaris longus (Fig. 77, *s*).—A flat fusiform muscle beneath the fascia on the medial border of the forearm.

Origin (Fig. 82, *p*) by a short flat tendon from the distal part of the medial surface of the medial epicondyle of the humerus.

About one centimeter from the wrist the muscle ends in a flat tendon which passes through the transverse ligament and divides on the hand into four or five (or sometimes only three) tendons (Fig. 77, *s'*) which diverge to the insertions. The ulnar portion of the flexor sublimis digitorum (Fig. 77, *x*) takes origin from the common tendon before its division.

Insertion.—Each tendon except the first gives off a branch which spreads out in the trilobed pad in the palm. The middle two of these may be traced to the integument covering the pad. The tendon is then inserted (Fig. 88, *a*) near the base of the first phalanx onto the outer surface of the perforated portion of the flexor sublimis tendon (*b*, *b'*) at its side, except that to the thumb, which divides near its distal end into two which are inserted into the sesamoid bones at the base of the first phalanx. The tendons of insertion are closely united to the fibrous pulley-ring at the base of the first phalanx, and each may send a slip to the base of the phalanx at either side of the ring.

Relations.—Outer surface with the superficial fascia and one head of the flexor sublimis (Fig. 77, *x*). Radial border with the flexor carpi radialis. Ulnar border with the flexor carpi ulnaris and a part of the flexor profundus digitorum. Inner surface with the flexor carpi radialis (*r*), the flexor carpi ulnaris (*t*), the flexor profundus digitorum (*u*), and the radial head of the flexor sublimis digitorum.

Action.—Flexor of the first phalanx of each of the digits.

M. flexor carpi ulnaris (Fig. 77, *t*, *t'*).

Origin.—There are two heads. The first or humeral head (*t'*) takes origin in common with the second part of the flexor profundus from the median surface of the distal end of the humerus just distad of the medial epicondyle (Fig. 82, *q*). The second or ulnar head (*t*) takes origin by fleshy fibres from the lateral surface of the olecranon and from the dorsal border of the ulna from the olecranon to a point distad of the semilunar notch (Fig 87, *f*). The two heads join proximad of the middle of the forearm. The muscle passes obliquely across the ventral surface of the forearm to its

Insertion by fleshy and tendinous fibres into the proximal surface of the pisiform bone.

Relations.—Outer surface with the integument and the palmaris longus (Fig. 77, *s*). Inner surface and ulnar border with the flexor profundus digitorum.

Action indicated by the name.

M. flexor sublimis digitorum (or perforatus).—This muscle is in two parts, which are given a common name only because of the similar structure and insertions of their tendons.

The **ulnar part** (Fig. 77, *x*) is a conical muscle taking origin from the outer surface of the tendon and muscle of the palmaris longus and from the adjacent ligament. It gives rise to two or three tendons (Fig. 88, *b*) which arise from distinct slips of the muscle; these pass to the ulnar two or three digits. That passing to the fourth or fifth digit receives an accessory slip from a small mass of fibres attached to the transverse ligament on the radial side of the palmaris tendon.

The **radial part** is a small flat triangular muscle which takes origin from the outer surface of the tendon formed by the junction of the tendons of the first and second parts of the flexor profundus. It divides into two slips, each giving rise to a tendon. These tendons (Fig. 88, *b′*) pass to the second and third digits. That to the third digit may divide into two, one of which goes to the fourth digit.

Each of the four tendons (Fig. 88, *b* and *b′*) is perforated by a tendon of the flexor profundus (Fig. 88, *c*) as it passes through the fibrous pulley-ring at the base of the first phalanx. It then continues beneath the flexor profundus tendon through the second pulley-ring (2) and is inserted into the base of the second phalanx.

Relations.—Outer surface of the ulnar part with the integument; inner surface with the palmaris longus (Fig. 77, *s*). Outer surface of the radial part with the palmaris longus; inner surface with the flexor profundus.

Action.—Flexor of the second phalanx of digits 2–5.

M. flexor profundus digitorum (or perforans).—This arises by five heads, the tendons of which join one another at the wrist to make the strongest and deepest of the flexor tendons.

The *first* or *ulnar head* has *origin* (Fig. 87, *g*) from the dorsal half of the medial (radial) surface of the ulna from the proximal lip of the semilunar notch to within a centimeter of the styloid process. Its fibres converge to a large flat tendon which forms the lateral (ulnar) and superficial part of the common tendon.

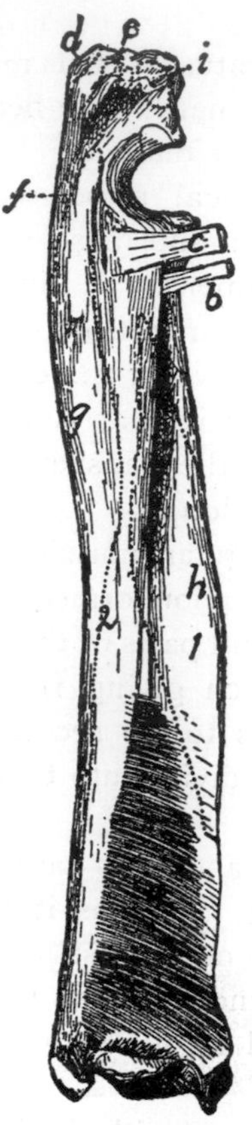

FIG. 87.—RADIUS AND ULNA, Medial or Flexor Side, with M. pronator quadratus and the Areas of Attachment of Other Muscles.

a, M. pronator quadratus; *b*, tendon of M. biceps; *c*, conjoined tendon of M. brachialis and M. clavobrachialis; *d*, insertion of caput longum of M. triceps; *e*, insertion of short portion of caput mediale of M. triceps; *f*, origin of M. flexor carpi ulnaris; *g*, origin of first head of M. flexor profundus digitorum; *h*, origin of fifth head of M. flexor profundus digitorum; *i*, intermediate portion of caput mediale of M. triceps.

The *second head* has *origin* (Fig. 82, *n*) from the distal end of the medial epicondyle of the humerus between the flexor ulnaris and the third and fourth heads of the profundus. It may be very closely attached to these muscles at their origins. Its tendon joins the radial border of the tendon of the first head. From this junction the radial part of the flexor sublimis arises.

The *third head* (Fig. 77, *u*) has *origin* (Fig. 82, *o*) by a strong tendon from the medial epicondyle of the humerus, between the palmaris (*p*) and flexor radialis (*m*). Its tendon forms the radial part of the common tendon.

The *fourth head* has *origin* by a strong tendon from the medial epicondyle of the humerus just ventrad of the origin of the second head and the flexor ulnaris, to which many of its fibres are attached. Its tendon forms the middle and superficial part of the common tendon.

The *fifth* or *radial head* (Fig. 75, *q*; Fig. 77, *u'*) has *origin* (Fig. 87, *h*) from the middle third of the ventral surface of the shaft of the radius over an area limited by two oblique bony ridges; from the adjacent parts of the interosseous membrane; and from the ventral part of the medial surface of the shaft of the ulna between a point about two centimeters distad of the semilunar notch and the junction of the middle and distal thirds of the shaft.

Its very thick tendon forms the middle and deep part of the common tendon.

The common tendon (Fig. 88, *c'*) covers the carpus and metacarpus ventrally. It divides into five tendons (*c*) which pass to the five digits and are *inserted* into the bases of the terminal phalanges. Those of the first four digits perforate the tendon of the flexor sublimis (*b*) at the base of the first phalanx of each digit. At the same place each passes through a fibrous pulley-ring attached to the base of the phalanx. Each then passes through a second pulley-ring (2) near the head of the phalanx and is finally inserted into the base of the terminal phalanx.

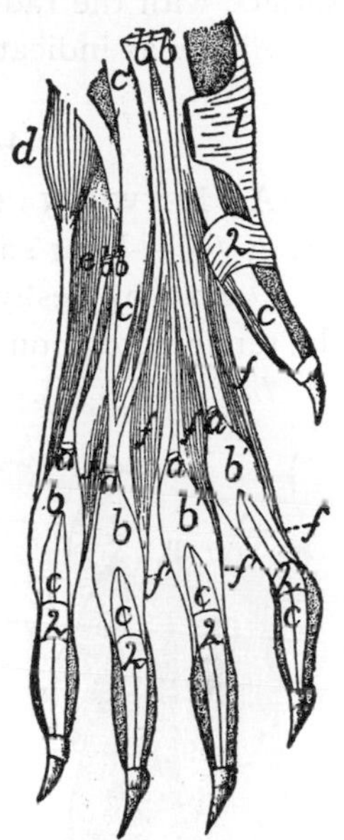

FIG. 88.—ARRANGEMENT OF THE TENDONS of M. palmaris longus, M. flexor sublimis digitorum, and M. flexor profundus digitorum, with Mm. lumbricales.

The integument, fibrous pads, and the palmaris longus (except the ends of its tendons) have been removed; the flexor sublimis has been cut. *a*, cut ends of tendons of M. palmaris longus; *b*, tendons of M. flexor sublimis digitorum, ulnar division; *b'*, radial part of M. flexor sublimis digitorum; *c*, tendons of M. flexor profundus digitorum (*c'*, the common tendon); *d*, M. abductor digiti quinti; *e*, M. flexor brevis digiti quinti; *f*, Mm. lumbricales (*f'*, their tendons). 1, transverse ligament of wrist; 2, annular ligaments.

Relations. — Outer surface with the pronator teres (Fig. 77, *q*), flexor carpi radialis (Fig. 77, *r*), palmaris longus (*s*), flexor carpi ulnaris (*t*), integument, and extensor carpi ulnaris (Fig. 75, *o*). Inner surface with the radius, ulna, interosseous membrane and pronator quadratus (Fig. 87, *a*).

Action.—Flexor of all the digits.

M. pronator quadratus (Fig. 87, *a*). —A thick quadrangular muscle whose fibres run obliquely between the distal ends of the ulna and radius.

Origin by fleshy fibres from about the distal half of the ventral (flexor) surface or border of the ulna and from the interosseous membrane adjacent to the area. The fibres pass obliquely distad toward the radial side to their

Insertion by fleshy fibres into the ventral (flexor) surface of the radius distad of the area of origin of the fifth head of the profundus.

Relations.—Outer surface with the flexor profundus. Inner surface with the radius, ulna, and interosseous membrane.

Action as indicated by the name.

4. Muscles of the Hand.

A. BETWEEN THE TENDONS.—**Mm. lumbricales** (Fig. 88, *f*, *f'*).—Four small muscle in the palm of the hand.

Origin by fleshy fibres from the outer (palmar) surface of the tendon common to the ulnar four parts of the profundus (*c'*).

Insertion (*f'*).—The four slips are flat at their origin. Each becomes cylindrical and curves about the base of one of the four ulnar digits and is inserted into the radial side of the base of the first phalanx close to its ventral border.

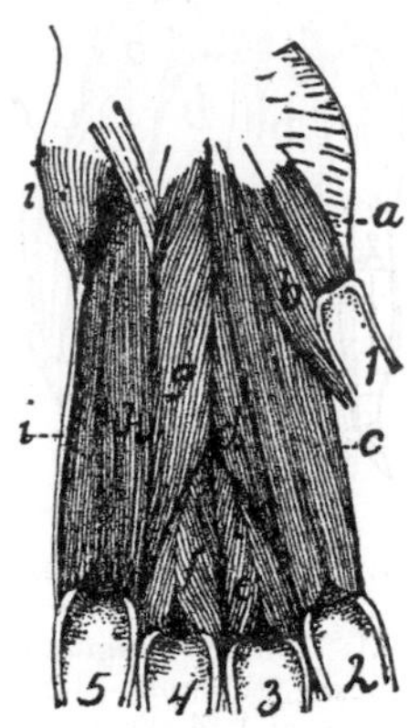

FIG. 89.—DEEP MUSCLES OF THE PALM OF THE HAND.

a, M. flexor brevis pollicis; *b*, M. adductor pollicis; *c*, M. interosseus of second digit (M. flexor brevis digiti secundi); *d*, M. adductor digiti secundi; *e*, M. interosseus of third digit; *f*, M. interosseus of fourth digit; *g*, M. opponens digiti quinti; *h*, M. interosseus of fifth digit (M. flexor brevis digiti quinti); *i*, M. abductor digiti quinti. 1–5, the digits in order.

Action.—Bend the digits toward the radial side.

B. MUSCLES OF THE THUMB.—**M. abductor brevis pollicis** (Fig. 77, *w*) (includes also the opponens pollicis of man).—A very minute, probably rudimentary muscle.

Origin from the transverse ligament (1) which connects the prominent fibrous, hairless projection that lies over the pisiform bone with the radial border of the head of the radius. The muscle passes radiodistad and ends in a very slender tendon, the insertion of which is into the base of the first phalanx of the thumb.

M. flexor brevis pollicis (Fig. 89, *a*).

Origin by fleshy fibres from the adjacent borders of the os magnum and scapholunar bones and from the fascia which bridges the intervening groove for the flexor carpi radialis.

Insertion by a short tendon into the base of the first phalanx of the pollex.

Action.—Flexor of the thumb.

M. adductor pollicis (Fig. 89, *b*).

Origin by fleshy fibres from the ventral border of the os magnum. It curves about the base of the first metacarpal on its ulnar side to its insertion.

Insertion by fleshy fibres into the base of the first phalanx of the pollex on its ulnar side.

C. MUSCLES LYING BETWEEN THE METACARPALS.—**Mm. interossei** (Fig. 89).—Small stout muscles lying on the palmar surfaces of the metacarpals of the second, third, fourth, and fifth digits.

Origin by fleshy fibres from the ventral or lateral surfaces of the bases of the metacarpals. Near the distal end of the metacarpal each divides into two masses which pass onto the lateral surfaces of the metacarpal, so as to leave the ventral surface of the distal end exposed.

Insertion partly onto the lateral surfaces of the base of the first phalanx and its sesamoids, and partly by a slender tendon (Fig. 84, *h*) which is continued dorsad to join the extensor tendon of the digit.

D. SPECIAL MUSCLES OF THE SEGOND DIGIT (THE INDEX).—**M. flexor brevis digiti secundi** (or indicis).—This name may be applied to M. interosseus of the second digit (Fig. 89, *c*).

M. abductor digiti secundi.—This name might be applied to a portion of the interosseus of the second digit which is sometimes differentiated from the remainder.

Origin from the radial and ventral surfaces of the base of the second metacarpal, and from the ventral surface of the trapezium.

Insertion into the radial side of the base of the first phalanx of the second digit and into its sesamoid.

M. adductor digiti secundi (Fig. 89, *d*).

Origin from the ventral surface of the os magnum.

Insertion into the ulnar side of the base of the first phalanx of the second digit.

E. SPECIAL MUSCLES OF THE FIFTH DIGIT.—**M. abductor digiti quinti** (Fig. 89, *i*).—A thick, small, conical bundle.

Origin from the distal surface of the pisiform bone and from the transverse ligament on the ulnar side of the pisiform. It ends in a slender tendon which runs along the ulnar side of the fifth metacarpal to its

Insertion into the ulnar side of the base of the first phalanx of the fifth digit.

M. flexor brevis digiti quinti (Fig. 89, *h*; Fig. 88, *e*).—This covers the ventral surface of the fifth metacarpal, and is really the interosseus of this digit.

Origin by fleshy fibres from the ventral surface of the base of the fifth metacarpal; from the ventral process of the unciform bone, and from the transverse ligament proximad of the fifth metacarpal.

Insertion by fleshy fibres into the ventral border of the proximal end of the first phalanx of the fifth digit.

M. opponens (adductor) digiti quinti (Fig. 89, *g*).

Origin by a flat tendon from the ventral surface of the os magnum on the ulnar side of the adductor pollicis (*b*). It passes toward the ulnar side and distad, the fibres diverging to their

Insertion (1) into nearly the whole of the radial surface of the fifth metacarpal, (2) into the base of its first phalanx.

V. MUSCLES OF THE PELVIC LIMBS.

1. Muscles of the Hip.

A. On the Lateral Surface of the Hip.

Fascia of the Thigh.—After the removal of the superficial fascia with its fat and blood-vessels, there is seen a strong glistening fascia, the **fascia lata** (Fig. 68, *z*, page 117), covering the vastus lateralis muscle over the dorsal half of the thigh. Ventrally it dips between the vastus lateralis and the biceps femoris and, becoming gradually thinner, is lost on the surface of the former muscle. Passing over the dorsal border of the thigh, it extends beneath the sartorius and is attached to the dorsal border of the vastus medialis. Toward its distal end the fascia is continuous with the tendon of the biceps femoris and dorsad with the border of the sartorius muscle, while between these points it is united with the tendon of the vastus lateralis; it thus gains insertion into the patella. At its proximal end the fascia receives the insertion of the tensor fasciæ latæ (Fig. 68, *r*).

M. tensor fasciæ latæ (Fig. 68, *r*, page 117; Fig. 92, *a*).—The tensor fasciæ latæ is a thick triangular muscle which may be recognized by its insertion into the proximal end of the fascia lata (Fig. 68, *z*; Fig. 92, *a'*).

Origin by fleshy fibres as a thick triangular prism from the outer margin of the ventral border of the ilium craniad of the auricular impression and from the fascia covering the ventral border of the gluteus medius (Fig. 90, *b*) over its cranial half. The caudal border of the muscle may be continuous with the cranial border of the gluteus maximus. The muscle spreads out in a fan-like manner, covering the proximal third of the dorsal surface of the thigh The cranial fibres pass farther distad than the others.

Insertion into the fascia lata (Fig. 68, *z*) along an irregular line which begins caudad at the base of the great trochanter and ends on the cranial side of the thigh at the junction of the first and second thirds.

Relations.—Outer surface with the cutaneus maximus (Fig. 62, *b*, page 94) and craniad with the sartorius (Fig. 68, *q*). Cranial border with the sartorius (*q*); caudodorsal border with the gluteus medius (Fig. 90, *b*). Inner surface with the gluteus medius, the rectus femoris (Fig. 92, *b*), and the vastus lateralis (Fig. 90, *d*).

Action indicated by the name. It also assists the quadriceps femoris in extending the leg.

M. gluteus maximus.—The gluteus maximus is a rather small quadrangular muscle in the angle between the gluteus medius (Fig. 90, *b*) and the caudal vertebræ.

Origin (Fig. 163, 3, page 401) by fleshy fibres from the tips of the transverse processes of the last sacral and the first caudal vertebræ, from the fascia covering the spinous muscles dorsad of the transverse processes of these vertebræ, and from the fascia covering the gluteus medius. The muscle passes laterad and slightly caudad to its

Insertion by tendon and muscle-fibres into a tubercle on the caudal side of the great trochanter at the middle of its distal end, and for a few millimeters into the ridge which continues distad from this tubercle.

Relations.—Outer surface with the caudofemoralis (Fig. 68, *s*, page 117), the superficial fascia, and a few fibres of the cutaneus maximus. Inner surface with the abductor caudæ internus, the tenuissimus (Fig. 90, *g*), the great sciatic nerve (Fig. 163, *a*), the obturator internus (Fig. 90, *e*), the gluteus medius (Fig. 90, *b*), the gemellus superior, and the pyriformis (Fig. 163, 7). Cranial border with the gluteus medius and the tensor fasciæ latæ. Caudal border with the caudofemoralis (Fig. 68, *s*).

Action.—Abducts the thigh.

M. gluteus medius (Fig. 90, *b*).—The gluteus medius is a very large triangular muscle which connects the ilium and the sacrum with the great trochanter (1).

Origin by fleshy fibres (1) from the superficial sacral fascia; (2) from the lateral surface of the fascia which covers the surface of the supraspinous extensor muscles of the tail; (3) from the fascia intervening between it and the tensor fasciæ latæ; (4) by tendon fibres from the dorsal half of the crest of the ilium and its dorsal border, and the dorsal half of the lateral surface craniad of the auricular impression; and (5) from the tips of the transverse processes of the last sacral and the first caudal vertebræ. The fibres converge to a strong internal tendon.

Insertion into the proximal end of the great trochanter.

Relations.—Outer surface with the gluteus maximus and tensor fasciæ latæ, and between these with the strong fascia lying beneath the cutaneus maximus muscle. Inner surface with the gluteus minimus, the pyriformis, and the gemellus superior. Cranial border with the tensor fasciæ latæ. Caudal border with the gluteus maximus.

Action.—Abducts the thigh.

M. pyriformis (Fig. 163, 7).—The pyriformis is a triangular muscle covered by the gluteus maximus and the gluteus medius (Fig. 90, *b*) and overlying the gemellus superior (Fig. 163, 6).

Origin by fleshy fibres from the tips of the transverse processes of the last two sacral and the first caudal vertebræ. The muscle passes laterad through the great sciatic notch to its

Insertion by a flat tendon into an elongated area on the proximal border of the great trochanter just outside (caudad) of the insertion of the gemellus superior.

Relations.—Outer surface with the gluteus medius (Fig. 90, *b*) and the gluteus maximus. Inner surface with the gemellus superior (Fig. 163, 6), the great sciatic nerve (Fig. 163, *a*), and the flexor caudæ longus (Fig. 68, *x*).

Action.—Abductor of the thigh.

M. gemellus superior (Fig. 163, 6).—The gemellus superior is a triangular muscle lying beneath the pyriformis (Fig. 163, 7). It is broader than the pyriformis, so that it projects beyond its borders both caudad and craniad. It is closely united craniad with the gluteus minimus, so that the limits of the two are definable only with difficulty. Its caudal border is closely united to the gemellus inferior.

Origin by fleshy fibres from an elongated area on the dorsal border of the ilium and ischium. The area is narrowed craniad. It does not quite reach the posterior inferior iliac spine in the one direction nor the spine of the ischium in the other direction. The fibres converge to a strong tendon the

Insertion of which is into a triangular area dorsad of the tip of the great trochanter.

Relations.—Outer surface with the gluteus medius (Fig. 90, *b*), the pyriformis (Fig. 163, 7), the great sciatic nerve (Fig. 163, *a*), and the gluteus maximus. Inner surface with the ilium, ischium, the capsularis, the caudal edge of the gluteus minimus (Fig. 163, 5), and the cranial edge of the obturator internus (Fig. 90, *e*).

Action.—Rotates the femur and abducts it so as to carry the foot outward.

M. gluteus minimus (Fig. 163, 5).—The gluteus minimus is a long triangular muscle beneath the middle of the gluteus medius (Fig. 90, *b*) and with its caudal border against or covering the cranial border of the gemellus superior (Fig. 163, 6), to which it is frequently closely united.

Origin from the ventral half of the ilium, from near its cranial end to a point midway between the posterior iliac spine and the spine of the ischium. The muscle ends in a strong flat tendon.

Insertion into an oval facet at the base of the dorsal surface of the great trochanter on its lateral side.

Relations.—Outer surface with the gluteus medius (Fig. 90, *b*) and at the caudal border with the gemellus superior (Fig. 163, 6). Inner surface with the capsularis and rectus femoris (Fig. 92, *b*).

Action.—Rotates the femur so as to carry the foot out.

M. capsularis (gluteus quartus, or epimeralis).—The capsularis is a small flat bundle of muscle-fibres which lies obliquely beneath the gluteus minimus (Fig. 163, 5) and gemellus superior (6) on the lateral or outer surface of the ilium.

Origin by fleshy fibres from the surface of the ilium over a triangular area between the origin of the rectus femoris (Fig. 92, *b*) ventrad, the gemellus superior (Fig. 163, 6) dorsad, and of the gluteus minimus (Fig. 163, 5) craniad and the acetabulum caudad. The muscle passes over the smooth surface of the ilium and the pubis ventrad of the acetabulum and then over the capsule of the joint.

Insertion by fleshy fibres for about one centimeter in the middle line on the dorsal surface of the femur distad of the great trochanter.

Relations.—Outer surface with the gluteus minimus (Fig 163, 5), the gemellus superior (6), and the vastus lateralis (Fig 90, *d*). Inner surface with the ilium, the rectus femoris (Fig 92, *b*), the capsule of the joint, and the vastus medialis (Fig 92, *c*).

Action.—Rotates the thigh so as to carry the foot inward hence antagonizes the iliopsoas.

M. gemellus inferior.—The gemellus inferior is a flat triangular muscle situated just caudad of the gemellus superior and beneath the obturator internus (Fig. 90, *e*), so that it is seen on reflecting the latter

Origin from the dorsal one-half of the whole lateral surface of the ischium between the ischial spine and the ischial tuberosity. The fibres converge toward its insertion. The inner surface of the muscle is covered by a strong tendon.

Insertion into the inner surface of the tendon of the obturator internus (Fig. 90, *e*) by tendon- and muscle-fibres. Some of the muscle-fibres are inserted into the capsule of the joint.

Relations.—Outer surface with the obturator internus (Fig. 90, *e*). Medial surface with the ischium. Caudal border with the quadratus femoris (Fig. 90, *f*). Cranial border with the gemellus superior.

Action.—Abductor of the thigh. The muscle may be considered as a separate head of the obturator internus (Fig. 90, *e*).

M. quadratus femoris (Fig. 90, *f*).—The quadratus femoris is a short thick muscle connecting the ischial tuberosity (2) and the proximal end of the femur. It lies just caudad of the obturator internus (*e*) beneath the proximal end of the biceps femoris (Fig. 68, *t*).

The *origin* is by fleshy fibres from a considerable triangular area on the lateral surface of the ischium near the tuberosity. The area lies between the origin areas of the gemellus inferior, biceps, semimembranosus, and the obturator externus.

Insertion into the distal two-thirds of the ventral border of the great trochanter and about half the adjacent surface of the lesser trochanter.

Relations.—Outer surface with the tenuissimus (Fig. 90, *g*), the biceps (Fig. 68, *t*), the semitendinosus (Fig. 90, *j*), and the great sciatic nerve (Fig. 163, *a*). Caudal border with the semimembranosus (Fig. 90, *i*). Ventral border with the adductor femoris (Fig. 90, *h*); dorsal border with the obturator internus (Fig. 90, *e*) and gemellus inferior.

Action.—Extensor of the thigh and rotator of the femur so as to carry the foot inward.

M. obturator externus.—The obturator externus is a flat triangular muscle beneath the adductor femoris (Fig. 92, *g*).

Origin by fleshy fibres from the median lip of the obturator foramen and from both dorsal and ventral surfaces of the rami of the pubis and ischium adjacent to the lip. Also from the outer surface of the ramus of the ischium as far as the area for the quadratus femoris (Fig. 90, *f*). The fibres converge to a strong flat tendon.

Insertion into the proximal portion of the bottom of the trochanteric fossa.

Relations.—Ventral surface with the adductor femoris (Fig. 92, *g*). Dorsal surface with the pubis and ischium. Caudal border with the quadratus femoris (Fig. 90, *f*).

Action. — Assists the iliopsoas.

B. MUSCLES ON THE MEDIAL SURFACE OF THE HIP.—

M. obturator internus (Fig. 90, *e*).—The obturator internus appears as a triangular muscle caudad of the gemellus superior.

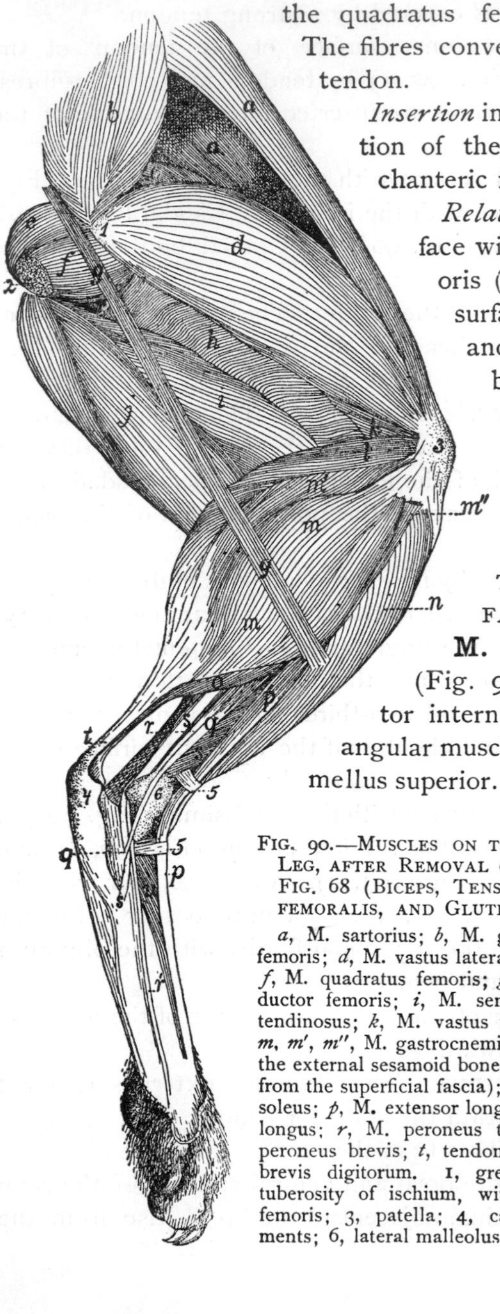

FIG. 90.—MUSCLES ON THE LATERAL SIDE OF THE LEG, AFTER REMOVAL OF THE MUSCLES SHOWN IN FIG. 68 (BICEPS, TENSOR FASCIÆ LATÆ, CAUDOFEMORALIS, AND GLUTEUS MAXIMUS).

a, M. sartorius; *b*, M. gluteus medius; *c*, M. rectus femoris; *d*, M. vastus lateralis; *e*, M. obturator internus; *f*, M. quadratus femoris; *g*, M. tenuissimus; *h*, M. adductor femoris; *i*, M. semimembranosus; *j*, M. semitendinosus; *k*, M. vastus intermedius; *l*, M. plantaris; *m*, *m′*, *m″*, M. gastrocnemius, outer head (*m*, part from the external sesamoid bone; *m′*, from the plantaris; *m″*, from the superficial fascia); *n*, M. tibialis anterior; *o*, M. soleus; *p*, M. extensor longus digitorum; *q*, M. peroneus longus; *r*, M. peroneus tertius (*r′* its tendon); *s*, M. peroneus brevis; *t*, tendon of Achilles; *u*, M. extensor brevis digitorum. 1, great trochanter of femur; 2, tuberosity of ischium, with cut origin of M. biceps femoris; 3, patella; 4, calcaneus; 5, transverse ligaments; 6, lateral malleolus.

Origin by numerous small separate heads from the dorsal surface of the ramus of the ischium along its symphysis and following its medial border from the symphysis nearly to the tuberosity. The fibres form a flat muscle which narrows and passes through the lesser sciatic notch, turns ventrad and ends in a strong flat tendon whose

Insertion is into the bottom of the trochanteric fossa of the femur. The tendon is continued proximad on the inner surface of the muscle and forms a smooth firm surface by which the muscle glides over the dorsal border of the ischium. Into the inner surface of this tendon near its insertion the tendon of the gemellus inferior is inserted.

Relations.—Medial surface within the pelvis with a mass of fat separating it from the pelvic organs. Dorsal or outer surface with the biceps femoris, the tenuissimus, the caudofemoralis, and the great sciatic nerve. Inner surface with the ischium and the great sciatic nerve. Caudal (or ventral) border with the quadratus femoris.

Action.—Abductor of the thigh.

M. iliopsoas (Fig. 162, 8; Fig. 91, *c*).—The iliopsoas (equivalent to the human psoas and iliacus) is a conical muscle emerging from the abdominal cavity onto the medial surface of the femur.

Origin.—(*a*) The portion corresponding to the human psoas (Fig. 162, 8) arises by ten vertebral heads. The first five of these come from the five cranial tendons of origin of the psoas minor (Fig. 162, 9); the sixth from a tendinous expansion which passes from the tendon of the first head over the ventral longitudinal muscles to the transverse process of the fifth lumbar vertebra. The seventh, eighth, ninth, and tenth heads arise by fleshy fibres from the ventral surfaces of the centra of the last four lumbar vertebræ.

(*b*) The portion corresponding to the human iliacus arises by fleshy fibres from the ventral border of the ilium, from opposite the auricular impression to the iliopectineal eminence. The portions of the muscle all converge to form a conical mass which ends in a strong tendon lying on its outer surface.

Insertion by tendon and fleshy fibres into the apex of the lesser trochanter of the femur.

Relations.—Dorsal surface with the quadratus lumborum (with which this muscle is partly united), the rectus femoris (Fig. 91, *d*), and, by the iliac head, with the gluteus minimus. Ventral and medial surface with the psoas minor (Fig. 162, 9) and the peritoneum. Lateral edge with the transversus abdominis (Fig. 162, 4).

Action.—Rotates the thigh so as to carry the foot out; also flexes the thigh.

2. Muscles of the Thigh.

M. biceps femoris (Fig. 68, *t*, page 117).—A very large flat muscle covering about two-thirds of the lateral side of the thigh.

Origin (Fig. 90, 2).—From the ventral surface of the tuberosity of the ischium by tendon- and muscle-fibres. The fibres diverge, and near the knee the mass has spread out, ending in a fascia. The dorsal border of the muscle and the common fascia are continuous dorsad with the superficial fascia of the thigh and with the tendon of the caudofemoralis (Fig. 68, *s*). Ventrad it is continuous with the superficial fascia of the shank.

Insertion into rather more than the proximal one-third of the dorsal border of the tibia along its lateral margin and into the lateral margin of the patella. In passing over the knee-joint it is closely united to the underlying ligaments and tendons.

Relations.—Outer surface with the superficial fascia and with a few of the most caudal fibres of the cutaneus maximus (Fig. 62, *b*, page 94). Cranial (or dorsal) edge with the caudofemoralis (Fig. 68, *s*) and the vastus lateralis (Fig. 90, *d*). Caudal border with the semitendinosus (Fig. 68, *u*) and a mass of fat. Inner surface with the caudofemoralis (Fig. 68, *s*), the tenuissimus (Fig. 90, *g*), the obturator internus (Fig. 90, *e*), the quadratus femoris (Fig. 90, *f*), the semitendinosus (Fig. 68, *u*), the semimembranosus (Fig. 90, *i*), the adductor femoris (Fig. 90, *h*), the great sciatic nerve (Fig. 163, *a*), and distad with the following muscles of the lower leg: the tibialis anterior (Fig. 90, *n*), the extensor longus digitorum (Fig. 90, *p*), the peroneus longus (Fig. 90, *q*), and the lateral head of the gastrocnemius (Fig. 90, *m*).

Action.—Abductor of the thigh, and flexor of the shank.

M. tenuissimus or **M. abductor cruris** (Fig. 90, *g*).—A very slender muscle, only three or four millimeters wide.

Origin from the tip of the transverse process of the second caudal vertebra, in common with the caudofemoralis (Fig. 68, *s*) or gluteus maximus. It passes obliquely beneath the biceps femoris (Fig. 68, *t*) distad and ventrad, to the distal end of the ventral border of that muscle. Here it becomes continuous with the ventral border of the biceps, ending in a continuation of the same fascia into which the biceps is inserted.

Relations.—Outer surface with the caudofemoralis (Fig. 68, *s*) and the biceps femoris (Fig. 68, *t*); distad with the integument. Inner surface with the obturator internus (Fig. 90, *e*), quadratus femoris (*f*), semitendinosus (*j*), adductor femoris (*h*), semimembranosus (*i*), and distad with the muscles of the lower leg.

M. caudofemoralis (parameralis, Strauss-Durckheim) (Fig. 68, *s*, page 117).

Origin by a flat tendon from the transverse processes of the second and third caudal vertebræ. The muscle forms a flat band which passes distad along the middle of the lateral side of the thigh over the pelvis and caudad of the great trochanter. At the middle of the thigh it ends in a very thin tendon. The tendon passes distad along the medial surface of the biceps femoris (Fig. 68, *t*), pierces the fascia lata near the knee, and passes to its

Insertion into the middle of the lateral border of the patella.

Relations.—Outer surface with the superficial fascia and a few fibres of the cutaneus maximus; distad with the biceps femoris (Fig. 68, *t*). Cranial border with the gluteus maximus; caudal border with the biceps femoris. Inner surface with the tenuissimus (Fig. 90, *g*), the gluteus maximus, the abductor caudæ internus, and with the obturator internus (Fig. 90, *e*); distad with the vastus lateralis.

Action.—Abducts the thigh and helps to extend the shank.

M. semitendinosus (Fig. 90, *j*).—A long slender muscle on the ventral (caudal) border of the thigh, between the semimembranosus (*i*) and the biceps femoris (Fig. 68, *t*).

Origin from the apex of the tuberosity of the ischium beneath the origin of the biceps femoris. The muscle passes to the medial side of the shank and ends in a thin but strong tendon (Fig. 92, *i'*) about five millimeters broad. The tendon curves proximad and passes beneath the gracilis tendon (Fig. 91, *b*) to its

Insertion into the crest (dorsal border) of the tibia one or two centimeters from its proximal end.

Relations.—Lateral surface with the biceps femoris (Fig. 68, *t*), the integument, a mass of fat, and distad with the gastrocnemius (Fig. 92, *j*) and popliteus (Fig. 92, *k*). Caudal surface with the integument. Medial surface with the semimembranosus (Fig. 90, *i*) and distad with the integument of the lower leg.

Action.—Flexor of the shank.

M. semimembranosus (Figs. 90 and 91, *i*; Fig. 92, *h*).—A thick prismatic muscle lying along the ventral (or caudal) side of the thigh between the semitendinosus (*j*) and the gracilis (Fig. 91, *b*).

Origin by short tendon-fibres from the caudal border of the tuberosity and the ramus of the ischium. The muscle mass is divided throughout most of its length into two portions (Fig. 92, *h* and *h'*), one of which (*h'*) lies laterad and caudad of the other. The two portions pass to the medial side of the knee. The caudal portion (*h'*) ends in a strong flat tendon five millimeters broad, the

Insertion of which is into the medial surface of the femur on the medial epicondyle, at the middle of its distal border and into the adjacent medial surface of the tibia behind the lateral ligament.

The dorsal part has its *insertion* into the distal one and one-half to two centimeters of the ridge which is continued from the medial epicondyle of the femur onto the shaft; and nto the sesamoid bone of the medial epicondyle.

Relations.—Lateral surface with the semitendinosus (Fig. 90, *j*), the biceps femoris (Fig. 68, *t*), and distad with a small part of the adductor femoris (Fig. 92, *g*), and with the gastrocnemius (Fig. 92, *j*). Medial surface with the gracilis (Fig. 91, *b*) and distad with the sartorius (Fig. 91, *a*). Cranial (or dorsal) border at the origin with the quadratus femoris (Fig. 90, *f*); for the remainder of its length with the adductor femoris (Fig. 90, *h*). Caudal border with the integument proximad.

Action. — Extensor of the thigh.

M. sartorius (Fig. 91, *a*; Fig. 68, *q*).—A large flat muscle along the medial side of the thigh near its cranial (dorsal) border.

Origin from the ventral half of the crest of the ilium and from the medial half of its ventral border craniad of the auricular impression. The caudal third of the origin is by a thin tendon, the rest by fleshy fibres.

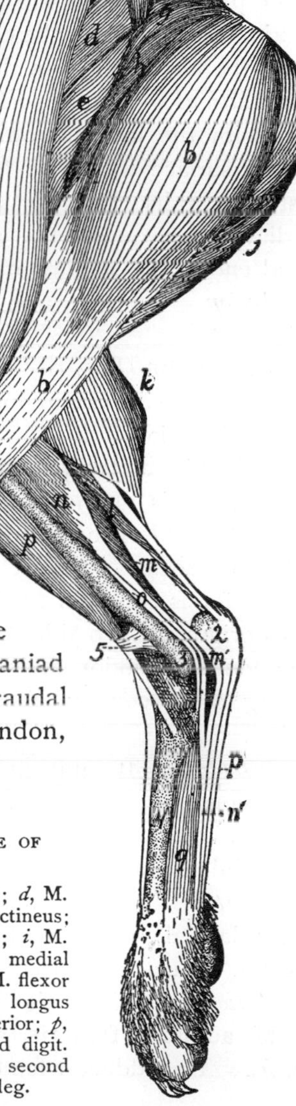

FIG. 91.—MUSCLES ON THE MEDIAL SIDE OF THE LEG.

a, M. sartorius; *b*, M. gracilis; *c*, M. iliopsoas; *d*, M. rectus femoris; *e*, M. vastus medialis; *f*, M. pectineus; *g*, M. adductor longus; *h*, M. adductor femoris; *i*, M. semimembranosus; *j*, M. semitendinosus; *k*, medial head of M. gastrocnemius; *l*, M. plantaris; *m*, M. flexor longus hallucis (*m'*, its tendon); *n*, M. flexor longus digitorum; (*n'*, its tendon); *o*, M. tibialis posterior; *p*, M. tibialis anterior; *q*, M. interosseus of second digit. 1, patella; 2, calcaneus; 3, medial malleolus; 4, second metatarsal; 5, transverse ligament of the lower leg.

Insertion on a long S-shaped line which begins on the dorsal border of the tibial shaft about two centimeters from its proximal end, passes thence to the middle of the proximal end of the medial surface of the tibia, thence across the ligaments of the knee-joint and the medial surface of the medial epicondyle to the patella, crosses the patella obliquely to the middle of its proximal end, and may be continued for some distance proximad along the middle line on the fascia.

Relations.—Medial surface with the integument and proximad with the internal oblique muscle (Fig. 68, *p*). Lateral (inner) surface with the tensor fasciæ latæ (Fig. 68, *r*), the vastus lateralis (Fig. 90, *d*), the superficial fascia, the vastus medialis (Fig. 92, *c*), the rectus femoris (Fig. 92, *b*), and the distal end of the semimembranosus (Fig. 92, *h'*).

Action.—Adducts and rotates the femur and extends the tibia.

M. gracilis (Fig. 91, *b*).—The gracilis is a flat, thin, subcutaneous muscle occupying the ventral half of the medial surface of the thigh.

Origin by a strong tendon from the caudal three-fourths of the symphysis of the ischium and pubis. The tendon may extend caudad of the symphysis in the middle line to the level of the tuberosity of the ischium. For about its first centimeter the tendon is common to the two muscles of opposite sides and gives origin on two sides to the fibres of the adductor femoris. The common tendon divides into two which pass laterad, each ending in a convex border from which the muscle-fibres spring.

Insertion.—It ends in a thin aponeurosis, part of which is continuous with that of the sartorius. The aponeurosis is finally inserted into the medial surface of the tibia near its proximal end, while distally it is continuous with the fascia.

Relations.—Outer (medial) surface with the integument Inner (lateral) surface with the semimembranosus (Fig. 91, *i*) and the adductor femoris (Fig. 91, *h*).

Action.—Adducts the leg and draws it caudad.

M. adductor femoris (magnus et brevis) (Fig. 92, *g*; Fig. 90, *h*).—The adductor femoris lies between the semimembranosus (Fig. 92, *h*) and the femur. Its proximal part is covered by the semimembranosus, while its distal part lies outside of it.

Origin by muscle-fibres from the rami of the pubis and the ischium along the whole of the length of the symphysis; from the ramus of the ischium between the symphysis and the tuberosity, and from the tendon of origin common to the two gracilis muscles.

Insertion into nearly the whole of the ventral surface of the shaft of the femur. The area begins at the base of the great trochanter opposite the proximal end and the insertion area of the gluteus maximus. It extends thence distad along the caudal border of the surface as an area about one millimeter wide. At the junction of the first and second thirds of the shaft the area expands and occupies the whole of the ventral surface of the bone, ending at the intercondyloid fossa.

Relations.—Lateral surface with the biceps (Fig. 68, *t*), the great sciatic nerve (Fig. 163, *a*), the tenuissimus (Fig. 90, *g*), and the semimembranosus (Fig. 92, *h*); dorsolateral border in contact with the vastus lateralis (Fig. 92, *c*). Dorsal surface with the quadratus femoris (Fig. 90, *f*) and obturator externus (Fig. 90, *e*). Caudal surface with the semimembranosus (Fig. 92, *h*). Medial surface with the gracilis (Fig. 91, *b*), adductor longus (Fig. 92, *f*), pectineus (Fig. 92, *e*), vastus medialis (Fig. 92, *c*), and distad with the medial head of the gastrocnemius (Fig. 92, *j*).

Action.—An extensor of the thigh.

M. adductor longus (Fig. 91, *g*; Fig. 92, *f*).—A thin muscle which covers the dorsal half of the medial surface of the adductor femoris (Fig. 92, *g*).

Origin by muscle-fibres from the median three-fourths of the cranial border of the pubis, the line of origin forming a medial continuation of that of the pectineus (Fig. 92, *e*).

Insertion by a thin aponeurosis into the external linea aspera of the femur along the second and third fifths of the bone.

Relations.—With its medial or cranial surface the adductor longus forms part of the boundary of a depression among the muscles at the proximal end of the medial side of the leg.

This depression is called the iliopectineal fossa; it contains the femoral vein and artery and saphenous nerve imbedded in fat (Fig. 127). The medial edge of the adductor longus is in relation with the integument; the lateral edge with the pec-

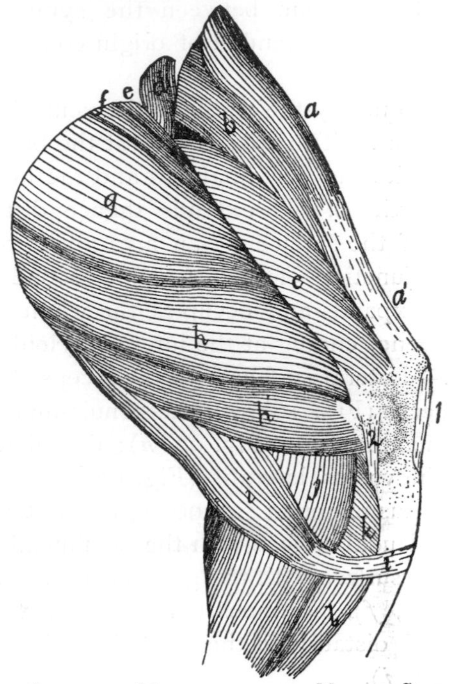

Fig. 92.—Second Layer of Muscles on the Medial Side of the Thigh.

a, M. tensor fasciæ latæ; *a'*, fascia lata; *b*, M. rectus femoris; *c*, M. vastus medialis; *d*, M. iliopsoas (cut); *e*, M. pectineus; *f*, M. adductor longus; *g*, M. adductor femoris; *h*, *h'*, M. semimembranosus; *i*, M. semitendinosus (*i'*, its tendon); *j*, medial head of M. gastrocnemius; *k*, M. popliteus; *l*, M. flexor longus digitorum. 1, patellar ligament; 2, ligamentum collaterale tibiale.

tineus (Fig. 92, *e*). Inner or caudal surface with the adductor femoris (Fig. 92, *g*).

Action.—Adductor of the thigh.

M. pectineus (Fig. 92, *e*).—A flat band of fibres closely united with the adductor longus (*f*), of which it appears to be a lateral continuation.

Origin by fleshy fibres from the lateral one-fourth of the cranial border of the pubis. The muscle passes over the smooth outer surface of the pubis between its origin area and the acetabulum, crosses the iliopsoas (*d*) obliquely and has its

Insertion by muscle-fibres into an elongated area (five millimeters in length) on the shaft of the femur just distad of the lesser trochanter and between the insertion of the adductor femoris (*g*) and that of the vastus medialis (*c*).

Relations.—The cranial edge forms part of the floor of the iliopectineal fossa. Lateral surface in relation with the iliopsoas (*d*) and vastus medialis (*c*); medial surface with the adductor longus (*f*) and adductor femoris (*g*).

Action.—Adductor of the thigh.

M. quadriceps femoris.—The quadriceps femoris is a very powerful extensor muscle on the front of the thigh. It consists of four muscles which unite to form the great extensor of the shank. It is inserted into the patella and through it, by the ligamentum patellæ, into the tibia. It may be compared to the triceps brachii. The parts are:

(1) **M. rectus femoris** (Fig. 92, *b*; Fig. 90, *c*).

Origin by strong tendon from an elongated triangular area which has its base at the acetabulum and its apex about five to seven millimeters craniad of the acetabulum, along the ventral border of the ilium. The area is between that for the capsularis and that for the iliopsoas. The muscle is flat near its origin, but soon becomes a triangular prismatic mass which is united to the dorsal border of the vastus lateralis (Fig. 90, *d*) at the junction of the middle and last thirds of the thigh.

Insertion into the oblique area on the outer surface of the patella near its proximal border in connection with the vastus lateralis.

Relations.—Outer or lateral surface at the origin with the gluteus minimus, the edge of the capsularis, the gluteus medius (Fig. 90, *h*), and farther distad with the vastus lateralis (Fig. 90, *d*). Medial surface with the tensor fasciæ latæ (Fig. 92, *a*), sartorius (Fig. 90, *a*), and vastus medialis (Fig. 92, *c*). Inner (caudal) surface with the vastus intermedius.

(2) **M. vastus lateralis** (Fig. 90, *d*).—A flat triangular prismatic mass joined distally to the preceding. It covers the dorsal part of the lateral surface of the thigh.

Origin from a triangular area on the dorsal and lateral surfaces of the shaft and the great trochanter of the femur. The base of the area is at the great trochanter, and its apex is at the junction of the second and third fifths of the shaft on the linea aspera. The linea aspera forms the ventral boundary of the triangle, while its dorsal boundary is formed by a line drawn from its apex to the dorsomedial angle of the great trochanter. The mass unites with the rectus femoris (*c*) by its dorsal border at the junction of the middle and distal thirds of the thigh.

Insertion into the oblique area on the outer surface of the patella near its lateral border in connection with the rectus femoris.

(3) **M. vastus medialis** (Fig. 92, *c*) lies on the medial side of the thigh.

Origin by fleshy fibres over a diamond-shaped area on the shaft of the femur lying between the medial branch of the linea aspera and the area for the vastus lateralis. Proximad the area is bounded by the spiral line, and distad it is bounded by a line parallel to the spiral line and having its proximal end at about the junction of the first and second thirds of the bone. The muscle forms a triangular, prismatic mass. It ends in a thin aponeurosis which is continuous dorsad with the border of the rectus femoris (Fig. 92, *b*), and ventrad sometimes with the tendon of the gracilis (Fig. 91, *b*).

Insertion into the medial border of the patella and the ligamentum patellæ. The insertion may extend onto the head of the tibia.

The adjacent surfaces of the vastus lateralis and the vastus medialis are connected over their distal thirds by an aponeurosis which passes transversely beneath the rectus femoris. The distal end of the aponeurosis is inserted into the proximal border of the patella. Its proximal end receives the insertion of some muscle-fibres which form a part of the vastus medialis as here described. This mass of fibres is described by Strauss-Durckheim as the **crural** muscle. Sometimes the transverse aponeurosis is continuous with only one of the two vasti and sometimes with neither, so that the insertion of the crural of Strauss-Durckheim becomes more or less independent.

Relations of the vastus medialis. Outer (medial) surface

with the sartorius (Fig. 91, *a*) and the structures in the ilio-pectineal fossa. Cranial (or dorsal) surface with the rectus femoris (Fig. 92, *b*) and vastus intermedius. Caudal (ventral) surface with the pectineus (Fig. 92, *e*), adductor longus (Fig. 92, *f*), adductor femoris (Fig. 92, *g*), and semimembranosus (Fig. 92, *h*).

(4) **M. vastus intermedius.**—A flat mass of muscle which lies beneath the rectus femoris.

Origin from nearly the whole of the dorsal surface of the shaft of the femur between the areas for the vastus medialis and vastus lateralis. The area of origin extends distad to an oblique line the middle of which is about one and one-half centimeters from the patellar surface, the lateral border of the area being longer than the medial border.

Insertion by muscle-fibres into the capsule of the joint. The central fibres are inserted about one centimeter proximad of the patella, while the lateral mass passes to the level of the proximal end.

Relations.—Outer surface with the rectus femoris (Fig. 92, *b*); borders with the vastus medialis (Fig. 92, *c*) and vastus lateralis (Fig. 90, *d*); inner surface with the femur.

Action.—The quadriceps extensor is an extensor of the shank. The vastus intermedius acting separately is a tensor of the capsule of the knee-joint.

3. Muscles of the Lower Leg (Crus).

A. On the Ventral Side.—**M. gastrocnemius.**—This is the great muscular mass of the calf. It arises by two heads, the caput laterale or lateral head (Fig. 90, *m*), and the caput mediale or medial head (Fig. 91, *k*), of the gastrocnemius.

Caput laterale (Fig. 90, *m*, *m′*, *m″*).—The origin of the lateral head is in four portions:

(1) From the tendon of origin of the plantaris which comes from the middle of the lateral border of the patella. The tendon ends in a small conical mass of fibres (*m′*) which joins the ventral part of the common head.

(2) By a slender flat tendon, distad of the first, from the

superficial fascia of the shank (*m''*). The tendon ends in a conical mass which joins the dorsal border of the common head.

(3) By a strong tendon and by muscle-fibres from the distal border of the lateral sesamoid bone (Fig. 61, 3) of the femur. These fibres (*m*) form the middle and outer part of the common head.

(4) By muscle-fibres from the middle of the outer surface of the aponeurosis covering the plantaris (Fig. 90, *l*) along rather more than the proximal half of the tibia. The lateral head thus formed is flat and fusiform in section.

Caput mediale (Fig. 91, *k*; Fig. 92, *j*).—The medial head resembles the lateral head closely.

Origin by a strong tendon from the medial sesamoid bone of the femur (Fig. 61, 4) and by muscle-fibres from the surface of the shaft for a short distance proximad of this.

The two heads unite by their contiguous borders at the junction of the first and second thirds of the tibia. The common muscle narrows rapidly and ends in a flat tendon which joins the tendon of the soleus to form the so-called tendon of Achilles (tendo calcaneus) (Fig. 90, *t*). This has its

Insertion into the proximal end of the calcaneus (Fig. 90, 4) near its ventral border. This tendon together with that of the soleus (Fig. 90, *o*) and the fascia of the shank forms a tubular sheath for the tendon of the plantaris.

Relations.—(1) Of the lateral head. Lateral (outer) surface with the biceps femoris (Fig. 68, *t*) and the superficial fascia. Medial (inner) surface with the popliteus (Fig. 92, *k*), the plantaris (Fig. 90, *l*) (to which it is closely united), the medial head of the gastrocnemius (Fig. 91, *k*), the soleus (Fig. 90, *o*), and the peroneus longus (Fig. 90, *q*). (2) Of the medial head. Medial (outer) surface with the superficial fascia and the tendons of the gracilis (Fig. 91, *b*), semimembranosus (Fig. 92, *h'*), and semitendinosus (Fig. 92, *i*). Lateral (inner) surface at the origin with the adductor femoris (Fig. 92, *g*), then with the plantaris (Fig. 91, *l*), the popliteus (Fig. 92, *k*), flexor longus digitorum (Fig. 91, *n*), and the lateral head of the gastrocnemius (Fig. 90, *m*).

Action.—Extensor of the foot. (It is to be noted that what is called **extension** in the foot is analogous to what is called **flexion** in the hand, so that the extensors of the foot are most readily to be compared with the flexors of the hand.)

M. plantaris (Fig. 90, *l*; Fig. 91, *l*).—A fusiform muscle covered distally by the gastrocnemius, but appearing between the two heads of the gastrocnemius at their proximal ends (Fig. 90, *l*).

Origin by a strong tendon from the middle of the lateral border of the patella and by fleshy fibres from the ventral border of the lateral sesamoid.

The patellar tendon ends in a flattened head which passes ventrad over the lateral epicondyle of the femur and then curves distad; it is closely united with the lateral head of the gastrocnemius. The muscle ends in a thick tendon which passes through a sheath formed by the tendons of the gastrocnemius and soleus, and the fascia of the shank. The tendon passes over the grooved proximal end of the calcaneus onto its ventral surface. It is held in place against the groove by two sheets of aponeurosis, which leave the tendon on either side for a distance of more than a centimeter and are attached to the lateral surfaces of the calcaneus at its proximal end. Lateral motion is thus hindered, while longitudinal motion is permitted.

Between this tendon and the tendon of Achilles is a synovial bursa which aids the gliding movement of the tendon. In the sole of the foot opposite the distal end of the calcaneus the tendon broadens and ends in the flexor brevis digitorum (pedis perforatus) muscle, which might also be considered as a second part of the plantaris. In man the plantaris is inserted into the calcaneus along with the gastrocnemius.

Relations.—The muscle is covered throughout by the two heads of the gastrocnemius (Fig. 90, *m*; Fig. 91, *k*), except at the proximal end (Fig. 90, *l*), where it is in contact with the integument. Inner surface in relation with the popliteus (Fig. 92, *k*), the soleus (Fig. 90, *o*), the flexor longus digitorum (Fig. 91, *n*), and flexor longus hallucis (Fig. 91, *m*).

M. soleus (Fig. 90, *o*).—A flat fusiform muscle lying beneath the plantaris.

Origin by muscle-fibres from the lateral surface of the head of the fibula, and by tendon-fibres from the proximal two-fifths of its ventral border.

Insertion.—The muscle ends in a slender tendon which joins the lateral border of the gastrocnemius tendon to form the tendon of Achilles (Fig. 90, *t*), which forms the sheath of the plantaris tendon.

Relations.—Outer surface with the gastrocnemius (Fig. 90, *m*) and plantaris (Fig. 90, *l*). Inner surface with the peroneus longus (Fig. 90, *q*), peroneus tertius (Fig. 90, *r*), and flexor hallucis (Fig. 91, *m*).

Action.—Assists the gastrocnemius to extend the foot.

M. triceps suræ.—The gastrocnemius and the soleus are sometimes considered as forming a single muscle, with three heads, under the name triceps suræ.

M. popliteus (Fig. 92, *k*).—A triangular muscle passing from the femur obliquely toward the medial side over the ventral surface of the proximal end of the tibia.

Origin by a strong tendon from the popliteal groove on the surface of the lateral epicondyle of the femur. In the tendon is a sesamoid bone, the popliteal bone (Fig. 61, 5, page 89), which glides over the ventral part of the lateral articular facet on the proximal end of the tibia. As the muscle passes over the joint it is closely attached to the joint capsule. From the popliteal bone, which with the tendon lies within the capsule of the knee-joint, the muscle-fibres diverge to their

Insertion into the proximal end of the ventral surface of the tibial shaft on the medial side of the medial oblique ridge. The area of insertion extends slightly onto the medial surface of the bone.

Relations.—Outer surface with the gastrocnemius (Fig. 92, *j*) and plantaris (Fig. 91, *l*), and with the tendon of the semitendinosus (Fig. 92, *i*). Distal border with the origins of the soleus and flexor longus digitorum. Inner surface with the capsule of the knee-joint and the tibia.

Action.—Rotates the thigh so as to turn the toes inward.

The three following deep muscles on the ventral surface of the shank are covered by a deep fascia (the deep crural fascia)

which separates them from the overlying muscles. This fascia stretches from the dorsal border of the tibia about the ventral side of the shank to the medial border of the tibia. It sends a slip beneath the border of the fibula.

M. flexor longus digitorum (Fig. 91, *m* and *n*).—Owing to the reduction of the first digit in the cat the tendon of the flexor longus hallucis (*m*) has become united to that of the flexor longus digitorum (*n*), so that the two might be considered separate heads of a single muscle. The head corresponding to the flexor longus hallucis (*m*) is much larger than that corresponding to the flexor longus digitorum (*n*). The two heads will be described separately.

(1) **M. flexor longus hallucis** (Fig. 91, *m*).—This lies against the ventral surface of the tibia and fibula beneath the popliteus (Fig. 92, *k*) and soleus (Fig. 90, *o*).

Origin by fleshy fibres, (1) from the sheet of deep crural fascia which dips between it and the tibialis posterior (Fig. 91, *o*) and the flexor longus digitorum (*n*). (2) From the ventral surface of the tibia distad of the lateral oblique line to within one to three centimeters of the distal end of the shaft. (3) From the medial surface of the shaft and head of the fibula and from the whole interosseous ligament. On the fibular side the origin may extend onto the tendon of the popliteus and the fascia of the peroneus longus. The fibres form a flat fusiform mass ending one centimeter from the heel in a strong flat tendon (*m'*) which passes over the groove on the distal surface of the astragalus and over the groove on the sustentaculum tali. The two grooves are converted into a continuous canal by strong transverse ligaments, and the canal is lined by an extension of the synovial bursa of the ankle-joint. Emerging from the canal the tendon broadens and receives on its medial side the insertion of the tendon of the flexor longus digitorum (*n*). The tendon gives origin on its outer surface to the lumbricales and to the common plantar ligament. The tendon continues to broaden until it reaches the middle of the length of the metacarpals; here it divides into four tendons which pass to the terminal phalanges of the digits.

Insertion.—The relations of the four tendons and their

insertions are identical with those of the flexor profundus digitorum of the hand.

Relations.—Outer surface with the soleus (Fig. 90, *o*) and plantaris (Fig. 91, *l*). Lateral border with the soleus, the peroneus tertius (Fig. 90, *r*), and peroneus brevis (Fig. 90, *s*). Medial border with the tibialis posterior (Fig. 91, *o*) and flexor longus digitorum (Fig. 91, *n*).

Action.—Flexor of the phalanges.

(2) **M. flexor longus digitorum** (Fig. 91, *n*).

Origin by muscle- and tendon-fibres from the ventral surface of the tibia over its proximal half between the oblique ridges; by fleshy fibres from an aponeurosis between it and the tibialis posterior (Fig. 91, *o*), and by tendon from the medial surface of the head of the fibula. At the junction of the middle and distal thirds of the bone the muscle ends in a slender tendon which passes through the ventral groove on the medial surface of the tibia and, curving onto the sole of the foot, becomes attached to the medial border of the common tendon described under the last.

Relations.—Outer surface with the medial head of the gastrocnemius (Fig. 91, *k*) and with the superficial fascia. Inner surface with the tibialis posterior (Fig. 91, *o*). Medial border at the proximal end with the popliteus (Fig. 92, *k*), lateral border with the tibialis posterior (Fig. 91, *o*), and flexor longus hallucis (Fig. 91, *m*).

Action.—Flexor of the phalanges.

M. tibialis posterior (Fig. 91, *o*).—A slender flat fusiform muscle beneath the flexor longus digitorum and between it and the flexor longus hallucis.

Origin by fleshy fibres from nearly the whole medial surface of the head of the fibula, from the inner surface of the aponeurosis between it and the flexor longus digitorum (*n*), and by a few fleshy fibres from the ventral surface of the tibia between the oblique ridges. Some fibres may also arise from the outer surface of the aponeurosis covering the flexor longus hallucis (*m*). The muscle ends at about the middle of the tibia in a slender flat tendon which passes parallel to the tendon of the flexor longus digitorum (*n*) through the dorsal groove on the medial surface of the distal end of the tibia. This groove is converted into a canal by a transverse ligament. Beyond the canal the tendon turns onto the plantar surface of the foot and passes through a groove on the ventral surface of the scaphoid bone. It then divides.

Insertion into the outer tuberosity on the surface of the scaphoid, and onto the proximal end of the ventral surface of the medial cuneiform.

Relations.—Outer and medial surface with the flexor longus digitorum (*n*). Lateral surface with the flexor longus hallucis (*m*)

Action.—Extensor of the foot.

B. MUSCLES ON THE DORSAL AND LATERAL SURFACES OF THE LOWER LEG.—**M. peroneus longus** (Fig. 90, *q*).—A slender, fusiform muscle lying superficially on the lateral side of the leg, dorsad of the soleus.

Origin by tendon-fibres from the lateral surface of the head of the fibula and from the proximal half of the lateral surface of its shaft.

At the junction of the middle and distal thirds of the lower leg the muscle ends in a slender tendon which passes through the groove on the lateral surface of the lateral malleolus. This groove is converted into a canal by a transverse ligament. The tendon passes through the groove on the peroneal tubercle of the calcaneus, then turns onto the sole of the foot and passes through the peroneal groove on the cuboid bone. It then turns mediad and passes through the groove between the ventral processes of the lateral cuneiform and the metatarsal until it reaches the first metatarsal. The entire groove is converted into a canal by the overlying ligaments.

Insertion into (1) the base of the fifth metatarsal, and (2) the outer side of the base of the first metatarsal, and (3) by slender branches into the bases of the other metatarsals.

Relations.—Outer (lateral) surface with the superficial fascia and the tendon of the biceps femoris. Inner surface with the peroneus tertius (*r*) and peroneus brevis (*s*), and with the extensor longus digitorum (*p*). At the proximal end the dorsal border touches the tibialis anterior (*n*).

Action.—Flexor of the foot.

M. peroneus tertius (Fig. 90, *r*).—A slender fusiform muscle beneath the peroneus longus (*q*).

Origin by fleshy fibres from about the second quarter of the lateral surface of the fibula. The muscle ends in a slender tendon (*r′*), which passes with that of the peroneus brevis (*s*) through the groove on the ventral border of the lateral malleolus. The groove is converted into a canal by a transverse ligament. Emerging from it, the tendon turns and passes along the outer margin of the foot. In passing the sesamoid at the base of the first phalanx of the fifth digit it is united to it by a band which passes from the sesamoid to the tendon.

The *insertion* is finally into the lateral border of the extensor tendon of the fifth digit as it passes from the first to the second phalanx.

Relations.—Outer surface with the peroneus longus (*q*), the soleus (*o*), and the superficial fascia. Ventral border with the soleus (*o*) and flexor longus hallucis (Fig. 91, *m*). Inner surface with the peroneus brevis (Fig. 90, *s*).

Action.—Extensor and abductor of the fifth digit and flexor of the foot.

M. peroneus brevis (Fig. 90, *s*) lies beneath the other peronei.

Origin by fleshy fibres from the distal half of the surface of the fibula, which it embraces. At the lateral malleolus the muscle ends in a thick tendon which passes through the canal on the ventral surface of the malleolus. In the canal it is enlarged and surrounded by a synovial bursa. It then turns onto the foot and passes over the dorsal surface of the calcaneus on its lateral side and has its

Insertion into the tubercle on the lateral side of the base of the fifth metatarsal.

Relations.—Outer surface with the peronei longus (*q*) and tertius (*r*). Inner surface with the bone.

Action.—Extensor of the foot.

M. extensor digitorum longus (Fig. 90, *p*).—A fusiform muscle which lies beneath the tibialis anterior (*n*), against the interosseous membrane, and between the tibialis anterior and the peronei.

Origin by a thin flat tendon from the lateral surface of the lateral epicondyle of the femur just dorsad of the origin of the popliteus. The tendon becomes narrower and thicker and passes through the capsule of the knee-joint and over a slight groove on the tibia just dorsad of the head of the fibula. The belly of the muscle extends the entire length of the tibia, passing beneath the transverse ligament (5) along with the tendon of the tibialis anterior (*n*). At the ankle it runs through a fibrous loop which is attached to the dorsal surface of the calcaneus (the annular ligament of the calcaneus); it then turns and passes onto the dorsum of the foot. The muscle ends in four slender tendons, the two middle of which begin at the transverse ligament, while the others begin at the fibrous loop. The tendons diverge to the four digits. Each tendon is connected with the fibrous sheath surrounding the base of the first phalanx, and each has a synovial bursa beneath it at this point. Near the distal end of the first phalanx the tendon is united on the lateral side to the conjoined tendon of the extensor brevis digitorum and an interosseus muscle, and on the medial side to the tendon of the interosseus. The lateral side of the most lateral tendon is not thus united, but is joined on the outer side by the tendon of the peroneus tertius.

Insertion.—The tendon thus formed on the dorsum of each phalanx by the junction of the two or three tendons above mentioned is firmly attached to the base of the second phalanx at its proximal end in the middle of its dorsal surface. In crossing the joint between the first and second phalanges the tendon forms a fibrous pad which protects the dorsum of the joint and glides over it. It then continues to be inserted into the base of the terminal phalanx.

Relations.—Outer surface with the tibialis anterior (*n*) and the superficial fascia. Inner surface with a part of the tibialis anterior, with the bones, the interosseous membrane, and the peroneus brevis (*s*).

Action.—Extensor of the phalanges.

M. tibialis anterior (Fig. 90, *n*).—This is the superficial muscle covering the lateral side of the tibia.

Origin by fleshy fibres from the proximal one-sixth of the lateral surface of the shaft of the tibia, from the proximal third of the medial border of the shaft and head of the fibula, and from the intervening interosseous ligament. The triangular body of the muscle covers the lateral surface of the tibia and the outer surface of the extensor longus digitorum (*p*). Near the malleolus it ends in a strong tendon which passes beneath the transverse ligament along with the tendon of the extensor longus (*p*). The tendon crosses the dorsal surface of the foot obliquely toward its medial side.

Insertion into the outer surface of the first metatarsal.

Relations.—Outer surface with the superficial fascia and the tendon of the biceps femoris. Inner surface with the extensor longus (*p*), the tibia, and the interosseous membrane.

Action.—Flexor of the foot.

4. Muscles of the Foot.

A. MUSCLES ON THE DORSUM OF THE FOOT.—**M. extensor brevis digitorum** (Fig. 90, *u*).—A broad thin muscle covering the tarsus and part of the metatarsus on the lateral side of the dorsum of the foot. It may be divided into three slips.

Origin from the distal border of nearly the whole calcaneal annular ligament (5), and from the proximal end of the dorsal surface of the three lateral metatarsals. At the middle of the metatarsals the muscle ends in three flat tendons which pass into the three interspaces between the four tendons of the extensor longus. Each tendon is divided into two branches.

Insertion.—The lateral branch of each tendon is inserted into the cartilaginous plate which lies in the metatarsophalangeal articulation of the digit on the outer side. The medial branch joins the lateral side of the extensor longus tendon on the dorsum of the first phalanx.

Action.—Extensor of the digits.

B. MUSCLES OF THE SOLE OF THE FOOT.—**M. flexor brevis digitorum (pedis perforatus).**—This is the direct continuation of the tendon of the plantaris. It lies immediately beneath the superficial plantar fascia. The flat belly of the muscle has its medial border attached by an oblique tendinous band to the medial surface of the scaphoid and the medial cuneiform. It divides into four slips which diverge to the four toes, each ending in a flat tendon. The slips decrease in size from the lateral to the medial side. The three lateral ones overlap one another proximally.

Insertion.—Each tendon expands at the distal end of the metatarsal and is wrapped about the tendon of the deep flexor which perforates it. The two halves unite beneath the perforating tendon and pass together with the perforating tendon through fibrous rings, the annular ligaments. One of these is attached to the sesamoids at the base of the phalanx. The other is attached to the head of the first phalanx. The tendons are finally inserted into the bases of the second phalanges.

The two annular ligaments are connected by fascia so as to form a continuous canal for the tendons. This canal is lined by a synovial membrane. Covering this canal is a more superficial layer of fascia. Before passing into the proximal annular ligament the two middle tendons unite each with the tendon of the corresponding lumbrical muscle. Each also gives off a branch, the lateral one on its lateral side and the medial one on its medial side. These branches, like those of the two middle ones, are inserted into the common phalangeal fascia.

Action.—Flexor of the second phalanges of the digits.

M. quadratus plantæ (called also the plantar head of the flexor longus digitorum) is a thin flat muscle which takes *origin* from the dorsal part of the lateral surface of the calcaneus and the cuboid. Its fibres converge to a flat tendon which passes transversely across the flexor longus digitorum and beneath the flexor brevis digitorum and calcaneometatarsal.

Insertion.—Into the medial part of the outer surface of the tendon of the flexor longus digitorum.

Action.—It holds the flexor longus tendon in place.

Mm. lumbricales.—These are six.

Origin.—The three larger ones have origin from the outer surface of the expanded portion of the flexor longus digitorum on its distal half. Each ends in a slender tendon.

Insertions.—The tendons unite with the divisions of the

tendon of the flexor brevis which pass to the three lateral digits, at their entrance to the first annular ligament. The one to the fifth digit is sometimes absent.

The other three have *origin* from the tendon of the flexor longus digitorum at the point where it divides. Each occupies one of the three intervals between the four divisions, and its fibres originate from the proximal ends of the two tendons which bound its interval.

Insertion by a very slender tendon into the medial side of the first phalanges of the third, fourth, and fifth digits near their bases.

Action.—Move the third, fourth, and fifth digits toward the medial side.

Mm. interossei.—The interosseus of the second digit forms five portions, which cover the ventral surface of the digit.

Origin.—(1) By two tendons from the ventral process of the lateral cuneiform. The muscle divides into four parts, three of which pass to the medial side of the digit and act as abductors. They are called the long, short, and middle abductors (abductor longus, brevis, and intermedius digiti secundi).

Insertions.—The short head into the medial sesamoid of the metatarsophalangeal joint, the middle into the medial side of the base of the first phalanx, and the long into the extensor communis tendon near the distal end of the first phalanx. The names long, short, and middle refer to the lengths of the tendons as determined by their points of insertion.

The *fourth* portion which comes from the lateral cuneiform has its *insertion* into the lateral side of the extensor tendon near the distal end of the first phalanx. It is therefore an adductor longus digiti secundi. In some cases there is an adductor brevis from this same head.

(2) The fifth part of the interosseus of the second digit has *origin* from the middle of the ligament covering the peroneal canal, along with the middle adductor of the fifth digit. The two muscles diverge. *Insertion* into the outer side of the base of the first phalanx of the second digit. It is an adductor medius digiti secundi.

The interossei of the third and fourth digits are alike.

Origin from the ventral surface of the base of the metatarsal. The muscles cover the ventral surface of the shaft. At the head each divides and passes onto the sides of the metatarsal.

Insertion.—Each half of the muscle shows a tendency to divide into two parts. One of these, the more superficial and ventral, ends in a tendon which joins the extensor tendon near the distal end of the first phalanx. The other part is inserted by short tendon- and muscle-fibres into the side of the base of the first phalanx; one of the parts is therefore a middle, and the other a long, adductor or abductor, the adductores and abductores digiti tertii and quarti.

The fifth digit has five short muscles.

M. abductor medius digiti quinti.

Origin from the ventral surface of the calcaneus and from the fifth metatarsal.

Insertion by a slender tendon into the lateral side of the base of the first phalanx of the fifth digit.

M. adductor medius digiti quinti.

Origin with the adductor medius digiti secundi.

Insertion on the inner side of the base of the phalanx of the fifth digit.

M. opponens digiti quinti.

Origin by a flat tendon from the middle of the ligament which covers the peroneal canal. It passes obliquely outward parallel to the last.

Insertion on the inner side of the shaft of the fifth metatarsal.

The two remaining muscles of the fifth digit take *origin* from the outer part of the ligament covering the peroneal canal. They cover the ventral surface of the shaft.

Insertion.—The lateral one is inserted into the lateral sesamoid and is therefore an abductor brevis. The medial one is inserted into the extensor tendon and is therefore an adductor longus.

C. Muscles of the Tarsus.—**M. calcaneometatarsalis** (part of M. adductor minimi digiti ?).—A weak muscle made up largely of tendon-fibres, some of which pass directly from origin to insertion. It may be regarded as a ligament.

Origin, the lateral and ventral surface of the calcaneus near the proximal end. It passes distad and slightly laterad outside of the quadratus plantæ.

Insertion, the lateral side of the base of the fifth metatarsal, and the adjacent surfaces of the cuboid and calcaneus.

Action.—Probably causes slight motion of the cuboid on the head of the calcaneus.

M. scaphocuneiformis.—A small muscle lying on the sole of the foot in the depression between the lateral cuneiform, medial cuneiform, and the lateral tubercle of the scaphoid. It is hidden by the overlying ligaments.

Origin, the lateral tubercle of the scaphoid bone. It passes distad and laterad.

Insertion, the lateral surface of the medial cuneiform.

Action.—Rotates the medial cuneiform on the scaphoid and would thus act as an opponens of the great toe if the great toe were present.

THE VISCERA.

I. THE BODY CAVITY.

The greater part of the viscera are situated in the body cavity or cœlom. This is divided by the diaphragm into two parts, the **thoracic** and the **abdominal cavities.** Each is lined by a serous membrane, in which the part covering the outer wall of the cavity is distinguished as the **parietal layer** from the part covering the viscera, the **visceral layer.**

The thoracic cavity is bounded by the thoracic vertebræ the ribs, the sternum, and the diaphragm. The cranial opening of the cavity is filled by the trachea and œsophagus as they enter from the neck region. The cavity is lined by two layers of thin tissue, the outer one of which is the **fascia endothoracica** (Fig. 92a, *5*), while the inner is the **pleura** (Fig. 92a, *F*). The fascia endothoracica is a sheet of connective tissue which lines the entire inner surface of the thoracic cavity, descending from the dorsal median line to the heart, and passing into the fibrous layer of the pericardium. The pleura is a thin membrane covering the fascia endothoracica and corresponding to the peritoneum of the abdominal cavity. It forms two sacs, the **pleuræ,** lining the right and left halves of the thoracic cavity respectively. Each of these sacs is closed, the viscera being suspended within them by folds of the membrane, so that the cavity is everywhere separated from the viscera by a sheet of the pleura. That portion of the pleura which lines the thoracic wall is known as the parietal layer (Fig. 92a, *F*); it may be divided into that covering the ribs (**costal** pleura), and that covering the diaphragm. That portion which covers the viscera is the visceral layer, or, since it covers chiefly the lungs, it may be distinguished as the **pulmonary** pleura (Fig. 92a, *D*). The medial walls of the two pleural sacs come in contact in the median plane, forming a median vertical partition passing lengthwise of the thoracic cavity, the **mediastinal septum** (Fig. 92a, *G*). The space between the two layers which make up the mediastinal septum is known as the **mediastinum,** or the **mediastinal cavity** (Fig. 92a, *H*, *H'*); it contains numerous organs of the thorax. Three parts are usually distinguished in this cavity: a **ventral** mediastinal cavity, containing chiefly blood vessels and the thymus gland; a **middle** cavity (Fig. 92a, *H*) which includes the heart, the anterior and posterior venæ cavæ, the vagus and phrenic nerves, the bifurcation of the trachea, bronchi, and pulmonary arteries and veins; and a **dorsal** mediastinum (Fig. 92a, *H'*) which contains the trachea, œsophagus, aorta, azygos vein, thoracic duct and splanchnic nerves.

The abdominal cavity extends caudad from the diaphragm to the region enclosed by the innominate bones and the sacrum. It has been described in two parts; the **abdominal cavity proper,** craniad of the edge of the pubis, and the **pelvic** cavity, caudad of that edge. Both parts are lined by the peritoneum. Lack of sharp limits between these parts and continuity of their common lining of peritoneum leads us to describe the abdominal cavity as undivided.

The **peritoneum,** a thin transparent sheet of connective tissue supporting on its surface a layer of flattened epithelial cells, forms a sac which lines the entire abdominal cavity. This sac is closed in the male; in the female it communicates with the exterior through the uterine tubes and the uteri. All the organs of the abdominal cavity are outside the sac. In the course of their development these organs have encroached on the peritoneal sac. Each has grown against the outer wall of the sac and has forced a part of this wall ahead of it into the cavity. In some cases the encroachment has gone so far that the organ in question lies apparently within the peritoneal cavity, suspended from the wall of the sac by a fold of that wall. The wall may thus be divided into three portions. One of these, the **parietal** layer (Fig. 92b, *C*), lines the wall of the body cavity. The second (the **mesentery** in case of the alimentary canal, or a **ligament** in the case of another organ) suspends the

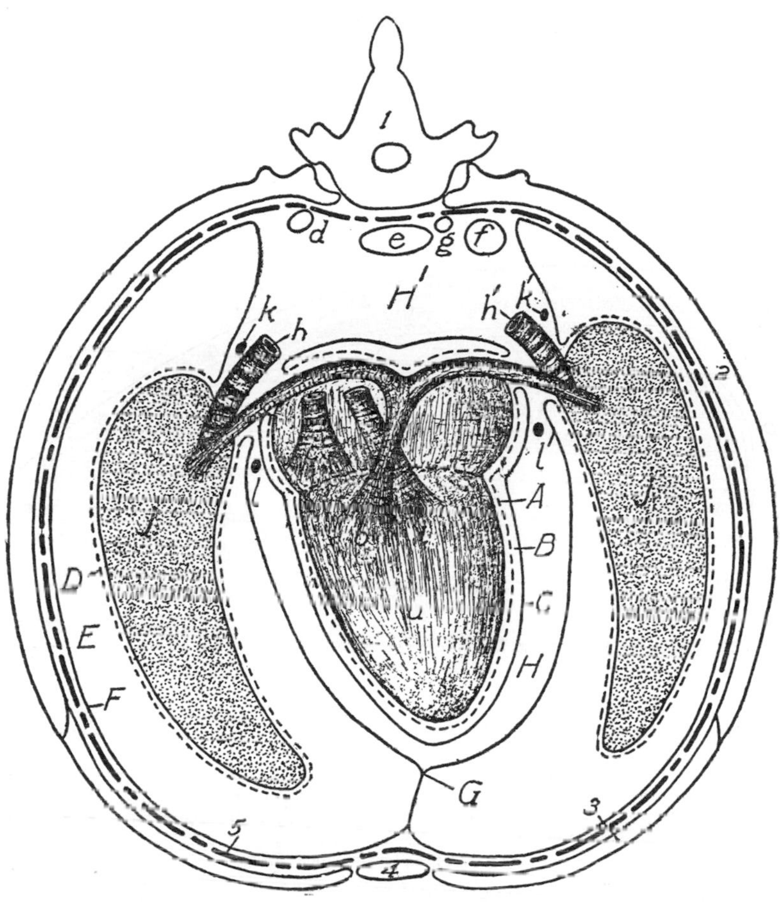

FIG. 92a.—DIAGRAM OF A CROSS SECTION THROUGH THE THORAX AT THE LEVEL OF THE ROOT OF THE LUNGS TO SHOW THE RELATIONS OF THE VISCERA TO THE PLEURAL AND PERICARDIAL CAVITIES.

1, thoracic vertebra; *2*, rib; *3*, costal cartilage; *4*, sternum; *5*, fascia endothoracica; *a*, heart; *b*, pulmonary artery; *c*, superior vena cava; *d*, azygos vein; *e*, œsophagus; *f*, dorsal aorta; *g*, thoracic duct; *h*, *h'*, right and left bronchi; *i*, aorta; *j*, lung; *k*, *k'*, vagus nerves; *l*, *l'*, phrenic nerves; *A*, visceral pericardium; *B*, pericardial cavity; *C*, parietal pericardium; *D*, visceral pleura; *E*, pleural cavity; *F*, parietal pleura; *G*, mediastinal septum; *H*, *H'*, middle and dorsal mediastinum.

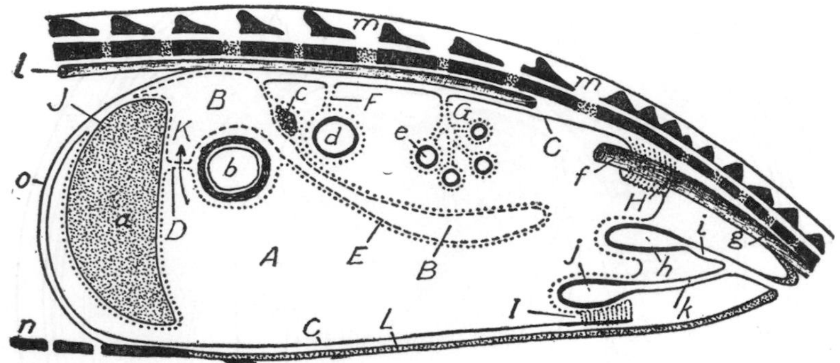

FIG. 92b.—DIAGRAM OF MIDSAGITTAL SECTION THROUGH THE ABDOMINAL CAVITY TO SHOW THE PLAN OF REFLECTION OF THE PERITONEUM.

The whole lining of the lesser peritoneal cavity is shown by a broken line. The visceral layer of the greater peritoneal cavity and of mesenteries and omenta is shown by a dotted line, the parietal layer by a solid line. *a*, liver; *b*, stomach; *c*, pancreas; *d*, transverse colon; *e*, small intestine; *f*, rectum; *g*, anal canal; *h*, uterus; *i*, vagina; *j*, urinary bladder; *k*, urethra; *l*, aorta; *m*, vertebral column; *n*, sternum; *o*, diaphragm; *A*, greater peritoneal cavity; *B*, lesser peritoneal cavity; *C*, parietal peritoneum; *D*, lesser omentum; *E*, greater omentum; *F*, transverse mesocolon; *G*, mesentery; *H*, mesorectum; *I*, suspensory ligament of bladder; *J*, bare area of bladder; *K*, foramen of Winslow, position shown by arrow; *L*, ventral body wall.

organ from the body wall. Between the layers of each mesentery or ligament blood vessels pass to the organs. The third portion or **visceral** layer covers the organ in question, forming its **serous** covering.

The reflection of the peritoneum to form the mesenteries and ligaments may be thus described:

Caudally the peritoneum covers the whole surface of the bladder and is reflected from its ventral wall to the linea alba as the **suspensory ligament** (Fig. 92b, *I*) of the bladder. Farther craniad the peritoneum suspends the rectum and the colon from the middorsal line, forming the **mesorectum** (Fig. 92b, *H*) and **mesocolon** (Fig. 92b, *F*). The mesocolon continues craniad to the level of the caudal end of the right kidney and is broadest at its cranial end. At this end the mesocolon passes into the **mesentery** proper (Fig. 92b, *G*), which suspends the small intestine. Its dorsal border is attached to the median line opposite the caudal end of the kidneys and is very short compared to its very long ventral or intestinal border. Toward the cranial end the mesentery of the jejunum passes gradually into the very much shorter duodenal mesentery. This is drawn out at the caudal end of the duodenum into a fold, the **duodenorenal** ligament which attaches the duodenum to the kidney.

The **mesogastrium** or peritoneal fold for the stomach passes from that part of the medial dorsal line lying between the kidneys and the diaphragm, to the greater curvature of the stomach. It does not pass directly to the stomach, but passes first ventrad of the small intestine as far as the pelvis. Thence it turns craniad to reach the greater curvature of the stomach, forming a fold, the **greater omentum** (Fig. 92b, *E*). It forms the dorsal and ventral walls of a sac, the **omental sac,** which encloses the **lesser peritoneal cavity** (Fig. 92b, *B*). The descending limb of the fold forms the dorsal wall of the sac, and its ascending limb forms the ventral wall. Each of these walls is double like a mesentery, so that the greater omentum consists of four sheets. Between the two sheets forming the descending limb lies the left half of the pancreas (Fig. 92b, *c*), which passes thence to the right into the duodenal mesentery. A transverse fold passes from the descending limb of the omentum along the cranial border of the pancreas to the duodenal mesentery. Farther to the right the descending limb of the omentum, which is here shorter, encloses the spleen and holds it in position parallel to the greater curvature of the stomach and about one centimeter from it. This part of the greater omentum is called the **gastrosplenic** or **gastrolienal** omentum.

The greater omental sac communicates with the peritoneal sac by an opening, the **foramen epiploicum** or **foramen of Winslow** (Fig. 92b, *K*). This opening lies caudad and dextrad of the caudate lobe of the liver. Along the ventral border of the foramen pass the common bile-duct from the liver and the portal vein to the liver.

The size of the great omental sac is increased by the **lesser omentum** (Fig. 92b, *D*). This is a double sheet of peritoneum which stretches horizontally from the liver to the duodenum and the lesser curvature of the stomach. It covers ventrad the caudate lobe of the liver. Its right border is at the foramen epiploicum. The part of it which stretches to the duodenum is called the **duodenohepatic** ligament and contains the bile-duct, the portal vein and the hepatic artery. The part that stretches to the stomach is called the **gastrohepatic** ligament. The peritoneum covers the caudal and cranial surfaces of the liver and is reflected to the adjacent parts to form the ligaments of the liver.

The **suspensory** ligament of the liver passes from the caudal surface of the diaphragm and the median ventral line for about one or two centimeters caudad of the diaphragm, to the liver, and extends between its two halves. The **ligamentum teres** or **round ligament** is the thickened free caudal border of the suspensory ligament. It is the remains of the fœtal umbilical vein. From the dorsal border of the liver the peritoneum which covers its cranial surface turns ventrad onto the caudal surface of the diaphragm, while that which covers its caudal surface turns dorsad onto the caudal surface of the diaphragm to reach the dorsal body wall. Between these two sheets a small linear part of the surface of the liver is closely applied to the diaphragm without intervening peritoneum (Fig. 92b, *J*). The two sheets which bound this area constitute the **coronary** ligament of the liver. This ligament is broader where it passes from the left lateral lobe to the diaphragm and is called the **triangular** ligament. (There is perhaps a corresponding right triangular ligament, from the cranial division of the right lateral lobe.) The caudal division of the right lateral lobe is held to the kidney of that side by the **hepatorenal** ligament.

II. THE ALIMENTARY CANAL. APPARATUS DIGESTORIUS.

The alimentary canal may be divided into mouth, pharynx, œsophagus, stomach, small intestine, and large intestine. With these are associated certain accessory structures,—the salivary glands, the liver, and the pancreas. The spleen, though not belonging to the digestive system, is usually described in connection with it. The respiratory organs are almost throughout in close relation with the organs of the digestive system.

1. **The Mouth. Cavum oris.**—The mouth cavity extends from the lips to the pharynx. It is narrower toward the lips, broadens caudad as far back as the last teeth, then becomes narrowed to form the **isthmus faucium,** by which it communicates with the pharynx. The mouth cavity is divisible into the **vestibule** of the mouth (**vestibulum oris**), which comprises that part outside the jaws proper, bounded externally by the lips and cheeks, and the **mouth cavity proper** (**cavum oris proprium**), which lies within the teeth. That portion of the vestibule which is bounded by the cheeks is sometimes farther distinguished as the **buccal cavity.** The entire mouth cavity (except the teeth) is lined by the mucous membrane or **mucosa.**

The **lips** (**labia oris**) are thick folds of skin bounding the entrance to the mouth cavity. The outer surface is covered with hair; the inner surface is covered with the mucous membrane. The upper lip is marked in the median line by a deep external groove which extends upward to the septum of the nose. Along the inner surface of this groove the lip is closely united to the jaw by a thick fold, the **frenulum** of the upper lip. For some distance on each side of the frenulum the inner surface of the lip bears numerous large papillæ. The **lower** lip is also united to the jaw by a frenulum in the median line; it is again united to the jaw just caudad of the canine tooth, in the space between the latter and the first premolar. Caudad the two lips pass into each other (forming the **commissura labiorum**), and unite with the cheek. The muscles of the lips have been described (page 105).

The **cheeks** (**buccæ**) in the cat are comparatively thin and small, extending from the lips caudad to the ramus of the mandible. The outer surface is covered with hair; the inner surface is smooth and somewhat folded. The buccal cavity is rather small. On the inner surface of the cheek open the duct of the parotid (Steno's duct), the ducts of the molar gland, and that of the infraorbital gland.

The roof of the mouth cavity is formed by the hard and soft palates. The hard palate (**palatum durum**) forms the cranial part of the roof; it is supported by the palatal plates of the maxillary and palatine bones. The mucosa of the hard palate is elevated to form seven or eight curved transverse ridges, which are concave caudad. Between the ridges are rows of papillæ. In front of the most cranial ridge is a papilla in the middle line, and at each side of the papilla is the opening of a small duct (the **incisive duct** or **Stenson's duct**), which leads dorsad through the incisive foramen to the **vomeronasal** organ (or **organ of Jacobson**), which lies on the floor of the nasal cavity. Caudad of the hard palate the roof of the mouth is formed by the soft palate or **velum palatinum,** described below.

The floor of the mouth cavity is formed chiefly by the tongue, which extends as far caudad as the isthmus faucium. Ventrad of the free edge of the tongue the mucosa forms a prominent median vertical fold which unites the tongue with the floor of the mouth beneath it; this fold is the frenulum linguæ. On each side of the median line at the cranial border of the floor of the mouth is a prominent papilla, at the apex of which open the ducts of the submaxillary and sublingual glands, the former on the lateral side of the apex, the latter on the medial side.

The sides of the mouth cavity are formed by the teeth and the gums, covering the alveolar borders of the mandible, maxillaries, and premaxillaries.

The mouth cavity presents further for examination the **glands,** the **teeth,** the **tongue,** and the **soft palate.**

THE GLANDS OF THE MOUTH (GLANDULÆ ORIS).—There are five pairs of salivary glands which open into the mouth cavity.

1. The **parotid gland** (**glandula parotis**) (Fig. 65, 1; Fig. 131, 10) is flattened, rather finely lobulated, and lies ventrad of the external auditory meatus and beneath the dermal muscles. Its cranial border follows the caudal border of the masseter muscle and overlies it somewhat; its caudal border is about three centimeters caudad of the border of the masseter. Its borders are unevenly lobed. The parotid duct (**ductus parotideus:** frequently called **Stenon's** or **Steno's** duct) is formed by the union of several smaller ducts near the ventral end of the cranial border of the gland. It passes craniad imbedded in the fascia covering the masseter. At the cranial border of the masseter it turns inward and lies close against the mucous membrane of the mouth, so that from the inside of the mouth it appears as a white ridge on the mucosa. It opens on the inside of the cheek opposite the most prominent cusp of the last premolar tooth. Along the course of the parotid duct in some cases one or more small **accessory parotid glands** are found.

2. The **submaxillary gland** (**glandula submaxillaris**) (Fig. 65, 2, page 109, and Fig. 131, 11) is approximately kidney-shaped. Its surface is nearly smooth, the lobulations not being apparent externally. It lies ventrad of the parotid, at the caudal edge of the masseter muscle, just caudad of the angular process of the mandible. The posterior facial vein (Fig. 131, *b*) crosses its outer surface, and its cranioventral border is hidden by two lymphatic glands (Fig. 131, 12) lying at the sides of the anterior facial vein. The **submaxillary duct** (**ductus submaxillaris,** frequently called **Wharton's duct**) leaves the inner surface of the gland and passes beneath the digastric and mylohyoid muscles and against the outer surface of the styloglossus. From the point where the styloglossus

passes into the tongue the duct continues craniad close against the oral mucosa and parallel to the mandibula. It is accompanied by the duct of the sublingual, which lies at first dorsad of it and then mediad. It opens at the apex of the prominent papilla which lies at the side of the middle line at the cranial end of the floor of the mouth.

3. The **sublingual gland** is elongated and conical in form, with its base against the submaxillary, of which it appears to be a continuation. It stretches along the submaxillary duct for about one and one-half centimeters, lying between the masseter and digastric muscles. The **sublingual** duct leaves its ventral side, passes close to the submaxillary duct, at first dorsad and then mediad of it, and opens on the medial side of the apex of the same papilla with the submaxillary duct.

4. The **molar gland** (**glandula molaris**) (Fig. 65, 9) lies between the orbicularis oris and the mucosa of the lower lip. It stretches from the cranial border of the masseter to a point between the first premolar and the canine. It is flat, broad caudad, and ends in a point craniad. It has several ducts which pass straight through the cheek and open on the mucous surface of the mouth.

5. The **infraorbital** (or **orbital**) **gland** lies in the lateral part of the orbit on its ventral floor. It is ovoid and about one and one-half centimeters long and one-third as thick. Its ventral end rests against the mucosa of the mouth just caudad of the molar tooth. Its duct leaves the ventral end and opens into the mouth at a point about three millimeters caudad of the molar tooth.

THE TEETH. DENTES.—The adult cat has thirty teeth, fourteen in the lower jaw and sixteen in the upper jaw. There are twelve **incisors,** four **canines,** ten **premolars,** and four **molars.** The tooth formula for the cat is then

$$i\frac{3-3}{3-3},\quad c\frac{1-1}{1-1},\quad pm\frac{3-3}{2-2},\quad m\frac{1-1}{1-1}.$$

The teeth are implanted in the alveolar borders of the premaxillaries, maxillaries, and mandible. In each tooth can be distinguished the **root,** imbedded in the socket of the bone, the **crown,** which projects above the gums, and a narrow **neck** connecting the two. The root is composed of one or more separate fangs; the crown bears one or more points or cusps.

At the cranial end of each jaw are six **incisor** teeth (Figs. 93 and 94, *a*). These are imbedded in the alveolar borders of the premaxillaries and the mandible. The incisor teeth are small, with a crown bearing a sharp edge which is notched so as to form three minute cusps. The root of each has a single fang. The lateral incisors are the largest in each jaw, and those of the upper jaw are larger than those of the lower.

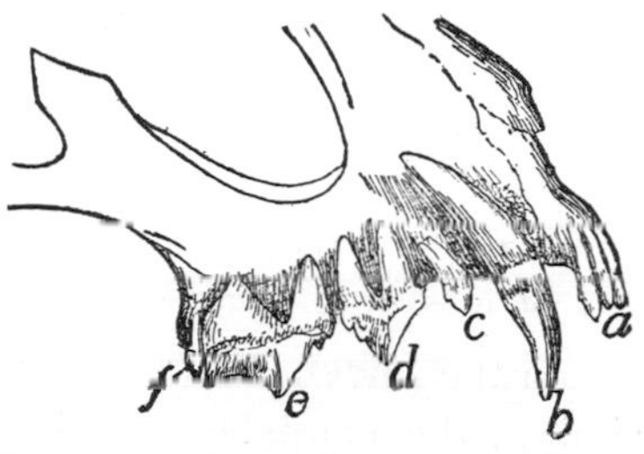

FIG. 93.—UPPER JAW, WITH ROOTS OF THE TEETH LAID BARE.

a, incisors; *b*, canine; *c*, first premolar; *d*, second premolar; *e*, third premolar; *f*, molar.

Caudad of the incisors, and in the upper jaw separated from them by a slight interval, are the **canines** (*b*), two in each jaw. These are long, strong, pointed teeth, deeply imbedded in the mandible and maxillaries, their large sockets causing a rounded swelling on the external surface of the bones. Each has a single fang and a single cusp. When the mouth is closed the upper canines lie laterocaudad of the lower ones.

Caudad of the canines there is in each jaw a considerable interval free from teeth: this is called the **diastema.** Caudad of the diastema are the **premolar** teeth, three pairs (*c*, *d*, *e*) in the upper jaw and two pairs (*c*, *d*) in the lower jaw. These teeth are compressed sideways, and those of the lower jaw fit inside of those of the upper jaw. In the **upper** jaw (Fig. 93) the first premolar (*c*) is small and usually has but a single cusp and a single fang, though occasionally there is a small supplementary cusp and fang. The second premolar is larger (*d*); it has a large central cusp, with a single smaller cranial cusp and two small caudal cusps, making four in all. This tooth has two fangs. The third premolar (*e*) is the largest tooth in the jaws; it has three large cusps in longitudinal series and a small cusp lying on the medial side of the first one in the row. Its root has three fangs. The **molar** tooth (*f*) of the upper jaw is small and lies caudomediad of the last premolar. It has two small cusps and two fangs.

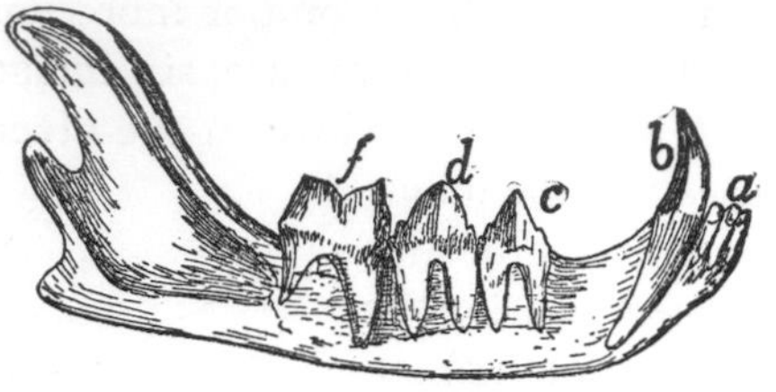

FIG. 94.—MANDIBLE, WITH ROOTS OF THE TEETH LAID BARE.
a, incisors; *b*, canine; *c*, first premolar; *d*, second premolar; *f*, molar.

In the **lower** jaw (Fig. 94) the two premolars (*c* and *d*) are similar, the caudal one being a little larger. Each has four cusps; a single large one, a small one craniad of this, and two small ones caudad of it. Each has two fangs. The single molar (*f*) is the largest tooth of the lower jaw; it has two large cusps and two fangs.

The Deciduous Teeth.—At birth the cat has no teeth. There appears later a set of twenty-six teeth: twelve incisors, four canines, and ten molars (six in the upper jaw and four in the lower). These teeth are later replaced by the permanent ones above described. The deciduous teeth of the cat are fully described by Jayne ("Mammalian Anatomy," vol. I. p. 319), where also an account is given of the order of appearance of the teeth.

THE TONGUE. LINGUA (Fig. 95).—The **tongue** is a muscular organ covered with mucous membrane; in life it is very mobile. It is an elongated organ, flat above, broadest in the middle, and very slightly narrowed at each end. It extends from the incisor teeth to the isthmus faucium and nearly fills the mouth cavity. The caudal third of the tongue forms the floor of the mouth cavity, so that the tongue has here no ventral surface, but is directly continuous with underlying organs. It is in this region that the extrinsic muscles of the tongue (except the genioglossus) enter it. The cranial two-thirds of the tongue is partly or entirely free from the floor of the mouth, the cranial one-third being completely free and movable. In about the middle third the ventral surface of the tongue is held to the floor of the mouth by the fold known as the **frenulum linguæ.** The frenulum contains parts of the two genioglossus muscles, which enter the tongue through it. The ventral surface and lateral borders of the tongue are smooth, soft, and free from papillæ. The dorsal surface is raised into papillæ of various kinds, and has a slight median longitudinal furrow. The caudal part of the dorsal surface is softer, redder, and marked with papillæ of a different kind from those of the rest of the tongue. From the caudal end a small median vertical fold, the **frenulum** (or **plica**) **glossoepiglottica** passes from the dorsal surface of the tongue to the cranial surface of the epiglottis.

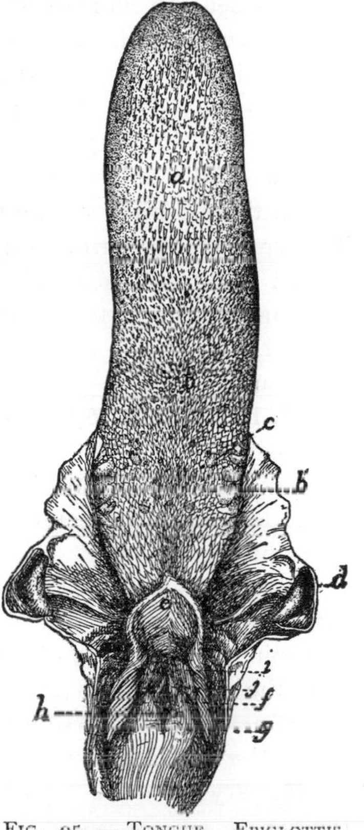

FIG. 95. — TONGUE, EPIGLOTTIS, AND OPENING OF LARYNX.

a, filiform papillæ; *b*, fungiform papillæ; *b'*, very large papillæ at the sides of the tongue; *c*, circumvallate papillæ; *d*, tonsils; *e*, epiglottis; *f*, plica aryepiglottica; *g*, arytenoid cartilages (covered with mucosa); *h*, glottis; *i*, false vocal cords; *j*, true vocal cords.

The **papillæ** of the tongue are of three kinds. 1. The very numerous **filiform papillæ** (*a*) (**papillæ filiformes**); many of them are horny and tooth-like, with points turned caudad. These are most numerous at the middle of the free end of the tongue. 2. The **fungiform papillæ** (*b*) (**papillæ fungiformes**) are found scattered over the surface of the middle of the tongue caudad of the large filiform papillæ. They are enlarged at their free ends. There is a prominent row of very large ones (*b'*) opposite the circumvallate papillæ at the borders of the tongue. 3. The **circumvallate papillæ** (*c*) (**papillæ vallatæ**) are blunt and each is surrounded by a trench which is bounded in turn by a raised wall. They are in two rows of two or three each, which converge near the base of the tongue so as to form a V with the apex directed caudad.

MUSCLES OF THE TONGUE (Fig. 96).—**M. genioglossus** (*f*) passes from the symphysis of the lower jaw into the tongue and lies beneath (dorsad of) the geniohyoid (*g*).

Origin from the medial surface of the mandible near the symphysis and dorsad of the origin of the geniohyoid.

Insertion.—The fibres pass dorsad, diverging in a fan-like manner and forming a flat vertical plate closely applied to the muscle of the opposite side. This plate extends along the caudal three-fourths of the tongue, i.e. as far as it is attached. The cranial fibres arch craniad to the tip of the tongue, the caudal fibres arch caudad to the root of the tongue. Dorsad the muscle is confounded with the muscle of the opposite side.

Action.—Draws the root of the tongue forward and the tip backward.

M. hyoglossus (*h*).—From the body of the hyoid bone to the tongue.

Origin.—(1) From the ventral surface of the body of the hyoid laterad of the geniohyoid (*g*), and (2) by a second head from the ceratohyal.

Insertion.—Both heads penetrate into the tongue between the styloglossus (*e*) and the genioglossus (*f*). The fibres intermingle with those of the styloglossus (*e*) and thus help to form the lateral parts of the tongue. They finally end in the integument on the dorsum of the tongue at the sides.

Action.—Retracts the tongue and depresses it.

M. styloglossus (*e*).—From the stylohyal bone to the tongue.

Origin from the mastoid process of the temporal bone, from the stylomandibular ligament (2) (which connects the border of the external auditory meatus with the angular process of the mandible) and from the proximal cartilaginous portion of the cranial cornu of the hyoid bone. The fibres pass mediad, diverging between those of the digastric and hyoglossus (*h*) into the lateral part of the tongue.

Insertion.—The fibres pass toward the tip of the tongue, where the mass finally ends in a point, the superficial ones gaining insertion into the integument at the sides of the tongue.

Relations.—Outer surface with the digastric (Fig. 65, *b*) and mylohyoid (Fig. 65, *c*). Inner surface with the ptery-

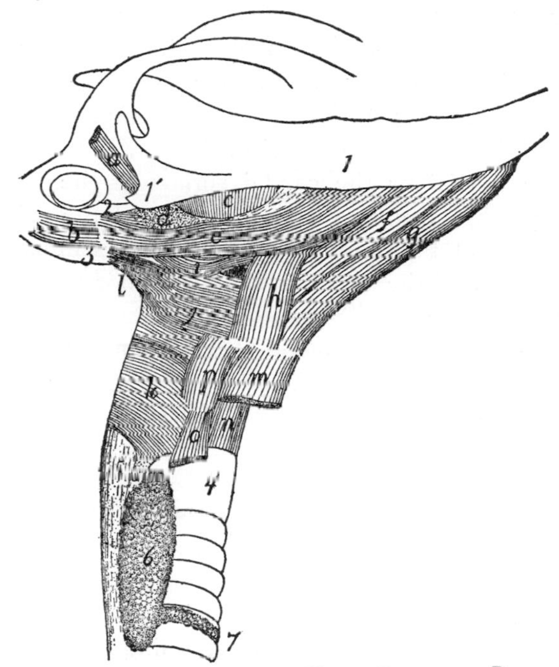

FIG. 96.—MUSCLES OF TONGUE, HYOID BONE, AND PHARYNX.

a, M. tragicus lateralis; *b*, M. jugulohyoideus; *c*, M. pterygoideus externus; *d*, partially cut surface of M. pterygoideus internus; *e*, M. styloglossus; *f*, M. genioglossus; *g*, M. geniohyoideus; *h*, M. hyoglossus; *i*, M. glossopharyngeus; *j*, M. constrictor pharyngis medius; *k*, M. constrictor pharyngis inferior; *l*, M. stylopharyngeus; *m*, M. sternohyoideus (cut); *n*, M. cricothyreoideus; *o*, M. sternothyreoideus (cut); *p*, M. thyreohyoideus. 1, mandible; 1′, angular process of mandible; 2, stylomandibular ligament; 3, bulla tympani; 4, trachea; 5, œsophagus; 6, thyroid gland; 7, isthmus of the thyroid gland.

goideus internus (Fig. 96, *d*), the cranial cornu of the hyoid, and the tympanic bulla.

Action.—Retracts the tongue and raises it.

The **intrinsic muscles** of the tongue (those entirely within it) are attached to its integument at both their ends. There are three sets of fibres: a longitudinal, a transverse, and a vertical one. These are seen most readily in cross-sections.

The SOFT PALATE. VELUM PALATINUM (Fig. 66, page

112).—The soft palate is the free curtain-like structure which forms the caudal part of the roof of the mouth. It is attached to the caudal border of the palatal plates and the ventral border of the perpendicular plates, of the palatine, and to the pterygoid processes and hamuli of the sphenoid, and extends some distance caudad of the hamuli. It thus forms a rather long and narrow curtain separating the caudal part of the nasal cavity from the mouth. Caudad it ends in a free arched border (Fig. 66, 4) which is at about the level of the epiglottis, and may lie against the cranial or the caudal surface of the latter. The narrowed passage bounded by the margin of the velum palatinum dorsad and the tongue ventrad is the **isthmus faucium.** From the sides of the velum a short distance from the caudal border a fold of mucosa passes ventrad to the side of the tongue; a short distance caudad of this a similar fold passes to the floor of the pharynx. These folds form the cranial and caudal **pillars of the fauces.** Between these folds is a shallow pocket, from the bottom of which there arises a prominent projection or swelling which is one of the two **tonsils** (Fig. 95, *d*). Each tonsil is a reddish, lobulated gland, lymphoid in the adult, nearly a centimeter in length, and about one-third as long as broad, with its long axis craniocaudad.

The velum palatinum consists of two layers of mucous membrane, oral and nasal, with intervening muscular and connective tissue. The muscles of the soft palate in the cat are as follows:

M. tensor veli palatini (Fig. 66, *d*, *d'*, page 112).

Origin from the ventral surface of the body of the sphenoid between the foramen ovale and the groove for the Eustachian tube. The muscle ends in a flat tendon which passes over the hamular process (3) of the pterygoid bone.

Insertion by spreading out in the soft palate into an aponeurosis which joins the aponeurosis of the opposite muscle and lies between the mucous membrane of the mouth and that of the nose.

Action.—Stretches the palate.

M. levator veli palatini (Fig. 66, *e*, *e'*).—A flat triangular muscle which lies within the tensor.

Origin from the surface of the body of the sphenoid mediad of the groove for the Eustachian tube, from the styliform process of the bulla tympani, and in part from the Eustachian tube. The muscle passes caudad, and its fibres then diverge into the velum palatinum.

Insertion into the velum palatinum, some of the fibres meeting in the middle line.

Action indicated by the name.

A number of other muscles have been described in the soft palate of the cat; they are, however, poorly developed and not easily distinguished. For an account of these, see Stowell, Proceedings of the Am. Soc. of Microscopists, 1889.

2. **The Pharynx.**—At the caudal end of the mouth cavity the passage for the food and that for the air cross; at the cranial end the food-passage (mouth) is ventral, the respiratory passage (nasal cavity) dorsal. Farther caudad the food-passage (œsophagus) is dorsal, while the respiratory passage (larynx and trachea) is ventral. In the region of crossing there is therefore for a certain distance a common passageway for food and air, and this is known as the **pharynx.** It extends from the isthmus faucium, at the free caudal margin of the soft palate, to the beginning of the œsophagus, at the dorsal or caudal margin of the opening of the larynx. The dorsal wall of the pharynx is separated from the base of the skull and the centra of the cervical vertebræ only by intervening muscles (**longus capitis, levator scapulæ ventralis,** and **longus colli,** Fig. 72, page 143). Its lateral and ventral walls are supported by the hyoid bone and the cartilages of the larynx.

Craniad the pharynx continues, usually, without break into the cavity lying dorsad of the soft palate. But at the time of swallowing the free edge of the soft palate is pushed dorsad against the dorsal wall of the pharynx, while the caudal part of the pharynx is drawn craniad, so as to form a cavity continuous with that of the mouth. In this way the cavity above the soft palate is completely separated at the time of swallowing from the rest of the pharynx. This separated portion is known as the **nasopharynx:** it is strictly a portion of the respiratory passage, as the food does not pass into it. The nasopharynx is continuous craniad by the **choanæ** with the nasal cavity; it forms a horizontal tube between and ventrad of the perpendicular plates of the palatine bones, and has the same craniocaudal extent as the soft palate. Its dorsal wall lies against the basis cranii and the longus capitis muscles; its lateral walls against the pterygoid muscles and the perpendicular plates of the palatine bones; its ventral wall is the soft palate. At the middle of its length, at the junction of its dorsal and lateral wall, are two longitudinal slits about three millimeters long. These are the medial openings of the **Eustachian tubes,** by which the nasopharynx communicates with the tympanic cavity.

The **pharynx proper,** situated caudad of the nasopharynx, is smaller than the latter. It is bounded craniad by the epiglottis and the margin of the soft palate, and is continuous between the two, by the isthmus faucium, with the mouth cavity. Its floor is formed by the cranial end of the larynx. At its caudal end it passes dorsally into the œsophagus, while ventrally it communicates with the larynx. Its walls are muscular.

MUSCLES OF THE PHARYNX (Fig. 96).—**M. glossopharyngeus** (*i*).

Origin.—Some fibres on the ventral and lateral part of the genioglossus (*f*) leave that muscle near its caudal end. They form a thin band of diverging fibres which pass outside of the cranial horn of the hyoid. A similar sheet of fibres leaves the midventral part of the styloglossus (*e*). The two sheets unite and the united muscle crosses the hyoid, turns dorsad, and has its

Insertion into the median dorsal raphe of the pharynx.

Action.—Constrictor of the pharynx.

M. constrictor pharyngis inferior (*k*).—A thin sheet of muscle covering the sides of the pharynx at its caudal end.

Origin from the lateral surfaces of the thyroid and the cricoid cartilages. The fibres pass dorsad and craniad, the cranial ones covering the fibres of the middle constrictor (*j*).

Insertion.—The median longitudinal raphe on the dorsum of the pharynx. The caudal fibres are transverse and continuous with the circular fibres of the œsophagus. The cranial fibres may pass as far as the base of the sphenoid.

Action.—Constrictor of the pharynx.

M. constrictor pharyngis medius (*j*).—A thin sheet which covers the middle part of the lateral surface of the pharynx.

Origin.—The ventral two pieces of the cranial horn and the whole of the caudal horn of the hyoid. The fibres diverge, passing dorsad.

Insertion into the median dorsal raphe of the pharynx. The cranial fibres are inserted into the base of the sphenoid bone. The muscle covers part of the stylopharyngeus (*l*) and the superior constrictor (Fig. 66, *f*, page 112) and is partly covered by the glossopharyngeus (Fig. 96, *i*).

Action.—Constrictor of the pharynx.

M. stylopharyngeus (*l*).

Origin from the tip of the mastoid process of the temporal bone and from the inner surface of the cartilaginous piece between the tympanohyal and the stylohyal bones. The parallel fibres form a flat band which passes ventrocaudad over the outer surface of the constrictor superior.

Insertion.—The ventral fibres pass beneath the middle constrictor (*j*) at its cranial border and, continuing toward the middle line of the pharynx, gradually lose themselves among the fibres of the superior constrictor. The dorsal fibres pass onto the outer surface of the middle constrictor and are lost among its fibres.

Action.—Constrictor of the pharynx.

M. constrictor pharyngis superior or **pterygopharyngeus** (Fig. 66, *f*, page 112).—A flat, triangular sheet beneath the constrictor medius.

Origin.—The tip of the hamular process of the pterygoid bone. The muscle passes caudad, the fibres diverging, and dips beneath the cranial border of the constrictor medius.

Insertion into the median dorsal raphe of the pharynx. The dorsal fibres are inserted into the base of the sphenoid. The ventral fibres pass lengthwise of the pharynx, closely connected with those of the stylopharyngeus (Fig. 96, *l*), and finally reach the level of the larynx.

Action.—Constrictor of the pharynx.

3. **The Œsophagus.**—The œsophagus is a straight tube, dorsoventrally flat when empty, which extends from the pharynx to the stomach. It has a uniform diameter when moderately dilated of about one centimeter. It lies dorsad of the trachea and against the longus colli muscles (Fig. 72, *g'*) covering the centra of the cervical vertebræ, until it reaches the caudal end of the thyroid gland (Fig. 96, 6); then it passes to the left and lies laterodorsad of the trachea until it reaches the bifurcation of the trachea. It there returns to the median line, passes gradually distad, separated from the vertebræ by the aorta, and finally pierces the diaphragm about two centimeters from the dorsal body wall, and enters the stomach. Its attachment to the diaphragm is loose enough to permit of longitudinal motion. In passing through the thoracic cavity it lies in the posterior mediastinum ventrad of the aorta. Its wall consists of a muscular coat, a submucosa, and a mucosa, and its inner surface presents many longitudinal folds. It has no serous covering, its side walls being merely in contact with the halves of the mediastinal septum.

4. **The Stomach. Ventriculus** (Fig. 97).—The stomach is the widest part of the alimentary canal. It is a pear-shaped sac, the long axis of which is curved nearly into a semicircle. The broad end of the sac lies to the left and dorsad; here the stomach communicates with the œsophagus (*a*). The narrowed end extends to the right and lies more ventrad than the other end; it passes here into the duodenum (*g*). That portion of the stomach which communicates with the œsophagus is known as the **cardiac** end (*b*); the opposite is the **pyloric** end. Owing to the curved form of the stomach above mentioned it is possible to distinguish a concave and a convex side. The concave side is directed craniad and dextrad; it is called the **lesser curvature** of the stomach (*c*). The longer convex border is directed caudad and to the left; it is called the **greater curvature** (*d*). The greater curvature extends to the left, next to the œsophagus, into a prominent convexity known as the **fundus** (*e*) of the stomach.

The stomach lies at the cranial end of the abdominal

cavity, mostly to the left of the middle line. Its cardiac end is in contact by its dorsal surface with the dorsal, nearly horizontal, portion of the diaphragm. On its ventral side the cardiac end does not touch the diaphragm, so that a small part of the œsophagus passes here for a short distance into the abdominal cavity, to join the stomach. The communication of œsophagus and stomach is by a simple conical increase in

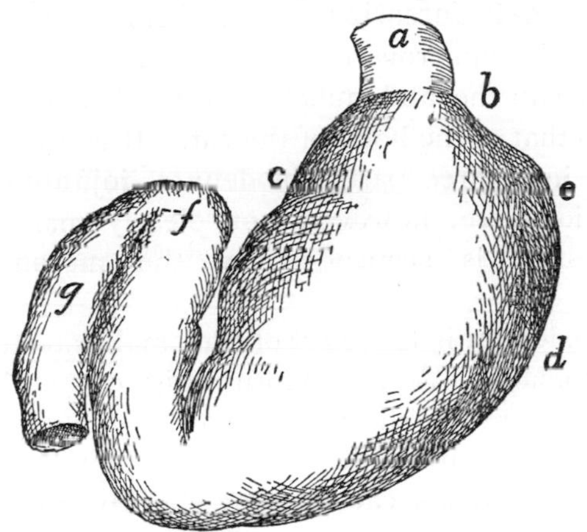

FIG. 97.—STOMACH, VENTRAL VIEW.

a, œsophagus; *b*, cardiac end of the stomach; *c*, lesser curvature; *d*, greater curvature; *e*, fundus; *f*, pyloric valve; *g*, part of duodenum.

size of the former. The pyloric end of the stomach extends to the right of the middle line, becoming constantly smaller; at its junction with the duodenum there is a constriction which marks the position of the **pyloric valve** (*f*). This valve is formed by a ring-like thickening of the circular muscle-fibres of the alimentary canal, forming a sphincter muscle at the junction of the stomach and duodenum and causing a projection of the mucosa into the lumen of the canal. The ventral surface of the stomach lies against the liver except when the stomach is much distended with food, when the ventral surface comes to lie against the ventral abdominal wall.

The stomach is supported by the **great omentum** and the **gastrohepatic** ligament. It is connected with the duodenum by the **gastroduodenal** ligament: with the spleen by the **gastrolienal** ligament.

The inner surface of the stomach presents longitudinal folds at its pyloric end and along the greater curvature as far as the fundus. The prominence of these depends on the degree of distension. Its walls are composed of an external peritoneal layer, an internal mucous layer, and an intervening muscular layer. This may be seen with the unaided eye in sections of the wall.

5. **The Small Intestine. Intestinum tenue.**—The small intestine lies in numerous coils which take up the greater part of the space in the abdominal cavity. It has a length about three times that of the body of the cat. It is usually considered as divided into three parts, **duodenum, jejunum,** and **ileum;** these divisions are, however, not clearly marked off. The small intestine is suspended by the **mesentery** already described.

The **duodenum** is that part of the small intestine which follows the stomach. At the pylorus (Fig. 97, *f*) the alimentary canal makes a rather sharp turn so that the first part of the duodenum forms an angle with the pyloric portion of the stomach, and extends caudad and slightly toward the right, soon becoming directed almost entirely caudad and lying along the right side. About eight or ten centimeters caudad of the pylorus it makes a U-shaped bend, extending thus craniosinistrad for four or five centimeters. Here it passes without definite limit into the jejunum, the duodenum being considered to end at the next turn caudad. The entire duodenum is about fourteen to sixteen centimeters in length. Between the two limbs of the U-shaped bend formed by the duodenum, the duodenal half of the pancreas is enclosed (Fig. 102, *a*).

The walls of the duodenum are composed of the serous (peritoneal) investment, a muscular coat which is made up of an outer thin, longitudinal layer of fibres and an inner thick, circular layer, a submucous coat, and inside this a mucous coat. The mucosa is thrown up into numerous delicate finger-like **villi** which give to it a velvety appearance. On the dorsal wall of the duodenum, about three centimeters distad of the pylorus, the mucosa presents a slight papilla, at the apex of which is seen the oval opening of the **ampulla of Vater.** This is an ovoid space in the wall of the duodenum. The space is encroached upon by numerous folds of the walls. The common bile-duct and the pancreatic duct open into it, the former extending from the bottom of the ampulla nearly to its mouth, and the latter extending from the bottom about half-way to the mouth. Two centimeters caudoventrad of the opening of the ampulla of Vater is the opening of the accessory pancreatic duct. It can usually be demonstrated only by passing a bristle into the duodenum through an opening in the duct.

The **jejunum** is the part of the small intestine following the duodenum. It is not separated from the part of the small intestine following it by any sharp line. In man it constitutes two-fifths of the small intestine exclusive of the duodenum, and is characterized by its emptiness after death and by the absence from it of Peyer's agminated glands (Peyer's patches).

The **ileum** is the portion of the small intestine between the jejunum and colon. It lies suspended by its mesentery in numerous folds in the caudal part of the abdominal cavity, separated from the ventral abdominal wall only by the great omentum. It is of nearly uniform diameter, but its caudal portion is thinner-walled than its cranial portion. Its walls have a microscopic structure like that of the duodenum and jejunum. On its inner surface and on the inner surface of the jejunum are seen close-set villi, but these become rather sparser toward the caudal end of the ileum and disappear about one centimeter from the opening into the colon. Among the villi of the caudal end of the ileum are numerous rounded elongations free from villi. These are the solitary follicles or solitary glands (lymphatic) of the intestine. These glands when aggregated together form the agminated glands or patches of Peyer. The ileum passes at the caudal end into the colon, the opening being guarded by the **ileocolic valve** (Fig. 99). This is formed by a marked projection of the mucosa (*f*) and transverse muscle layer (*e*) of the ileum into the colon. Its surface is free from villi.

6. **The Large Intestine. Intestinum crassum.** — The large intestine is divided into **colon** and **rectum.** The **colon** or first part of the large intestine lies against the dorsal body

wall and is separated from the ventral body wall by the folds of the ileum. It has a diameter about three times that of the ileum. The opening of the ileum into it is on its side between one and two centimeters from its cranial end (Fig. 98). The

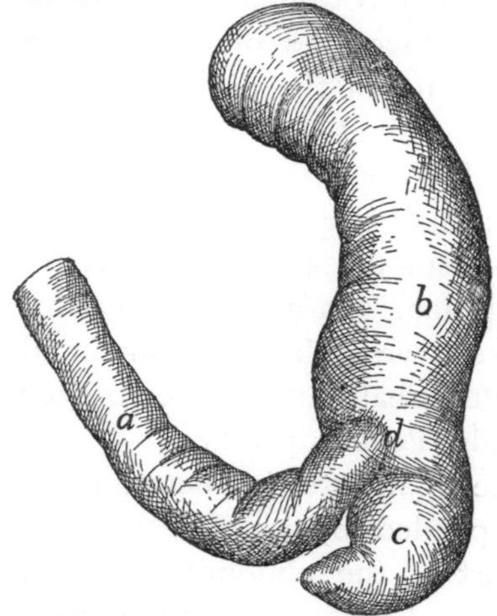

FIG. 98.—JUNCTION OF SMALL AND LARGE INTESTINE.

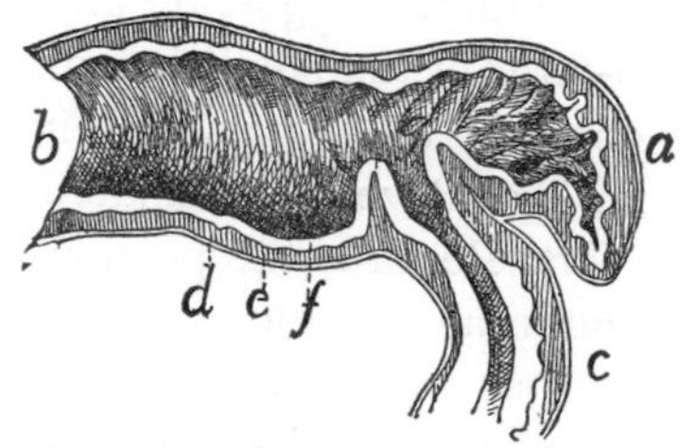

FIG. 99. — SECTION OF THE ILEO-COLIC VALVE.

Fig. 98.—*a*, ileum; *b*, ascending colon; *c*, cæcum; *d*, position of ileocolic valve.
Fig. 99.—*a*, cæcum; *b*, colon; *c*, ileum; *d*, longitudinal muscle layer; *e*, transverse muscle layer; *f*, mucosa; *g*, ileocolic valve (opened, as when material is passing into the colon).

blind pouch thus formed by the cranial end of the colon is the **cæcum** (Fig. 98, *c*; Fig. 99, *a*). The cæcum ends in a slight conical projection which may be considered as the rudiment of a vermiform appendix. The colon lies at first on the right side and passes at first craniad; then transversely to the left, then caudad, lying nearly in the middle line and next to the dorsal abdominal wall. The colon may thus be distinguished according to its direction into **ascending, transverse,** and **descending** colon. At its caudal end the colon passes without sharp limit into the rectum.

At the bottom of the cæcum on its inner surface is seen a collection of solitary glands forming one of the agminated glands of Peyer, or Peyer's patches. The mucous membrane is without villi. It presents a few considerable elevations, probably solitary glands.

The **rectum** is the terminal portion of the large intestine lying in the median line close to the dorsal body wall, from which it is suspended by the short mesorectum. Its structure is like that of the colon. It opens externally at the anus. The entire large intestine has a length about one-half that of the animal. At each side of the anus are two large secreting sacs, the **anal sacs** or **glands,** each about a centimeter in diameter. These open into the anus one or two millimeters from its caudal boundary.

Muscles of the Rectum and Anus.—Owing to the close interrelation of the muscles of the rectum and anus with those of the urogenital organs, all these muscles will be described together at the end of the description of the urogenital system.

7. **The Liver, Pancreas,** and **Spleen.**—**The Liver. Hepar.**—The liver (Figs. 100 and 101) is a large red-brown organ occupying the cranial part of the abdominal cavity. It is closely applied to the caudal surface of the diaphragm and extends thence ventrad of the stomach so as to conceal all but its pyloric end. Owing to the position of the stomach the larger mass of the liver is on the right side and it extends somewhat further caudad on this side.

The liver is divided by the dorsoventral suspensory ligament into the **right** and **left** lobes, and each half is again divided into lobes. On the left is a small **left median** (*b*) and a larger **left lateral** lobe (*a*). The left lateral (*a*) extends caudad with a thin edge which covers the greater part of the ventral surface of the stomach. On the right there is a large **right median** (or **cystic**) lobe (*c*, *c'*). Its cranial surface is dome-shaped and fitted against the right two-thirds of the caudal surface of the diaphragm. Its ventral edge is thin, its dorsal edge thick, and its caudal surface marked by a deep dorsoventral cleft in which lies the gall-bladder (Fig. 101, *f*). Dorsad and caudad of the cystic lobe is the **right lateral** lobe (*d*, *d'*), which is deeply cleft. Its elongated caudal division (*d'*) extends in a point to the caudal end of the right kidney and is adapted to the medial half of its ventral surface. Its smaller and more compact cranial division (*d*) ends ventrally in a thin edge. It lies between the caudal division (*d'*) and the cystic lobe (*c*), and

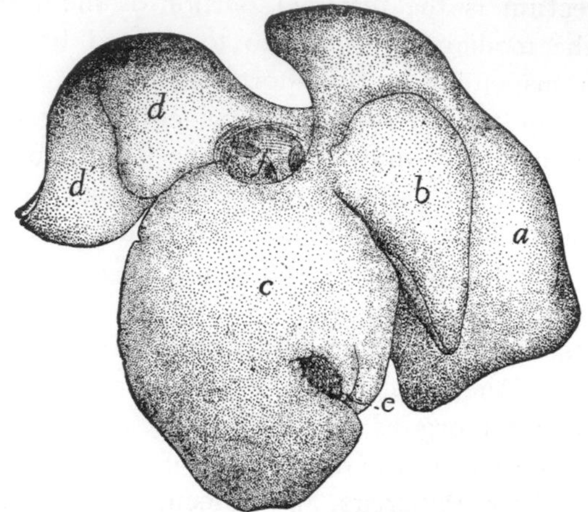

FIG. 100.—LIVER, CRANIAL SURFACE.

a, left lateral lobe; *b*, left median lobe; *c*, right median lobe; *d*, *d'*, right lateral lobe; *e*, gall-bladder; *f* opening of posterior vena cava, with the smaller openings of the hepatic veins.

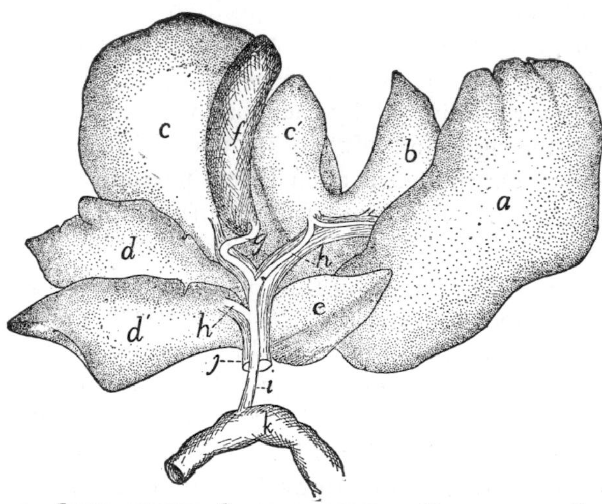

FIG. 101.—LIVER TURNED CRANIAD, SHOWING DORSOCAUDAL SURFACE.

a, left lateral lobe; *b*, left median lobe; *c*, *c'*, right median (or cystic) lobe; *d*, *d'*, cranial and caudal divisions of the right lateral lobe; *e*, caudate lobe; *f*, gall-bladder; *g*, cystic duct; *h*, hepatic ducts; *i*, common bile-duct; *j*, portal vein; *k*, part of duodenum.

its dorsal surface is adapted to the suprarenal body. The **caudate** or **Spigelian** lobe (Fig. 101, *e*) is an elongated, triangular, pyramidal lobe. It lies in the omental sac and partly closes the foramen epiploicum (foramen of Winslow). At its base it is connected with the caudal division of the right lateral lobe (*d'*).

The **Gall-bladder** (Fig. 101, *f*) is pear-shaped and lies in a cleft on the caudal (or dorsal) surface of the right median lobe (*c*, *c'*) of the liver. Its larger end is directed caudad (or ventrad) and is free. By one surface it is in contact with the liver and not covered by peritoneum, while the other surface is covered by peritoneum. The peritoneum in passing from the larger free end to the liver forms one or two ligament-like folds. By its smaller end the gall-bladder is continuous with the **cystic duct** (*g*). This duct is about three centimeters long and has a sinuous course. At its distal end it is joined by two (or more) **hepatic ducts** (*h*), bringing the bile from the lobes of the liver. The relation of these to the cystic duct varies. They may open into it by a common trunk or separately. Of these hepatic ducts one is made up by the junction of smaller hepatic ducts from the left half of the liver and the left half of the cystic lobe, while the other is similarly formed by smaller ducts from the right half of the cystic lobe, from both divisions of the right lateral lobe and from the caudate lobe. The duct formed by the junction of the hepatic and cystic ducts is the **common bile-duct (ductus communis choledochus)** (*i*). It passes in the free right border of the gastroduodenal omentum to the duodenum (*k*) and opens into it by way of the ampulla of Vater, in common with the pancreatic duct, at a point on the dorsal surface of the duodenum and about three centimeters from the pylorus.

Pancreas.—The pancreas (Fig. 102, *a*) is a flattened, closely lobulated gland of irregular outline, about twelve centimeters long, varying in width from one to two centimeters. It is bent nearly at right angles at about its middle. One of the halves (*a'*) into which it is divided by its bend lies in the descending limb of the great omentum, and is near the greater curvature of the stomach (*d*) and parallel to it. The free end of this half is in contact with the spleen (*e*). The other half (*a*) lies in the duodenal omentum between the limits of the duodenal U (*c*) and reaches to the bottom of the U. The pancreas has two ducts. The larger **pancreatic duct** (*b*) (sometimes known as the duct of Wirsung) collects the pancreatic fluid from both halves of the gland, the ductlets from each half uniting to make two larger ducts, which then unite near the angle of the gland to make the pancreatic duct. This is short and broad and opens into the ampulla of Vater together with the common bile-duct. The **accessory pancreatic duct**

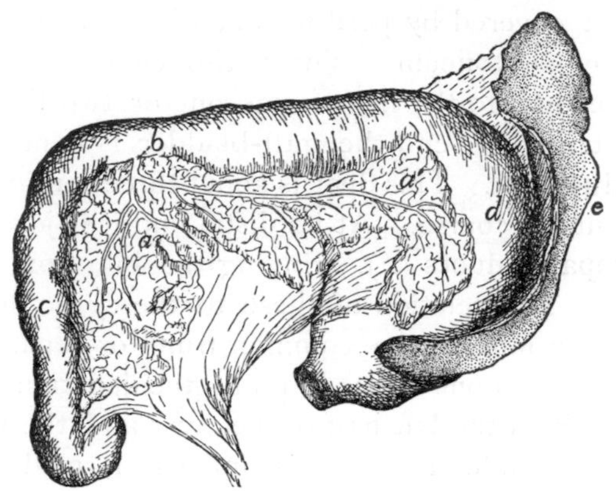

FIG. 102.—PANCREAS AND SPLEEN.

The œsophagus has been cut and the stomach turned caudad, so that the dorsal surface of the stomach and the ventral surface of the duodenum are seen. *a*, pancreas (*a*, duodenal portion; *a'*, gastric portion); *b*, pancreatic duct; *c*, duodenum; *d*, stomach; *e*, spleen.

(duct of Santorini) opens into the duodenum about two centimeters caudoventrad of the ampulla of Vater. It is formed by the union of branches which anastomose with those of the pancreatic duct. It is apparently sometimes lacking.

Spleen. Lien.—The spleen (Fig. 102, *e*) is a deep red, flattened, elongated gland belonging to the lymphatic system. One of its ends, the left, lies against the free end of the gastric half of the pancreas and is broader than the other end. The spleen is curved and is suspended in the descending limb of the great omentum so that it follows the greater curvature of the stomach (*d*).

III. RESPIRATORY ORGANS. APPARATUS RESPIRATORIUS.

The **organs of respiration** consist of the **nasal cavity,** the **nasopharynx,** the **pharynx** (also a food-passage), the **larynx** (also the organ of the voice), the **trachea,** the **bronchi,** and the **lungs.** With them are usually described also the **thyroid** and **thymus glands.**

1. **The Nasal Cavity. Cavum nasi.**—The osseous framework of the nasal cavity has already been described (page 59), and in connection with this description the boundaries of the cavity and its connections with other cavities have been given. It consists essentially of a large cavity bounded by the facial bones and divided by a longitudinal partition into two lateral halves. The two cavities thus formed are nearly filled by (1) the labyrinths of the ethmoid (ethmoturbinals), (2) the superior nasal conchæ or nasoturbinals, projecting into the dorsal part from the ventral surface of the nasal bones, and (3) the inferior nasal conchæ, or maxilloturbinals, projecting into the ventral portion from the medial surfaces of the maxillaries.

There remain to be considered, in addition to the bones, the **cartilaginous** framework of certain parts of the nose, and the **mucous membrane.** The lamina perpendicularis is continued by cartilage, especially craniad, in such a way as to make a complete septum separating the two cavities. This septum extends from the septum of the external nose caudad to the lamina cribrosa, and from the internasal suture ventrad to the vomer and the suture of the premaxillaries. All parts of the nasal cavity are lined by mucous membrane. This is continuous at the nares with the integument, while at the choanæ it passes into the mucosa of the pharynx. It covers the conchæ nasales and the labyrinths of the ethmoid, passing into the cellules of the latter. Owing to the crowding together of the conchæ nasales and the labyrinths the nose is almost completely filled, only three narrow passageways being distinguishable. The ventral one of these, known as the **ventral** or **inferior meatus** of the nose, lies ventrad of the inferior nasal concha, next to the nasal septum. It passes caudad beneath the horizontal plate formed by the vomer and ethmoid, and opens caudad at the **choanæ** into the nasopharynx. The **dorsal** or **superior meatus** of the nose lies just ventrad of the superior nasal concha, next to the median septum; it leads to the frontal sinus, the lamina cribrosa, and the caudal parts of the ethmoid. The **middle meatus** of the nose has almost disappeared in the cat; it is simply the narrow space between the superior and inferior meati. It is practically filled by the ethmoid, into the cells of which it leads. The mucosa is continued from the nasal cavity into the sinuses of the frontals and presphenoid.

At the sides of the nasal septum, near the ventral edge, and about one to one and a half centimeters caudad of the nares, there is on each side a small curved cartilaginous tube, about one centimeter or less in length. This, the **vomeronasal** organ, or **organ** of **Jacobson,** lies against the septum, between it and the mucosa. It begins at the incisive canal or anterior palatine foramen, in the roof of the mouth, curves thence caudodorsad close against the side of the nasal septum, and ends blindly in the nasal cavity.

The **nares** or cranial openings of the nasal cavity are supported by a number of cartilages which form the framework of the **snout** or external nose. The cartilaginous continuation of the lamina perpendicularis extends some distance craniad of the tips of the nasal and premaxillary bones, forming the septum of the external nose (Fig. 103, *a*). From the dorsal edge of this projecting cartilaginous septum, two thin cartilaginous wings (*b*) extend laterad, forming the dorsal wall of the narial opening. Each then turns ventrad to form the lateral wall of the opening, but does not form the ventral floor; instead it curves mediad and finally dorsad, thus extending from the floor of the opening as a prominent ridge (*c*) within the nares. The cartilaginous wing is thus rolled into a sort of spiral, ending with a free edge within the narial opening. From the ventral edge of the median cartilaginous septum there

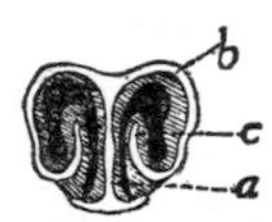

FIG. 103. — CROSS-SECTION OF THE CARTILAGES OF THE EXTERNAL NOSE.

a, cartilage of the median septum; *b*, "wings"; *c*, ridge formed by internal portion of wing.

are likewise lateral extensions, which form part of the ventral boundary of the nares; these do not quite reach the ventral parts of the dorsal wings, however, so that a small part of the narial opening is not bounded by cartilage. A section of the narial cartilages is shown in Fig. 103. The wings from the dorsal edge of the septum do not extend quite to the cranial tip of the nose, so that a notch is formed on the ventrolateral side of the nares; a section in this region would therefore differ from that figured.

The framework of the external nose thus formed is covered externally by thick hairless skin, containing many glands. From the ventral end of the internarial septum a groove passes ventrad, partly dividing the upper lip.

The inner surfaces of the cartilages are covered by the **mucosa,** which forms a number of ridges. The narial opening is almost completely divided by the prominent ridge which is supported by the free edge (*c*) of the cartilaginous wing above described. This free edge is covered by a thick layer of mucosa, and the entire ridge so formed is continuous caudad with the inferior nasal concha. On the medial side of the partial partition formed by this ridge and near the ventral side there begins a slight distance caudad of the outer opening another ridge, supported by the ventrally incurved portion of the cartilaginous ring. This soon becomes a thick swelling; beneath it opens the lachrymal canal, and that part of the passageway that lies ventromediad of it is the beginning of the inferior meatus of the nose. About one or two centimeters caudad of the external opening a third ridge projects from the dorsolateral wall of the cavity toward the large ridge first described; dorsomediad of it is a narrow passage which is the entrance to the **superior meatus** of the nose.

The **olfactory mucosa,** or that part to which the olfactory nerve is distributed, and which therefore acts as the sensory surface, is confined to the dorsocaudal parts of the nasal cavity, in the region occupied by the cells of the ethmoid. The air penetrates to this region probably only by a definite act of snuffing, the inferior meatus serving as the usual passageway of air to the lungs.

The **nasopharynx** and **pharynx** are considered under the alimentary canal (page 231).

2. **The Larynx.**

The larynx is the enlarged upper end of the air-passage which leads from the pharynx to the lungs. It is a box composed of pieces of cartilage connected by ligaments and moved by muscles, and it is lined by mucous membrane. At the root of the tongue about one centimeter caudad of the body of the hyoid bone is the triangular leaf-like **epiglottis** (Fig. 95, *e*, page 227). When food is taken this closes the opening into the larynx, and the food passes over it into the œsophagus. It is so curved that its apex is directed craniad. A fold of mucous membrane, the **plica glossoepiglottica** or **frenulum** of the epiglottis, extends from the middle of its cranial surface to the root of the tongue, and on each side of this fold is a depression.

From each side of the base of the epiglottis a fold, **plica aryepiglottica** (Fig. 95, *f*), extends caudad to the base of the arytenoid cartilage (*g*). Dorsad of this fold and separated from it by a depression is a ridge which marks the position of the caudal hyoid cornu. The plicæ aryepiglotticæ (*f*) and the epiglottis (*e*) form the boundaries of the **aditus laryngis,** or opening into the larynx.

The cavity of the larynx is divided into three portions. The upper one of these is the **vestibule** of the larynx. It is bounded caudad by two folds of mucosa (*i*) that stretch from the caudal surface of the epiglottis near its base to the tips of the arytenoid cartilages. These folds are the **false vocal cords** (*i*). Their vibration is said to produce purring. Caudad of the false vocal cords two folds of the mucosa stretch from the apices of the arytenoid cartilages to the thyroid cartilages, near the base of the epiglottis. These folds are nearer the median plane than the false vocal cords. They are the **true vocal cords** (*j*). The **middle portion** of the laryngeal cavity is that between the true and the false vocal cords. It is produced laterally into a very small pouch or pocket on each side, the **ventriculus.** The narrow slit between the true vocal cords is the **glottis** (*h*). It can be narrowed and widened by the action of muscles. The vocal cords, which bound it, are set vibrating by currents of air transmitted from the lungs, and the voice-sounds are thus produced. The **caudal portion** (inferior portion) of the laryngeal cavity is that between the glottis and the first tracheal cartilage. It is narrowed near the glottis.

CARTILAGES OF THE LARYNX (Fig. 104).—There are three unpaired cartilages, the **thyroid** (1), **cricoid** (3), and **epiglottic** (2), and two paired cartilages, the **arytenoids** (4).

The **thyroid** cartilage (**cartilago thyreoidea**) (1) has nearly the form of a visor of a cap, but is relatively broader at its ends than a cap visor. It forms about two-thirds the circumference of a circle, and is so situated that it embraces the other carti-

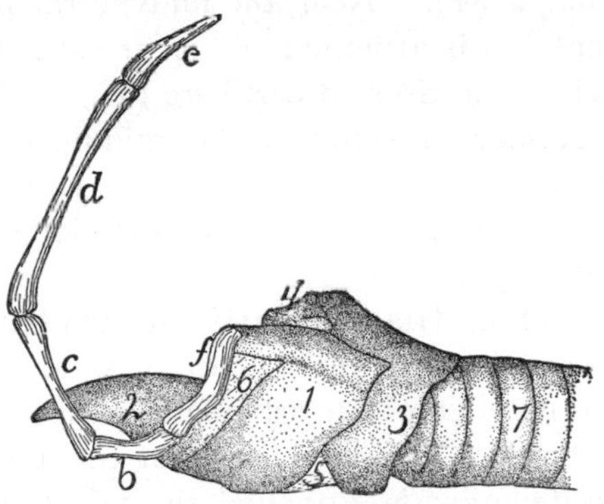

FIG. 104.—CARTILAGES OF LARYNX, WITH SIDE VIEW OF HYOID BONE.
b, ceratohyal; *c*, epihyal; *d*, stylohyal; *e*, tympanohyal; *f*, thyrohyal. 1, thyroid cartilage; 2, epiglottis; 3, cricoid cartilage; 4, arytenoid cartilage; 5, cricothyroid ligament; 6, thyrohyoid ligament; 7, trachea.

lages ventrally and laterally. Its caudal and cranial borders are oblique to its caudocranial axis and are directed dorso-caudad. To the middle of the cranial border is attached the epiglottic cartilage (2), and the whole cranial margin is connected by membrane (6) to the body and caudal cornua (*f*) of the hyoid bone. The dorsal border projects craniad into a considerable cornu which is attached to the free end of the caudal hyoid cornu (*f*). The border also projects caudad into a process which articulates with a facet on the lateral surface of the cricoid cartilage (3). In the middle of the dorsal surface is a longitudinal ridge for attachment of the vocal cords and origin of the thyroarytenoid muscles (Fig. 105, *d*), and at the caudal end of this ridge the caudal border presents a considerable rounded notch.

The **cricoid cartilage (cartilago cricoidea)** (3) has the form of a seal ring with its broader part dorsad. The broad dorsal part of the ring is partly embraced by the wings of the thyroid cartilage (1). Its caudal border is undulating and nearly at right angles to its caudocranial axis. It is connected by membrane with the first tracheal ring. The cranial border is oblique to the long axis and lies in a plane which passes from the ventral side craniodorsad. Near the median line on each side it articulates by an oblique facet with one of the two arytenoid cartilages (4). Near the midventral line the cricothyroid ligament (5) is attached and it stretches thence to the midcaudal notch of the thyroid cartilage (1).

The outer surface presents at the middle of each side a facet for articulation with the thyroid, and is marked in the median dorsal line by a ridge for the posterior cricoarytenoid muscle (Fig. 105, *b*).

The **arytenoid cartilages (cartilago arytenoidea)** (Fig. 104, 4) are triangular pyramids with base and sides nearly equilateral triangles. One side articulates with an oblique facet on the cranial border of the cricoid near the mid-dorsal line. Near the opposite apex is attached the vocal cord. At the lateral angle of the base is attached on its dorsal side the posterior cricoarytenoid muscle (Fig. 105, *b*), and on its ventral side the thyroarytenoid (Fig. 105, *d*) and lateral cricoarytenoid (Fig. 105, *c*) muscles. The movements produced by these muscles carry the arytenoid ends of the vocal cords toward or from the median plane and thus open or close the glottis.

The **epiglottic cartilage** (Fig. 104, 2) is flexible (fibrocartilage) and of a cordate form. It is so curved that its caudal surface is convex dorsoventrally and concave from side to side. It supports the epiglottis. Its cranial surface presents a slight median ridge for attachment of muscles. By its base it is attached to the midventral part of the cranial border of the thyroid cartilage (1). Its position varies so that it either stands erect with its apex directed craniad to allow the passage of air to the lungs, or, as in the act of swallowing, it is turned caudad over the aditus laryngis so as to allow food to pass over it and into the œsophagus.

The **vocal cords** are two fibrous elastic bands. Each is attached at one end to the apex of the arytenoid cartilage, and at the other end to the median ridge on the dorsal surface of the thyroid. Each supports a projecting fold of mucous membrane, the vibration of which causes the voice.

MUSCLES OF THE LARYNX.—1. Muscles moving the entire larynx.

A. **Elevators.** **M. thyreohyoideus** (Fig. 96, *p*, page 229). —A flat band on the lateral side of the larynx.

Origin on the lateral part of the caudal border of the thyroid cartilage.

Insertion on the medial two-thirds of the caudal border of the caudal cornu of the hyoid.

Action.—Raises the larynx.

The stylohyoid (Fig. 65, *d*, page 109) and the median and inferior constrictors (Fig. 96, *j* and *k*) of the pharynx, already described, have the same action.

B. **Depressors.**—The sternothyroid (Fig. 65, *g'*), already described (p. 141).

2. Muscles which move the parts of the larynx one upon another.

A. **Muscles on the Outer Surface of the Larynx.**

M. cricothyreoideus (Fig. 96, *n*).—A broad flat band which with its fellow covers the ventral surface of the cricoid cartilage and the cricothyroid ligament.

Origin.—The lateral half of the ventral surface of the cricoid cartilage. The muscles diverge so as to leave a part of the cricothyroid ligament between them.

Insertion.—The ventral part of the caudal border of the thyroid cartilage laterad of the median ventral notch.

M. cricoarytenoideus posterior (Fig. 105, *b*).—The two muscles cover the dorsal surface of the larynx.

Origin.—From the dorsal part of the caudal border of the cricoid cartilage (3) and from its median dorsal crest. The fibres pass craniolaterad, converging. The lateral fibres are nearly longitudinal in direction.

Insertion.—The dorsal border of the caudal end of the arytenoid cartilage (4).

Action.—Moves the arytenoid on its oblique articulation with the thyroid. The apex of the arytenoid is thus carried laterad, and the vocal cords are separated so as to widen the glottis.

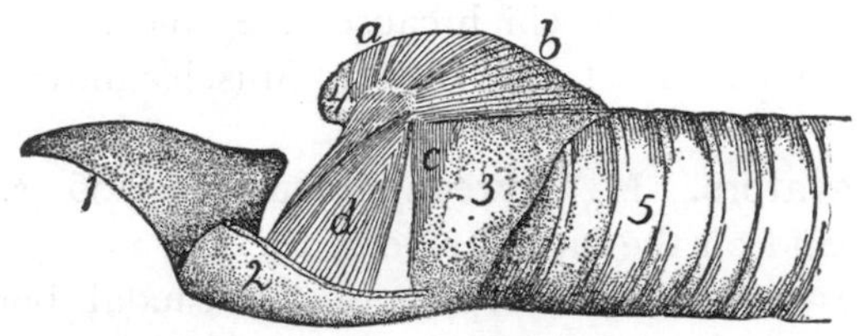

FIG. 105.—MUSCLES OF THE LARYNX, AS EXPOSED BY REMOVAL OF MOST OF THE LEFT HALF OF THE THYROID CARTILAGE.

1, epiglottis; 2, portion of the thyroid cartilage (cut); 3, cricoid cartilage; 4, arytenoid cartilage; 5, trachea. *a*, M. arytenoideus transversus; *b*, M. cricoarytenoideus posterior; *c*, M. cricoarytenoideus lateralis; *d*, M. thyreoarytenoideus.

M. arytenoideus transversus (Fig. 105, *a*).—A small unpaired muscle running transversely between the caudal ends of the arytenoid cartilages, just beneath the mucous membrane and parallel to the cranial border of the cricoid cartilage.

M. glossoepiglotticus.—A small longitudinal muscle, lying by the side of its fellow in the frenulum of the epiglottis.

Origin.—The median fibrous septum of the tongue.

Insertion.—The dorsal (cranial) surface of the epiglottic cartilage in the median line near its attached border.

Action.—Draws the epiglottis craniad.

M. hyoepiglotticus is a small bundle of parallel fibres lying in the frenulum of the epiglottis craniad and dorsad of the body of the hyoid bone.

Origin.—The lateral end of the cranial surface of the body of the hyoid. The two muscles pass craniodorsad, converging, and unite with the preceding.

Insertion with the preceding. (The lateral portion of the muscle may continue craniad to the tongue as a second part of the hyoglossus.)

Action.—Like the preceding.

B. **Muscles on the Inner Surface of the Cartilages of the Larynx.**

M. thyreoarytenoideus (Fig. 105, *d*).—The thyroarytenoid is a triangular, flat muscle of considerable size. It lies within the wing of the thyroid cartilage (2), and its fibres are nearly dorsoventral in direction.

Origin.—The median longitudinal crest on the dorsal surface of the thyroid cartilage (2).

Insertion.—The fibres converge to the insertion into the cranial lip of the laterocaudal angle of the arytenoid cartilage (4).

Action.—Turns the arytenoid on its oblique articulation so as to close the glottis.

M. cricoarytenoideus lateralis (Fig. 105, *c*).—Triangular, a little smaller than the preceding, caudad of which it is situated, so that it also is covered by the wing of the thyroid.

Origin.—The lateral part of the cranial border of the cricoid cartilage (3). The fibres converge, passing dorsad.

Insertion.—The caudal lip of the laterocaudal angle of the arytenoid cartilage (4).

Action.—Similar to the preceding, so that it closes the glottis.

3. **The Trachea** (Fig. 105, 5; Fig. 106, *a*).—The trachea is that part of the air-passage which extends from the larynx to the bronchi (Fig. 106). It is a straight tube composed of a lining mucosa with ciliated epithelium, and a connective-tissue covering which encloses supporting cartilages. Each tracheal cartilage is incomplete dorsally where it lies against the œsophagus, the gap between the two free ends of each ring being filled with muscular and connective tissue. As a result of this the diameter of the trachea is not fixed, but can be increased and diminished. The first ring is broader than the others. Where the œsophagus leaves the median line, the dorsal surface of the trachea lies against the longus colli muscles (Fig. 72, *g''*). Its ventral surface is against the sternohyoid (Fig. 65, *e*) and sternothyroid (Fig. 65, *g'*) muscles. Its lateral surfaces are partly covered by the thyroid gland (Fig. 96, 6), and are in close relation with the carotid artery

(Fig. 119, *a*, page 284), the vagus and sympathetic nerves (Fig. 156, *i*), and the internal jugular vein (Fig. 119, *b*). In the thoracic cavity the great vessels coming from the heart lie against the ventral surface of the trachea (Fig. 129, 2). At about the level of the sixth rib the trachea divides into the two main **bronchi** (Fig. 106). Each bronchus is supported by incomplete rings of cartilage like those of the trachea and has otherwise in general the structure of the trachea. In the lungs the bronchi become divided into many branches (Fig. 106), in the manner described in the account of the lungs.

4. **The Lungs. Pulmones.**—Immediately after division of the trachea the two bronchi enter the lungs (Fig. 106). These are two large, much-lobed organs, which fill the greater part of the thoracic cavity. The main lobes of the lungs are completely separated from each other, except in so far as they are connected by the bronchi and connective tissue; the main lobes may also be partly subdivided into secondary lobes that are not thus completely separated. The two lungs are completely separated from each other, except at the **radix,** where they are united by the bronchi; they lie in the right and left halves of the thoracic cavity, with the mediastinal septum between them. The bronchi on entering the lungs divide in the following manner. Each divides at first into two main branches. The cranial branch on the right side is known as the **eparterial** bronchus (*b*), because it lies craniad of the pulmonary artery. All the others are **hyparterial;** i.e., they lie caudad of the pulmonary artery. The right cranial bronchus does not further subdivide into large bronchi, but gives off numerous small branches. The right caudal bronchus divides into three main branches. There are thus four main branches of the right bronchus. The left cranial bronchus divides into two main branches; the left caudal bronchus continues caudad as a main trunk giving off small branchlets. Of the left bronchus there are thus but three main subdivisions. The main subdivisions of the bronchi on the two sides correspond, as will be seen, with the lobulation of the lungs.

The **right** lung (Fig. 106, 1-4) is slightly larger than the left (1′-3′). It divides into three smaller proximal lobes (1-3), and one large distal one (4). The most cranial one of the proximal lobes (1) is sometimes partly subdivided. The third one of the proximal lobes (3) lies mediad of the others; it is partly subdivided and one-half projects into a pocket in the

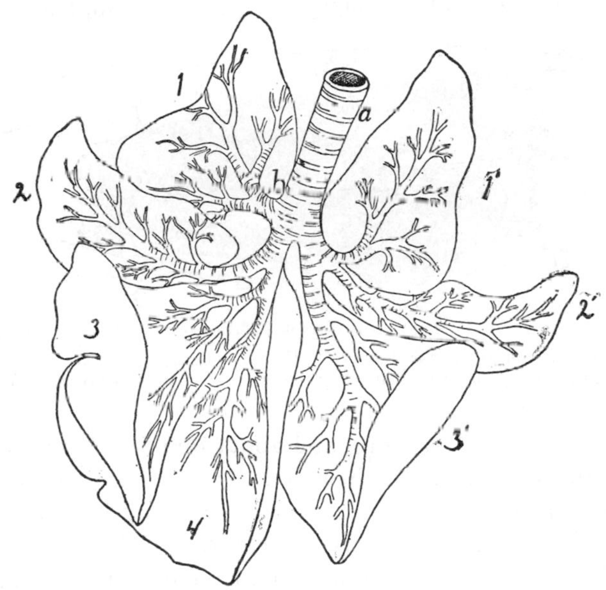

FIG. 106. RAMIFICATIONS OF THE BRONCHI, WITH OUTLINES OF THE LOBES OF THE LUNGS, VENTRAL VIEW.

1–4, lobes of the right lung; 1′–3′, lobes of the left lung. *a*, trachea, *b*, eparterial bronchus.

mediastinum, so that it comes to lie across the middle line, extending a short distance onto the left side. This lobe is frequently called the **mediastinal** lobe (3). The caudal lobe (4) of the right lung is large and flat, containing about half the substance of the lung.

The **left** lung is divided into three main lobes (1′-3′); the two cranial ones (1′-2′) are, however, partly united at the base, so that they may be considered subdivisions of but a single lobe; thus the left lung has but two distinctly separated lobes.

Each lung is attached to the aorta, vertebral column, and diaphragm by a fold of pleura, the **pulmonary ligament.** This is broadest at the caudal lobe of each lung. Each pulmonary ligament is double, being formed of two sheets of the pleura.

The Thyroid Gland. Glandula thyreoidea (Fig. 96, 6).—The thyroid gland consists of two lateral lobes (6) and a median lobe or **isthmus** (7). Each lateral lobe (6) is an elongated, flattened, lobulated mass with round ends. It is

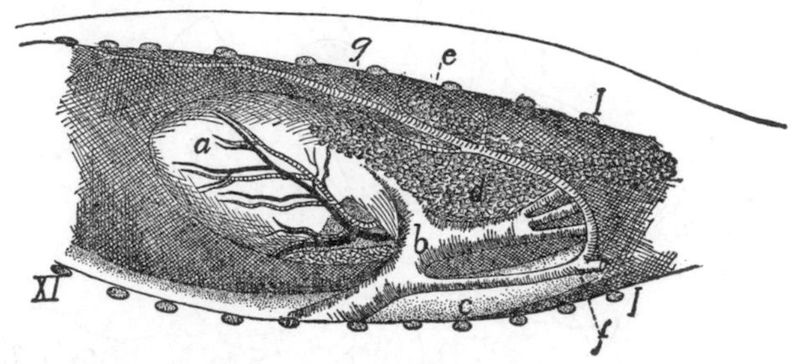

FIG. 107.—POSITION OF THYMUS GLAND, FROM LEFT SIDE.

a, heart; *b*, aorta; *c*, œsophagus; *d*, thymus gland; *e*, lymphatic gland; *f*, left subclavian artery; *g*, internal mammary artery. *I*, cut ends of first rib; *XI*, eleventh rib.

about two centimeters long and about one-fourth as broad. It lies at the side of the trachea (4), dorsad of the lateral margin of the sternohyoid muscle. Its cranial end is at the level of the caudal border of the cricoid cartilage. The **isthmus** (7) is a delicate band two millimeters wide which connects the caudal ends of the two lateral lobes. It passes ventrad of the trachea and in close contact with it. The thyroid has no duct.

The Thymus Gland. Glandula thymus (Fig. 107, *d*).—The thymus gland is best developed in young kittens; in the adult cat it has partly or almost completely degenerated. It is an elongated, flattened organ, of a pinkish-gray color, which lies in the mediastinal cavity, between the two lungs and against the sternum. It extends caudad as far as the heart (*a*), overlying the pericardium at its posterior end. At its cranial end it projects, when well developed, a short distance (about one centimeter) outside of the thoracic cavity into the neck region. The caudal end is forked, and the left lobe thus formed is usually larger than the right. The cranial end may also show indication of a division into two lobes, but this is frequently not the case.

IV. THE UROGENITAL SYSTEM. APPARATUS UROGENITALIS.

1. The Excretory Organs.

KIDNEY. REN (Figs. 108 and 109).

The kidneys of the cat are compact (i.e., not lobulated) and have the usual kidney or bean form. They lie in the abdominal cavity, one on either side of the vertebral column, against the dorsal body wall, in the region between the third and fifth lumbar vertebræ. The right kidney is one or two centimeters farther craniad than the left, and the long axes of the two converge craniad a little. Each is covered by peritoneum on its ventral surface only (i.e., it is retroperitoneal). At the border of the kidney, where the peritoneum passes from it to the body wall, there is an accumulation of fat, which is most abundant at the cranial end of the kidney. Within the peritoneal investment the kidney is enclosed in a special loose fibrous covering, the **capsule** or **tunica fibrosa,** which is continuous with the fibrous coat of the ureter and pelvis. In the middle of the median border of each kidney is a notch, the **hilus.** It gives exit to the ureter (Fig. 108, *c*) and renal veins

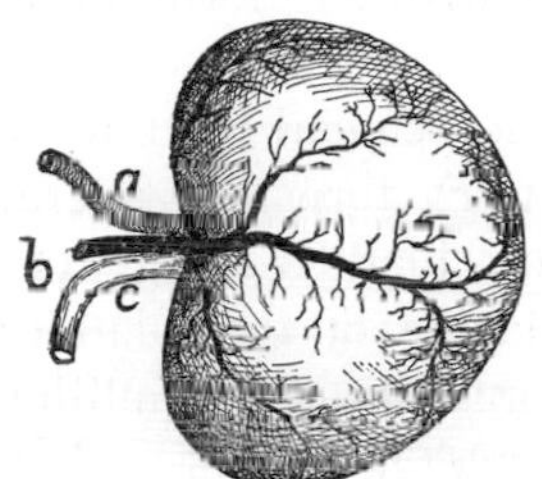

FIG. 108.—LEFT KIDNEY, VENTRAL SURFACE.

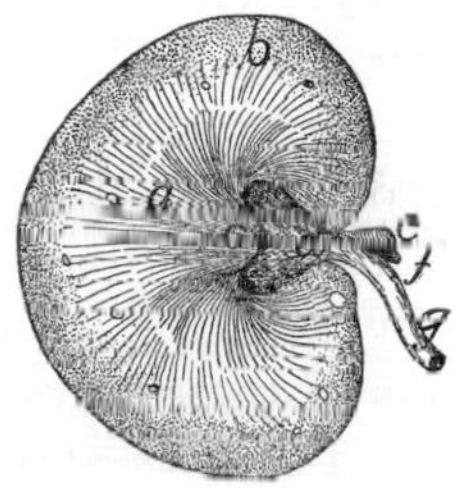

FIG. 109. MEDIAN LONGITUDINAL SECTION OF KIDNEY.

Fig. 108.—*a*, renal artery; *b*, renal vein; *c*, ureter.
Fig. 109.—*a*, medullary portion; *b*, cortical portion; *c*, papilla; *d*, pelvis; *e*, renal artery; *f*, renal vein; *g*, ureter.

(*b*), and entrance to the renal artery (*a*). On the ventral surface of the kidney within the capsule are seen grooves radiating from the hilus. They contain blood-vessels. If the substance of the kidney is sliced away parallel to the ventral surface for some distance (Fig. 109), there is exposed a cavity, the **sinus,** which lies near the medial border and the opening of which is the hilus. It contains the pelvis (*d*) (the expanded beginning of the duct of the kidney), and also renal vessels (*e* and *f*) with their branches. These structures are enclosed in fat, which fills the remainder of the sinus. Upon opening the pelvis the kidney substance is seen to project into it in the form of a cone, the **papilla** (*c*), the apex of which is directed mediad. On the apex of the papilla are the numerous openings of the uriniferous collecting-tubes, some of them opening at the bottom of an apical depression of the papilla.

In a section made parallel to the ventral surface and in the median plane, the substance of the kidney is seen to consist of a peripheral darker and more granular **cortical portion** (Fig. 109, *b*), and of a central, lighter, less granular **medullary portion** (*a*). Both portions are marked by lines which converge to the apex of the papilla (*c*).

THE URETER (Fig. 108, *c*; Figs. 111 and 112, *b*).—The duct of the kidney begins as the **pelvis** (Fig. 109, *d*), a conical sac the base of which encloses the base of the papilla. From the apex of the papilla the urine passes into the pelvis. The outer wall of the pelvis is continuous with the capsule of the kidney. At the hilus the pelvis narrows to form the **ureter** (Fig. 109, *g*). The ureter passes caudad in a fold of peritoneum which contains fat. Near its caudal end it passes dorsad of the vas deferens (Fig. 111, *c*), turns ventrocraniad, and pierces the dorsal wall of the bladder (Fig. 111, *a*) obliquely near the neck. On the inside of the bladder the openings of the ureters appear as pores about five millimeters apart, and each is surrounded by a white, ring-like elevation of the surface.

THE BLADDER. VESICA URINARIA.—The bladder (Fig. 111, *a*) is pear-shaped. It lies in the abdominal cavity between its ventral wall and the rectum and a short distance craniad of the pubic symphysis. Caudad it is continued into a rather long, narrow **neck** (*f*) which passes dorsad of the symphysis to the pelvic cavity.

The bladder is covered by peritoneum and is held in place by its neck and by three folds of the peritoneum. One of these passes from its ventral wall to the linea alba and is the **suspensory** ligament. Two others pass one from each side of the bladder to the dorsal body wall at the sides of the rectum. They are the **lateral** ligaments of the bladder. They form the walls of a partly isolated peritoneal pocket into which the rectum passes; this pocket opens craniad into the peritoneal cavity. The wall of the bladder is composed of an internal epithelium, a layer of plain muscle-fibre bundles which cross one another in various directions, and the external peritoneal layer.

SUPRARENAL BODIES. GLANDULÆ SUPRARENALES.—The suprarenal bodies are two ovoid bodies about a centimeter in the longest diameter, lying craniomediad of the kidneys, but usually not touching them. In a fresh condition they are of a pinkish or yellow color. They are usually imbedded in fat and are covered by peritoneum on their ventral surface. They have no ducts, being known as ductless glands or endocrine glands.

2. The Genital Organs.

A. THE MALE GENITAL ORGANS. *External Genital Organs.*—The external genital organs are the **scrotum** and **penis.**

The **scrotal sac** or **scrotum** is a pouch of integument which lies ventrad of the anus in the median line against the ischiatic symphysis. It is marked by a median groove which indicates the position of an internal septum dividing its cavity into lateral halves, within each of which is one of the **testes.**

The **penis** (Fig. 111, *l*; Fig. 113, 6; see also page 262) lies ventrad of the scrotal sac. It projects caudad. It is covered by the integument, which projects at its end as a free fold, the **prepuce.** Within the prepuce is the projecting **glans penis** (Fig. 113, 7). It is conical and bears on the ventral side of its free end the opening of the **urethra,** the common urinogenital opening. On the side on which the urethra opens the glans is connected to the prepuce by a fold of integument, the **frenulum.** The surface of the glans is covered with sharp, recurved, horny papillæ.

The Scrotum and Testes, and the Ducts of the Testes.—The scrotum contains the two **testes**, one in each of its compartments. Each testis lies in a diverticulum of the abdominal cavity, which is lined by an extension of the peritoneum. The testis has the same relation to this peritoneal diverticulum that the intestine has to the abdominal cavity; i.e., it does not lie within the cavity of the diverticulum, but is suspended apparently within it by means of a fold of its wall which acts as a mesentery. The peritoneal diverticulum is called the **tunica vaginalis propria** and consists thus of a **parietal** layer and a **visceral** layer.

The **tunica vaginalis propria** consists of a slender proximal part through which the blood-vessels pass to the testis and the vas deferens from it, and of an expanded distal part in which lies the testis. Only the distal part lies within the scrotum. The blood-vessels and vas deferens are suspended in the narrow part of the tunica vaginalis propria by means of a mesenterial fold similar to that which suspends the testis, and continuous with it. This fold and the blood-vessels and vas deferens contained within it form the **spermatic cord** (Fig. 111, *d*) which passes from the abdomen to the scrotal sac in the narrow part of the tunica vaginalis propria. In the formation of the human tunica vaginalis the various layers of the body wall are carried out by it and form the tunics, or coats of the testis. The one of these coats next the tunica vaginalis propria (which is reckoned as one of the coats) is the **tunica vaginalis communis** (or **fascia propria**) and is formed by the transversalis fascia. Outside of the tunica vaginalis communis is the **cremaster muscle,** an incomplete layer formed from the fibres of the internal oblique muscle. Next is the **cremasteric** (or **inter-columnar**) fascia from the aponeurosis of the external oblique muscle, and outside of this is the integument forming the scrotum. In this integument there is a layer of smooth muscle which is sometimes described as the **tunica dartos.** In the cat the tunica dartos and the cremaster muscle are wanting. The cremaster is replaced by the elevator scroti muscle. The coats of the testis are thus five, as follows:

1. The **scrotum** (the integument).

2. **Cremasteric fascia** (subcutaneous fascia).

3. The **levator scroti muscle** (subcutaneous muscle-layer) (Fig. 113, *j*).

4. **Tunica vaginalis communis** (transversalis fascia).

5. **Tunica vaginalis propria** (peritoneum).

The tunica vaginalis communis is inseparably united with the parietal layer of the tunica vaginalis propria. Where the spermatic cord passes from the abdominal wall to the scrotum it is covered by integument and cremasteric fascia on its ventral surface only, but is entirely surrounded by the tunica vaginalis propria and tunica vaginalis communis. The canal by which the spermatic cord passes through the body wall is known as the **inguinal canal.** The end by which it opens into the abdominal cavity is the **internal inguinal ring,** and the opposite end is called the **external inguinal ring.**

The **internal inguinal ring** is merely the point of connection between the proximal tubular portion of the tunica vaginalis propria and the abdominal cavity. It is circular, and is situated close against the lateral side of the lateral ligament of the bladder at its middle.

The **external inguinal ring** is an oval opening in the aponeurosis of insertion of the external oblique muscle. The aponeurosis of this muscle ends caudally in a free border along the cranial edge of the pubis, from the ilium to the pubic tubercle. The external ring is just craniad of the end of this aponeurosis.

The **inguinal canal** between these rings lies along the lateral border of the rectus muscle. It is one to one and a half centimeters long. Its medial wall rests on the rectus muscle; its dorsal wall on the fat contained within the lateral ligament of the bladder. The lateral and ventral walls lie on the transversus muscle proximally, on the internal oblique near the distal end. The wall itself is composed of tunica vaginalis propria and communis. As it passes within the caudal border of the internal oblique muscle it receives some aponeurotic fibres from it. A thin aponeurosis is also continued from the border of the external ring onto the tunica vaginalis propria.

The **testes** (Fig. 110) are the organs which produce the spermatozoa. They lie one in each compartment of the scrotal sac, enveloped in the membranes or tunics described when treating of the scrotum. Each is attached to the dorsal wall of its peritoneal pouch by a mesenteric fold. The testis is surrounded by the visceral layer of the tunica vaginalis propria, and within this, by a dense fibrous covering, the **tunica albuginea,** which sends septa into its interior. Within the fibrous covering it is made up of numerous coils of seminiferous tubules which are readily seen by the naked eye.

The **epididymis** (Fig. 110, *c*) is the beginning of the efferent duct of the testis. It appears as a flat band with a broad rounded end which lies on the medial surface of the testis at its cranial end (*b*). From this point it passes about the cranial end of the testis from its medial to its lateral surface, forming thus a semicircle with the convexity ventrad. Thence it passes as a narrower band (*c*) along the dorsal side of the testis, laterad of the suspending mesentery, to the caudal end of the testis (*d*). At the caudal end of the testis it is enlarged, passes from its lateral to its medial surface, and turns at the same time craniad to become continuous with the vas deferens (*e*).

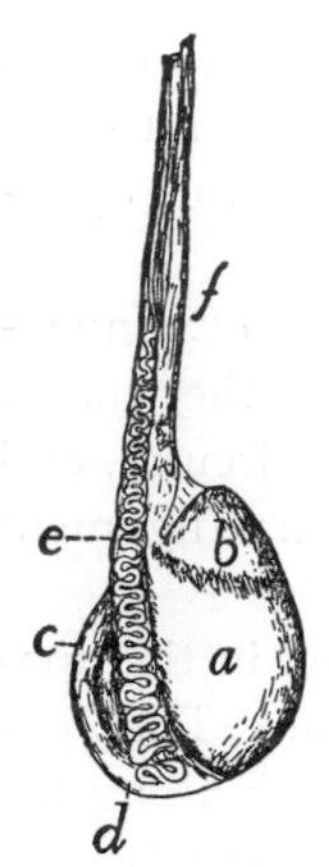

FIG. 110.—TESTIS. *a*, testis; *b*, caput epididymis; *c*, epididymis; *d*, cauda epididymis; *e*, vas deferens; *f*, spermatic cord.

The enlarged cranial end is the **caput epididymis** (*b*); the enlarged caudal end the **cauda epididymis** (*d*). The whole epididymis is encased in a tough fibrous covering similar to that of the testis. The fibrous covering (**albuginea**) of the testis and that of the epididymis are connected by fibrous tissue. Within the fibrous covering the head of the epididymis is made up of tubules which pass from the testis into its end: these are the **vasa efferentia testis.** The vasa efferentia unite within the caput into a single vessel which passes in a very tortuous course to the cauda. Its numerous windings form the cauda, from the end of which it passes craniad as the **vas deferens** (*e*).

The **vas deferens** (Fig. 110, *e*; Fig. 111, *c*) is a slender tube much convoluted at its beginning. It passes from the cauda epididymis (*d*) along the mesenterial fold of the testis on its medial side, to the spermatic cord (Fig. 111, *d*). It leaves the spermatic cord at the internal inguinal ring and, curving over the ureter (Fig. 111, *b*), bends craniad and approaches the vas deferens of the opposite side dorsad of the neck of the bladder (Fig. 111, *f*). The two vasa deferentia pass caudad together as far as the cranial border of the pubis. There they enter the prostate gland (*g*), pierce the dorsal wall of the neck of the bladder, and open close together on the inner surface. The two openings are separated by a slight elevation, the **veru montanum.**

The Urethra (Fig. 111, *h*).—The urethra is the common urinogenital duct which is formed by the union of the neck of the bladder (*f*) and the vasa deferentia (*c*) dorsad of the cranial border of the pubis. It extends thence to the end of the penis. It is divided into three portions.

1. The **prostate** portion is the commencement of the urethra; it is surrounded by the prostate gland (*g*).

2. The **membranous** portion (*h*) extends from the prostate portion to a point between the crura of the penis. This portion is surrounded by the thick compressor urethræ muscle, so that its wall appears much thicker than it really is.

3. The **spongy** portion (pars cavernosa) extends along the ventral side of the penis to its end in the groove between the corpora cavernosa penis. At its beginning is an enlargement formed by the bulbocavernosus muscle. This is known as the **bulbus urethræ.** The walls of the spongy portion are thick and vascular and form the **corpus cavernosum urethræ** or **corpus spongiosum.** At its end the corpus cavernosum urethræ is greatly enlarged and forms the **glans penis** (*m*).

Glands of the Urethra.—1. The **prostate** (Fig. 111, *g*) is a bilobed gland lying on the dorsal wall of the urethra and surrounding the ends of the vasa deferentia (*c*). It opens into the urethra at its beginning by numerous small ducts visible to the naked eye on the inner surface of the urethra.

2. The **bulbourethral** or **Cowper's glands** (Fig. 111, *i*).—There are two bulbourethral or Cowper's glands, one on either side of the bulbus of the urethra between the ischiocavernosus and bulbocavernosus muscles. Each has a covering of muscle-

fibres derived from the neighboring bulbocavernosus (Fig. 113, *l*). Each is said to open by a single duct into the urethra at the root of the penis.

The penis (Fig. 111, *l*; Fig. 113, 6) is a cylindrical organ with the apex directed backward. It is covered by integument

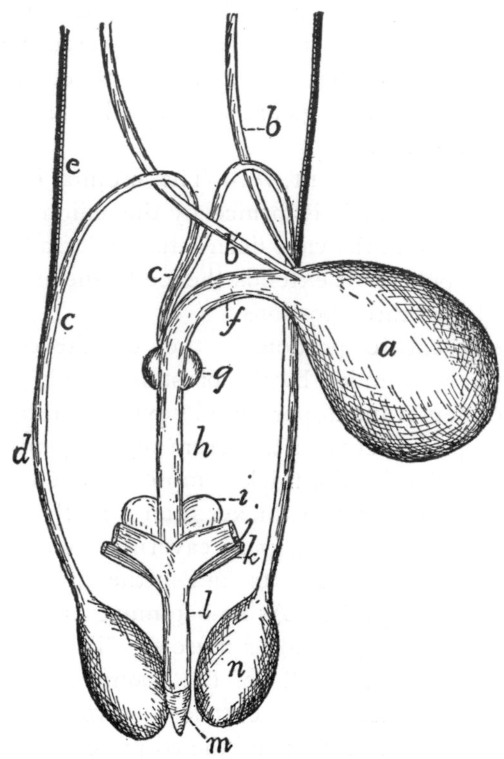

FIG. 111.—MALE GENITAL ORGANS.

a, bladder; *b*, *b'*, ureters; *c*, vasa deferentia; *d*, spermatic cord; *e*, spermatic artery and vein; *f*, neck of bladder; *g*, prostate gland; *h*, urethra; *i*, bulbourethral (or Cowper's) gland; *j*, corpus cavernosum penis, cut from ischium; *k*, ischiocavernosus muscle (cut); *l*, penis; *m*, glans penis; *n*, testis.

which projects at its free end in the form of a fold, the **prepuce** (Fig. 113), which ensheaths the glans (Fig. 113, 7) of the penis. Beneath the integument is a layer of strong fibrous subcutaneous fascia continuous with that of the surrounding parts. On the dorsum of the penis a thin band of fibrous tissue, **the ligamentum suspensorium penis,** is continued from the middle line beneath the pelvic symphysis. This band divides distally, and its halves ensheath the glans and thus form a support of the penis.

The penis is formed by three bodies, the two **corpora cavernosa penis** and the single **corpus cavernosum urethræ** (corpus spongiosum).

The **corpora cavernosa penis** (Fig. 111, *j*). Each is a cylindrical sheath of dense fibrous tissue within which are trabeculæ separating blood-sinuses. Each corpus cavernosum is attached by the one pointed end to the caudal border of the ramus of the ischium near the symphysis. From their attachments the corpora cavernosa approach one another, forming the **crura** of the penis. They become closely united by their medial surfaces and pass thus to the free end of the penis where their somewhat pointed distal ends are imbedded in the glans (*m*). A groove is left between the corpora cavernosa on the dorsum of the penis, and there is a second groove on the ventral side. In the latter groove lies the urethra.

The **corpus cavernosum urethræ** is the spongy portion of the urethra which lies in the groove on the ventral surface of the penis, between the corpora cavernosa penis. It becomes greatly enlarged at the distal end of the penis, forming the **glans** (*m*). A small bone (**os penis**) is imbedded in the distal end of the penis.

B. Female Genital Organs (Fig. 112).—The urinal organs of the female are like those of the male. The neck (*k*) of the bladder is, however, much longer, extending almost to the border of the ischiatic ramus. The urethra is consequently short.

The genital organs consist of the **ovaries** (*c*) (the organs which produce the eggs), the **oviducts** or **uterine tubes** (*e*) (**Fallopian tubes**), which receive the eggs from the ovaries; a bifid **uterus** (*f* and *i*) in which the ova undergo their development, and a **vagina** (*m*) which leads from the uterus to its junction with the neck of the bladder.

The neck of the bladder (*k*) unites with the vagina to form the **urogenital sinus** (*n*) which is very short, leads to the external opening, and is comparable to the male urethra.

Ventrad of the external orifice of the urogenital sinus is the **clitoris,** a rudimentary structure homologous with the penis of the male.

The Ovaries (*c*).—The ovaries lie in the abdominal cavity in the same longitudinal line with the kidneys and a short distance caudad of them. Each is an ovoid body about one centimeter long and one-third to one half as broad. On its surface are numerous whitish projecting vesicles, the larger of which show clear centres. They are the **Graafian follicles** (best seen in section), which contain the eggs. There may be present one or more elevations of the size of the largest Graafian follicles, but of a bright red or brown color. They are the **corpora lutea** (sing. corpus luteum),—Graafian follicles from which the eggs have been discharged.

The ovary is held in position by the **broad ligament** of the uterus, a fold of the peritoneum, which passes here from the uterine tube to the adjacent body wall. The ovary lies in a sort of a pocket formed by the broad ligament. In the natural position the pocket opens ventrolaterad. The ovary is further held in position by the ligament of the ovary (**ligamentum ovarii**), a short thick cord which passes from the ventral face of the ovary at its uterine end to the adjacent ventral surface of the uterus.

The Uterine Tubes (*e*).—The uterine (or Fallopian) tubes or oviducts are the tubes which convey the ova from the ovary (*c*) to the uterus (*f*). Each begins with an expanded trumpet-shaped opening, the **ostium tubæ abdominale** (*d*). Its walls are thin, and the mucosa of its inner surface is thrown up into undulating, radiating ridges.

The ostium (*d*) lies on the lateral side of the ovary (*c*) at its cranial end, and the trumpet partly clasps the ovary. From the ostium the tube (*e*) turns craniad, then mediad, and then caudad, so as to describe a curve about the cranial end of the ovary. It then extends caudad on the mediodorsal aspect of the ovary to its junction with the uterine cornu (*f*). It is sinuous throughout its course, and the first two-thirds (the **vestibulum**) is of considerably greater diameter than the last third. Throughout the last two-thirds of its course it lies in

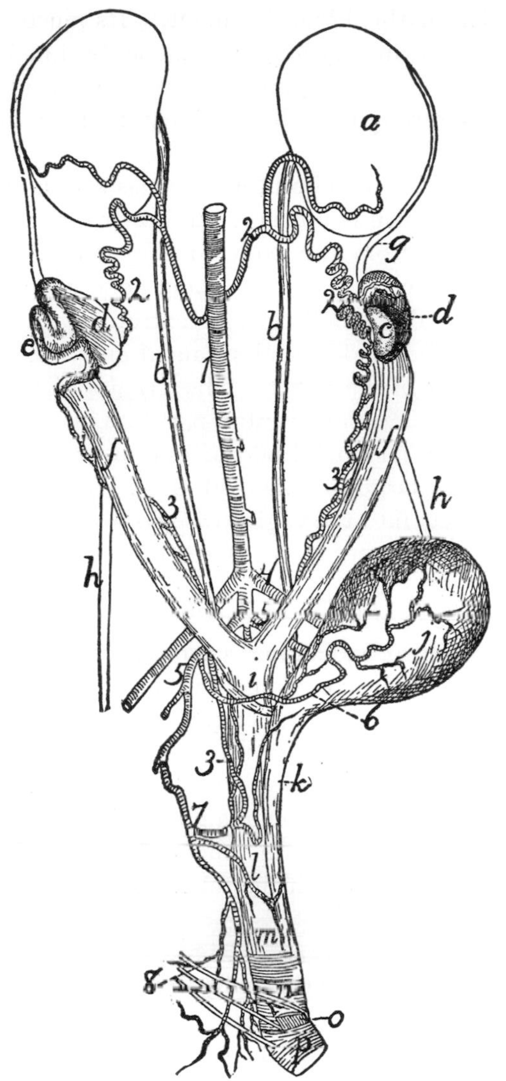

FIG. 112.—FEMALE UROGENITAL ORGANS, OBLIQUELY VENTRAL VIEW.

a, kidney; *b*, ureter; *c*, ovary; *d*, ostium tubæ abdominale; *e*, uterine (Fallopian) tube; *f*, cornua of the uterus; *g*, cranial edge of broad ligament; *h*, round ligament of the uterus; *i*, body of the uterus; *j*, bladder; *k*, neck of the bladder; *l*, position of cervix uteri; *m*, vagina; *n*, urogenital sinus or vestibule, with M. urethralis; *o*, corpus cavernosum clitoridis, with M. ischiocavernosus (cut); *p*, fibres of M. constrictor vestibuli. 1, aorta; 2, internal spermatic arteries; 3, uterine arteries; 4 external iliac arteries; 5, hypogastric arteries; 6, umbilical artery; 7, inferior hemorrhoidal artery; 8, branches of N. pudendus.

the free border of the broad ligament. Its mucosa is thrown into irregular folds, mostly longitudinal, and is lined by ciliated epithelium. From the foregoing description it is seen that the ova must pass through the body cavity in order to reach the ostium tubæ.

The Uterus (*f*, *i*).—The **uterus** consists of a median portion or **body** (*i*) which is unpaired, and of two **horns** or **cornua** (*f*) which extend from the body to the uterine tubes. The body (*i*) of the uterus is a tube about four centimeters long which lies in the abdominal cavity, ventrad of the rectum and between it and the bladder. Its caudal end is at the level of the cranial border of the pubis. The cranial end of its cavity is divided by a median dorsoventral partition into lateral halves, while the cavity of its caudal portion is unpaired. The mucosa is thrown up into large longitudinal folds. At its caudal end the uterus projects into the vagina (*m*), so that when the vagina is opened the end of the uterus is seen projecting into it as a prominent papilla. The portion of the uterus thus enclosed by the vagina is the **cervix uteri** or **neck** of the uterus. Its free end is directed ventrocaudad, and a prominent ridge is continued from its caudodorsal side along the mid-dorsal wall of the vagina. The uterine cavity communicates with the vaginal cavity by a V-shaped opening, the **os uteri,** which looks ventrocaudad and has its apex directed cranioventrad. Each horn (*f*) of the uterus passes craniolaterad in a nearly straight course from the body (*i*) to the uterine tube (*e*). It narrows rapidly and becomes continuous with the tube. The mucosa is thrown into longitudinal folds.

Ligaments of the Uterus.—**The Broad Ligament.**—The uterus is held in place principally by the broad ligaments. These are two folds of the peritoneum, each of which is attached to the whole length of one of the cornua and the adjacent part of the uterine tube and to the corresponding lateral surface of the body of the uterus. Each ligament ends craniad in a concave free border. Its attached border forms a curved line which begins laterad of the kidney and extends thence to the lateral ligament of the bladder. From the lateral ligament of the bladder the broad ligament extends caudad into the **recto-**

vesical pouch of the peritoneum, which lies between the rectum and the bladder. It holds the body of the uterus to the lateral wall of this pouch, and together with the opposite ligament and the body of the uterus forms thus a transverse partition, which divides the rectovesical pouch into dorsal and ventral portions.

The **round ligament** (*h*) is a fibrous band which extends from a point of the body wall, which corresponds exactly to the internal inguinal ring of the male, to the cornu of the uterus about two centimeters from the cranial end. It is attached to the broad ligament by an intervening fold of peritoneum.

The Vagina (*m*).—The **vagina** extends from the os uteri (at *l*) dorsad of the symphysis of the pelvis to a point a short distance craniad of the caudal border of the ischiatic symphysis. At this point it joins the neck of the bladder (*k*) to form the **vestibulum** or **urogenital sinus** (*n*), which is homologous with the urethra of the male.

Urogenital Sinus (*n*).—The **urogenital sinus** extends from the caudal end of the vagina (*m*) to the external opening, which is situated ventrad of the anal opening. It is about a centimeter long and nearly as wide, and is marked off from the vagina by a circular fold of mucosa, while its inner surface presents longitudinal folds. On its ventral wall at its cranial end is the opening of the neck of the bladder, which is enclosed by a ring-like elevation of the mucosa, most prominent at the sides. The external entrance to the urogenital sinus forms the **vulva**.

The Clitoris.—The **clitoris** is a minute organ homologous with the penis and lying on the ventral floor of the urogenital sinus. Its distal end lies at the entrance of the urogenital sinus on its ventral border. In adult specimens the **prepuce** of the clitoris appears as a slight elevation of the integument surrounding a central vascular structure which appears red in the fresh organ. From the clitoris there are two small **corpora cavernosa clitoridis** (*o*) passing craniad and then diverging to be attached to the ischiatic rami. The ischiatic portion of each is covered by a muscle (ischiocavernosus). The clitoris is said to contain a bone.

Mammary Glands.—The mammary glands secrete the milk, and lie on the ventral surface of the body beneath the integument. The separate glands are closely gathered into two chief masses, one on each side the ventral middle line. Each of these extends from about the region of the fourth rib to the caudal end of the abdomen, ending over the pubic symphysis. On each side the glands are gathered into five groups, each of which is furnished with a **nipple.** The nipple is a projection of the integument, having near its distal end numerous fine openings for the ducts of the glands. The first two nipples are on the thorax, the other three on the abdomen, the most caudal ones being about two or three centimeters in front of the cranial edge of the pubis.

Rudimentary mammary glands and nipples are present in the male.

MUSCLES OF THE UROGENITAL ORGANS, RECTUM, AND ANUS (Figs. 113 and 114).—The muscles connected with the caudal openings of the alimentary canal and of the urogenital organs are closely interrelated, a single muscle sometimes acting on parts of both systems. For this reason all these muscles are described together.

The region lying between the anus and the external opening of the urogenital organs is known as the **perineum.** The perineum is formed chiefly by muscles and fascia.

a. Muscles common to the Male aud Female.—**M. sphincter ani externus** (Fig. 113, *i*; Fig. 114, *a*).—This muscle is confounded with the levator scroti (Fig. 113, *j*) or the levator vulvæ (Fig. 114, *b*). The two take origin in common from the integument on the dorsum of the root of the tail dorsad of the fifth caudal vertebra. There the fibres from the opposite sides are intermingled. The common muscle passes ventrad about the tail as a flat band close to the integument. Dorsad of the anus the inner fibres of the muscles of the opposite sides are united. They then separate and surround the anus as a band five millimeters wide situated beneath the integument. Ventrad of the anus the fibres are again intermingled. Some fibres on each side then continue to the scrotum as the levator scroti (Fig. 113, *j*) or to the vulva as the levator vulvæ (Fig. 114, *b*). Fibres also pass onto the anal pouch and unite with the sphincter ani internus, forming the **constrictors of the anal pouch** (Strauss-Durckheim).

M. sphincter ani internus (Fig. 113, *h*; Fig. 114, *c*).—The sphincter ani internus is a broad and thick band of striated muscle-fibres which surrounds the rectum at the anus. Dorsad the band is about two centimeters broad, while ventrad it is less than one. In the ventral median line some of the fibres pass craniad to help in forming the bulbocavernosus muscle. The muscle surrounds the anal sac.

(The muscle here described under this name is that described under the same name in the cat by Strauss-Durckheim and Mivart; it corresponds, however, to a part of the sphincter ani externus of the dog, as described by Ellenberger and Baum.)

M. levator ani (or **pubiocaudalis**) (Fig. 162, 11).—This muscle lies in the pelvic cavity. Each muscle forms a nearly vertical sheet, and between the two are the rectum and the urethra.

Origin from the symphysis of the pelvis.

Insertion into the midventral line of the centra of the third, fourth, and fifth caudal vertebræ, close to the muscle of the opposite side. This muscle is frequently continuous with the iliocaudalis (Fig. 162, 11').

Action.—Bends the tail and compresses the rectum.

M. ischiocavernosus (Fig. 113, *m*; Fig. 114, *e*).—A small, flat, spindle-shaped muscle which lies upon the crus of the penis or clitoris. Each has

Origin from the caudal border of the ramus of the ischium, about one centimeter from the median line.

Insertion, in the male, into the whole outer surface of the crus penis, or bulb of the corpus cavernosum penis. In the female the muscle is smaller than in the male, and the insertion is into the ventral surface of the urogenital sinus, at the base of the clitoris.

M. transversus perinei (Fig. 114, *i*).—A small bundle of fibres which arises from the medial surface of the ischium, just dorsad of the origin of the ischiocavernosus, and passes mediad to join the sphincter ani internus (*c*).

M. caudoanalis (S.-D.) (Fig. 113, *f*; Fig. 114, *g*).—A slender, flat bundle of fibres having origin on the middle line of the ventral surface of the second and third caudal vertebræ. It passes caudoventrad, lying between the levator ani and the

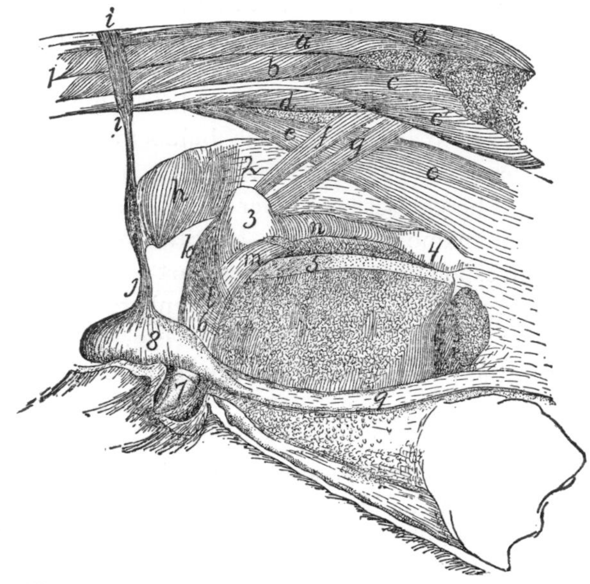

FIG. 113.—MUSCLES OF THE ANUS, UROGENITAL ORGANS, AND TAIL IN THE MALE (SLIGHTLY SCHEMATIC).

One side of the pelvis has been removed. *a*, *a'*, M. extensor caudæ lateralis; *b*, M. abductor caudæ externus; *c*, *c'*, M. flexor caudæ longus; *d*, M. flexor caudæ brevis; *e*, M. caudorectalis; *f*, M. caudoanalis; *g*, M. caudocavernosus; *h*, M. sphincter ani internus; *i*, M. sphincter ani externus; *j*, M. levator scroti; *k*, M. rectocavernosus; *l*, M. bulbocavernosus; *m*, M. ischiocavernosus (cut); *n*, M. compressor urethræ membranaceæ. 1, tail; 2, rectum; 3, bulbourethral or Cowper's gland; 4, prostate gland; 5, symphysis pubis; 6, penis; 7, glans penis; 8, testis; 9, spermatic cord.

caudorectal (Fig. 113, *e*; Fig. 114, *j*), and unites with the ventral portion of the sphincter ani internus (Fig. 113, *h*).

Action.—Draws the anus craniodorsad.

M. caudorectalis (Fig. 113, *e*; Fig. 114, *j*).

Origin from the ventral surface of the sixth and seventh caudal vertebræ. A small, at first unpaired band two or three millimeters wide is formed, which passes cranioventrad, soon dividing into two lateral halves. These spread out over the sides of the rectum, forming a broad sheet of fibres which pass into the walls of the rectum, among the transverse fibres of the latter. This muscle is covered by the caudoanalis (Fig. 113, *f*), caudocavernosus (*g*) (or caudovaginalis, Fig. 114, *h*), iliocaudalis, and levator ani.

b. Muscles Peculiar to the Male (Fig. 113).—**M. levator scroti** (*j*).—This is a band of fibres which passes ventrad in the median line from the sphincter ani externus (*i*) onto the scrotum. Here it spreads out beneath the skin, forming especially a well-marked bundle in the median furrow between the two testes.

M. rectocavernosus, or **retractor penis** (*k*).—A small bundle of fibres which arises in two parts from the ventral surface of the sphincter ani internus (*h*). The two parts unite into a single bundle which passes caudad on the middle line of the ventral surface of the penis; it is inserted into the corpus cavernosum just proximad of the glans. The muscle is covered only by integument, and overlies the ischiocavernosus (*m*).

M. caudocavernosus (S.-D.) (*g*).—A slender bundle just craniad of the caudoanalis (*f*).

Origin on the median ventral line of the first two caudal vertebræ. The muscle passes caudoventrad, lying between the levator ani and the caudorectal (*e*). It divides into two bands, one of which is inserted into the base of the corpus cavernosum, while the other extends farther caudad and is inserted at the distal extremity of the corpus cavernosum.

Action.—Flexes the penis (bends it backward).

M. bulbocavernosus (accelerator urinæ) (*l*).—The two muscles cover the ventral surface of the penis.

Origin of each from a median raphe, which passes from the bulbous portion of the urethra toward the anus. The fibres pass toward the distal end of the penis and have their

Insertion into the distal half of the lateral surface of the corpus cavernosum penis.

M. compressor urethræ membranaceæ (*n*).—A thick layer of striated muscle-fibres which surrounds the urethra between Cowper's gland (3) and the prostate (4). The fibres have a circular course, and the cranial ones are attached to the crura of the penis. The other fibres have no fixed attachment.

c. Muscles Peculiar to the Female (Fig. 114).—**M. levator vulvæ** (Strauss-Durckheim), or **constrictor cunni** (*b*).—This is homologous with the levator scroti of the male. It consists of a band of fibres which pass ventrad from the external sphincter ani (*a*) and surround the vulva (3), lying immediately beneath the integument.

M. constrictor vestibuli, or **rectovaginalis** (Strauss-Durckheim) (*d*).

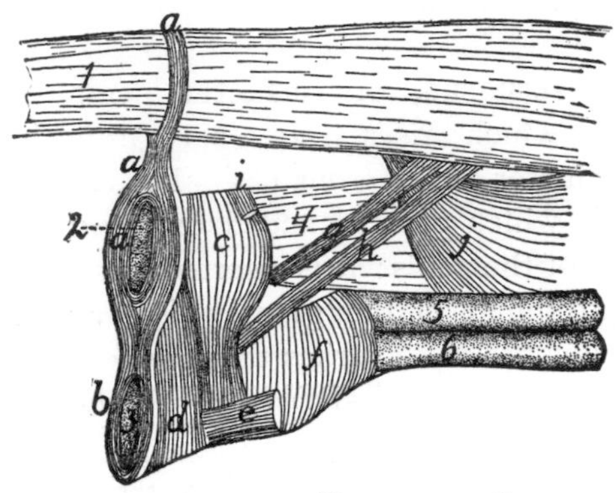

FIG. 114.—MUSCLES OF THE ANUS AND UROGENITAL ORGANS IN THE FEMALE.
a, M. sphincter ani externus; *b*, M. levator vulvæ; *c*, M. sphincter ani internus; *d*, M. constrictor vestibuli; *e*, M. ischiocavernosus (cut); *f*, M. urethralis; *g*, M. caudoanalis; *h*, M. caudovaginalis; *i*, M. transversus perinei; *j*, M. caudorectalis. 1, the tail; 2, anus; 3, vulva; 4, rectum; 5, vagina; 6, neck of the bladder.

Origin from the sides of the sphincter ani internus (*c*). The muscle forms a distinct bundle two or three millimeters wide, which passes ventrocaudad and is *inserted* into the ventral surface of the urogenital sinus, caudad of the insertion of the ischiocavernosus (*e*).

M. caudovaginalis (Strauss-Durckheim) (*h*).—A slender band just craniad of the caudoanalis (*g*), and corresponding to the caudocavernosus of the male.

Origin from the median line of the ventral surface of the first two caudal vertebræ. The muscle passes caudoventrad, lying between the levator ani and the caudorectal (*j*), and is *inserted* into the ventral side of the urogenital sinus, at the base of the clitoris.

M. urethralis (*f*).—This consists of fibres surrounding the cranial part of the urogenital sinus and the caudal parts of the vagina and neck of the bladder.

Origin partly on the caudal part of the symphysis of the ischium, partly from the ventral surface of the urogenital sinus, where the fibres are attached to the corpora cavernosa clitoridis. The fibres pass dorsad over the surface of the sinus, and over the surface of the union of the vagina and neck of the bladder, to be inserted into the sides of the vagina and the dorsal surface of the urogenital sinus.

THE CIRCULATORY SYSTEM.

I. THE HEART. COR.

The heart lies in the mediastinum, enclosed in the pericardial sac (Fig. 92a), and projects rather more toward the left than toward the right. It is an ovoid or pear-shaped organ, with its long axis directed approximately craniocaudad. Its caudal end or apex is, however, directed slightly ventrad and to the left, while the larger cranial end or base faces slightly dorsad as well as craniad.

Laterally and dorsally the heart is largely covered by the lungs. The ventral side and a considerable portion of the lateral surface are, however, not thus covered, so that they lie against the thoracic wall. The heart extends from about the fourth or the fifth to the eighth rib, and its apex touches the diaphragm.

The cavity of the heart is divided by a longitudinal dorsoventral septum into lateral halves—a right and a left side. Each side is again divided by a transverse dorsoventral septum (**auriculoventricular**) into two chambers, one of which, the **auricle,** lies at the base; the other, the **ventricle,** lies at the apex of the heart. There are thus right and left auricles and right and left ventricles. An external groove, partly filled with fat, separates the auricular portion of the heart from the ventricular part; this groove is known as the **sulcus coronarius.**

Each auricle or ventricle has a single set of blood vessels either leaving it or entering it. Thus the blood enters the right auricle by the **inferior** and **superior** venæ cavæ (Fig. 116, *d* and *e*) (postcava and præcava). It passes thence into the right ventricle, and from the right ventricle to the lungs by a single **pulmonary artery** (Fig. 115, *f*). It returns to the left auricle by the numerous **pulmonary veins** (Fig. 116, *g*, *h*, *i*), and passes thence to the left ventricle. From the left ventricle it passes to the body by a single **aorta** (Fig. 115, *g*).

When the heart is viewed from the ventral surface (Fig. 115), a considerable blood vessel, the **coronary artery** (*q*), running from the base to a point a little to the right of the apex, indicates the position of the septum (ventricular septum), between the right (*a*) and left (*b*) ventricles. The apex thus belongs to the left ventricle. From the cranial end of the right ventricle the pulmonary artery (*f*) is seen passing obliquely craniad and toward the left. Beneath the pulmonary artery the aorta (*g*) appears rising from the middle of the base of the heart and passing directly craniad. At the base appears a part of the auricular appendage of the left auricle (*d*), and at the right a part of the right auricular appendage (*c*). The former (*d*) is larger and bent at right angles, so that its free end is directed toward the apex.

In the dorsal view (Fig. 116) the position of the ventricular septum is not indicated. On the surface of the left ventricle a short distance from the ventricular septum and nearly parallel to it are seen branches of the coronary artery and the coronary vein passing toward the apex. Craniad of the left ventricle is seen the left auricle (*b*) with the pulmonary veins (*g*, *h*, *i*) opening into it. Craniad of the right ventricle (*a*) is the right auricle (*c*) with the venæ cavæ (*d* and *e*) opening into it near the middle. Coming from beneath the auricles are seen the pulmonary artery (*j*) and the aorta (*f*).

The **chambers of the heart.**

1. The **right auricle** (atrium dextrum) (Figs. 115 and 116, *c*). Externally the right end of the right auricle projects so as to form its **auricular appendage** (Fig. 115, *c*) which lies at the right of the base of the aorta (Fig. 115, *g*). The superior vena cava (Fig. 116, *e*) is seen entering near the cranial end of the auricular septum opposite the base of the aorta. The inferior vena cava (Fig. 116, *d*) enters the auricle near the coronary sinus and close to the auricular septum. The netted appearance which the wall, especially that of the

appendage, presents externally is due to the muscular thickenings of the wall (**musculi pectinati**).

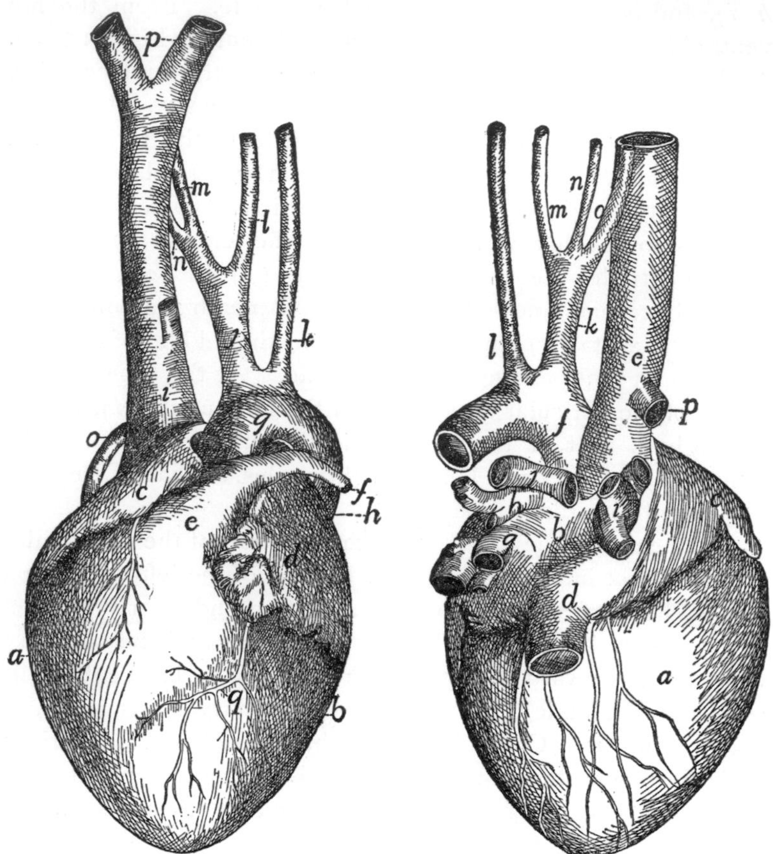

FIG. 115.—HEART, VENTRAL VIEW. FIG. 116.—HEART, DORSAL VIEW.

Fig. 115.—*a*, right ventricle; *b*, left ventricle; *c*, right auricular appendage; *d*, left auricular appendage; *e*, conus arteriosus; *f*, pulmonary artery; *g*, aortic arch; *h*, thoracic aorta; *i*, vena cava superior; *j*, innominate artery; *k*, left subclavian artery; *l*, left common carotid; *m*, right common carotid; *n*, right subclavian; *o*, azygos vein; *p*, the two innominate veins; *q*, coronary artery.

Fig. 116.—*a*, right ventricle; *b*, left auricle; *c*, right auricle; *d*, vena cava inferior; *e*, vena cava superior; *f*, aorta; *g*, *h*, *i*, groups of pulmonary veins (*g*, dorsal group; *h*, sinistral group; *i*, dextral group); *j*, pulmonary artery (division into two); *k*, innominate artery; *l*, left subclavian; *m*, left common carotid; *n*, right common carotid; *o*, right subclavian; *p*, azygos vein.

The cavity (including that of the auricular appendage) is somewhat egg-shaped, with its long axis transverse. The musculi pectinati, which branch and unite into a network, are most abundant on its dorsal wall at the right. The axes of the two venæ cavæ if produced into the cavity of the auricle would meet one another at its centre and nearly at right angles. Caudad of the opening of the inferior vena cava is seen the slit-like opening of the **coronary sinus,** guarded craniad by the semilunar **valve of the coronary sinus** (or valve of Thebesius). The coronary sinus receives blood from **coronary veins,** which collect it from the walls of the heart.

In the auricular septum ventrad of the opening of the inferior vena cava is seen a faintly marked smooth oval depression, the **fossa ovalis.** When the auricular septum is examined by transmitted light it is seen to be thinner over the fossa ovalis. There is an opening, **foramen ovale,** at this point in fœtal life, so that the blood of the inferior vena cava then passes directly from the right auricle to the left auricle. Caudad the cavity of the right auricle communicates with that of the ventricle by the large oval auriculoventricular opening, which is guarded by the tricuspid valves (Fig. 117).

2. The **right ventricle** (ventriculus dexter) (Figs. 115 and 116, *a*) does not reach quite to the apex of the heart, so that it makes up less than one-half of its ventricular portion. It makes a half-spiral turn about the left ventricle, from its lateral side at the apex toward its ventral side at the base, where it ends in the pulmonary artery (Fig. 115, *e*). Its wall is very thin as compared with that of the left ventricle. Its cavity (Fig. 117) is nearly flat on its medial side, convex on its lateral side. It communicates with the auricle craniodorsad. Cranioventrad the cavity is narrower and turns around toward the ventral side of the heart and opens into the pulmonary artery. That portion of the ventricle between the auriculoventricular opening and the pulmonary artery is the **conus arteriosus** (Fig. 115, *e*; Fig. 117, *f*). Internally the wall presents many muscular **trabeculæ** (Fig. 117, *a*) of various sizes. These are more numerous over the ventricular wall than on the septum. They do not occur on the conus (*f*). Surrounding the auriculoventricular opening is the **tricuspid valve** (Fig. 117, *d*, *d'*, *d''*). It consists of three flaps. One of these (*d'*) is septal

(i.e., it lies against the septum), while of the two others which do not lie against the septum, one is dorsal (*d''*) and the other ventral. Each flap is thin, semicircular, and membranous, and is attached to the border of the auriculoventricular opening by the diameter of the semicircle. The free border of each is attached to the wall of the heart by numerous delicate tendinous bands, the **chordæ tendineæ** (*c*), some of which are attached to the lower face of each valve. The chordæ tendineæ

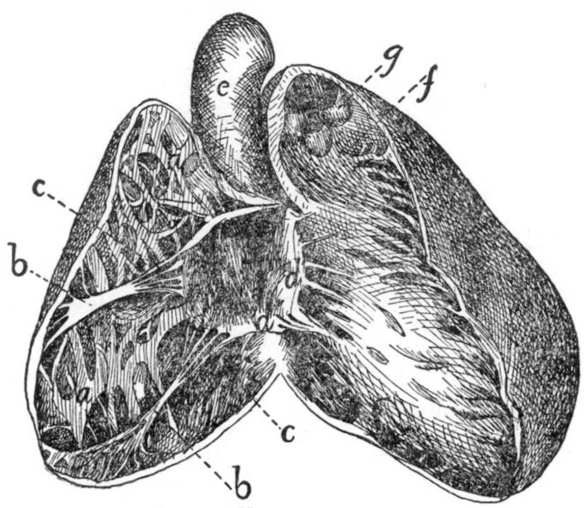

FIG. 117.—HEART, WITH RIGHT VENTRICLE LAID OPEN TO SHOW THE TRICUSPID VALVE.

a, trabeculæ; *b*, columnæ carneæ; *c*, chordæ tendineæ; *d*, *d'*, *d''*, the three flaps of the tricuspid valve; *e*, aorta; *f*, conus arteriosus, laid open; *g*, semilunar valves of the pulmonary artery.

of the septal valve (or most of them) are attached at their opposite ends to the septum directly, while those of the dorsal and ventral flaps are attached to the ends of three or more band-like muscles, **columnæ** (or trabeculæ) **carneæ** (*b*), which are fixed by their opposite ends to the ventricular wall.

Between the conus arteriosus (*f*) and the pulmonary artery are three pocket-like **semilunar valves** (Fig. 117, *g*), one ventral, one dextral, and one sinistral. Between each valve and the wall of the pulmonary artery there is an enlargement of the cavity of the artery, one of the **pulmonary sinuses** (or sinuses of Valsalva). Beyond the sinuses the pulmonary artery divides into right and left branches (Fig. 116, *j*).

3. The **left auricle** (atrium sinistrum) (Fig. 115, *d*; Fig. 116, *b*). The auricular appendage (Fig. 115, *d*) is bent at right angles and its apex turned caudad. The cavity is thus irregular. Muscular trabeculæ occur only in the auricular appendage. When the auricular septum is examined by transmitted light the position of the fossa ovalis is indicated at about the middle of the septum as seen from the left side. Ventrad of it is a fold of the septal wall.

The **pulmonary veins** enter the dorsal wall of the auricle in three groups (Fig. 116, *g*, *h*, *i*). Each group opens into a more or less pronounced sinus or extension of the auricular cavity. The sinuses may be called, on account of their position, dorsal (*g*), sinistral (*i*), and dextral (*h*).

4. The **left ventricle** (Fig. 115, *b*) occupies rather more than the left half of the base of the heart. Its walls are two or three times as thick as those of the right ventricle. Internally its walls present a few muscular bands, comparable to the trabeculæ of the left ventricle. There are two very large columnæ carneæ, one dorsad and one ventrad. At the cranial end it communicates near the lateral wall with the left auricle by the auriculoventricular opening, and near the septum with the aorta. The **bicuspid valve** (or mitral valve), which guards the auriculoventricular opening, consists of two flaps, one septal and one lateral. Their chordæ tendineæ, which come from their free borders as well as from their outer surfaces, are attached to the columnæ carneæ, chordæ passing from both valves to each columna carnea.

The opening into the aorta is guarded by three **aortic semilunar** valves, each of which partly conceals an **aortic sinus** (or sinus of Valsalva). One valve is dorsal, one sinistral, and one dextral. In the dextral sinus is the opening of one of the **coronary arteries,** which carry blood to the walls of the heart.

Pericardium.

The pericardium is a sac enclosing the heart. It lies in the middle mediastinum, and the two halves of the mediastinal septum with their fat may be dissected away from it. Its wall is composed of two layers, an external firm fibrous layer and an internal layer of flattened epithelial cells similar to the peritoneal epithelium (**serous** layer). The fibrous layer forms a sac which repeats roughly the form of the heart. This sac is attached to the aorta at the point of origin of the subclavian artery, to the pulmonary artery at its bifurcation, and to the venæ cavæ and pulmonary veins near their entrance into the heart. At these points it is continuous with the fibrous coats of the vessels named, and from them it is reflected over the heart, forming a complete sac enclosing it but not attached to it anywhere. The heart lies within this sac. The serous layer lines the fibrous sac and gives to the surface of the heart and fibrous layer a smooth glistening appearance. It is reflected over the heart. The relation of the heart to it is much the same as the relation of the intestine to the peritoneal sac. The serous layer consists therefore of two portions, **parietal,** lining the sac, and **visceral,** covering the heart. The parietal and visceral portions are continuous along a line which runs approximately parallel to the auriculoventricular groove and encloses all the great blood vessels. Within this line the heart lies against the fibrous layer of pericardium and is not covered by the serous layer. The serous layer is easily dissected free from the heart-wall, but its parietal portion is closely adherent to the fibrous layer.

II. THE ARTERIES. ARTERIÆ.

1. A. pulmonalis, the Pulmonary Artery (Fig. 115, *f*).

The pulmonary artery passes craniodorsad and slightly to the left from the cranial end of the conus arteriosus. One to one and a half centimeters from the conus it divides into right and left branches (Fig. 116, *j*). Just before the division the dorsal surface of the pulmonary artery is connected by the short **ligamentum arteriosum,** or ligamentum Botalli, with the aorta. This is the remnant of a canal which in fœtal life forms a free communication between the pulmonary artery and the aorta; this canal is known as the **ductus Botalli.** The ligament is almost or quite obliterated in the adult cat.

The left branch of the pulmonary artery passes to the left lung, crossing ventrad of the thoracic aorta. It then divides

into branches which pass to the lobes of the left lung. The point of division of the left branch of the pulmonary artery lies craniad of all the lobes of the lung, so that the lobes of the left lung are said to be all **hyparterial,** i.e., below (or caudad of) the artery.

The right branch passes under (dorsocaudad of) the aortic arch, and reaches the right lung at about the junction of the cranial lobe with the remainder of the lung. The cranial lobe of the right lung is therefore said to be **eparterial,** since it is craniad of the pulmonary artery; the other lobes are hyparterial. The right branch divides at its entrance to the lung and is distributed to its lobes.

2. **Aorta** (Fig. 115, *g*; Fig. 118, *a*).

The aorta is the single great vessel which conveys blood from the left ventricle. It makes a sharp semicircular curve dorsad (Fig. 118, *a′*) and to the left, passes caudad at the left side of the vertebral column, and passes between the crura of the diaphragm to reach the abdominal cavity. It is divisible into **thoracic aorta** (Fig. 118) and **abdominal aorta** (Fig. 126).

A. **Thoracic Aorta** (Fig. 118).—The first portion of the thoracic aorta, curved as above described, is the **aortic arch** (*a′*). It lies in the thoracic cavity opposite the interval between the third and fourth or fourth and fifth ribs. It is separated from the vertebral column on the right by the superior vena cava (*y*), and on the left by the œsophagus (4). At its beginning it lies a little to the right of the median plane; but it passes at once to the left side of the vertebral column.

BRANCHES OF THE THORACIC AORTA.

1. **Aa. coronariæ.**—The coronary arteries are two. They arise from the aortic sinuses. The left one (Fig. 118, *p*) leaves the aorta on the left side, passes dorsad of the pulmonary artery, and divides into two branches, one of which follows the auriculoventricular groove (sulcus coronarius) to the dorsal side of the heart and sends branches to the adjacent heart-walls, while the other runs onto the ventricles, following approximately the ventral border of the ventricular septum. The **right coronary** artery passes in the auriculoventricular groove toward the right and dorsad, and supplies the adjacent walls of the heart.

2. **A. anonyma** (Fig. 115, *j*; Fig. 118, *b*).—The innominate artery passes craniad from the convexity of the aortic arch (*a'*). It gives rise first to a small **mediastinal artery** (*m*) which

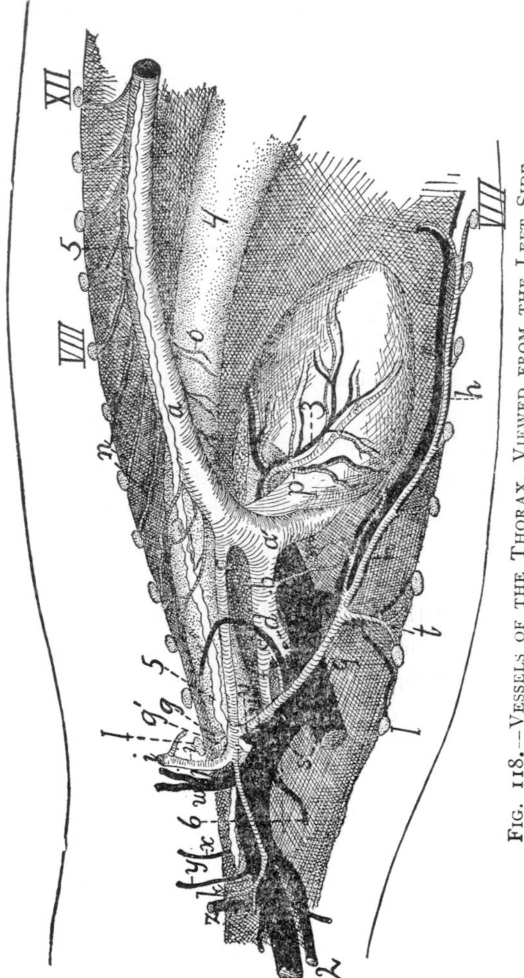

FIG. 118.—VESSELS OF THE THORAX, VIEWED FROM THE LEFT SIDE.

a, aorta (*a'*, aortic arch); *b*, innominate artery; *c*, left subclavian; *d*, right subclavian; *e*, right common carotid; *f*, left common carotid; *g*, costocervical axis; *g'*, vertebral artery; *h*, internal mammary artery; *i*, axillary artery; *j*, thyrocervical axis; *k*, A transversa scapulæ; *m*, mediastinal artery; *n*, intercostal arteries; *o*, œsophageal arteries; *p*, left coronary artery; *q*, superior vena cava; *r*, internal mammary vein; *s*, the two innominate veins; *t*, sternal artery; *u*, costocervical vein; *v*, vertebral vein; *w*, axillary vein; *x*, vein to clavo-trapezius and lateral ends of the pectoral muscles; *y*, vein accompanying second branch of A. transversa scapulæ; *z*, thyrocervical vein. 1, external jugular vein; 2, internal jugular vein; 3, vena cordis magna; 4, œsophagus; 5, thoracic duct; 6, one of the lymphatic ducts from the neck. *I*, first rib (cut); *VIII*, eighth rib (cut); *XII*, twelfth rib (cut).

passes ventrad into the mediastinum, then to the **left common carotid** (Fig. 115, *l*), then to the **right common carotid** (Fig. 115, *m*). Sometimes the carotids are given off from a common trunk. Beyond the right common carotid the innominate is continued as the **right subclavian** (Fig. 115, *n*).

3. **A. subclavia sinistra** (Fig. 115, *k*; Fig. 118, *c*).—The left subclavian passes craniad from the convexity of the aortic arch. It curves about the first rib (Fig. 118, *I*) to enter the armpit, where it becomes the **axillary artery** (*i*).

4. **Aa. intercostales** (*n*).—The intercostal arteries are given off from the dorsal side of the aorta. Each passes to an intercostal space and divides into three branches. One of these passes ventrad along the caudal margin of the cranial one of the two ribs between which it extends. Another goes to the deep muscles of the back, and the third enters the spinal canal through the intervertebral foramen. The arteries for the first and second (and sometimes the third) intercostal space usually arise from the subclavian (costocervical axis, Fig. 118, *g*).

5. **Aa. bronchiales.**—The bronchial arteries are two, and arise either from the aorta opposite the fourth intercostal space or from the fourth intercostal arteries. They accompany the bronchi to the lungs.

6. **Aa. œsophageæ** (Fig. 118, *o*).—The œsophageal arteries are small branches of varying origin passing to the œsophagus.

7. **Aa. lumbales.**—The lumbar arteries correspond to the intercostals, but pass off between the lumbar vertebræ. The obliquity of the diaphragm throws the origin of one or two pairs of them within the thorax.

A. CAROTIS COMMUNIS. THE COMMON CAROTID ARTERY. (Fig. 115, *l* and *m*; Fig. 119, *a*).

The two common carotid arteries arise from the innominate artery in the manner already described. Each passes craniad along the side of the trachea. In the thorax (Fig. 118, *f*) the common carotid lies mediad of the subclavian artery (Fig. 118, *c*) and dorsad of the superior vena cava (Fig. 118, *q*). In the neck (Fig. 119) the artery lies, accompanied by the vagus and sympathetic nerves and the internal jugular vein (*b*), in the space between the longus capitis muscle (7) and the trachea (14); it is covered ventrally by the sternomastoid and sternothyroid (2) muscles, lying close to the lateral border of the latter. Near its origin the common carotid may give rise to the small **inferior thyroid** artery. It then passes to about the level of the larynx without giving off branches; here it gives off the **superior thyroid** (*c*) on the ventral side and one or more muscular branches (*e*) on the dorsal side. One or two centimeters further craniad it gives oft on the dorsal side the **internal carotid** (*g*) and the **occipital** artery (*f*). The main artery now takes the name **external carotid** (*m*).

Branches of the common carotid:

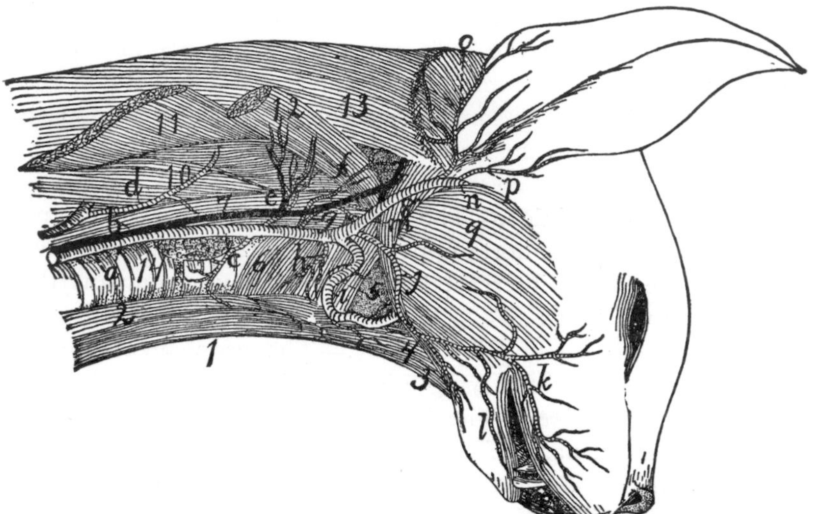

FIG. 119.—COMMON CAROTID ARTERY AND INTERNAL JUGULAR VEIN.

a, common carotid artery; *b*, internal jugular vein; *c*, superior thyroid artery; *d*, cervicalis ascendens artery; *e*, large muscular branches; *f*, occipital artery; *g*, internal carotid; *h*, branch to larynx; *i*, lingual artery; *j*, external maxillary; *k*, superior labial; *l*, inferior labial; *m*, external carotid; *n*, internal maxillary; *o*, posterior auricular; *p*, superficial temporal. 1, M. sternohyoideus; 2, M. sternothyreoideus; 3, M. geniohyoideus; 4, M. genioglossus; 5, M. constrictor pharyngis medius; 6, M. constrictor pharyngis inferior; 7, M. longus capitis; 8, M. digastricus; 9, M. masseter; 10, M. scalenus; 11, M. levator scapulæ (cut); 12, M. levator scapulæ ventralis (cut); 13, M. splenius; 14, trachea.

1. **A. thyreoidea ima.**—The inferior thyroid is a small artery which arises either from the common carotid near its origin, or from the innominate before the origin of the carotid. It passes craniad on the trachea as far as the thyroid gland, giving branches to the trachea and œsophagus.

2. **A. thyreoidea superior** (*c*).—The superior thyroid leaves the carotid opposite the thyroid cartilage and passes mediad and caudad, sending branches to the thyroid gland, and the

sternothyroid (2) and sternohyoid (1) muscles. A small branch, the **superior laryngeal,** passes to the larynx, and supplies those muscles of the larynx which are not enclosed by the cartilages.

3. **Rami musculares** (*e*).—One or two branches, usually of considerable size, leave the common carotid at about the same level as the superior thyroid and pass to the muscles on the dorsal side of the neck, the main trunk of the artery passing between the longus capitis (7) and scalenus muscles (10).

4. **A. occipitalis** (*f*).—The occipital artery arises from the common carotid at about the same point as the internal carotid. It immediately sends a large branch dorsad, passing between M. longus capitis (7) and the vertebral column, to the deep muscles of the neck. The occipital then crosses the outer surface of the digastric muscle (8) to the back of the skull, and runs along the lambdoidal crest just beneath the splenius muscle. It sends a number of branches to the muscles of the back of the neck; and one of its branches may unite with the vertebral artery as it lies in the groove on the atlas, or with a branch of the vertebral.

5. **A. carotis interna** (*g*).—The internal carotid artery is one of the terminal branches of the common carotid. It is very small. It is given off near or in common with the occipital artery, passes toward the cranial end of the tympanic bulla, enters the bulla with the Eustachian tube, and passes into the skull at the foramen lacerum (page 59). It is much convoluted before entering the foramen. Within the skull (Fig. 121, *g*) it joins the posterior cerebral artery (Fig. 121, *f*) at the side of the hypophysis.

6. **A. carotis externa** (Fig. 119, *m*).—After giving off the internal carotid the continuation of the common carotid artery receives the name **external carotid** (*m*). It passes craniad and laterad between the digastric (8) and styloglossus muscles, where it gives off cranioventrad the **lingual artery** (*i*) and a number of small muscular branches; also sometimes the small **laryngeal** artery. At the dorsolateral border of the digastric (8) it gives off the **external maxillary** artery (*j*), and about one centimeter farther craniad the **posterior auricular** (*o*). It now

turns mediad, lying against the cartilaginous auditory meatus, on its cranial side, and gives off the **superficial temporal** (*p*). The artery then continues mediad, taking the name **internal maxillary** (*n*)—so that the internal maxillary artery is to be considered the terminal branch of the external carotid.

Branches of the external carotid artery (Fig. 119):

a. **A. lingualis** (Fig. 119, *i*; Fig. 120, *d*).—The lingual artery leaves the external carotid near its beginning and passes craniomediad along the ventral border of the digastric muscle (Fig. 120, 9), accompanied by the hypoglossal nerve. It gives off numerous small branches to the hyoid and pharyngeal muscles, then passes dorsad of the hyoglossus muscle (Fig. 120, 6), where it gives off a branch which passes transversely across the middle line to communicate with the artery of the other side. Beneath the hyoglossus the artery turns craniad and passes into the tongue. Here it runs along the medial border of the styloglossus to the tip of the tongue, giving off numerous branches into the substance of this organ.

b. **Rami musculares.** — Muscular branches pass to the digastric and to the hyoid muscles. A small branch (Fig. 119, *h*), which may arise either from the external carotid or from the common carotid near the beginning of the external carotid, passes to the larynx and supplies the thyroarytenoid and lateral cricoarytenoid muscles of the larynx.

c. **A. maxillaris externa** (Fig. 119, *j*).—The external maxillary artery leaves the external carotid (*m*) opposite the angle of the jaw and at about the dorsal border of the digastric muscle (8). It passes craniad, lying at first beneath the digastric muscle and sending a branch to the submaxillary gland. Opposite the caudal border of the mylohyoid muscle it gives off the **submental** artery, turns dorsad, emerges from beneath the digastric, and passes along the cranial border of the masseter onto the face. Here it divides into **superior** (*k*) and **inferior** (*l*) **labial** branches, which pass along the upper and lower lips, respectively, giving off numerous branches.

The **submental** artery passes to the symphysis menti between the digastric and mylohyoid muscles, giving off on its course collateral branches to the muscles of this region.

d. **A. auricularis posterior** (Fig. 119, *o*).—The posterior auricular leaves the external carotid (*m*) opposite the middle of the bulla tympani and beneath the submaxillary gland. It passes about the base of the ear on its caudal and dorsal sides outside of the deep muscles of the occipital region, but beneath the auricular muscles, and sends several branches to the muscles of the external ear, passing onto the caudal surface of the concha. It sends also a large branch mediad to the muscles of the occiput, especially to the temporal muscle, within which it ramifies. A large branch (**anterior auricular,** Fig. 131, *u*) passes from the caudal side of the concha craniodorsad, and appears on the cranial side of the external ear, running along the cranial margin of the auditory opening.

e. **A. temporalis superficialis** (Fig. 119, *p*; Fig. 120, *h*).—The superficial temporal artery arises from the external carotid as the latter lies between the cartilaginous auditory meatus and the caudal border of the masseter muscle. It passes dorsad and gives off soon after its origin a muscular branch to the masseter, and an **auricular** branch which passes distad along the concha auris and ramifies over its cranial surface. The superficial temporal itself passes onto the surface of the temporal muscle (Fig. 120, 11), to which it gives numerous branches. It extends to the caudal angle of the eye (Fig. 131, *s*), where it divides. One branch passes into the lower eyelid; the larger branch passes along the dorsal side of the eye, sending a branch into the orbit and small branches onto the dorsal surface of the nose.

f. **A. maxillaris interna** (Fig. 119, *n*; Fig. 120, *i*).—The internal maxillary artery is the continuation of the external carotid. It turns caudad at the caudal end of the mandible, then passes craniad, lying dorsad of the pterygoid muscles (Fig. 120, 10), and against the medial surface of the mandible. It gives off the **inferior alveolar** artery (Fig. 120, *j*), then the **middle meningeal** (*k*), and then continuing mediad divides into three or four branches. The branches redivide, and the twigs form a complicated plexus, the **carotid plexus** (Fig. 120, *l*), which surrounds the maxillary division of the fifth nerve near its exit from the foramen rotundum. One of the larger branches of the plexus enters the skull through the orbital fissure, lying beside the hypophysis; it divides in the manner described below.

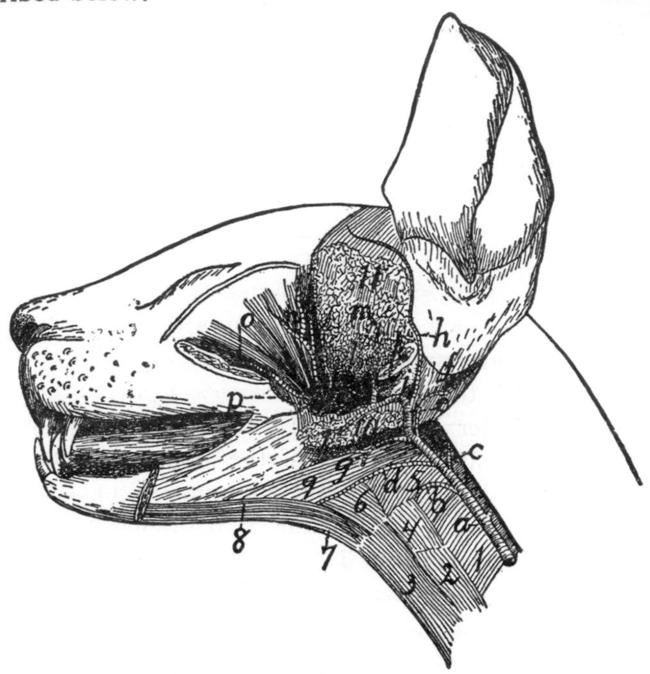

FIG. 120.—BRANCHES OF EXTERNAL CAROTID ARTERY.

a, common carotid; *b*, branch to larynx; *c*, internal carotid; *d*, lingual; *e*, external carotid; *f*, posterior auricular; *g*, external maxillary; *h*, superficial temporal; *i*, internal maxillary; *j*, inferior alveolar; *k*, middle meningeal; *l*, carotid plexus; *m*, branch to temporal muscle; *n*, ophthalmic; *o*, infraorbital; *p*, lesser palatine. 1, M. constrictor pharyngis inferior; 2, M. sternothyreoideus; 3, M. sternohyoideus; 4, M. thyreohyoideus; 5, M. constrictor pharyngis medius; 6, M. hyoglossus; 7, M. geniohyoideus; 8, M. genioglossus; 9, M. digastricus; 10, Mm. pterygoidei externus and internus (cut); 11, M. temporalis (cut).

Beyond the carotid plexus a main trunk which may be considered the continuation of the internal maxillary passes craniad, lying on the dorsal surface of the external pterygoid muscle; nearly opposite the molar tooth it divides into the **infraorbital** (Fig. 120, *o*) and the **sphenopalatine** arteries.

Branches of the internal maxillary artery and of the carotid plexus:

1. **A. alveolaris inferior** (Fig. 120, *j*).—The inferior alveolar (or inferior dental) artery leaves the inferior maxillary just

opposite the condyloid process of the mandible. It enters the mandibular canal by the mandibular foramen, along with the nerve of the same name, and traverses the canal, furnishing branches to the lower teeth. It emerges at the mental foramen, and its terminal branches are distributed to the chin, but a branch is continued in the bone beyond the mental foramen and supplies the incisor and canine teeth of the lower jaw.

2. **A. meningea media** (Fig. 120, *k*).—The middle meningeal is a large vessel which leaves the internal maxillary at about the same level as the inferior alveolar. It passes into the foramen ovale and ramifies in the dura mater. Its branches leave distinct impressions on the inner surface of the bones of the skull.

3. A large branch (Fig. 121, *h*) from the plexus passes into the cranial cavity through the orbital fissure and lies within the skull at the side of the hypophysis. It gives off the following branches:

a. A **posterior communicating** branch, very short, which extends caudad and joins the internal carotid artery (Fig. 121, *g*).

b. **A. cerebri media** (Fig. 121, *i*).—The middle cerebral artery passes dorsad on the side of the cerebral hemisphere along the fissure of Sylvius and divides into numerous branches which are distributed to the surface of the cerebrum.

c. **A. cerebri anterior** (Fig. 121, *j*) passes dorsad between the cerebral hemispheres. Just craniad of the optic chiasma the two anterior cerebral arteries are united by a small communicating branch, thus completing the circulus arteriosus or circle of Willis (Fig. 121), surrounding the hypophysis (see page 292).

4. From the carotid plexus several branches pass, arising either separately or in common, to the masseter, temporal, and pterygoid muscles.

5. **A. ophthalmica** (Fig. 120, *n*).—The ophthalmic artery passes from the carotid plexus to the structures in the orbit. It gives off numerous branches which supply the muscles of the eyeball, and other structures of this region. It sends an **ethmoidal** branch into the nasal cavity through the ethmoidal

foramen in the orbital plate of the frontal bone, then continues distad to emerge from the orbit on the medial side of the eye; here it anastomoses with branches of the superficial temporal.

6. **A. palatina minor** (Fig. 120, *p*).—The lesser palatine artery leaves the internal maxillary distad of the carotid plexus, near the caudal border of the maxillary bone. It passes ventrocaudad into the soft palate.

7. **A. sphenopalatina.**—The sphenopalatine is one of the terminal branches of the internal maxillary; it passes mediad through the sphenopalatine foramen into the nasal cavity, and divides into numerous branches which supply the mucous membrane of the nose. It gives off just before it enters the sphenopalatine foramen the **descending palatine** (**A. palatina descendens**), which passes into the posterior palatine canal and emerges on the surface of the hard palate, where it ramifies.

8. **A. infraorbitalis** (Fig. 120, *o*).—The infraorbital artery is a direct continuation craniad of the internal maxillary. It sends off numerous small branches to the teeth of the upper jaw, and a rather large branch which passes to the lower eyelid. It then enters the infraorbital foramen, at the same time dividing usually into two or three branches; these emerge from the foramen and supply the parts of the nose and upper lip adjacent to the foramen (Fig. 131, *r*).

A. SUBCLAVIA. THE SUBCLAVIAN ARTERY.

The **left subclavian** (Fig. 118, *c*) arises from the convexity of the aortic arch just distad of the origin of the innominate artery, and about two or three centimeters from the heart. It passes craniad and slightly to the left, and turns into the left arm just craniad of the first rib.

The **right subclavian** (Fig. 115, *n*) is a direct continuation of the innominate, the artery receiving the name subclavian after the right common carotid is given off, usually at about the level of the second or third intercostal space.

The subclavian has the following branches: the **vertebral artery** (Fig. 118, *g'*), the **internal mammary** (Fig. 118, *h*), the **costocervical axis** (Fig. 118, *g*), the **thyrocervical axis** (Fig. 118, *j*). Beyond the last-named branch it continues into the arm as the **axillary** artery (Fig. 118, *i*; Fig. 122, *g*).

a. **A. vertebralis** (Fig. 118, *g'*).—The vertebral artery arises from the dorsal surface of the subclavian opposite the first rib. It passes craniad and dorsad at the side of the thoracic portion of the longus colli muscle, and enters the foramen transversarium of the sixth cervical vertebra. It passes thence craniad through the foramina transversaria (which together form the **vertebrarterial canal**) and gives off at the intervertebral foramina branches to the muscles of the neck and branches which pass across the ventral surface of the spinal cord to join A. spinalis anterior. Craniad of the foramen transversarium of the atlas the vertebral artery turns dorsad in the groove on the lateral surface of the atlas. Here it gives off a large branch which passes laterodorsad to the muscles of the neck and may anastomose with a branch of the occipital artery. The vertebral artery then passes into the vertebral canal through the atlantal foramen. It passes to the ventral side of the spinal cord and unites at about the level of the foramen magnum with the vertebral artery of the opposite side (Fig. 121, *a*) to form the **basilar artery** (**A. basilaris**) (Fig. 121, *c*), which passes craniad along the ventral middle line of the brain. Just before their union the two vertebral arteries (*a*) give off each a branch which passes caudomediad. These two branches soon unite in the middle line, forming the **anterior spinal artery** (**A. spinalis anterior**) (*b*), which passes caudad the entire length of the spinal cord, lying on its ventral middle line and receiving many communicating branches from the vertebral, intercostal, and lumbar arteries.

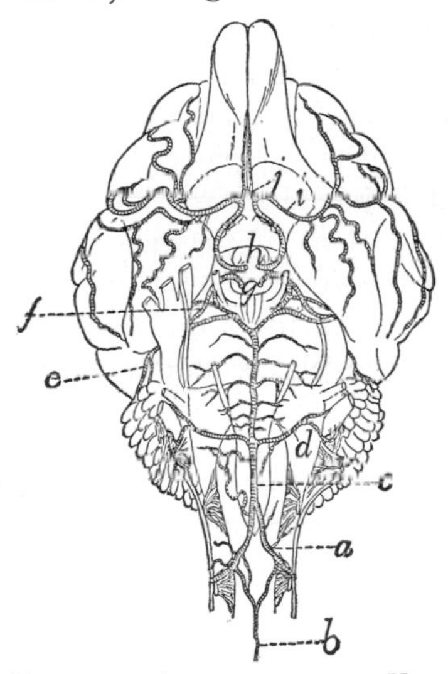

FIG. 121.—ARTERIES OF THE VENTRAL SURFACE OF THE BRAIN.

a, A. vertebralis; *b*, A. spinalis anterior; *c*, A. basilaris; *d*, A. cerebelli inferior posterior; *e*, A. cerebelli anterior; *f*, A. cerebri posterior; *g*, cut ends of the two internal carotid arteries; *h*, cut ends of branches from the carotid plexus (*g* and *h* are placed within the circulus arteriosus or circle of Willis); *i*, A. cerebri media; *j*, A. cerebri anterior.

A. basilaris (*c*).—This arises by the union of the two vertebral arteries. It passes craniad along the ventral middle line of the medulla and pons and gives many small branches to them. A large branch, **A. cerebelli inferior posterior** (*d*), passes on each side to the caudal surface of the cerebellum, on which it ramifies. At the cranial margin of the pons the basilar artery divides. From each division a very large branch passes on each side across the pedunculi cerebri to the cranial part of the cerebellum; this is **A. cerebelli anterior** (*e*). Just craniad of this, arising from nearly the same point, the smaller **A. cerebri posterior** (*f*) passes laterad to the caudal part of the cerebrum; it is joined by the internal carotid artery (*g*). The small continuations of the two halves of **A. basilaris** then pass craniad at the side of the hypophysis to join the posterior communicating branches from the carotid plexus. As other branches of the carotid plexus unite across the middle line craniad of the optic chiasma, an arterial circle is formed on the ventral surface of the thalamus portion of the brain, surrounding the hypophysis and the optic chiasma. This is known as the **circulus arteriosus,** or circle of Willis (page 289).

b. **A. mammaria interna** (Fig. 118, *h*).—The internal mammary artery rises from the ventral surface of the subclavian opposite the first rib, and passes ventrocaudad in the mediastinum to reach the sternum opposite the third intercostal space. It sends two or three small branches craniad to the midventral part of the thoracic wall and then extends caudad at the side of the sternum. It sends off lateral branches to the ventral thoracic wall, branches to the mediastinum and pericardium, a branch to the diaphragm which anastomoses with the phrenic; and finally it passes out of the thoracic cavity caudad of the last costal cartilage, extends caudad in a zigzag course at the lateral border of the rectus muscle and anastomoses with the inferior epigastric artery (superior epigastric of man).

c. **Truncus costocervicalis** (Fig. 118, *g*).—The costocervical axis arises from the subclavian opposite the first rib, passes craniodorsad, and divides almost at once into two branches. The smaller one of these, the **superior intercostal**

(**A. intercostalis suprema**), passes caudad and, dividing, supplies the first and second intercostal spaces, and then passes to the deep muscles of the back. The other branch divides almost immediately into two. One of these, **A. transversa colli,** passes laterad in front of the first rib and enters the serratus anterior muscle. In this it passes dorsad, giving off branches to this muscle and to the levator scapulæ, till it reaches M. rhomboideus, which it likewise supplies. The other branch (**A. cervicalis profunda**), which seems to form a continuation of the main artery, passes directly dorsad and leaves the thoracic cavity between the heads of the first and second ribs. Here it passes into the deep muscles of the neck; it can be traced in the substance of the complexus muscle as far forward as the atlas.

d. **Truncus thyreocervicalis** (Fig. 118, *j*).—The thyrocervical axis (or thyroid axis) arises from the subclavian beneath the first rib, a short distance distad of the origin of the costocervical axis. It passes laterocraniad and dorsad, lying on the mediocranial side of the brachial plexus. A short distance from its origin it gives off a branch, varying much in size, the **cervicalis ascendens** (Fig. 119, *d*), which passes craniad on the ventral side of the neck, supplying the sternomastoid, sternohyoid, the cervical portion of the scalenus, and sometimes other muscles of the neck region. Other branches pass from the thyroid axis to the inner surface of the clavotrapezius (Fig. 122, *a*) and to the ventral end of the pectoral muscles. At the level of the cranial border of the scapula the artery takes the name **A. transversa scapulæ,** or **suprascapularis.** This divides into three main branches. The first branch, sometimes large, sometimes small, passes to the lymphatic gland in the hollow of the shoulder, and to the adjacent muscles; it supplies the clavotrapezius, acromiotrapezius, levator scapulæ ventralis, splenius, occipitoscapularis, and rhomboideus. A second branch passes between the subscapularis and supraspinatus muscles, dividing into various branches which supply the muscles named. The third branch pierces the supraspinatus muscle, just craniad of the acromion process, and ramifies in that muscle.

e. **A. axillaris** (Fig. 122, *g*).—The axillary artery is the continuation of the subclavian laterad of the first rib. It lies caudad of the brachial plexus and parallel to it. It sends off the following branches:

1. **A. thoracica anterior** (Fig. 122, *h*).—The anterior thoracic is a slender artery which leaves the ventral side of the axillary opposite the first rib and passes caudomediad, to supply the medial ends of the pectoral muscles (*g*).

2. **A. thoracica longa** (*p*).—The long thoracic artery is larger than the preceding, leaves the axillary a short distance laterad of it, and passes caudad to the middle portions of the pectoral muscles (8) and continues to the inner surface of the latissimus dorsi.

A short distance beyond the long thoracic the axillary divides into two. The more cranial one of these is the **subscapular** (*l*); the other is the **brachial** (*g'*).

3. **A. subscapularis** (*l*).—The subscapular artery passes laterad and gives off a short distance from its origin the **A. thoracicodorsalis** (*t*) and **A. circumflexa humeri posterior** (see below); it may also give rise to the **circumflexa anterior humeri** (*l'*), and to the **profunda brachii** (*u*); these two branches, however, rise more frequently from the brachial artery (*g'*) and are described in connection with it. The subscapular artery then passes through the triangular interval between the scapular end of the long head of the triceps, the latissimus dorsi, and the glenoid border of the scapula. Within this interval it sends muscular branches to the long head of the triceps, the subscapularis, and the latissimus dorsi. That to the latter muscle is very large. At the border of the scapula, opposite the tuberosity of the spine, it turns craniad, passes over the lateral surface of the infraspinatus muscle, supplying it; crosses the spine, and sends branches into the supraspinatus fossa in both directions parallel to the scapular spine. These supply the supraspinatus, acromiotrapezius, and spinotrapezius, and anastomose with the branches of the transversa scapulæ. As the subscapularis turns craniad onto the surface of the infraspinatus it sends dorsad a small branch, the **circumflexa scapulæ,** which passes in the infraspinatus fossa close to its

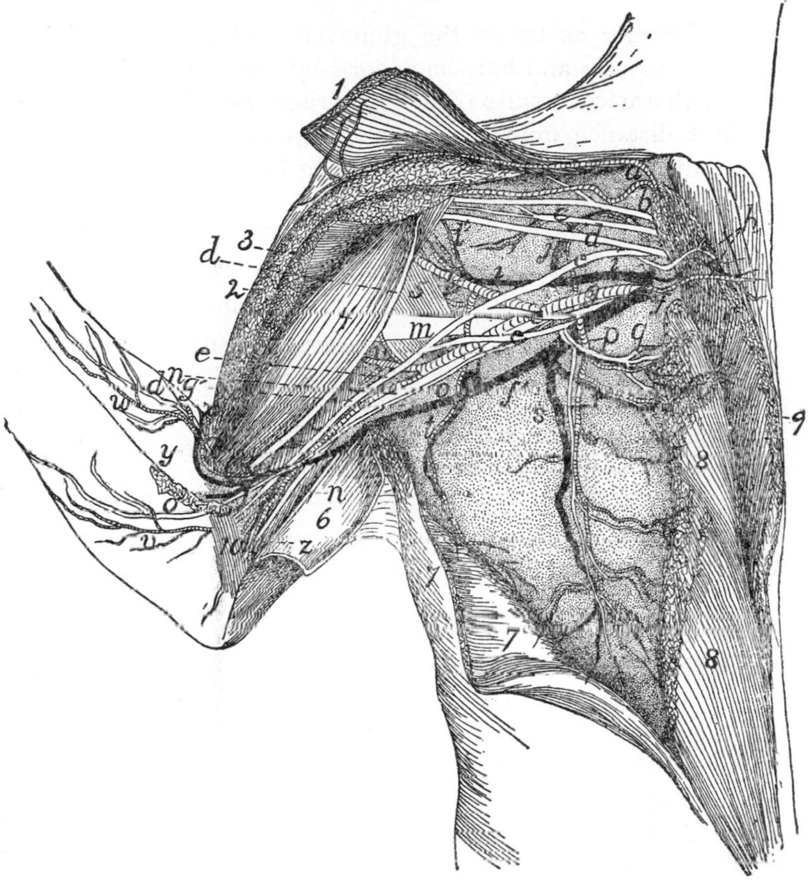

FIG. 122.—BLOOD-VESSELS AND THE MORE VENTRAL NERVES OF THE AXILLA, VENTRAL VIEW.

The pectoral and clavobrachial muscles have been cut and laid aside, their ends being shown; only a part of the nerves are exhibited. 1, M. clavobrachialis; 2, cut end of M. pectoralis major; 3, cut end of M. pectoralis minor; 4, M. biceps; 5, M. teres major; 6, M. epitrochlearis, partly cut and turned back; 7, M. latissimus dorsi, partly cut; 8, M. pectoralis minor; 9, M. pectoralis major; 10, short portion of caput mediale of M. triceps brachii. *a*, branches of the thyrocervical axis to clavobrachial and clavotrapezius muscles; *b*, suprascapular nerve; *c*, first subscapular nerve; *d*, musculocutaneous nerve; *e*, median nerve; *f*, V. axillaris; *f'*, V. brachialis; *g*, A. axillaris; *g'*, A. brachialis; *h*, first anterior thoracic nerve, accompanied by the anterior thoracic artery and vein; *i*, V. subscapularis; *j*, large muscular branch (to subscapular muscle) of the subscapular vein and brachial artery; *l*, A. subscapularis; *l'*, A. circumflexa humeri anterior; *m*, radial nerve; *n*, ulnar nerve; *o*, medial cutaneous nerve; *p*. A. thoracica longa; *q*, *r*, second anterior thoracic nerve; *s*, V. longa thoracica; *t*, A. and V. thoracicodorsalis; *u*, A. profunda brachii; *v*, branch of brachial artery accompanying medial cutaneous nerve; *w*, branch of A. collateralis radialis superior; *x*, A. collateralis radialis superior; *y*, V. mediana cubiti; *z*, A. collateralis ulnaris.

glenoid border as far as the glenovertebral angle, supplying the infraspinatus and latissimus dorsi by lateral branches.

A. thoracicodorsalis (*t*).—This arises from the subscapular a short distance from its origin and passes across the teres major to the latissimus dorsi (7), giving branches to both these muscles and to the epitrochlearis.

A. circumflexa humeri posterior.—The posterior circumflex artery arises from the A. subscapularis close to the origin of the latter. It passes between the subscapularis muscle and the teres major, close to the border of the biceps, then between the lateral and long heads of the triceps. It gives off a branch to the inner surface of the spinodeltoid and acromiodeltoid, then passes distad to supply the lateral and long heads of the triceps.

4. **A. brachialis** (*g'*).—The brachial artery is the continuation of the axillary (*g*) into the arm beyond the origin of the subscapular (*l*). It passes along that side of the biceps which lies next to the humerus. It passes thus, accompanied by the brachial vein (*f'*) and median and ulnar nerves, through the bicipital arch and afterwards between the biceps (4) and the intermediate division of the medial head of the triceps to the supracondyloid foramen of the humerus, through which it passes with the median nerve to reach the concavity of the elbow. It gives off the following branches:

a. **A. circumflexa humeri anterior** (*l'*).—The anterior circumflex artery usually leaves the brachial near its origin (but may arise from the subscapular (*l*) or one of its branches); it passes to the biceps (4) near the origin of the latter and sends a branch proximad to the head of the humerus.

b. **A. profunda brachii** or **superior profunda** (*u*).—This arises from the first part of the brachial or it may come off from one of the branches of the axillary (e.g., the subscapularis). It passes along with the radial nerve onto the dorsal side of the humerus and supplies the triceps muscle. It also sends branches to the epitrochlearis (6) and latissimus dorsi (7).

c. **Rami musculares.**—Muscular branches are given off near the supracondyloid foramen to the biceps (4), epitrochlearis (6), and brachialis muscles. A nutrient artery leaves the brachial proximad of the supracondyloid foramen, either separately or in common with the muscular branches, and passes into the nutrient foramen at the junction of the middle and distal thirds of the shaft of the humerus, supplying the bone.

d. **A. collateralis ulnaris** (superior) (or A. anastomotica magna) (*z*).—This leaves the brachial artery just proximad of the supracondyloid foramen and passes to the convexity of the elbow, supplying the structures about the olecranon.

e. **A. collateralis radialis superior** (Fig. 130).—This rises from the axillary artery just proximad of the supracondyloid foramen (Fig. 122, *x*), in company with the vena mediana cubiti (*y*), passes across the surface of the biceps (4), beneath the pectoantibrachialis, into the concavity of the elbow. Here it gives branches to the pectoantibrachialis, clavobrachialis, and extensor muscles of the forearm. It then passes onto the ventroradial border of the forearm (Fig. 130) and runs along this border, in company with the vena cephalica (Fig. 130, *c*) and the superficial radial nerve (*g*), to the wrist, sending off branches to the integument. At the wrist it turns onto the dorsum of the hand, passing in a gentle curve to the ulnar side and distad, and giving off a branch for the space between each pair of metacarpal bones. These branches (Fig. 130, *e*) (**Aa. digitales dorsales**) pass distad and anastomose with branches coming from the palm.

f. **A. radialis** (Fig. 123). Distad of the convexity of the elbow the brachial artery takes the name **radial artery.** It passes from the supracondyloid foramen on the medial side of the biceps tendon (1) and beneath the pronator teres muscle (5), giving off small branches, as far as the middle of the forearm, where it gives off the ulnar artery (*k*). It then passes from beneath the pronator teres (5) and lies on the surface of the fifth part of the flexor profundus (8), covered only by the fascia and integument. Near the wrist it sends off a branch (*m*) toward the ulnar side of the arm, which passes into the palm on the surface of the tendon of the flexor profundus, giving twigs to the digits and to the pad in the palm. A branch from this may join the ulnar, and the common trunk thus formed passes into the hand and gives origin to the branches described under the ulnar artery. The presence and size of this branch of the radial varies with the size of the ulnar artery, it being smaller or absent as the ulnar is larger. It is shown at *m*, Fig. 123. The radial artery (*g*) now turns gradually dorsad and passes beneath the tendon of the extensor brevis pollicis onto the dorsum of the hand. It passes over the oblique groove on the dorsal surface of the base of the second metacarpal beneath the tendon of the extensor carpi radialis longus and passes between the bases of the second and third metacarpals into the palm of the hand. Here it passes to the ulnar side and anastomoses with the ulnar artery to form the palmar arch.

Branches of the Radial Artery.

1. **A. radialis recurrens** (*i*).—The radial recurrent arises in the concavity of the elbow and sends a branch proximad to the structures in the concavity; it then continues to the radial side of the forearm at the elbow, supplying adjacent parts of the brachialis (2), the extensor carpi radialis, and the extensor communis digitorum.

2. **A. ulnaris recurrens** (*j*).—The ulnar recurrent arises on the medial side of the tendon of the biceps and supplies structures in the concavity of the elbow on the ulnar side, also the pronator teres (5) and proximal ends of the flexor carpi radialis and flexor profundis digitorum.

3. **Rami musculares.**—Muscular branches are given off along the course of the artery, to adjacent muscles. A nutrient artery to the radius leaves the radial artery about two centimeters distad of the supracondyloid foramen.

4. **Aa interosseæ** (**anterior** (*l*) and **posterior**) are given off usually separately between the origin of the ulnar artery and the biceps tendon. Sometimes they arise as a common trunk which soon divides. The **posterior interosseous artery** passes distad, supplying the flexor muscles of the forearm. It also sends a branch to the pronator teres. The **anterior interosseous** (*l*) may arise from the ulnar artery. It passes dorsad to the interosseous membrane, on which it runs distad; sends a nutrient branch to the ulna, and then passes to the wrist in the

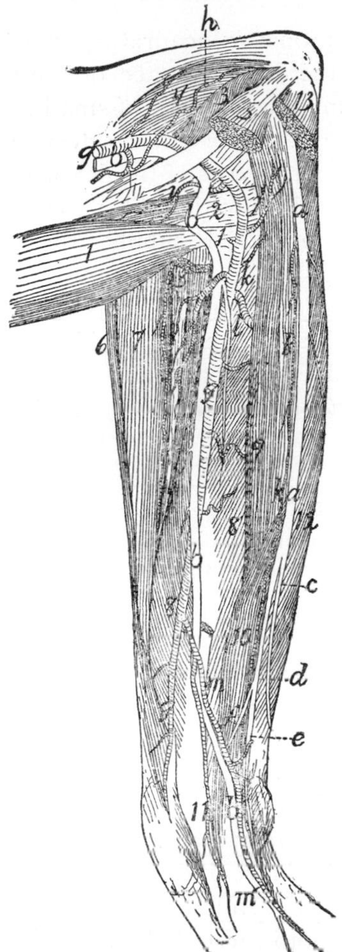

FIG. 123.—NERVES AND ARTERIES OF THE FOREARM, SEEN FROM THE FLEXOR SIDE.

Mm. palmaris longus, flexor carpi radialis, flexor carpi ulnaris, and the third and fourth heads of flexor profundus digitorum have been removed; also part of M. pronator teres. 1, biceps; 2, conjoined tendon of brachialis and clavobrachialis; 3, short portion of caput mediale of triceps brachii; 4, intermediate portion of caput mediale of triceps brachii; 5, cut ends of pronator teres; 6, brachioradialis; 7, extensor carpi radialis longus and brevis; 8, fifth head of flexor profundus digitorum; 9, second head of flexor profundus digitorum; 10, radial part of flexor sublimis digitorum; 11, common tendon of flexor profundus digitorum; 12, first head of flexor profundus digitorum; 13, cut origin of flexor carpi ulnaris. *a*, ulnar nerve; *b*, median nerve; *c*, dorsal cutaneous branch of the ulnar nerve; *d*, palmar branch of ulnar nerve; *e*, deep palmar branch; *f*, superficial palmar branch; *g'*, A. brachialis; *g*, A. radialis; *h*, A. collateralis ulnaris superior; *i*, A. radialis recurrens; *j*, A. ulnaris recurrens; *k*, A. ulnaris; *l*, A. interossea anterior; *m*, large branch of A. radialis, joining A. ulnaris.

substance of the pronator quadratus, which it supplies. It sends a branch to the dorsal surface of the wrist; this ramifies on the carpus, forming a network of small arteries.

5. **A. ulnaris** (*k*).—The ulnar artery passes beneath the second, third, and fourth parts of the flexor profundus digitorum (but outside of the origin of the fifth part), to the inner surface of the flexor carpi ulnaris. It supplies the flexor carpi ulnaris, the flexor profundus and palmaris longus, and passes on the inner surface of the flexor carpi ulnaris to the wrist. Near the wrist it sends a branch onto the side of the forearm, and another to its midventral part, and ends in a small branch to the wrist on the radial side of the pisiform bone. This branch anastomoses with the radial to form the palmar arch, described below.

6. The **palmar arch** (Fig. 124) is formed by the termination of the radial artery (*a*) in the palm and its junction with the end of the ulnar (*f*). The radial artery reaches the palm between the bases of the second and third metacarpals and passes thence toward the ulnar side and distad, piercing the interosseus muscle of the third digit and lying on the outer surface of the interossei of the third and fourth digits beneath the adductors of the second and fifth digits. A small communicating branch from the radial passes to it between the first and second metacarpals.

Branches of the palmar arch :

A. princeps pollicis et indicis (*c*) leaves the palmar arch near its radial end and sends a branch onto the ulnar side of the thumb and one onto the radial side of the index.

The **palmar interosseæ** (*d*) are three in number. They leave the palmar arch (*b*) and pass distad and dorsad in the intervals between the four ulnar digits. The radial one passes along the ulnar side of the first digit, the ulnar one along the radial side of the fifth digit. The middle one divides and supplies the contiguous sides of the third and fourth digits. Each of these interosseous arteries sends off muscular branches (*e*) to the short muscles in the palm, and branches into the fibrous pad which occupies the palm of the hand. The palmar arch also sends branches onto the dorsum of the hand at the sides of the fourth metacarpal. Branches pass from these proximad to the wrist.

B. Aorta abdominalis. The Abdominal Aorta.—The abdominal aorta emerges into the abdomen from between the crura of the diaphragm, at about the level of the second lumbar vertebra. It passes caudad along the dorsal middle line, lying to the left of the inferior vena cava. It gives off **parietal** branches to the body wall, and **visceral** branches to the viscera, and ventrad of the first sacral vertebra it gives off two large branches on each side, the **external iliac** (Fig. 126, *k*) and the **hypogastric** (Fig. 126, *l*)—a very small median vessel, the **sacralis media** (Fig. 126, *o*), continuing the course of the aorta and passing into the tail.

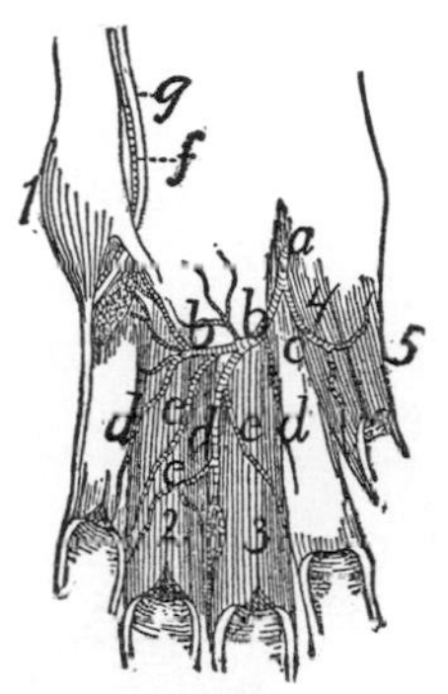

Fig. 124.
The Palmar Arch and its Branches in the Palm of the Hand.
The interosseous muscles have been removed, except those of the third and fourth digits. 1, M. abductor digiti quinti; 2, 3, Mm. interossei of third and fourth digits; 4, M. adductor pollicis; 5, M. flexor brevis pollicis. *a*, termination of radial artery; *b*, palmar arch; *c*, A. princeps pollicis et indicis; *d*, Aa. interosseæ; *e*, muscular branches of the same; *f*, A. ulnaris; *g*, deep palmar branch of ulnar nerve.

The aorta gives off the following branches: **A. cœliaca; A. mesenterica superior; Aa. adrenolumbales; Aa. renales; A. mesenterica inferior; Aa. iliolumbales; Aa. lumbales** (seven pairs); **Aa. iliacæ externæ; Aa. hypogastricæ.**

A. **A. cœliaca** (Fig. 125).—The cœliac artery is a large branch which is given off from the aorta one centimeter or less caudad of the opening in the diaphragm. It passes directly ventrad about three or four centimeters, then divides, usually at once, into three branches. The most cranial of these is the **hepatic** (*d*), the next is the **gastrica sinistra** (*e*), while the third and largest, seeming to form a continuation of the cœliac, is the **splenic** (*f*) (**A. lienalis**). The cœliac artery may give rise also, before its division, to the two **phrenic** arteries (which, however, usually arise from the adrenolumbales), and either before or at the point of division to one or two small **Aa. ventriculi dorsales,** which, however, frequently arise from the gastrica sinistra.

Branches of the cœliac artery:

1. **A. hepatica** (*d*).—The hepatic artery passes cranioventrad, pierces the descending limb of the great omentum and passes craniad to the liver, lying, together with the portal vein and common bile-duct, in the ventral boundary of the foramen

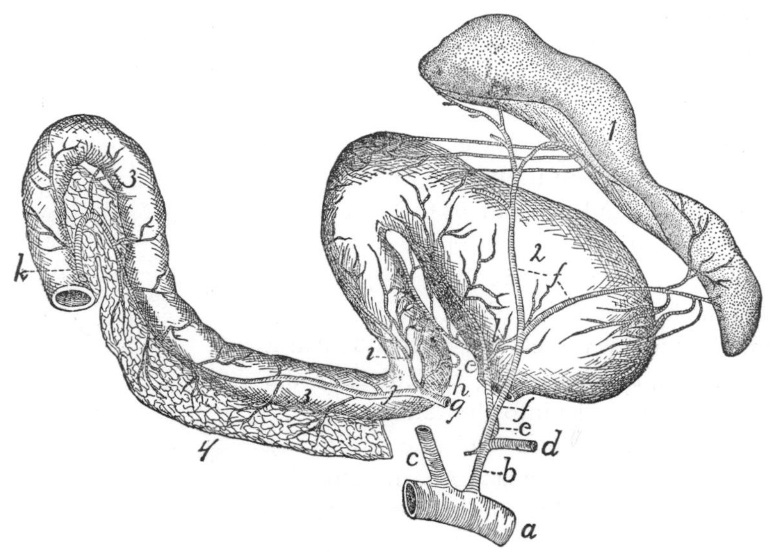

FIG. 125.—THE CŒLIAC ARTERY AND ITS BRANCHES.

a, abdominal aorta; *b*, A. cœliaca; *c*, A. mesenterica superior (cut); *d*, A. hepatica (cut); *e*, A. gastrica sinistra; *f*, A. lienalis; *g*, A. gastroduodenalis (cut from A. hepatica); *h*, A. pylorica; *i*, A. gastroepiploica dextra; *j*, A. pancreaticoduodenalis superior; *k*, A. pancreaticoduodenalis inferior (cut from inferior mesenteric); *l*, A. ventriculi dorsalis. 1, spleen; 2. stomach; 3, duodenum; 4, pancreas.

epiploicum (foramen of Winslow) and contained, together with the last-named vessels, in a fibrous sheath called the capsule of Glisson. Just before entering the sheath it gives off the **gastroduodenalis** (*g*). At its termination the hepatic artery divides, sending branches to the lobes of the liver and a **cystic** artery to the gall-bladder.

a. **A. gastroduodenalis** (*g*).—This arises from the hepatic near the pylorus and passes caudad, dividing one or two centimeters from its origin into three branches, **A. pylorica** (*h*), **A. pancreaticoduodenalis superior** (*j*), and **A. gastroepiploica dextra** (*i*). The **pylorica** (*h*) (which may arise directly from the hepatic) passes to the pylorus, thence along the lesser curvature of the stomach, dividing into numerous branches and anastomosing with the gastrica sinistra. The **pancreaticoduodenalis superior** (*j*) passes to the duodenum, supplying it and the duodenal part of the pancreas and anastomosing with the pancreaticoduodenalis inferior (*k*). The **gastroepiploica dextra** (*i*) passes along the greater curvature of the stomach from the pyloric end and supplies the walls of the stomach, sending branches also to the ascending limb of the great omentum. These branches anastomose with the terminal branches of the splenic artery.

2. **A. gastrica sinistra** (*e*).—This arises from the cœliac artery and passes to the lesser curvature of the stomach, extending along this to the right. It gives off many branches to the walls of the stomach, and anastomoses with A. pylorica.

A. ventriculi dorsalis (*l*).—One or two small arteries which arise either from the gastrica sinistra or the cœliac artery, and pass toward the dorsal part of the greater curvature of the stomach near its cardiac end.

3. **A. lienalis** (*f*).—The splenic artery is the largest of the branches of the cœliac axis, of which it appears to be the direct continuation. It divides into two large branches, one to the cranial end, the other to the caudal end, of the spleen (1). From the latter a large branch passes to the pancreas and descending limb of the great omentum.

B. **A. mesenterica superior** (Fig. 126, *d*).—The superior mesenteric artery is larger than the cœliac. It supplies the blood to the small intestines and caudal portion of the pancreas and to the ascending and transverse colon. It arises from the ventral side of the abdominal aorta about one centimeter caudad of the cœliac axis and passes caudoventrad, forming a curve with the convexity dextrad. It gives off the **pancreaticoduodenalis inferior, colica media, colica dextra, ileocolica,** and numerous branches to the small intestine.

1. **A. pancreaticoduodenalis inferior** (Fig. 125, *k*).—This passes to the caudal end of the pancreas and a part of the duodenum, anastomosing with the pancreaticoduodenalis superior.

2. **A. colica media** is a large branch to the transverse and

descending portions of the large intestine. It divides and sends branches in both directions which anastomose with the colica dextra and with branches from the inferior mesenteric arteries.

3. **A. colica dextra.**—A small branch which passes to the ascending and transverse colon, anastomosing with the colica media and ileocolica. It is sometimes absent.

4. **A. ileocolica.**—This passes to the cæcum and supplies that structure, sending branches to the ileocolic valve and the caudal end of the ileum, and anastomosing with the colica dextra and the intestinal branches of the superior mesenteric.

5. The superior mesenteric now divides into about sixteen terminal branches which pass to the small intestine. In many cases these branches unite near the intestine, forming arches, and from these arches numerous short branches pass to the intestine.

3. **A. adrenolumbalis** (or **lumboabdominalis**) (Fig. 126, *e*).—This rises from the aorta, one on each side, about two centimeters caudad of the superior mesenteric. Each passes laterad onto the dorsal body wall, supplying the muscles of this region. A large branch passes caudad along the surface of the muscles dorsad of the kidney and anastomoses with the ilio-lumbar artery. From the adrenolumbalis rises usually:

A. phrenica (*f*).—The phrenic artery rises either from the cœliac (*c*) or the adrenolumbalis (*e*) and passes to the diaphragm, near its dorsal border. In the diaphragm it passes ventrad, lying at the medial margin of the costal portion of the diaphragm, as far as its sternal portion, where it unites with the artery of the opposite side. The two thus form an arch, from which radiating arteries pass off to supply the diaphragm.

4. **A. renalis** (*g*).—The two renal arteries arise from the sides of the aorta, usually at about the same point, so that the left passes caudolaterad and the right craniolaterad (owing to the position of the kidneys). The artery usually divides just before entering the kidney (2). It passes dorsad of the vein (*t*). The renal artery sometimes sends a branch to the supra-renal body (1). It also occasionally gives origin to the spermatic artery (*h*).

5. **A. spermatica interna** (*h*).—This rises from the aorta

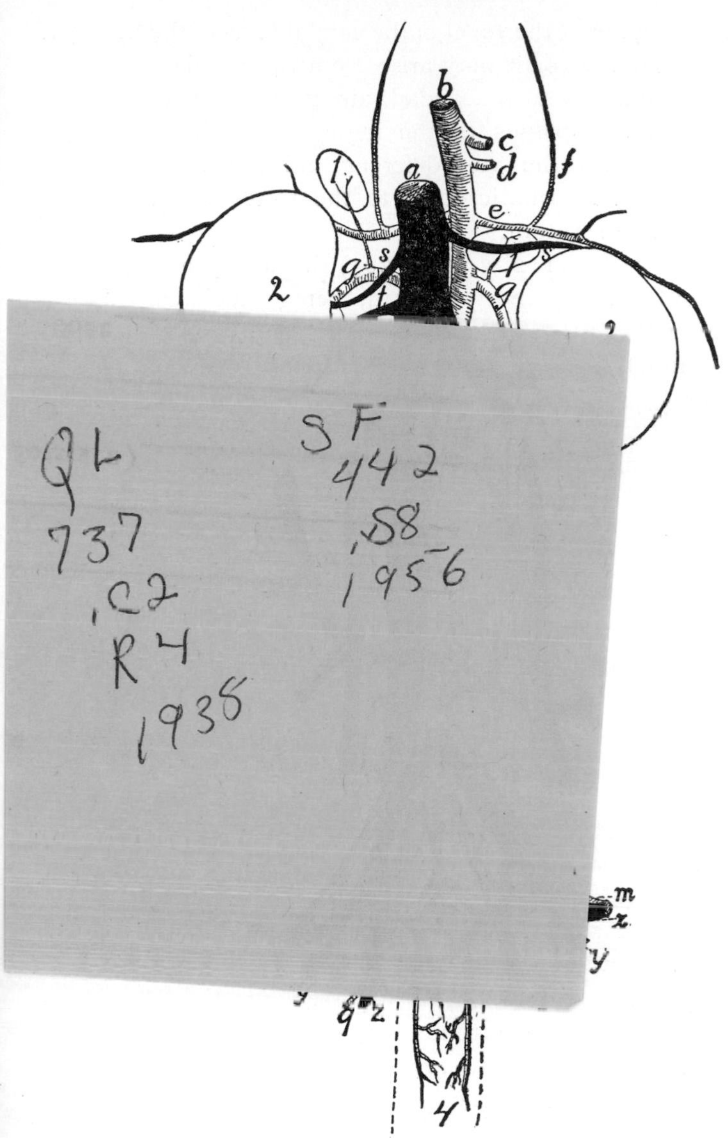

FIG. 126.—ABDOMINAL BLOOD-VESSELS, VENTRAL VIEW.

a, vena cava inferior; *b*, abdominal aorta; *c*, A. cœliaca (cut); *d*, A. mesenterica superior (cut); *e*, A. adrenolumbalis; *f*, A. phrenica; *g*, A. renalis; *h*, A. spermatica interna; *i*, A. mesenterica inferior (cut); *j*, A. iliolumbalis; *k*, A. iliaca externa; *l*, A. hypogastrica; *m*, beginning of A. femoralis; *n*, A. umbilicalis; *o*, A. and V. sacralis media (*o*, the artery; *o'*, the vein); *p*, A. glutea superior; *q*, A. glutea inferior; *r*, A. and V. hemorrhoidalis media; *s*, V. adrenolumbalis; *t*, V. renalis; *u*, V. spermatica interna; *v*, V. iliolumbalis; *w*, V. iliaca communis; *x*, V. femoralis; *y*, V. and A. profunda femoris; *z*, V. hypogastrica. 1, suprarenal body; 2, kidney; 3, ureter; 4, outline (broken) of rectum.

on each side at about the level of the caudal ends of the kidneys, and passes laterad (or it may arise from the renal). In male specimens the artery turns caudad, along with the corresponding vein (*u*), and passes to the inguinal canal. Thence it passes along with the vas deferens and the vein (forming all together the spermatic cord) to the testes and the other structures in the scrotum.

In females (Fig. 112, 2, page 265) the artery is larger and passes more nearly directly laterad, being much convoluted. It passes to the ovary, being now called the **ovarian artery.** It sends branches into the ovary (*c*) and to the cranial end of the uterus (*f*); the latter anastomosing with branches of the uterine artery (3).

6. **A. mesenterica inferior** (Fig. 126, *i*).—The inferior mesenteric artery has its origin from the aorta at about the level of the last lumbar vertebra. It passes toward the large intestine, and near it divides into two branches, the **colica sinistra,** which passes craniad along the descending colon, anastomosing with the colica media, and the **superior hemorrhoidal,** which passes caudad along the descending colon and rectum and anastomoses with the middle hemorrhoidal (page 308).

7. **A. iliolumbalis** (Fig. 126, *j*).—The iliolumbar arteries arise from the aorta about two centimeters caudad of the inferior mesenteric and pass laterad over the ventral surface of the psoas minor and iliopsoas muscles. Each divides into two main branches, one passing caudad and the other craniad; these supply the muscles of this region. The cranial branch anastomoses with branches of the adrenolumbalis (*e*). The caudal branch sends an artery through the abdominal wall to appear at the cranial edge of the thigh; it passes onto the lateral surface of M. sartorius and extends here some distance distad.

8. **A. lumbalis.**—There are usually seven pairs of lumbar arteries, passing almost directly dorsad from the dorsal surface of the aorta; the first pair arising just craniad of the diaphragm, the last at the same level as the origin of the external iliac. The two arteries of a pair usually arise from the aorta one behind the other, or they may arise by a common trunk. They correspond to the intercostal arteries. They pass

between the centra of the vertebræ and the muscles of the dorsal region, and send one main branch laterad, the other dorsad; both supply the dorsal muscles. From the dorsal branch small arteries pass into the vertebral canal to join the anterior spinal artery.

9. **A. iliaca externa** (Fig. 126, *k*).—The external iliac artery passes obliquely caudad from the aorta, lying ventrad of the common iliac vein and against the medial surface of the psoas minor muscle. It passes onto the ventral surface of this and the iliopsoas and at the same time reaches the tendon of the abdominal muscles; through a small opening in this tendon lying ventrocaudad of that for the iliopsoas, it leaves the abdominal cavity. On its emergence from the abdominal cavity onto the medial surface of the thigh it receives the name **A. femoralis** (*m*). The branches of the external iliac artery are described below (page 309).

10. **A. hypogastrica** (or iliaca interna) (Fig. 126, *l*).—The hypogastric or internal iliac arteries are given off from the aorta usually within a centimeter caudad of the external iliac. Each passes caudolaterad, lying on the medial side of the common iliac vein, and divides into branches which supply the structures within the pelvis and the muscles about the pelvic wall. There is much variation in the origin and relations of the branches of this artery. The following seems to be a very common arrangement: A very short distance from the origin the **umbilical** artery (*n*) is given off. The hypogastric artery then extends two or three centimeters and gives off **A. glutea superior** (*p*), which passes at once to the pelvic wall. A little farther caudad the hypogastric divides into the **middle hemorrhoidal** (*r*), to the rectum, and the **glutea inferior** (*q*), which passes out of the pelvis.

Branches of the hypogastric artery:

a. **A. umbilicalis** (Fig. 126, *n*).—This small artery arises from the hypogastric about one centimeter from the beginning of the latter, and passes ventrad to the bladder. Here it divides into two branches—the **superior vesical** to the sides of the bladder, the **inferior vesical** to the neck of the bladder and the urethra.

b. **A. glutea superior** (Fig. 126, *p*).—This passes dorsolaterad from the hypogastric and reaches the pelvic wall against the medial surface of the ilium. Here it divides into two branches. One passes between the iliopsoas muscle and the ventral border of the ilium to the medial surface of the gluteus maximus; it gives branches to the gluteus muscles, the pyriformis, and the rectus femoris. The other branch passes dorsad of the ilium, sending a branch to the medial surface of the gluteus medius, and a small branch which joins the lateral sacral artery and enters thus the sacral canal.

c. **A. hemorrhoidalis media** (Fig. 126, *r*).—The middle hemorrhoidal passes ventrad from the hypogastric, onto the lateral surface of the rectum. It passes caudad near the ventral side of the rectum as far as the anus. A short distance from the origin it gives off a branch which passes almost directly ventrad toward the beginning of the urethra. In the male this branch is small, sending twigs to the urethra and the prostate. In the female it is much larger, forming **A. uterina** (Fig. 112, 3, page 265). The uterine artery turns craniad onto the uterus, which it supplies, passing to the cranial end of the uterine cornu and anastomosing with the ovarian artery.

The middle hemorrhoidal gives off in the female branches to the vagina (Fig. 112, *m*) and neck of the bladder (*k*), and a large branch to the urogenital sinus (*n*); it then supplies the anal glands and other structures about the anus, and anastomoses with the terminal branches of the hemorrhoidalis superior. In the male branchlets are given to the urethra, to the bulbourethral (or Cowper's) gland, and to the penis. The **A. dorsalis penis** is a small branch which passes along the median dorsal groove of the penis to the glans. The middle hemorrhoidal then supplies the structures about the anus and anastomoses with the superior hemorrhoidal, as in the female.

d. **A. glutea inferior** (Fig. 126, *q*).—This is the terminal portion of the hypogastric. It passes along with the great sciatic nerve to the great sciatic notch, and reaches the medial surface of M. pyriformis. It divides into branches which supply the gluteus and pyriformis muscles, while a small branch accompanies the great sciatic nerve. A small branch also passes onto the lateral surface of the tail, extending caudad along its side.

11. **A. sacralis media** (Fig. 126, *o*).—This is the continuation of the aorta into the sacral and caudal regions. It extends to near the end of the tail, lying in the ventral middle line against the sacral and caudal vertebræ. In the caudal region it passes through the hæmal arches, covered by the chevron bones. Between the vertebræ it gives off side branches comparable to the intercostal and lumbar arteries of the aorta.

Branches of the sacralis media:

a. **A. sacralis lateralis.**—Behind the first sacral vertebra a large branch, the lateral sacral, is given off on each side. This enters the first anterior sacral foramen, gives a branch to the structures in the sacral canal, and sends a dorsal branch out through the posterior sacral foramen to the muscles on the dorsal side of the sacrum.

Similar but smaller branches are given off between the succeeding vertebræ, sacral and caudal.

The External Iliac and its Branches.—The origin of the external iliac (Fig. 126, *k*) is described above (page 307). It gives off the following branches:

1. **A. profunda femoris** (Fig. 126, *y*).—This is given off just before the external iliac leaves the abdominal cavity. It passes caudad, and about one centimeter from its origin it gives off three branches, sometimes all separately, sometimes two in common. One of these passes mediad in the lateral ligament of the bladder and ramifies on the lateral surface of that organ. A second passes through the abdominal wall and into the fat on the medial surface of the thigh; it sends a branch caudad toward the external genital organs, while its main trunk passes distad in the subcutaneous fat almost to the knee. From one of these two a small branchlet passes in the male to the spermatic cord and accompanies this to the testis; it represents thus the **external spermatic artery.** The third branch, **A. epigastrica inferior,** passes directly to the ventral surface of the rectus abdominis muscle, on which it passes craniad, sending branches to the muscles of the abdominal walls. It anastomoses with terminal branches of the internal mammary artery.

The profunda femoris itself passes between the iliopsoas and the pectineus muscles, then to the medial surface of the adductor femoris. It divides into branches which supply the pectineus, adductor longus, adductor femoris, caudofemoralis, quadratus femoris, semimembranosus, and semitendinosus.

2. **A. femoralis** (Fig. 127).—This is the continuation of the external iliac onto the medial surface of the thigh. The artery lies in a triangular depression between the borders of the sartorius (1) and gracilis (9) muscles. The floor of the depression is formed by the adductor longus (6), pectineus (5), vastus internus, and rectus femoris (3) muscles. This triangular depression is known as the **ilio-pectineal** fossa, or Scarpa's triangle; it contains also the femoral vein (*a*) and saphenous nerve (*g*), which pass along with the artery.

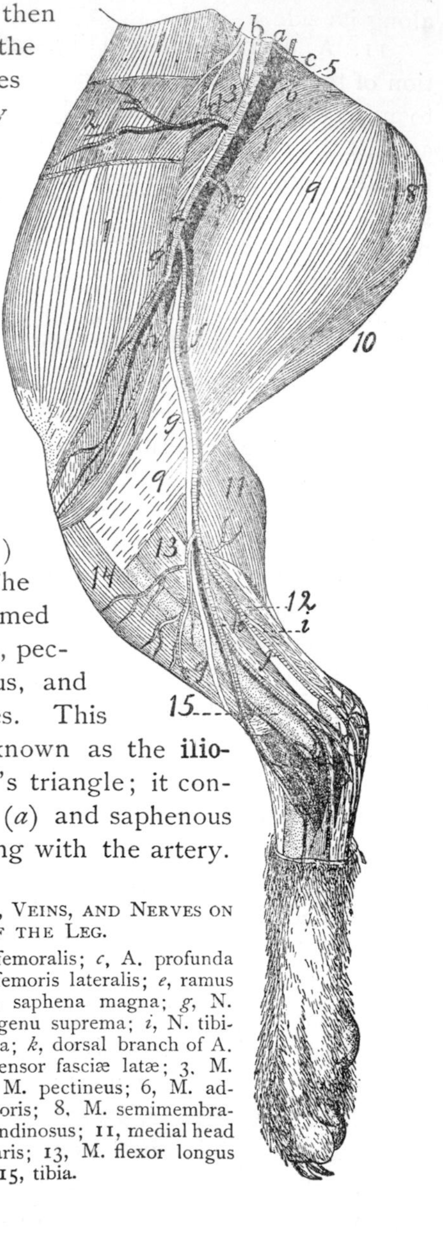

FIG. 127.—SUPERFICIAL ARTERIES, VEINS, AND NERVES ON THE MEDIAL SIDE OF THE LEG.

a, A. and V. femoralis; *b*, N. femoralis; *c*, A. profunda femoris; *d*, A. and V. circumflexa femoris lateralis; *e*, ramus muscularis; *f*, A. saphena and V. saphena magna; *g*, N. saphenus; *h*, A. and V. articularis genu suprema; *i*, N. tibialis; *j*, plantar branch of A. saphena; *k*, dorsal branch of A. saphena. 1, M. sartorius; 2, M. tensor fasciæ latæ; 3, M. rectus femoris; 4, M. iliopsoas; 5, M. pectineus; 6, M. adductor longus; 7, M. adductor femoris; 8, M. semimembranosus; 9, M. gracilis; 10, M. semitendinosus; 11, medial head of M. gastrocnemius; 12, M. plantaris; 13, M. flexor longus digitorum: 14, M. tibialis anterior; 15, tibia.

The artery extends distad, and at about the middle of the length of the thigh it passes, along with the vein and nerve, into a groove between the vastus medialis and the adductor femoris. This groove is converted into a canal by the overlying aponeurosis; it is known as **Hunter's canal** or the **canalis adductorius.** At the distal end of the adductor femoris the femoral artery ceases to be superficial and passes between the vastus medialis and the semimembranosus to the popliteal space; it now receives the name **A. poplitea.**

Branches of the femoral artery:

a. **A. circumflexa femoris lateralis** (Fig. 127, *d*).—The lateral circumflex arises from the femoral about one centimeter from its emergence from the abdominal cavity. It passes craniad and laterad and divides into two main portions. One part passes between the rectus femoris and vastus medialis, gives branches to these muscles, and sends an ascending branch to the structures about the hip-joint, and a descending branch into the vastus medialis muscle. The remainder of the lateral circumflex passes along the inner (lateral) surface of the sartorius (1) to the cranial border of the leg, giving branches to the sartorius (1) and tensor fasciæ latæ (2).

b. A large **muscular** branch (*e*) passes caudad (or ventrad) and distad across the distal end of the adductor femoris (7) and between the gracilis (9) and semimembranosus, supplying these muscles. Other small muscular branches may be given off from both sides of the femoral.

c. **A. articularis genu suprema** (*h*).—The superior articular artery arises from the femoral, either in common with the saphenous artery or separately, a little proximad of the point where the femoral ceases to be superficial. It passes toward the knee, between the vastus medialis and semimembranosus, and covered by the sartorius (1), and ramifies over the medial surface of the knee-joint and in the structures just proximad of the joint.

d. **A. saphena** (*f*).—The saphenous artery frequently takes origin in common with the superior articular (*h*), but may arise separately at about the same level. It passes distad across the gracilis (9), accompanied by the saphenous nerve (*g*) and vein, sends several branches dorsad (toward the knee), and at about the middle of the lower leg it divides into two main branches, a **dorsal** branch (*k*), passing to the dorsum of the foot, and a **plantar** branch (*j*), to the sole of the foot. The dorsal branch is accompanied by the main saphenous nerve (*g*) and vein. It sends one or two branches to the medial side of the ankle-joint, passes then onto the dorsum of the foot, and divides into four main branches. The medial one passes along the medial side of the medial digit; the other three pass to the intervals between the digits. Each divides into two branches which supply the contiguous sides of the two digits between which the interval lies. The dorsal branch thus supplies arteries to the sides of all the digits except to the lateral side of the lateral digit. This is supplied by A. suralis.

The plantar branch (*j*) is larger than the dorsal. It passes distad on the medial surface of the flexor longus hallucis, accompanied by the tibial nerve, and across the space between the tendon of Achilles and the flexor. It gives superficial and deep branches to the structures about the ankle-joint, and sends inward a branch from the lateral side (Fig. 128, *d*) which joins the termination of A. tibialis anterior to form the plantar arch. It then passes distad along the plantar surface of the foot, nearer its medial border. Beneath the pad in the sole of the foot it divides into three branches which supply the interosseous spaces between the three digits.

e. **A. poplitea.**—The main trunk of the femoral artery passes between the vastus medialis and the semimembranosus and then through the distal portion of the adductor femoris to reach the popliteal space. This is the space ventrad (or caudad) of the knee, between the biceps femoris on one side and the semimembranosus on the other. Here the artery receives the name **A. poplitea,** or popliteal artery. The popliteal artery gives off a number of large branches as it passes through the popliteal space, passes between the condyles of the femur and underneath the popliteal muscle, and finally turns dorsolaterad between the tibia and fibula, just distad of the head of the fibula. It now receives the name **A. tibialis**

anterior and passes distad along the dorsal (anterior) border of the fibula.

Branches of the popliteal artery:

1. **A. suralis.**—This is a large branch which passes distad from the caudal side of the popliteal artery. It sends branches to the biceps and to the fat in the popliteal space, and passes onto the ventral border of the lateral head of the gastrocnemius. It sends branches to both heads of the gastrocnemius and to the popliteus, passes distad onto the lateral surface of the tendon of Achilles, and may be traced to the proximal portion of the dorsolateral side of the foot, where it sends many branches to the integument about the ankle-joint. It then passes along the lateral side of the foot and supplies the artery on the lateral side of the fifth digit.

2. **Aa. genu posteriores.**—Several small arteries which pass to the knee-joint.

3. **Rami musculares.**—Numerous small branches to the muscles about the popliteal space.

4. **A. tibialis posterior.**—This is the largest branch of the popliteal artery, which it leaves just before the latter passes beneath the popliteal muscle. The tibialis posterior passes at first mediad, then turns distad, passes across the popliteus muscle onto the surface of the flexor longus hallucis, and ramifies in the substance of this muscle and its tendon. It gives branches also to the gastrocnemius and soleus. (It does not pass into the foot as does the corresponding artery in man.)

5. **A. tibialis anterior.**—The anterior tibial artery is the continuation of the popliteal after its passage through the interosseous membrane between tibia and fibula to the dorsal side of the lower leg. Here it passes distad, lying against the interosseous membrane, between the extensor longus digitorum and the tibialis anterior muscle, or partly imbedded in the substance of the latter. It passes, lying beneath the tendons of these muscles, through the transverse ligament proximad of the malleoli, thus reaching the dorsum of the foot. It extends distad across the tarsus to the space between the second and third metatarsals, and through this space to the plantar side of the

foot (Fig. 128). Here it receives one or two small branches (*a* and *d*) from the plantar branch of A. saphena (forming with them the **plantar arch** (*c*)), and passing distad and slightly laterad, divides into three main portions (*e*). These (**Aa. digitales plantares**) pass to the three intervals between the digits. The medial one passes along the lateral side of the second digit; the next divides, sending a branch to the lateral side of the third digit and the medial side of the fourth; the lateral one passes along the medial border of the fifth digit. The Aa. digitales plantares send numerous branches to the interosseous muscles.

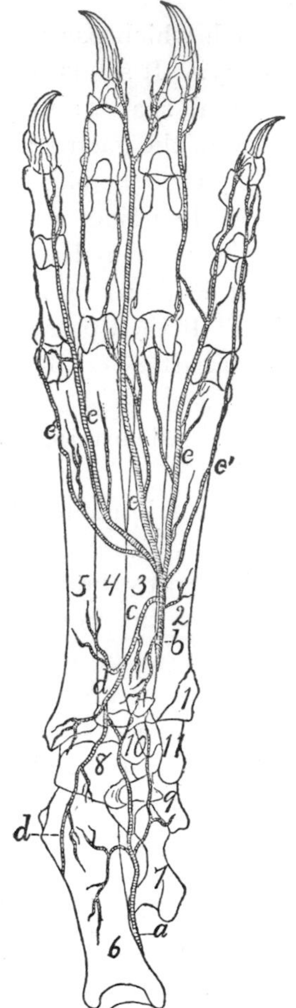

FIG. 128.—DEEP ARTERIES ON THE PLANTAR SURFACE OF THE FOOT.

a, medial twig from plantar branch of A. saphena; *b*, A. tibialis anterior (or plantaris profunda); *c*, plantar arch; *d*, lateral twig from plantar branch of A. saphena; *e*, terminal branches from A. tibialis anterior.

Branches of the tibialis anterior:

a. **A. tibialis recurrens.**—Immediately after passing through the interosseous membrane the anterior tibial sends a small artery proximad to the knee-joint.

b. **Rami musculares.**—Numerous short branches throughout the course of the artery, to the muscles about it.

c. **Ramus superficialis.**—A larger branch leaves the lateral surface of the artery about one-third the distance from the knee to the ankle and passes along with the superficial peroneal nerve, at first beneath M. peroneus longus, then superficially. It passes onto the dorsal surface of the foot and becomes connected with terminal branches of **A. saphena.**

d. **A. tarsea medialis.**—This arises from the tibialis anterior just distad of the transverse ligament through which it passes at the ankle, passes over the medial surface of the astragalus, and is distributed to the ligaments about the ankle-joint. It anastomoses with the plantar branch of A. saphena.

e. **A. metatarsea.**—The metatarsal artery passes laterad from the tibialis anterior at the distal boundary of the tarsus, on the dorsal surface of the foot. It sends branches distad in the intervals between the third and fourth and the fourth and fifth metatarsals.

The distal branches (Fig. 128) of the tibialis anterior have been described in the general description of the artery.

THE VEINS. VENÆ.

Venæ pulmonales. The Pulmonary Veins.

The pulmonary veins follow in the lungs the course of the bronchi. They enter the left auricle in three groups (Fig. 116, page 276). The first of these (*i*) comes from the anterior and middle lobes of the right side, the second (*h*) from the corresponding lobes of the left side, and the third (*g*) from the terminal lobes of both sides. Each group is composed of two or three veins and opens into a sinus or extension of the auricle. The sinuses are from their position dextral (*i*), sinistral (*h*), and dorsal (*g*).

The Veins of the Body.

The veins of the body may be classified into three main groups: (1) the veins of the heart; (2) the superior vena cava and its branches; (3) the inferior vena cava and its branches. The portal system of veins will be considered with the inferior vena cava.

1. Veins of the Heart.

The veins of the heart consist of one large vein, the **vena cordis magna,** and a number of small veins.

Vena cordis magna (Fig. 118, 3).—This arises as a number of scattered branches on the surface of both ventricles. These unite to form two main trunks. One of these, on the ventral side of the heart, marks externally the septum between the two ventricles. It passes beneath the left auricular appendage, then turns to the left and passes along the sulcus coronarius to the dorsal side of the heart. Here it unites with the second main trunk which ramifies over the surface of the left ventricle. Arriving at the base of the right auricle it enters this by the coronary sinus, which lies just beneath the opening of the inferior vena cava.

In addition to the vena cordis magna and its branches there are a number of small veins, especially in the wall of the right ventricle. These enter the right auricle by a number of small separate openings along the sulcus coronarius.

2. **Vena cava superior** (Fig. 129, *b*).

The superior vena cava is the great vein returning the blood from the head, fore-limb, and cranial part of the trunk. It extends from the level of the first rib on the right side of the vertebral column to the right auricle. Its caudal end lies dorsad of the aortic arch. Opposite the right rib it is formed by the junction of the two innominate veins (*m*).

Branches of the superior vena cava:

1. **V. azygos** (*d*).—The first branch of the superior vena cava is the azygos vein, which enters the vena cava on the right side a centimeter or less craniad of the root of the right lung. It is formed in the abdominal cavity by the confluence of two or three small veins, which collect the blood from the muscles of the dorsal wall of the abdomen. The small median trunk thus formed enters the thoracic cavity between the crura of the diaphragm and lies on the ventral surface of the centra of the thoracic vertebræ, slightly to the right of the middle line. The azygos receives the **intercostal** veins (*n*), which correspond to the intercostal arteries and have the same course and distribution. In the caudal part of the thoracic cavity the intercostals enter the azygos separately, but the intercostals of

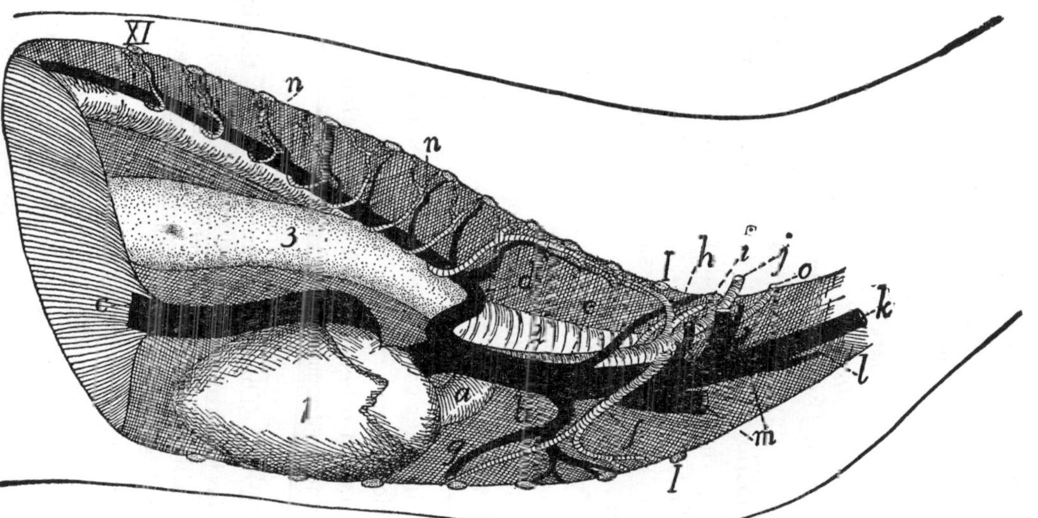

FIG. 129.—THORACIC BLOOD-VESSELS, FROM THE RIGHT SIDE.

a, aorta; *b*, vena cava superior; *c*, vena cava inferior; *d*, V. azygos; *e*, A. subclavia dextra; *f*, A. mammaria interna; *g*, V. mammaria interna; *h*, costocervical axis; *i*, united trunk of vertebral and costocervical veins; *j*, A. and V. axillaris; *k*, V. jugularis externa; *l*, V. jugularis interna; *m*, the two innominate veins; *n*, intercostal arteries and veins; *o*, thyrocervical axis. 1, heart; 2, trachea; 3, œsophagus; *I–XI*, cut ends of the first eleven ribs.

the cranial intercostal spaces usually unite two or three together and enter the azygos by one or more common trunks. The azygos also receives **bronchial** and **œsophageal** veins, corresponding to the similarly named arteries.

2. **V. mammaria interna** (*g*).—The internal mammary veins follow the corresponding arteries. The two veins unite to form a common trunk, the **sternal vein,** which, after receiving a branch from the cranial part of the sternum, enters the vena cava opposite the third rib.

3. **Vv. anonymæ** (Fig. 129, *m*; Fig. 115, *p*).—The innominate veins unite opposite the first intercostal space to form the vena cava superior. Each extends from the cranial end of the vena cava superior craniolaterad to a point a short distance craniad of the first rib and is there formed by the union of the **external jugular** (Fig. 129, *k*) and **subclavian** (*j*) veins. The innominate vein has the following branches:

A and B. **Vv. vertebralis** and **costocervicalis** (*i*).—The vertebral and costocervical veins unite to form a single trunk which enters the innominate about opposite the first rib. These two veins follow the corresponding arteries. (Sometimes the vertebral and costocervical veins enter the innominate separately, and in other cases one or more of the components of the costocervical veins (e.g., the transversa colli) may enter the axillary vein. In other cases the entire common trunk of the vertebralis and costocervicalis may enter the superior vena cava directly.)

C. **V. subclavia.**—The subclavian vein enters the innominate at about the level of the first rib. Outside of the thorax it is called the axillary vein (*j*); this comes from the arm.

Veins of the Arm.—The blood is returned from the arm by two systems of veins,—a deep and a superficial system.

The deep system is composed of veins which correspond to the branches of the axillary artery, follow in general the same course, and receive the same names (Fig. 122). They unite to form the axillary vein. The brachial vein does not pass with the brachial artery through the supracondyloid foramen.

The superficial system comprises the vena cephalica and its branches.

V. cephalica (Fig. 130).—Several superficial branches lying in the palm of the hand unite to form a common trunk which curves about the radial side of the wrist and here unites with a similarly formed trunk from the dorsum of the hand. The vein formed by this union, vena cephalica (antibrachii) (*c*), passes to the elbow accompanying the radial nerve (*g*) and the collateral radial artery (*d*), and lying on the extensor carpi radialis longus muscle just beneath the integument. It receives small lateral superficial branches. At the elbow it divides into two: these are the vena cephalica (humeri) (*a*) and the **vena mediana cubiti** (*b*). The latter passes beneath the pectoantibrachialis muscle, across the biceps, and unites with the brachial vein in the concavity of the elbow.

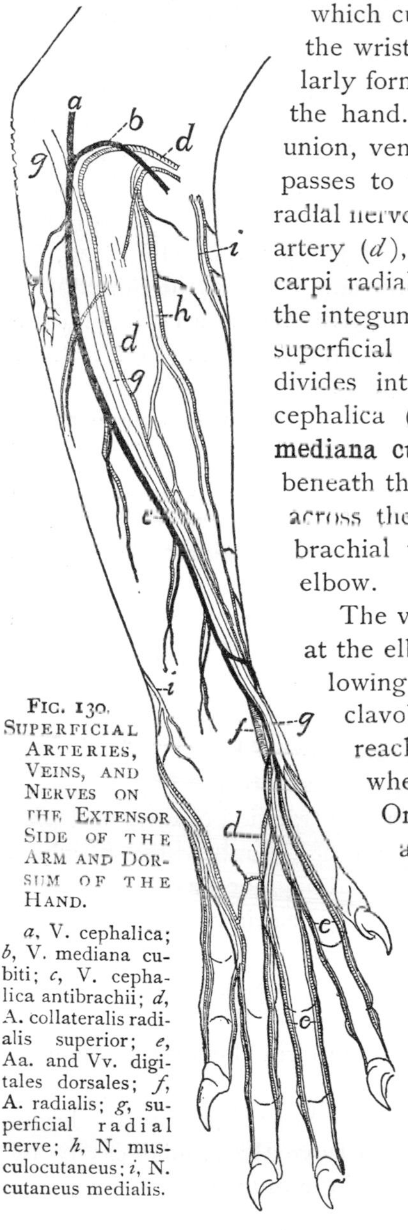

FIG. 130. SUPERFICIAL ARTERIES, VEINS, AND NERVES ON THE EXTENSOR SIDE OF THE ARM AND DORSUM OF THE HAND.

a, V. cephalica; *b*, V. mediana cubiti; *c*, V. cephalica antibrachii; *d*, A. collateralis radialis superior; *e*, Aa. and Vv. digitales dorsales; *f*, A. radialis; *g*, superficial radial nerve; *h*, N. musculocutaneus; *i*, N. cutaneus medialis.

The vena cephalica (humeri) passes at the elbow onto the upper arm, following the lateral border of the clavobrachial muscle. It thus reaches the acromiodeltoid muscle, where it divides into two branches. One passes inward beneath the acromiodeltoid, and joins the vena circumflexa posterior (a branch of the axillary). The second continues over the outer surface of the shoulder, and finally joins the vena transversa scapulæ (a branch of the external jugular).

D. **V. jugularis externa** (Fig. 131; Fig. 65, 5, page 109).—The external jugular vein comes from the head and face. It is formed by the junction of the anterior (Fig. 131, *c*) and posterior (*b*) facial veins near the ventral border of the sternomastoid muscle. It passes thence obliquely across the sternomastoid to the triangular interval between it and the clavotrapezius. In the interval it receives a small branch which accompanies the branch of the transversa scapulæ artery to the clavobrachialis muscle, receives next the common trunk of the vena cephalica and transversa scapulæ, and opposite the cranial end of the manubrium receives the internal jugular vein (Fig. 129, *l*). It then unites with the subclavian to form the innominate vein. Near the point where it receives the internal jugular the external jugular vein receives the **thoracic duct** (Fig. 118, 5).

Branches of the external jugular:

a. **V. transversa scapulæ.**—This follows the course of the artery of the same name. One of its branches receives one of the two terminal divisions of the vena cephalica (q. v.). In many cases veins which correspond to branches of the transversa scapulæ artery enter the external jugular separately (as shown in Fig. 118, *x* and *y*).

b. **V. cervicalis ascendens.**—A small branch which follows the corresponding branch of the thyrocervical axis.

c. **V. jugularis interna** (Fig. 118, 2; Fig. 119, page 284). —The internal jugular vein varies much in size and in the place where it joins the external jugular. The point of junction is usually at about the level of the first rib, but may be much farther craniad. It arises on the ventral side of the basal portion of the occipital by the junction of a number of veins which are described below. The internal jugular passes caudad in the neck region at the side of the trachea, in company with the common carotid artery and the vagus and sympathetic nerves. In this region it receives branches which accompany the branches of the common carotid artery.

The veins which by their union form the internal jugular vein are the following:

(1) One or two veins from the venous sinuses of the brain, the **inferior cerebral veins,** which leave the cranial cavity by the jugular foramen. (See veins of the brain.)

(2) A large communicating branch from the posterior facial.

(3) The **vena occipitalis,** a large branch coming from the vertebral column (which it leaves by the atlantal foramen) and from the back of the head.

d. **V. facialis anterior** (Fig. 131, *c*).—The anterior facial vein collects the blood from the face, the tongue, and adjacent parts; it joins the **posterior facial** (*b*) caudad of the angle of the jaw to form the external jugular vein.

The anterior facial begins over the frontal bone caudad of the orbit, where it is known as the **frontal** vein (*c''*). This runs along the dorsal border of the orbit, into which it dips. It sends a communicating branch into the orbit, and receives small veins (**superior palpebral**) from the upper eyelid. It then turns ventrad, passing along the cranial angle of the eye between the levator labii superioris proprius (5) and the orbicularis oculi (8) muscles, being called in this region the **angular vein** (*c'*). This receives branches (**external nasal veins,** *k*) from the side of the nose. The vein crosses the malar bone obliquely (now receiving the name **anterior facial,** *c*) and follows the cranioventral border of the masseter muscle (9). As it passes the infraorbital foramen it receives through the foramen a small vein from within the orbit. It receives also the **inferior palpebral** (*j*) from the lower eyelid, and the **superior labial** vein (*i*) from the upper lip. Just caudad of the angle of the mouth it receives from beneath the cranioventral margin of the masseter the **V. facialis profunda** (*h*) described below. Still farther caudad it receives the **inferior labial** vein (*g*) from the lower lip, and a small branch from the masseter muscle. Caudad of the middle of the cranioventral border of the masseter it receives from beneath the lymphatic gland of this region the large **submental** vein (*f*). Next the anterior facial vein receives a large communicating branch (**V. transversa,** *d*) which passes transversely across the ventral surface of the throat and connects the two anterior facial veins of the opposite sides. From the middle of this communicating branch an unpaired trunk passes caudad in the middle line and divides into the two **laryngeal** veins, which pass to the larynx; a small branch is continued from the unpaired trunk craniad into the tongue. The communicating branch receives also near its junction with the anterior facial a rather large superficial branch (*e*) which comes from the sides of the lower jaw and passes

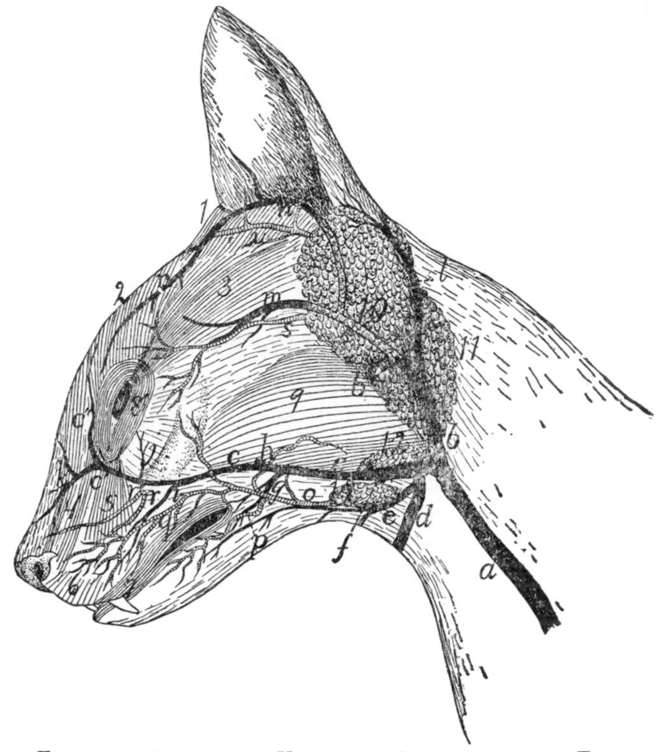

FIG. 131.—SUPERFICIAL VEINS AND ARTERIES OF THE FACE.

a, external jugular vein; *b*, posterior facial vein; *c*, anterior facial vein (*c'*, angular vein; *c''*, frontal vein); *d*, communicating branch with opposite anterior facial; *e*, superficial branch from lower jaw; *f*, submental vein; *g*, inferior labial vein; *h*, deep facial vein; *i*, superior labial vein; *j*, inferior palpebral vein; *k*, external nasal veins; *l*, posterior auricular vein; *m*, superficial temporal vein; *n*, anterior auricular vein; *o*, external maxillary artery; *p*, inferior labial artery; *q*, superior labial artery; *r*, infraorbital arteries; *s*, superficial temporal artery; *u*, anterior auricular branch of posterior auricular artery. 1, M. adductor auris superior; 2, M. corrugator supercilii medialis; 3, M. corrugator supercilii lateralis; 4, M. levator labii superioris alæque nasi; 5, M. levator labii superioris proprius; 6, M. myrtiformis; 7, M. orbicularis oris; 8, M. orbicularis oculi; 9, M. masseter; 10, parotid gland; 11, submaxillary gland; 12, lymphatic glands.

across the lymphatic gland (12) to join the communicating branch.

The following larger branches of the anterior facial are not described above:

V. facialis profunda (Fig. 131, *h*).—The deep facial vein enters the anterior facial from beneath the masseter, just caudad of the angle of the mouth. It collects branches from the soft and hard palates and the teeth, these branches passing along with the corresponding arteries for a distance, then uniting and passing ventrolaterad beneath the zygomatic arch to join the anterior facial. The deep facial vein also receives branches which come from the venous plexus that lies in the same region as the arterial carotid plexus.

V. submentalis (Fig. 131, *f*).—This enters the anterior facial vein at the ventral border of the masseter muscle and near the cranial end of the two superficial lymph-glands (12) in this region. The submental vein is formed at the dorsal border of the digastric muscle by two branches emerging from between the digastric and the mandible. The more cranial of these, **V. lingualis,** collects branches from the tongue, from its middle to the tip; it passes through the middle of the lateral border of the mylohyoid muscle to join the other branch. The second branch emerges from between the mandible and the pterygoid muscles. It comes from near the caudal end of the mandible, where it becomes continuous with a communicating branch from the posterior facial vein, and receives a branch which comes from the mandibular canal; also small branches from the adjacent parts.

c. **V. facialis posterior** (Fig. 131, *b*).—The posterior facial vein arises from the region of the internal maxillary artery, its terminal branches following the branches of the artery. It collects blood from the pterygoid, masseter (9), and temporal muscles, and forms a plexus which is interwoven with the carotid (arterial) plexus in the region of the orbital fissure. It is connected with the submental vein by a communicating branch. From the posterior facial a branch extends ventrad close against the outer surface of the tympanic bulla and then turns caudad, receives a branch from the pharynx, then continues to join the internal jugular. The posterior facial itself passes laterad along the caudal border of the masseter (9) and the ventral border of the parotid gland (10), then becomes superficial and turns ventrad over the outer surface of the submaxillary gland (11) to join the anterior facial (*c*) caudad of the angle of the jaw.

As it passes ventrad of the parotid gland (10), just before becoming superficial, the posterior facial receives the **superficial temporal** (*m*). This at first follows the superficial temporal artery (*s*), then enters the substance of the parotid gland, joining the posterior facial near the ventral border of the latter. The superficial temporal receives the **anterior auricular** (*n*), a large vein passing along the cranial border of the auricular opening and arising dorsad of the eye.

The posterior facial receives also, at the point where it passes from beneath the parotid gland, the **posterior auricular** or **great auricular** vein (*l*). This collects blood from the back of the head and the external ear, its branches following those of the artery of the same name. It passes along the caudal border of the parotid gland to join the posterior facial.

VEINS OF THE BRAIN AND SPINAL CORD.—The veins of the brain form a large number of small vessels which pour their blood into larger veins lying in folds of the dura mater; these are known as the **venous sinuses** of the dura mater. These sinuses communicate with the venous plexus about the orbital fissure, coming from the posterior facial vein; with the internal jugular through the jugular foramen, and with the vertebral veins, in the vertebral canal. The chief sinuses of the dura mater on the dorsal side of the brain are as follows:

1. **Sinus sagittalis superior.**—This lies in the dorsal part of the falx cerebri, between the two hemispheres of the cerebrum. It receives veins from the dorsal and middle parts of the cerebrum, and passes caudad to the tentorium. Here it enters the sinus transversus. It receives the **vena cerebri magna,** a large vein coming from the interior of the brain and passing directly dorsad at the caudal end of the corpus callosum to enter the sinus sagittalis.

2. **Sinus transversus.**—This lies in a canal in the dorsal border of the tentorium. It receives numerous small veins from the cerebellum, roof of the skull, etc. One or two centimeters on each side of the middle line the sinus transversus passes out of the canal onto the caudal surface of the tentorium.

thence proceeds caudoventrad obliquely over the surface of the cerebellum, unites with veins from the ventral side of the brain, leaves the skull by the jugular foramen, forming thus the **inferior cerebral** vein, and joins the internal jugular vein.

On the ventral side of the brain are the following sinuses of the dura mater:

3. **Sinus cavernosus.**—A short broad venous sinus, one on each side of the hypophysis, on the body of the sphenoid. It receives veins from the side and ventral surface of the brain. The two sinuses are connected by communicating branches craniad and caudad of the hypophysis. From them branches pass out through the orbital fissure to join the plexus formed by the branches of the posterior facial vein.

4. **Sinus petrosus inferior.**—This arises from the sinus cavernosus and passes caudolaterad in the groove between the edge of the petrous bone and the basilar portion of the occipital. Reaching the jugular foramen it divides; part joins the termination of the sinus transversus to form the **inferior cerebral vein,** which passes through the jugular foramen to join the internal jugular vein. The other portion of the sinus petrosus inferior passes through the condyloid canal of the occipital bone, communicates by a strong transverse branch across the surface of the basioccipital with the vein of the opposite side, and enters the spinal canal through the foramen magnum. Here it joins the sinus of the vertebral column.

5. **Sinus columnæ vertebralis.**—On the ventral surface of the vertebral canal, beneath the periosteum, are two wide venous sinuses, one on each side of the middle line. These sinuses extend the entire length of the spinal cord. At the atlantal foramen each sends a strong branch to the internal jugular vein. Farther caudad they send branches to the vertebral, intercostal, and lumbar veins, and communicate with each other by numerous transverse branches. They receive many small veins from the spinal cord.

3. **Vena cava inferior** (Fig. 129, *c*; Fig. 126, *a*).

The inferior vena cava (Fig. 126, *a*) is formed at about the level of the last lumbar vertebra by the union of the two common

iliac veins (Fig. 126, *w*). It passes craniad near the dorsal median line, lying at first dorsad of the aorta (*b*), then to the right, then ventrad. It enters the dorsal part of the caudate lobe of the liver, traverses that organ, then pierces the diaphragm near the ventrolateral edge of its central tendon, to pass craniad in the thoracic cavity (Fig. 129, *c*) ventrad of the caudal lobe of the right lung and enter the right auricle.

It receives the (Fig. 126): **lumbar, iliolumbalis** (*v*), **right spermatica interna** (*u*) (the left internal spermatic usually joins the left renal), **renal** (*t*), **adrenolumbalis** (*s*), **phrenic,** and **hepatic** veins. All but the last two accompany the arteries of the same name.

V. phrenica.—The phrenic veins gather the blood from the diaphragm and empty into the vena cava as it penetrates the diaphragm.

V. hepatica.—The hepatic veins vary in number. They gather the blood from the liver (sent in by the portal vein and hepatic arteries) and enter the vena cava just caudad of the diaphragm.

VENA PORTÆ. THE PORTAL VEIN (Fig. 132, *a*).—The **portal** vein is the large vein carrying the blood from the abdominal digestive viscera to the liver. Within the liver the portal vein breaks up into capillaries; these collect to form the **hepatic** veins, which enter the vena cava inferior. The portal vein (*a*) is formed near the pyloric end of the stomach (1) by the union of the **superior mesenteric** (*b*) and **gastrosplenic** (*c*) veins and passes thence along the ventral border of the foramen epiploicum (foramen of Winslow) to the liver (2), where it divides, going to the lobes of the liver. On its way to the liver it may receive the **pancreaticoduodenalis** (*d*), **gastroepiploica** (*e*), and **coronaria ventriculi** (*f*). These may unite with the portal separately, or any two or all three may unite to form a single trunk before entering the portal vein.

1. **V. coronaria ventriculi** (*f*) gathers the blood from the lesser curvature of the stomach and anastomoses with the gastrosplenic veins. It usually empties into the portal vein near the pylorus.

2. **V. pancreaticoduodenalis** (*d*) receives the blood from

the pancreas and first part of the duodenum, and empties into the vena portæ near to or with the preceding.

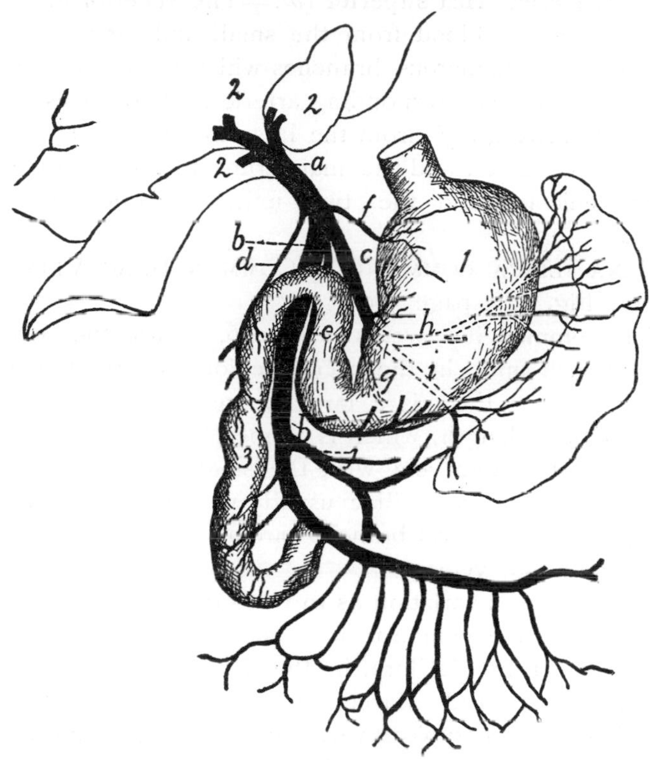

Fig. 132.—Portal Vein.

a, portal vein; *b*, superior mesenteric; *c*, gastrosplenic; *d*, pancreaticoduodenalis, *e*, gastroepiploica; *f*, coronaria ventriculi; *g*, *h*, *i*, branches of gastrosplenic; *j*, inferior mesenteric. 1, stomach; 2, liver; 3, duodenum; 4, spleen.

3. **V. gastroepiploica** (*e*) comes from the greater curvature of the stomach and ascending limb of the great omentum. It empties into the vena portæ ventrodextrad of the opening of the coronaria ventriculi, or sometimes in common with it.

4. **V. gastrolienalis** (*c*).—The gastrosplenic is one of the veins which unite to make up the portal vein. It is formed by three branches: one (*g*) from the horizontal or gastric portion of the pancreas, one (*h*) from the stomach and gastric end of the spleen, the third and largest (*i*) from the caudal end of the spleen and descending limb of the great omentum. The three

branches unite and the common trunk joins the superior **mesenteric** vein (*b*) to form the portal vein as above described.

5. **V. mesenterica superior** (*b*).—The superior mesenteric vein receives the blood from the small and large intestines. It is formed by numerous branches which follow and have the same name as the corresponding arteries. It receives also the **inferior mesenteric** (*j*) from the large intestine. The numerous branches unite, and the main trunk thus formed joins the gastrosplenic (*c*), and the two united become the portal vein (*a*).

VENA ILIACA COMMUNIS. COMMON ILIAC VEIN (Fig. 126, *w*; Fig. 127, page 310).

The common iliac veins (Fig. 126, *w*) are the two large vessels which unite in the sacral region to form the inferior vena cava (*a*). Each is a large vessel, usually four or five centimeters in length, which is formed by the junction of the large **external iliac** vein with the smaller **hypogastric** vein (*z*). The left common iliac usually receives the **V. sacralis media** (*o*); other lateral branches are as a rule not received by the common iliac veins.

There is much variation as to the formation of the common iliac veins and their union to form the vena cava. On this subject the paper by McClure, in the *American Naturalist*, vol. XXXIV. pp. 135–198 (March, 1900), may be consulted with profit. The more typical variations may be classified as follows: (1) The two common iliac veins may be longer than usual, so that the vena cava is formed farther craniad than usual. (2) There may be in the abdominal region two separate veins (**venæ cardinales**) representing the inferior vena cava, these uniting in the region of the kidneys. (3) The vena sacralis media may enter into the left common iliac (the usual condition); or the right common iliac (as in Fig. 126); or it may fork, one branch passing to the left, the other to the right common iliac.

Branches of the common iliac veins:

1. **V. sacralis media** (Fig. 126, *o*).—This follows the course of the corresponding artery and usually enters the left common iliac.

2. **V. hypogastrica** (or **iliaca interna**) (*z*).—The hypogastric or internal iliac vein joins the medial side of the external iliac to form the common iliac (*w*). Its branches follow the branches of the corresponding artery except that the vein from the bladder (umbilical vein) joins the **V. hemorrhoidalis media.** Also the **vena glutea inferior** receives a large superficial communicating branch (Fig. 163, *k'*) from the **vena saphena parva.** This branch leaves the saphena parva (Fig. 163, *k*) at the popliteal space, and passes over the lateral surface of the biceps muscle to its proximal end. Here it passes between the biceps and caudofemoralis to join the vena glutea inferior.

3. **V. iliaca externa** (Fig. 127, page 310).—This vein follows the corresponding artery, collecting the blood from the posterior extremity. Its branches are the same and have in general the same distribution as those of the artery. The vein has, however, certain branches in addition to those of the artery, resulting in a somewhat different general arrangement of vessels; it will be necessary therefore to give an account of the system of veins from the foot and lower leg.

The blood is collected from the foot into two sets of veins which may be distinguished as the **deep** and the **superficial** sets. The veins of the deep set are those which accompany the branches of the popliteal and anterior tibial arteries. Those of the superficial set are larger and carry most of the blood. On the dorsum of the foot blood is collected from the third, fourth, and fifth digits by two or three superficial metatarsal veins, which unite opposite the proximal end of the metatarsus into a single vein. This receives a similar branch coming from the dorsum of the second digit, and has numerous branches in the ankle region which form here a network, communicating with the vena saphena parva (Fig. 163, *k*), and with branches from the plantar side of the foot. From this network two or three main veins pass proximad on the medial side of the leg, along with the branches of the arteria saphena, and unite with a similar vein from the plantar side of the foot to form the **vena saphena magna** (Fig. 127, *f*, page 310), which accompanies the arteria saphena to join the femoral vein (*a*).

On the plantar side of the foot small veins pass from the digits to a superficial **venous plantar arch,** which lies just proximad of the fibrous pad on the sole of the foot. At its medial side this arch extends proximad and dorsad to join that branch of the vena saphena magna which comes from the dorsum of the second digit. On the lateral side it extends proximad along the lateral margin of the foot, sends a communicating branch dorsad to the branches of the V. saphena magna, and continues along the lateral border of the foot to the ankle. It forms the beginning of the **V. saphena parva** (Fig. 163, *k*, page 401). This receives branches from the lateral surface of the ankle, which anastomose with those of the saphena magna. The saphena parva then passes proximad along the lateral surface of the leg, close to its ventral border, to the popliteal space. At the distal end of the popliteal space it divides into two branches. One passes inward through the fat of the popliteal space, receiving branches from the lymphatic gland situated here, and joins the popliteal vein. The other (*k'*) remains superficial and continues proximad over the lateral surface of the biceps to the proximal end of that muscle. Here it passes between the biceps and caudofemoralis to join the inferior gluteal vein.

IV. THE LYMPHATIC SYSTEM. SYSTEMA LYMPHATICUM.

The lymphatic system of the cat has not been worked out in detail, so that only the main features of the system are given in the following account.

The lymphatic system consists of a number of vessels, the **lymphatics,** containing a colorless fluid called **lymph,** and of **lymphatic glands,** connected with the lymphatic vessels. The lymphatic vessels are found throughout the body as slender tubes, frequently united into networks, and containing many valves. They take origin from the spaces in the connective tissue, so that they are at first without definite walls. The fluid in the connective-tissue spaces gradually flows together into tubes with definite walls, and these tubes, the lymphatic vessels, finally join the venous system. In their passage through the lymphatic glands the vessels break up into fine channels which again unite on leaving the gland. In the gland lymph-cells are added to the fluid, and probably other changes are produced.

Most or all of the lymphatic vessels of the body finally unite into two trunks before entering the veins. The largest trunk is the **thoracic duct** (Fig. 118, 5, page 282), which collects the lymph from the entire caudal half of the body, and from the left forelimb and the left side of the thorax, head, and neck. It passes along the dorsosinistral side of the thoracic aorta, lying against its surface, and enters the left external jugular vein at its junction with the subclavian. The second main trunk is the **right lymphatic duct**; this collects the lymph from the right side of the thorax, the right forelimb, and the right side of the neck and head; it enters the right external jugular.

1. **Lymphatics of the Head.**—A number of lymphatic vessels arise on the sides of the face, especially in the upper and lower lips. They form a superficial network of vessels, lying over the ventral half of the masseter muscle and an area ventrad of it. These lymphatic vessels all enter two large lymphatic glands (Fig. 131, 12, page 322) lying at the ventro-caudal angle of the masseter muscle, covering the union of the anterior and posterior facial veins. Into these glands pass also a number of lymph vessels from the back of the head. From these two lymphatic glands two or three small lymphatic vessels pass caudad, lying on the surface of the external jugular vein. Near the point of the shoulder, some distance craniad of the junction of the external and internal jugular veins, these vessels enter another small lymphatic gland lying on the dorsal surface of the external jugular vein. Thence one or two vessels continue caudad, still on the surface of the external jugular, and finally unite with the deep lymphatics of the head and neck and those of the arm to enter the caudal end of the external jugular vein, usually (on the left side) after junction with the **thoracic duct**, from the thorax.

The deep lymphatics of the head come from the internal parts of the head,—tongue, pharynx, etc., and enter a large lymphatic gland situated close to the caudoventral surface of the tympanic bulla, at the side of the pharynx. Thence a large lymphatic trunk passes caudad at the side of the trachea, along with the common carotid artery and internal jugular vein, unites with the superficial vessels from the head, above described, joins (on the left side) the thoracic duct, and enters the external jugular vein.

2. **Lymphatics of the Neck.**—Two or three lymph-glands are found in the fatty mass in the neck beneath the clavotrapezius and levator scapulæ ventralis muscles. These receive lymphatics from the neck and side of the thorax. The vessels which arise from them join those from the head and arm to enter the external jugular vein.

3. **Lymphatics of the Thoracic Limbs.**—The lymphatics of the forelimbs begin as a number of vessels on the dorsum and palm of the hand. These all pass toward the radial side, and at about the base of the first metacarpal the vessels from both sides of the hand unite to form two or three main trunks. These pass towards the elbow, accompanying the vena cephalica (Fig. 130). There are usually two of these main trunks, one lying on each side of the vena cephalica. They accompany this vein over the shoulder, following that portion which finally joins the external jugular. In the hollow of the shoulder they enter the **cervical lymph-glands,** one or two lymph-glands imbedded in the fat lying beneath the clavotrapezius and levator scapulæ ventralis in this region. From the cervical lymph-glands a single trunk passes mediocaudad, unites with the lymphatics from the head, and usually (on the left side) with the cranial end of the thoracic duct, and enters the external jugular vein at its junction with the subclavian. The common trunk from the head and arm may enter the jugular separately, but close to the termination of the thoracic duct. On the right side the common trunk is joined by one or more small vessels coming from the lymphatic glands of the thorax and forming the right lymphatic duct.

There is said to be also a deep system of lymphatics in the arm, in addition to the superficial system above described; this is said to accompany the branches of the brachial vein. If this system is present in the cat, it is much less easily demonstrated than the superficial system.

4. **Lymphatics of the Thorax and Abdomen.**—In the thorax are a number of lymphatic glands which are apparently not constant in number and position. One is commonly found dorsad of the bifurcation of the superior vena cava, one ventrad of the mammary vein, several small ones about the bifurcation of the trachea, one or more in the region of the aortic arch, and a number of small ones scattered in the mediastinum. The vessels from these glands finally join either the right lymphatic duct or the thoracic duct; the details have not been worked out and are probably variable.

In the abdominal cavity a number of **mesenteric** glands, of considerable size, are found in the mesentery and in the mesocolon. In the mesocolon these are usually separate, forming a chain of glands following the colon about one and a half centimeters from it. In the mesentery the glands are mostly united into a very large one, formerly known as the **pancreas aselli**; this is the largest lymph-gland in the body. It is a curved structure, four or five centimeters in length, lying in the central region of the mesentery.

Into the mesenteric glands pass lymphatic vessels from the viscera of the abdomen. From the mesenteric glands one or two large lymphatic vessels pass craniodorsad, at first with the portal vein, then dorsad of it. This vessel reaches the dorsal side of the aorta near the cranial end of the kidney, where it enters a large fusiform vessel, the **receptaculum chyli,** which stretches from the cranial end of the kidney craniad between the crura of the diaphragm into the thorax. The receptaculum receives other lymphatics from the various organs of the abdominal cavity as well as vessels coming from the pelvic region, and from the **iliac** glands. These lie beside the iliac artery, receive lymphatics from the hind limbs, and send lymphatics craniad to the receptaculum chyli. The latter forms the beginning of the **thoracic duct.**

The thoracic duct (Fig. 118, 5, page 282) enters the thoracic cavity between the crura of the diaphragm as a continuation of the receptaculum chyli. It lies on the dorsal side of the aorta (*a*), somewhat to the left. It passes along the aorta, gradually coming to lie more on its left side, and finally leaves that vessel near the aortic arch. The duct continues thence straight craniad along the left side of the œsophagus till it reaches the external jugular vein at its junction with the subclavian. In this region the thoracic duct usually unites with the lymphatics coming from the head and arm, then enters the external jugular vein, or the innominate at the point of union of external jugular and subclavian.

In its passage through the thorax the duct frequently divides into two or three divisions which pass along parallel to each other for a distance, then reunite. Such division into two or three parts is especially frequent just before the union with the jugular vein. The numerous valves in the thoracic duct give it a beaded appearance.

5. **Lymphatics of the Pelvic Limbs.**—A number of lymphatic vessels are formed on the dorsum and the sole of the foot. These pass to the lateral side, forming a network on the lateral and dorsal surface of the ankle-joint, and finally unite into two main trunks which accompany the vena saphena parva. In the popliteal space these enter the **popliteal gland** which lies imbedded in the fat of that region. From the popliteal gland one or two trunks accompany the superficial division of the vena saphena parva across the lateral surface of the biceps muscle, and finally thus reach the pelvic cavity. Here they join the lymphatics of the pelvic region, which all pour their lymph at last into the thoracic duct. Inguinal glands are either very small or not present in the cat.

The pelvic limbs have perhaps a deep system of lymphatics, accompanying the deep veins; if so, they are not easily demonstrable.

NERVOUS SYSTEM.

I. THE CENTRAL NERVOUS SYSTEM.

1. **The Spinal Cord. Medulla spinalis** (Figs. 133--136). —The spinal cord is that portion of the nervous system which occupies the vertebral canal; it is continuous craniad with the brain. It has the form of a somewhat flattened cylinder and extends from the foramen magnum into the caudal region. It diminishes in diameter after entering the sacral region.

The cord has a cervical and a lumbar enlargement, the former (Fig. 133) marking the origin of the nerves which pass to the fore limb, and the latter (Fig. 136) the origin of those which pass to the hind limb.

The **cervical** enlargement (Fig. 133) lies in that part of the vertebral canal bounded by the fourth to seventh cervical and first thoracic vertebræ. Caudad of the first thoracic vertebra the cord continues of nearly uniform diameter to the lumbar enlargement (Fig. 136) which stretches from the third to the seventh lumbar vertebræ (inclusive). Caudad of the seventh lumbar vertebra it diminishes uniformly in diameter and ends in a slender cord, the **filum terminale** (Fig. 136, *C*), which may be traced into the caudal region.

The surface of the cord is marked by a number of longitudinal grooves or **sulci,** and **fissures.** The most prominent of these is the **anterior median fissure** (Fig. 134, *c*), along the ventral median line; into this the pia mater dips. The **posterior median sulcus** (Fig. 133, *e*; Fig. 134, *a*) is a shallow furrow along the dorsal median line. The anterior fissure and the posterior sulcus thus divide the cord into lateral halves.

Each half is subdivided by the **anterior** and **posterior lateral sulci.**

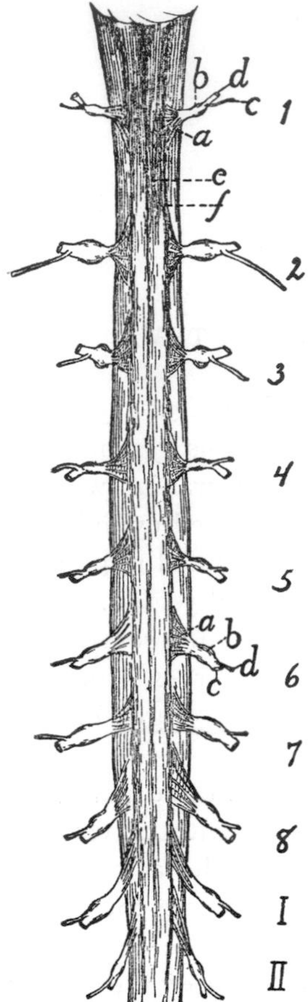

FIG. 133.—CRANIAL PORTION OF THE SPINAL CORD, WITH THE CERVICAL ENLARGEMENT. DORSAL VIEW.

1–8, the eight cervical nerves. *I–II*, first two thoracic nerves. *a*, dorsal roots (ventral roots not shown); *b*, spinal ganglia; *c*, dorsal rami; *d*, ventral rami; *e*, posterior median sulcus; *f*, posterior lateral sulcus.

The **posterior** lateral sulcus (Fig. 133, *f*; Fig. 134, *b*) lies at the side of the posterior median sulcus. It is broad and shallow and has the posterior roots of the spinal nerves emerging from its bottom.

The **anterior** lateral sulcus exists only after the forcible pulling out of the anterior (ventral) roots of the spinal nerves. It then marks the line along which they originate from the cord.

In cross-section (Fig. 134) the substance of the cord appears to the naked eye as composed of a darker central **"gray matter"** (*g*) and of an outer **"white matter"** (*f*). The gray matter has in section the form of the letter H. The cord is really tubular, having a **central canal** (*h*) which appears in section in the middle of the cross-bar of the H, while the two ends of each vertical bar extend toward the anterior and posterior lateral fissures.

The white matter is divided into funiculi (or columns) by the fissures and sulci, so that there is in each half of the cord an **anterior,** a **posterior,** and a **lateral** white funiculus.

In the cervical region (Fig. 134) there appears between the posterior lateral and posterior median sulci an **intermediate** sulcus which divides the posterior funiculus in this region into two. The median slenderer of these is the **fasciculus gracilis** (*d*) or column of

Goll. The lateral and thicker is the **fasciculus cuneatus** (*e*) or column of Burdach.

The membranes of the spinal cord :

The **dura mater** is a tough fibrous membrane directly continuous with the dura mater of the brain. It differs from the dura mater of the brain in two particulars:

1. At the foramen magnum it splits into two layers, one of which lines the bony vertebral canal and forms its periosteum, while the other covers the cord.

2. It is separated from the cord by a considerable space. The dura mater is continuous with the fibrous sheaths of the spinal nerves at their points of exit. Along the sides of the cord it is connected to the pia mater by a delicate strand of connective tissue probably equivalent to the "ligamentum denticulatum" of man.

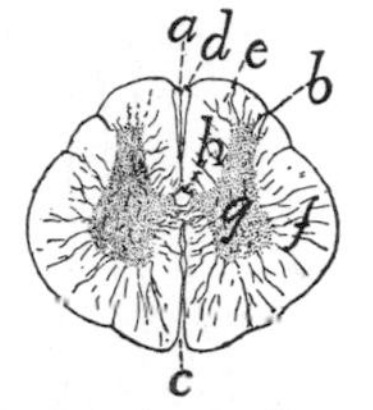

FIG. 134. — CROSS-SECTION OF THE SPINAL CORD IN THE CERVICAL REGION.

a, posterior median sulcus; *b*, posterior lateral sulcus; *c*, anterior median fissure; *d*, fasciculus gracilis; *e*, fasciculus cuneatus; *f*, white matter; *g*, gray matter; *h*, central canal.

The **arachnoid** is a delicate cellular membrane lying beneath the dura mater, between it and the pia mater. It forms a continuous investment for the cord, is not vascular, and is said not to dip into the fissures of the cord.

The **pia mater** invests the cord closely and contains some blood-vessels. It is a delicate membrane which dips into the fissures and sulci of the cord and is connected to it by numerous strands of connective tissue that pass from it into the substance of the cord. The nerves pierce it.

FIG. 135. — SECTION OF SPINAL CORD, SHOWING THE ORIGIN OF A PAIR OF SPINAL NERVES.

a, dorsal root; *b*, spinal ganglion; *c*, dorsal ramus; *d*, ventral ramus ; *e*, ventral root.

Spinal Nerves.— From the spinal cord arise the spinal nerves. Of these there are about thirty-eight pairs in the cat. Eight are **cervical,** thirteen **thoracic,** seven **lumbar,** three **sacral,** and seven or eight **caudal.** Those leaving the cervical (Fig. 133, 5-8 and *I*) and lumbar (Fig. 136) enlargements are larger than the others. The **first cervical** nerve leaves the vertebral canal through the atlantal

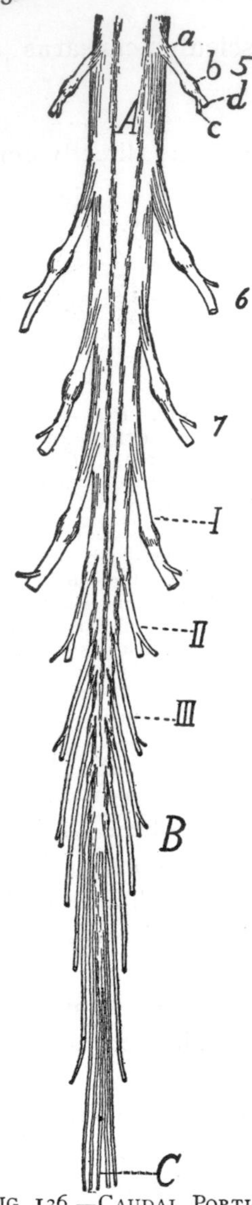

FIG. 136.—CAUDAL PORTION OF THE SPINAL CORD.

A, lumbar enlargement; *B*, cauda equina; *C*, filum terminale; 5–7, fifth to seventh lumbar nerves. *I–III*, the three sacral nerves. *a*, dorsal roots; *b*, spinal ganglia; *c*, dorsal rami; *d*, ventral rami.

foramen, the **second** leaves between the arches of the atlas and axis, while all the others leave the vertebral canal by way of the intervertebral foramina. Each nerve arises from the cord by a **dorsal** and a **ventral** root. The dorsal root is chiefly sensory, the ventral motor in character. The **dorsal** root (radix posterior) (Figs. 133, 135, and 136, *a*) begins as a number (twelve or more) of separate nerve-bundles which emerge from the posterior lateral groove. These roots lie nearly in a single plane and pass laterad, converging to penetrate a ganglion, the **spinal ganglion** (*b*) (or ganglion of the posterior root). All the spinal ganglia except the first and second are situated in the intervertebral foramina or within the vertebral canal. The first and second are situated among the muscles surrounding the place of exit of the nerves.

The **ventral root** (radix anterior) (Fig 135, *e*) arises as a larger number of small fibre-bundles which do not lie in a single plane, so that in a transverse section several rootlets may appear in a single section. The rootlets converge to form a single mass which joins the dorsal root just as it emerges from the spinal ganglion. The nerve formed by the junction of the ventral and dorsal roots is one of the **spinal nerves.**

The direction in which the nerves leave the cord varies. In the cervical region (Fig. 133) and cranial part of the lumbar region it is nearly laterad; at the cervical and lumbar enlargements it is laterocaudad. The nerves in the sacral and caudal regions pass almost directly caudad to reach the intervertebral foramina and form thus a brush which surrounds the filum terminale (Fig. 136, *C*) and is called the **cauda equina** (Fig. 136, *B*).

Each spinal nerve immediately after leaving the intervertebral foramen divides into two branches, a **dorsal** or **posterior** branch or **ramus** (*c*), and a **ventral** or **anterior ramus** (*d*). The dorsal ramus is in each case small (except in the first and second cervical nerves), and is distributed to the longitudinal muscles and integument of the back.

The ventral rami are larger and each is connected a short distance beyond its origin with the sympathetic system by short **rami communicantes** (Fig. 163a, *G*, *F*) or communicating branches. Each is then distributed to the integument and muscles of the ventral part of the body, including the limbs.

The ventral rami which pass to the limbs are much larger than the others. The ventral rami are further distinguished from the dorsal by the fact that they frequently unite with one another to form plexuses.

The peripheral distribution of the spinal nerves is described later.

2. **The Brain. Encephalon.**—The brain is that portion of the central nervous system that is included within the cranial cavity. It is a direct continuation of the spinal cord, and presents many of the same essential characters as the latter, with great modifications in details.

The structure of the brain can best be understood if it be considered as a modified continuation of the spinal cord, and the relation of the parts to the essential parts of the cord noted. The spinal cord is a nearly straight tube, with a central cavity and thick walls. The brain is likewise tubular, with the cavities enlarged or subdivided in places, with the walls greatly thickened, and with a number of bends and constrictions in the tube. The relation of the structure of the brain to that of the spinal cord is most easily perceived by an examination of the brain of some lower vertebrate, as the frog or shark, and such an examination should be made before proceeding to the study of the more complicated brain of the cat.

In the following account of the brain of the cat all parts will be described as far as possible in relation with the tubular structure of the brain. The brain will be considered as a hollow structure, having central cavities, and the solid portions will be brought into relation as parts of the roof, sides, or floor of the cavities. The cavities of the brain, forming a direct continuation of the central canal of the spinal cord, are known as **ventricles** (**ventriculi**).

In a general view of the cat's brain from the dorsal side (Fig. 137) four subdivisions are discernible. At the caudal

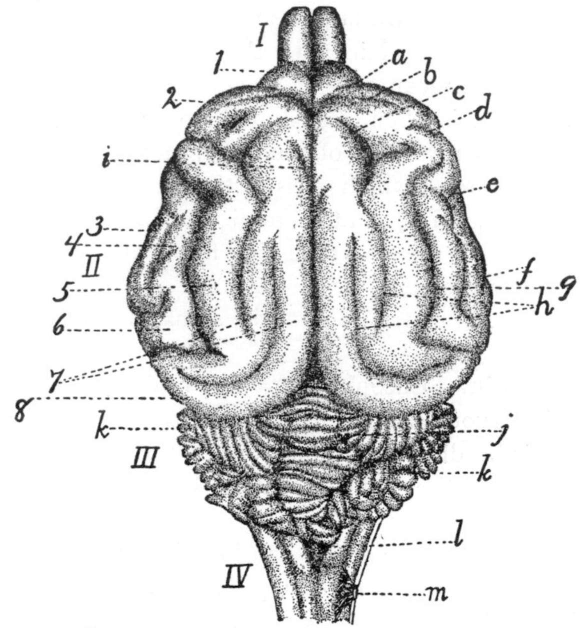

FIG. 137.—DORSAL SURFACE OF THE BRAIN.

I, olfactory bulbs; *II*, cerebral hemispheres; *III*, cerebellum; *IV*, medulla. *a*, præsylvian sulcus; *b*, cruciate sulcus; *c*, sulcus ansatus; *d*, coronal sulcus; *e*, anterior sulcus; *f*, posterior sulcus; *g*, suprasylvian sulcus; *h*, separate parts of the lateral sulcus; *i*, end of splenial sulcus; *j*, vermis of cerebellum; *k*, hemispheres of cerebellum; *l*, roof of fourth ventricle; *m*, first cervical nerve. 1, orbital lobe (or gyrus); 2, sigmoid gyrus; 3, anterior sylvian gyrus; 4, ectosylvian gyrus; 5, suprasylvian gyrus; 6, posterior sylvian gyrus; 7, parts of marginal gyrus; 8, gyrus compositus posterior.

end is a small stalk-like portion (*IV*) which is clearly a slightly modified continuation of the spinal cord; this is the **myelencephalon** or **medulla oblongata.** Just craniad of this, rising high above it, is an irregularly lobulated rounded portion, the **cerebellum** (*III*). This is produced as a thickening of the wall of the original tube; it forms the dorsal part of the **metencephalon.** These two portions of the brain have a common cavity, lying within the medulla oblongata and ventrad of the cerebellum, and formed by a widening of the cavity of the spinal cord; it is known as the **fourth** ventricle. Craniad of the cerebellum, separated from it by a deep transverse fissure, are two very large portions, the **hemispheres** of the **cerebrum** (*II*), separated from each other by a deep longitudinal fissure; they constitute together the **telencephalon.** The hemispheres are produced by a sort of forking of the original central tube; —by outgrowths on the sides of the tube, the central cavity extending into the outgrowths. The two outgrowths extend dorsad, as well as craniad and caudad from the original place of origin, forming the larger part of the brain; the extensions of the central cavity which they contain are known as the **lateral ventricles.** Finally, in front of the two hemispheres are seen the two small **olfactory bulbs** (*I*) which are mere extensions of the two hemispheres and contains cavities which are extensions of the lateral ventricles.

In a ventral view of the entire brain (Fig. 138) certain parts are visible which in the dorsal view are hidden by the large cerebral hemispheres. At the caudal end is seen, as before, the medulla oblongata, or myelencephalon, and craniad of this, on the ventral side of the cerebellum, a broad transverse tract, the **pons** (*i*); this, like the cerebellum, forms part of the metencephalon. All this part of the brain formed by the myelencephalon and metencephalon lies caudad of (behind) the rest of the brain and is marked off from it by a great fissure; it therefore receives as a whole the name hind-brain or **rhombencephalon.**

Just craniad of the pons are seen two short diverging arm-like bands of fibres (*g*), enclosing a small triangular space between them. These two arms with the space between them are all that is visible of a division of the brain which in dorsal view is completely covered by the backward projection of the cerebral hemispheres. This is the midbrain or **mesencephalon.**

In this portion of the brain the continuation of the central cavity is a narrow canal which receives the name **cerebral aqueduct** (**aqueductus cerebri**) or aqueduct of Sylvius.

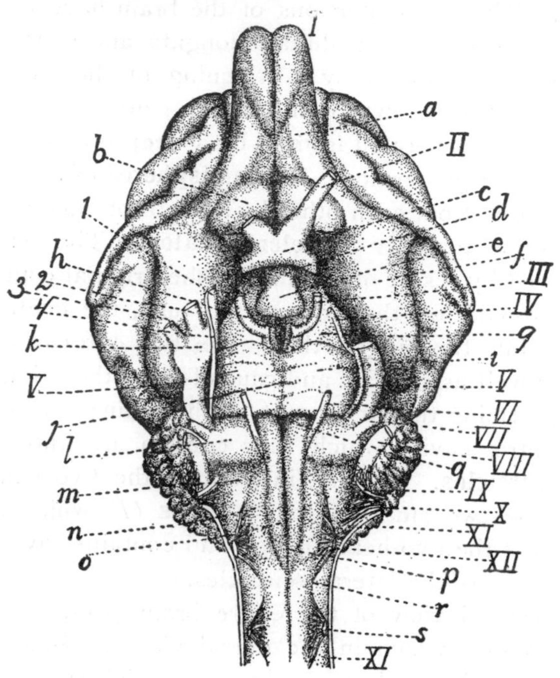

FIG. 138.—VENTRAL SURFACE OF THE BRAIN.

I–XII, the twelve cranial nerves in order; *I*, olfactory bulb; *II*, N. opticus; *III*, N. oculomotorius; *IV*, N. trochlearis; *V*, N. trigeminus (1, mandibular nerve; 2, maxillary nerve; 3, ophthalmic nerve; 4, sensory root); *VI*, N. abducens; *VII*, N. facialis; *VIII*, N. acusticus; *IX*, N. glossopharyngeus; *X*, N. vagus; *XI*, N. accessorius; *XII*, N. hypoglossus. *a*, tractus olfactorius; *b*, substantia perforata anterior; *c*, optic chiasma; *d*, infundibulum; *e*, hypophysis; *f*, lobus pyriformis, or tractus postrhinalis; *g*, pedunculi cerebri; *h*, substantia perforata posterior; *i*, pons; *j*, sulcus basilaris of pons; *k*, semilunar (or Gasserian) ganglion; *l*, trapezium; *m*, area ovalis; *n*, area elliptica; *o*, pyramidal tracts; *p*, anterior or ventral fissure; *q*, foramen cæcum; *r*, anterior lateral sulcus; *s*, first cervical nerve.

Just craniad of the midbrain is a small rather irregular area, bounded craniad by the band-like **optic chiasma** (*c*), from which arise the optic nerves (*II*), and showing caudad of this band a rounded irregular projection (*e*). This is a fourth division of the brain which is likewise covered dorsad by the hemispheres; it is the 'tween-brain or **diencephalon.** Its cavity is known as the third ventricle. Just craniad of the 'tween-brain, in the median line, is a deep fissure, showing that here in reality is the termination of the original tube, the further extension craniad being due to the pushing forward of the lateral outgrowths, or cerebral hemispheres, which extend in ventral view a considerable distance further craniad. The hemispheres lie also caudad, laterad, and dorsad of the mid-brain and 'tween-brain, so that these parts are almost enveloped by the hemispheres. The hemispheres and 'tween-brain are sometimes taken together as forming a single portion, the fore-brain or **prosencephalon.**

There are thus altogether five principal subdivisions of the brain, each enclosing a portion of the central cavity. These are the **myelencephalon,** the **metencephalon** (these two enclosing the **fourth** ventricle), the **mesencephalon** (enclosing the **cerebral aqueduct**), the **diencephalon** (enclosing the **third** ventricle), and the two cerebral hemispheres, constituting together the **telencephalon,** and enclosing the two **lateral ventricles.** A plan of the brain, considered as a tube enclosing cavities, is given in Figs. 139 and 140. Fig. 139 shows the plan considered as viewed from the dorsal side, Fig. 140 in a lateral view. These figures are of course pure diagrams, showing only what may be called the *plan* of structure, and omitting all details. In the actual conditions many important modifications even of the main features of the plan are met with.

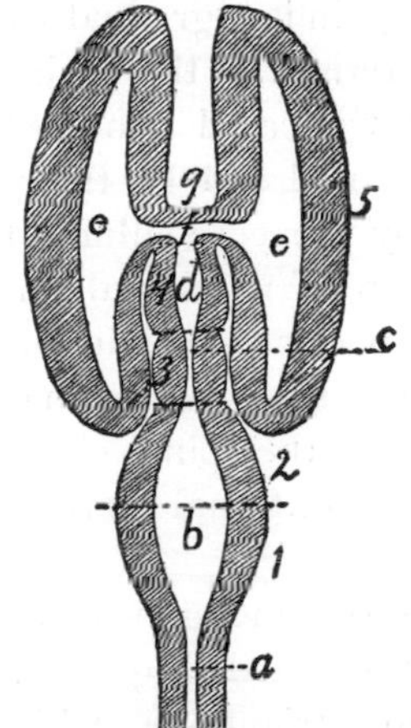

FIG. 139.—DIAGRAM OF BRAIN FROM ABOVE.

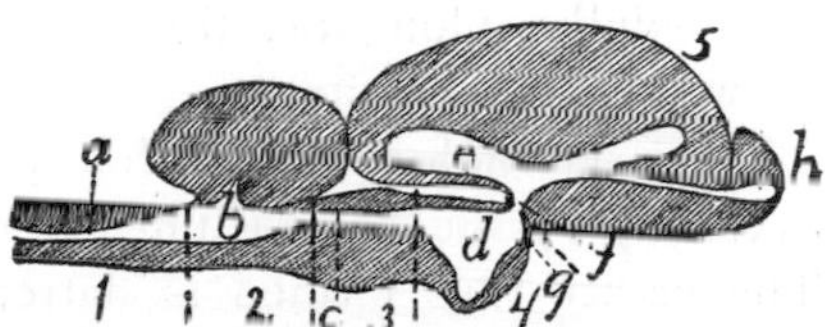

FIG. 140. — DIAGRAM OF BRAIN FROM THE SIDE.

1, myelencephalon; 2, metencephalon, 3, mesencephalon; 4, diencephalon; 5, telencephalon. *a*, canal of the spinal cord; *b*, fourth ventricle; *c*, cerebral aqueduct (aqueduct of Sylvius); *d*, third ventricle; *e*, lateral ventricle; *f*, interventricular foramen (or foramen of Monro); *g*, lamina terminalis; *h*, olfactory bulb.

In the following description the parts of the brain will be taken up in this order:

A. RHOMBENCEPHALON (primitive hindbrain).
   1. *Myelencephalon.*
   2. *Metencephalon.*

B. MESENCEPHALON (primitive midbrain).
   3. *Mesencephalon.*

C. PROSENCEPHALON (primitive forebrain).
   4. *Diencephalon.*
   5. *Telencephalon.*

A. RHOMBENCEPHALON.—1. *Myelencephalon.*—The myelencephalon or medulla oblongata is transitional between the spinal cord and the brain. It has in general the structural peculiarities of the cord, but these undergo in it a gradual transformation into the arrangements characteristic of the brain.

It has the form of a flattened and truncated cone, which widens craniad and is limited at the cranial end by the pons (Fig. 138, *i*) ventrally and laterally; by the cerebellum (Fig. 137, *III*) dorsally. The cranial portion of its dorsal surface is overhung by the cerebellum. The points of origin of the roots of the first pair of cervical nerves (Fig. 138, *s*) may be taken as indicating the boundary between the spinal cord and the medulla oblongata; there is no other external marking to show the limits of the two.

The central canal of that part of the medulla which is overhung by the cerebellum is greatly widened (Fig. 141, *h*). The cavity thus formed is flattened and triangular, with the apex of the triangle caudad, and is the caudal part of the **fourth ventricle** (Fig. 141, *h*). The roof is very thin (Fig. 143, *n*) and is intimately connected with the pia mater, so that in removing the latter the thin roof of the fourth ventricle is removed with it and the cavity of the fourth ventricle is left exposed. The thin roof of the fourth ventricle is known as the **velum medullare posterius** (Fig. 143, *n*).

The ventral (anterior) fissure (Fig. 138, *p*) of the cord passes onto the medulla oblongata and ends at the pons (*i*), its end being slightly deeper and forming what is known as the

foramen cæcum (*q*). The dorsal (posterior) sulcus (Fig. 141, *a*) is well marked; it ends at the caudal boundary of the fourth ventricle (*h*).

The anterior lateral sulcus (Fig. 138, *r*) may be traced craniad from the origin of the ventral roots of the first cervical nerves (*s*), along the lateral border of the area elliptica (*n*), then curving mediad to the lateral border of the pyramis (*o*), and finally reaching the pons (*i*). Its position is marked by the origin of the roots of the hypoglossal nerve (*XII*).

The posterior lateral sulcus (Fig. 141, *b*), marked on the spinal cord by the origin of the dorsal nerve-roots, curves laterad at the sides of the fourth ventricle (*h*) owing to the increasing width of the latter, and ends at an elevated area of oblique fibres, the **area ovalis** (*f*).

The columns or funiculi bounded by the longitudinal fissures present the following peculiarities:

The anterior white funiculus of the cord is replaced in the medulla by the **pyramidal tracts** (**pyramides**) (Fig. 138, *o*). The pyramidal tracts are formed by fibres which emerge from beneath the pons and pass caudad to disappear just craniad of the level of the first cervical nerve (*s*). The pyramidal tracts are bounded medially by the anterior median fissure (*p*), but laterally each is separated from the anterior lateral sulcus (*r*) over its caudal part by an elongated **area elliptica** (*n*), the human homologue of which is uncertain. It perhaps represents the **oliva.**

Laterad of the cranial portion of the pyramids is an irregular area known as the **trapezium** (*l*) which abuts caudad on the area elliptica (*n*) and the area ovalis (*m*). The **area ovalis** (Fig. 138, *m*; Fig. 141, *f*) (or zonula Arnoldi) is a broad band of oblique fibres which passes from the lateral side of the area elliptica craniodorsad to disappear under the cerebellum.

The posterior white funiculus was divided in the cervical region into two, the **fasciculus gracilis** (column of Goll) and the **fasciculus cuneatus** (column of Burdach). The fasciculus gracilis (Fig. 141, *c*) extends to the caudal end of the fourth ventricle (*h*) and ends there in an expansion, the **clava** (*d*), which forms the posterior boundary of the fourth ventricle.

The fasciculus cuneatus (*e*) passes laterad on account of the width of the fourth ventricle and appears to end at the area ovalis (*f*), but it may be seen passing beneath the area ovalis, emerging at its cranial border and turning dorsad to enter the cerebellum. It forms the side walls of a part of the shallow fourth ventricle.

The lateral funiculi are divided by longitudinal furrows into three divisions. The dorsal one of these is the **fasciculus cuneatus lateralis** or column of Rolando (Fig. 141, *g*). It accompanies the fasciculus cuneatus into the cerebellum.

The entire mass formed by the fasciculus gracilis, the fasciculus cuneatus medialis, and fasciculus cuneatus lateralis is known as the **corpus restiforme,** and since its fibres pass into the cerebellum it is sometimes known as the **pedunculus cerebelli** (or crus cerebelli ad medullam).

The following cranial nerves arise from the medulla oblongata (Fig. 138).

The twelfth nerve (*XII*) (**N. hypoglossus**) arises by ten or fifteen rootlets from the ventral surface of the medulla oblongata in the anterior lateral fissure (*r*) opposite the caudal portion of the area elliptica (*n*).

The eleventh cranial nerve (*XI*) (**N. accessorius**) arises by numerous rootlets from the lateral surface of the medulla oblongata and of the spinal cord as far caudad as the sixth or seventh cervical nerve. These rootlets join to form a nerve which enters the cranium through the foramen magnum and is closely associated at its point of exit with the glossopharyngeal (*IX*) and vagus (*X*) nerves. The line of origin on the medulla passes between the dorsal and ventral roots of the cervical nerves and is along the middle of the lateral white funiculi.

The tenth cranial nerve (*X*) (**N. vagus**) arises by about eighteen very delicate rootlets from the surface of the area ovalis. The rootlets are divided into a dorsal and a ventral series. The dorsal series (about twelve) arise in the groove which separates the fasciculus cuneatus medialis from the fasciculus cuneatus lateralis. The ventral series arise somehat ventrad of this groove. These rootlets are to be distinguished from those of the ninth nerve by their smaller size.

The ninth cranial nerve (*IX*) (**N. glossopharyngeus**) arises from the area ovalis from a line craniad of the dorsal line of origin of the vagus roots (*X*) and between these and those of the auditory (*VIII*). It arises by a number of rootlets which are larger than those of the vagus (*X*), with which this nerve is closely associated.

The eighth cranial nerve (*VIII*) (**N. acusticus**) appears at the lateral end of the trapezium (*l*). It arises from an elevation (Fig. 141, *i*) which is continued dorsomediad along the cranial border of the area ovalis.

The seventh cranial nerve (*VII*) (**N. facialis**) leaves the lateral border of the trapezium (*l*) near its cranial edge, between the fifth and eighth nerves. It is much smaller than the eighth nerve.

The sixth cranial nerve (*VI*) (**N. abducens**) arises by about six bundles from the groove between the pyramids and the trapezii and passes craniad.

2. *Metencephalon.*—The metencephalon includes the **pons** and the **cerebellum.**

The **pons** (Fig. 138, *i*) is a mass of transverse fibres which forms the ventral and cranial part of the primitive hindbrain. It is a modification of the latter brought about by the development of the cerebellum, and the degree of its development is in direct ratio to that of the cerebellar and cerebral hemispheres. The pons forms a projecting mass of fibres which is marked by a median longitudinal groove, the **sulcus basilaris** (*j*), which indicates the course of the basilar artery (Fig. 121, *c*). Laterad the fibres of the pons converge somewhat and turning dorsad disappear in the cerebellum, forming the **brachia pontis** (Fig. 141, *l*).

The fifth cranial nerve (Fig. 138, *V*) (**N. trigeminus**) arises by two roots from the caudal border of the pons, near the lateral end. The ventral root (4) is small; the dorsal one is much larger and soon forms the large semilunar ganglion (*k*) from which three branches (1, 2, and 3) diverge. The ventral root (4) joins one of these branches (1).

The **cerebellum** (Fig. 137, *III*) is formed by an increase in size of the cranial portion of the primitive hindbrain. This increase has affected principally the surface of the roof, so that as the cerebellum has grown it has been thrown into many folds, the exact form of which varies in different specimens. The cerebellum has at the same time increased in size and has thus extended laterad as well as caudad and craniad. It thus touches the cerebrum in front (separated from it by the tentorium) and aids it in concealing the midbrain and 'tween-brain in dorsal view, while caudad in the same view it conceals the greater part of the medulla. The connections of the cerebellum with adjacent parts of the brain are also overhung and concealed.

The whole surface of the cerebellum is thrown up into numerous folds or **gyri,** separated from one another by deep fissures or **sulci,** which appear at first to render the surface wholly irregular. The entire mass is, however, divisible into a central portion, which from its resemblance to a segmented worm is called the **vermis** (*j*) (its cranial part is the **superior vermis,** and its caudal part the **inferior vermis**), and into lateral portions, the **hemispheres** (*k*). The vermis (*j*) occupies a median longitudinal position, and its gyri and sulci are in the main transverse. It is not directly connected with adjacent parts, and its ventral surface extends farther caudad and craniad than that of the hemispheres. The ventral part of the superior vermis is fitted against the posterior corpora quadrigemina.

The **hemispheres** (*k*) may again be subdivided into groups of gyri which have received special names. One of these, the so-called appendicular lobe, fits into the appendicular fossa of the petrous bone.

The cerebellum is connected to the adjacent parts by three tracts of fibres. sometimes known as crura cerebelli. The tract connecting it with the medulla oblongata is the **corpus restiforme;** that connecting it with the pons is the **brachium pontis** (Fig. 141, *l*); these have been described. A third tract passes craniad to the corpora quadrigemina (Fig. 141, *p* and *q*); this is the **brachium conjunctivum** (Fig. 141, *k*).

The cerebellum is composed of white and gray matter, the latter on the surface (Fig. 143, *III*). The folds of its surface present thus a contrivance for increasing the amount of gray matter. The white matter forms a central mass from which tracts extend into the folds. The whole mass of white matter has thus in section (more particularly in a longitudinal section of the vermis) the appearance of a tree, whence the name **arbor vitæ** (Fig. 143).

The **fourth ventricle** (Fig. 141, *h*; Fig. 143, *m*) is the cavity of the original hindbrain. It begins caudad at the clava (Fig. 141, *d*) as a widening and continuation of the central canal of the spinal cord and extends craniad, becoming wider and passing ventrad of the cerebellum. It becomes narrower craniad and ends at the posterior corpora quadrigemina (*p*), where it becomes continuous with the aqueductus cerebri (Fig. 141, *o*; Fig. 143, *j*). The cavity is shallow and is encroached upon dorsally by the vermis of the cerebellum (Fig. 143).

The floor of the cavity is known as the **fossa rhomboidea** (Fig. 141, *h*). It is formed by the continuation of the gray matter which surrounds the central canal of the cord. It is marked by a median longitudinal groove. At its widest part are seen two considerable tracts of white fibres (**striæ medul lares**) which pass from near the median line laterad and extend into the auditory (eighth) nerves. The floor caudad and craniad of these striæ is marked by a number of elevations and depressions. Similarly situated elevations in the human brain differ from one another slightly in color, are made up of gray matter, and are the centres of origin of most of the cranial nerves. Their homologues in the cat appear not to have been determined.

The side walls of the fourth ventricle (Fig. 141) are formed by the following in order, beginning caudad: the **clava** (*d*), the **corpus restiforme, brachium pontis** (*l*), **brachium conjunctivum** (*k*), and **caudal corpora quadrigemina** (*p*) (**colliculi inferiores**).

The roof (Fig. 143) is formed caudad by a thin layer of non-nervous matter which is closely associated with the pia mater. This thin layer is known as the **velum medullare posterius** (*n*). It connects the dorsal surface of the medulla with the caudal border of the cerebellum. The pia mater covering this portion of the roof is vascular and is folded in toward the floor of the ventricle, forming the **choroid plexus** of the fourth ventricle. In the middle the roof of the fourth ventricle is the cerebellum, while craniad the roof is the **velum medullare anterius** (Fig. 143, *l*). This is a thin layer just craniad of the cerebellum, connecting it with the corpora quadrigemina, and attached laterally to the brachia conjunctiva. Here the fourth ventricle narrows craniad and becomes continuous with the slender **aqueductus cerebri** (Fig. 143, *j*) (aqueduct of Sylvius). The narrowed portion of the brain is frequently known as the **isthmus rhombencephali.**

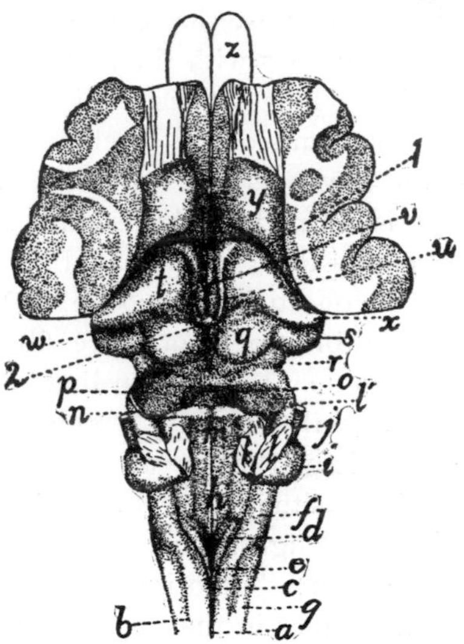

FIG. 141.—DORSAL SURFACE OF MYELENCEPHALON, MESENCEPHALON, AND DIENCEPHALON.

The cerebellum and the greater part of the cerebral hemispheres have been removed. *a*, posterior sulcus of cord; *b*, posterior lateral sulcus; *c*, fasciculus gracilis; *d*, clava; *e*, fasciculus cuneatus; *f*, area ovalis; *g*, fasciculus cuneatus lateralis; *h*, fossa rhomboidea or floor of fourth ventricle; *i*, projection formed by origin of auditory nerve; *j*, facial nerve; *k*, cut end of brachium conjunctivum; *l*, cut end of brachium pontis (*l'*, brachium pontis); *m*, velum medullare anterius; *n*, fourth nerve; *o*, depression marking caudal end of aqueductus cerebri (aqueduct of Sylvius); *p*, caudal corpora quadrigemina (colliculi posteriores); *q*, cranial corpora quadrigemina (colliculi anteriores); *r*, brachium quadrigeminum inferius; *s*, corpus geniculatum mediale; *t*, thalamus; *u*, striæ medullares; *v*, third ventricle; *w*, pulvinar; *x*, corpus geniculatum laterale; *y*, corpus striatum; *z*, outlines of olfactory bulbs. 1, boundary between hemispheres and 'tween-brain; 2, pineal body.

The fourth cranial nerve (Fig. 141, *n*; Fig. 138, *IV*) (**N. trochlearis**) arises from the brain at the craniolateral angle of the velum medullare anterius.

B. MESENCEPHALON.—3. *Mesencephalon.*—The mesencephalon or midbrain includes the **corpora quadrigemina** (Fig. 141) and the **pedunculi cerebri** (Fig. 142). In the primary midbrain there is a pronounced thickening of the walls accompanied by a reduction of the central canal. The midbrain does not thus become very large and is concealed in the dorsal view by the cerebellum and cerebrum, though its floor appears in the ventral view just craniad of the pons (Fig. 138, *g*). Its narrow canal is the **aqueductus cerebri** (**aqueduct of Sylvius**) (Fig. 143, *j*). Its roof forms the **corpora quadrigemina,** and its floor the **pedunculi cerebri.**

In a dorsal view (Fig. 141) the roof is seen to be marked by two pairs of elevations, the **corpora quadrigemina** (*p* and *q*). The cranial pair (*q*) (known as the colliculi superiores) are circular in outline, surrounded on all sides except the cranial one by a deep groove. From the cranial side a tract of fibres (**brachium quadrigeminum superius,** or arm of the cranial corpus) extends craniad and disappears beneath the thalamus (*t*). Between the anterior or cranial corpora quadrigemina lies the **pineal body** or epiphysis (corpus pineale) (Fig. 143, *y*; Fig. 141, 2), a portion of the roof of the 'tween-brain. The caudal corpora (Fig. 141, *p*) are larger than the cranial ones, and ovoid in shape with the long axis vertical. They are united in the median line, and the velum medullare anterius (*m*) stretches between their caudal borders. The brachium of the caudal corpus quadrigeminum (brachium quadrigeminum inferius) (*r*) extends craniad and disappears beneath a considerable elevation, the **corpus geniculatum mediale** (*s*).

Crossing this brachium is seen a small tract of fibres which extends ventrad, crosses the pedunculus cerebri, and reaches the medial border of the latter. It is the **tractus transversus peduncularis** (Fig. 142, *b*). Ventrad of the caudal corpus quadrigeminum is seen a triangular area of oblique fibres which corresponds in position to the human lemniscus.

The **pedunculi cerebri** (peduncles of the cerebrum) form the ventral part of the midbrain. They appear in a ventral view of the entire brain (Fig. 138) as two broad tracts of fibres (*g*) emerging from beneath the pons and diverging from one another as they pass craniad, finally disappearing beneath the cerebral hemispheres. Each is made up of many fibre-bundles, which are apparent in surface view (Fig. 142). The peduncles are separated by a small triangular space, which is marked by a median longitudinal sulcus. In this space, just caudad of the mammillary bodies, is a small area through which a number of blood-vessels pass into the brain. This is known as the **posterior perforated area** (or substance) (Fig. 142, *j*). The cerebral peduncles (*a*) are crossed by the tractus transversus peduncularis (*b*) (see above).

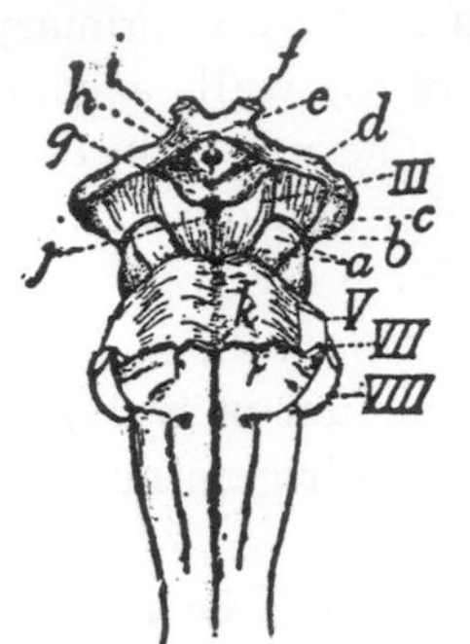

FIG. 142.—VENTRAL SURFACE OF THE MIDBRAIN AND 'TWEEN-BRAIN, WITH THE PONS.

a, pedunculi cerebri; *b*, tractus transversus peduncularis; *c*, corpus geniculatum mediale; *d*, optic tract; *e*, optic chiasma; *f*, optic nerve; *g*, mammillary bodies; *h*, tuber cinereum; *i*, opening for infundibulum (which has been removed); *j*, posterior perforated area; *k*, pons. *III*, *V*, *VII*, *VIII*, third, fifth, seventh, and eighth cranial nerves.

The third cranial nerve (Fig. 138, *III*) (**N. oculomotorius**) leaves the brain at the medial border of the cerebral peduncle (*g*), just caudad of the tractus transversus peduncularis.

The **aqueductus cerebri** (Fig. 143, *j*; Fig. 153, *d*) (or aqueduct of Sylvius) is the continuation craniad of the fourth ventricle. It is a narrow passage, one or two millimeters in diameter, lying dorsad of the pedunculi cerebri and ventrad of the corpora quadrigemina.

C. PROSENCEPHALON.—The prosencephalon or primitive forebrain includes the **diencephalon** or 'tween-brain and the **telencephalon** or cerebral hemispheres.

4. *Diencephalon.*—The diencephalon or 'tween-brain includes the **thalami** and the other parts bounding the third ventricle. The diencephalon is seen in entire brains only in ventral view (Fig. 138, *c*, *d*, *e*, etc.)

The diencephalon may be considered as forming almost or quite the most cranial portion of the median nervous tube,—the cranial wall of the third ventricle (the **lamina terminalis**) (Fig. 143, *d*), ending in the median line in the deep fissure between the hemispheres of the cerebrum. Parts of the brain which extend farther craniad than this are lateral portions, due to the forward growth of the lateral hemispheres. The two hemispheres of the cerebrum may be considered as lateral outgrowths of the central 'tween-brain; these outgrowths have extended dorsad, laterad, craniad, and caudad, so as to cover almost completely the 'tween-brain.

In early stages the cerebral hemispheres are projections from the *cranial end* of the 'tween-brain, so that the plane of junction was nearly transverse, the cranial end of the 'tween-brain joining the caudal end of the hemispheres. With the increasing size and backward growth of the latter, the attachment to the 'tween-brain has been shifted from a cranial to nearly a lateral position, and at the same time the originally lateral surface of the 'tween-brain has become nearly caudal. This is shown in Fig. 141, the deep fissure at 1 marking the line of attachment between the 'tween-brain and the hemispheres. The dorsoventral plane of junction of 'tween-brain and hemispheres is (as Fig. 141 shows) not wholly lateral, but oblique, passing from its cranial end near the middle line caudolaterad.

A second peculiarity of the 'tween-brain lies in the thinness of its roof. The roof is exceedingly thin and is so intimately connected with the pia mater that they cannot be removed separately. The ventral thick floor of the 'tween-brain is directly continuous with the similar floor of the cerebrum; but where the roof of the 'tween-brain joins the roof of the cerebrum along the oblique plane already indicated, the roof is very thin and is intimately connected to the pia mater, and is at the same time folded into the lateral ventricles to form, together with the pia mater, the **choroid plexuses** of the lateral ventricles (Fig. 148, *e*). When the pia mater is removed the thin roof of the brain along the line of junction of the 'tween-brain and the cerebrum is brought away and there *appears* to be a direct communication between lateral ventricles and the exterior.

We may now take up the parts of the diencephalon in detail.

a. **Thalamus** (Fig. 141, *t*).—The two thalami are large oblique rounded ridges, forming the sides of the 'tween-brain. They lie just craniad of the cranial corpora quadrigemina (*q*), but separated from them by a broad groove, and are completely covered by the caudally projecting part of the cerebral hemispheres. The medial larger end of each thalamus is near the middle line; thence the thalamus extends caudolaterad, and rises at its lateral extremity into a sharply rounded projection, the **corpus geniculatum laterale** (*x*). From this projection the thalamus is continued ventrad and then craniomediad as a large band of fibres, the **optic tract** (**tractus opticus**) (Fig. 142, *d*), which extends to the optic chiasma (*e*), where it passes into the optic nerves (*f*). On the caudal border of the thalamus, near the median line, is a very faint projection, the **pulvinar** (Fig. 141, *w*); this lies just craniad of the lateral border of the cranial corpus quadrigeminum (*q*). Just ventrad of the corpus geniculatum laterale (*x*) is the prominent rounded **corpus geniculatum mediale** (*s*); this is connected by a prominent ridge, the **brachium quadrigeminum inferius** (*r*), with the caudal corpus quadrigeminum (*p*). In a similar manner the **brachium quadrigeminum superius** passes from the cranial corpus quadrigeminum (*q*) into the thalamus itself.

Between the two thalami there exists a groove, the **sulcus hypothalamicus.** Over this groove lies the roof of the third ventricle, forming the **choroid plexus** of the third ventricle (Fig. 143, *w*). The medial surface of the two thalami are flat and extend directly ventrad, forming part of the lateral boundary of the third ventricle (Fig. 143, *h*). The two medial surfaces meet over a considerable area across the narrow cavity of the third ventricle, and unite, forming the **massa intermedia** (Fig. 143, *f*) or intermediate mass of the thalamus ("middle commissure"). This connection of the thalami of the two sides is thus not a primitive one, forming no part of the roof or floor of the central cavity, but is a secondary connection due to a growing together of a part of the two sides of the ventricle across its cavity. Along the dorsal edge of the medial border of each thalamus passes a distinct white strand, the **stria medullaris** (Fig. 141, *u*); the two striæ meet in an arch caudad, lying beneath the pineal body (2).

The thalamus is separated craniolaterad by a groove (1) from the corpus striatum (*y*), on the floor of the cerebral hemisphere.

b. The **roof** of the third ventricle is thin and united with the pia mater, as already stated. The pia mater bears many blood-vessels, and the two are folded into the groove between the optic thalami, forming the **lamina chorioidea epithelialis,** or choroid plexus of the third ventricle (Fig. 143, *w*). The roof is attached to the dorsomedial borders of the thalami and becomes continuous with the choroid plexus of the lateral ventricles (Fig. 148, *e*) at the craniolateral borders of the thalami.

The **pineal body** (**corpus pineale**) or epiphysis (Fig. 141, 2; Fig. 143, *y*) is a small conical or spheroidal, hollow body formed as an outgrowth of the caudal part of the roof of the third ventricle and containing an extension of the ventricle. It lies on the roof of the brain between the two cranial corpora quadrigemina (Fig. 141, *q*). From its craniolateral angles two white strands, the **habenulæ,** extend into the striæ medullares (Fig. 141, *u*) of the thalami.

Just ventrad of the pineal body is a transverse band of white fibres, lying in the caudal part of the roof of the third ventricle. This interconnects the two thalami, and forms the **posterior commissure** (Fig. 143, *z'*) (commissura posterior). From this commissure a thin sheet of tissue extends to the pineal body.

c. The **floor** of the third ventricle appears in a ventral view of the brain (Fig. 138, Fig. 142) as a somewhat diamond-shaped space craniad of the pedunculi cerebri (Fig. 142, *a*) and bounded along its cranial margin by the **optic tracts** (Fig. 142, *d*). The optic tracts come from the thalami, as already described; they converge and unite to form the optic chiasma (Fig. 142, *e*), from which the optic nerves (*f*) diverge.

Immediately caudad of the optic chiasma lies a considerable rounded gray elevation, the **tuber cinereum** (Fig. 142, *h*). This bears on its ventral surface in the natural condition the **infundibulum** (Fig. 138, *d*) with the **hypophysis** (Fig. 138, *e*); in cases where the two latter structures have been removed (Fig. 142) the tuber cinereum (*h*) bears a small longitudinal opening (*i*) for attachment of the infundibulum. The infundibulum (Fig. 138, *d*) is a hollow extension of the floor of the third ventricle, and is attached to the middle of the ventral surface of the tuber cinereum. It bears at its ventral end the hypophysis (pituitary body) (Fig. 138, *e*), a vascular non-nervous body of unknown function. The hypophysis is lodged in the sella turcica of the sphenoid bone.

At its caudal border the tuber cinereum bears two white elevations, the **mammillary bodies** (corpora mammillaria) (Fig. 142, *g*).

The **third ventricle** (Fig. 143, *h*; Fig. 141, *v*) is a very narrow slit-like space, of considerable extent dorsoventrally, but less than a millimeter in width; it lies between the medial

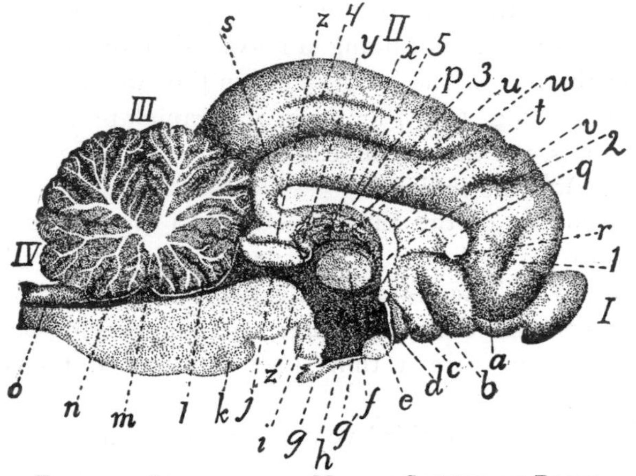

FIG. 143.—LONGITUDINAL MEDIAN SECTION OF BRAIN.

I, olfactory bulb; *II*, cerebrum; *III*, section of cerebellum, showing "arbor vitæ"; *IV*, medulla oblongata. *a*, tractus olfactorius; *b*, substantia perforata anterior; *c*, anterior commissure; *d*, lamina terminalis; *e*, optic chiasma; *f*, massa intermedia of thalamus; *g'*, infundibulum; *g*, hypophysis; *h*, third ventricle; *i*, mammillary body; *j*, aqueductus cerebri (or aqueduct of Sylvius); *k*, pons; *l*, velum medullare anterius; *m*, fourth ventricle; *n*, velum medullare posterius; *o*, continuation of canal of spinal cord; *p*, corpus callosum (body); *q*, genu of corpu callosum; *r*, rostrum; *s*, splenium; *t*, septum pellucidum; *u*, fornix; *v*, pillars of fornix; *w*, choroid plexus of third ventricle; *x*, stria medullaris; *y*, corpus pineale; *z*, cranial corpus quadrigeminum; *z'*, posterior commissure. 1, sulcus falcialis; 2, sulcus cruciatus; 3, sulcus splenialis; 4, sulcus marginalis; 5, sulcus supracallosalis (or callosalis).

ends of the thalami (Fig. 141), and extends ventrad into the tuber cinereum, and thence into the infundibulum (Fig. 143, *g'*). Dorsad it extends into the corpus pineale (Fig. 143, *y*). The third ventricle communicates caudally near its dorsal border with the aqueductus cerebri (*j*); craniolaterally with the lateral ventricles, through the **interventricular foramen**

(foramen of Monro). Its cranial boundary forms in the middle line a thin plate, the **lamina terminalis** (*d*), which is, morphologically, the cranial termination of the cerebrospinal axis; it lies at the bottom of the deep fissure between the cerebral hemispheres. At the dorsal border of the lamina terminalis is a strong transverse band of fibres connecting the two sides of the brain; this is the **anterior commissure** (*c*). The cavity of the third ventricle is much encroached upon by the meeting and secondary union of the two thalami across the middle line, forming the massa intermedia (*f*).

The boundaries of the third ventricle, in order, are as follows, beginning dorsocraniad of the communication with the aqueductus cerebri: the posterior commissure (Fig. 143, *z'*), the pineal body (*y*), the choroid plexus of the third ventricle (*w*), the columns of the fornix (*v*), the anterior commissure (*c*), the lamina terminalis (*d*), the tuber cinereum with the infundibulum (*g'*), the substantia perforata posterior, and the midbrain. The lateral boundaries are formed by the thalami (Fig. 141, *t*).

5. *Telencephalon.*—The telencephalon includes the two cerebral hemispheres. The name **cerebrum** is also applied to this portion of the brain; frequently, however, the name cerebrum is used as signifying the entire mass of the brain craniad of the rhombencephalon,—therefore including mesencephalon, diencephalon, and telencephalon. The term will here be used as synonymous with telencephalon.

The **cerebral hemispheres** arise as two lateral outgrowths from the cranial end of the primitive forebrain. They have undergone great increase in size in the course of evolution, so as to form the larger part of the brain; at the same time important modifications of structure have taken place. In the original condition the medial faces of the two hemispheres are not connected, the two being separate outgrowths of the 'tween-brain, and connected only through the latter. But secondary connections have been formed across the fissure between the two hemispheres, resulting in the production of the **corpus callosum** (Fig. 143, *p*; Fig. 147; Figs. 149–152, *a*), a broad transverse band of white fibres connecting the two hemispheres dorsad of the 'tween-brain. Ventrad of the corpus callosum another secondary union has resulted in the production of the **fornix** (Fig. 143, *u*).

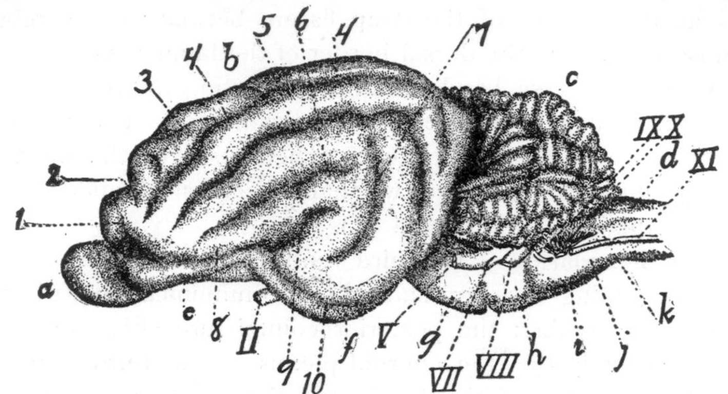

FIG. 144.—LATERAL SURFACE OF THE BRAIN.

a, olfactory bulb; *b*, cerebral hemisphere; *c*, cerebellum; *d*, medulla oblongata; *e*, tractus olfactorius; *f*, lobus pyriformis or tractus postrhinalis; *g*, pons; *h*, trapezium; *i*, pyramid; *j*, area elliptica; *k*, area ovalis. *II*, N. opticus; *V*, N. trigeminus; *VII*, N. facialis; *VIII*, N. acusticus; *IX*, N. glossopharyngeus; *X*, N. vagus; *XI*, N. accessorius. 1, sulcus præsylvius; 2, sulcus cruciatus; 3, sulcus ansatus; 4, sulcus lateralis; 5, sulcus suprasylvius; 6, sulcus anterior; 7, sulcus posterior; 8, sulcus rhinalis; 9, fissura Sylvii; 10, sulcus rhinalis posterior.

External Features.—With increase in size the mass of the cerebrum shows externally a tendency to divide into three lobes, one craniad, the **frontal** (Fig. 145, *A*); one caudoventrad, the **temporal** (*B*); and one caudodorsad, the **occipital** (*C*). The two latter are not distinctly marked off from one another. The limit between the temporal and frontal lobes is marked by a short deep fissure, the **lateral fissure** (**fissura cerebri lateralis**), or fissure of Sylvius (Fig. 144, 9; Fig. 145, *a*). Each lobe is thrown up into elevations or **gyri,** which are separated by grooves or **sulci**; these are described below. The homology of the cerebral gyri and sulci of the cat with those of man is in most cases uncertain.

The sulci and gyri of the cerebral hemispheres may be described briefly in their main features as follows: On the lateral surface of the hemisphere (Fig. 145) the lateral fissure (fissura cerebri lateralis), or fissure of Sylvius, separating temporal and frontal lobes, forms the most convenient point of departure for an understanding of the fissures. The fissure of Sylvius is short but deep, and is formed early during development. In man it covers an area, the **insula,** at its bottom, which may be seen by separating the sides of the fissure. In the cat the insula is rudimentary and can be demonstrated only with difficulty.

The lateral surface of the hemisphere is marked by fissures which form three concentric arches (*b–c*, *d*, and *e*), irregular and incomplete, about the fissure of Sylvius. These arches all open ventrad. The first arch (*b–c*) (that next to the fissure of Sylvius) lacks the central part, the keystone, so that a com-

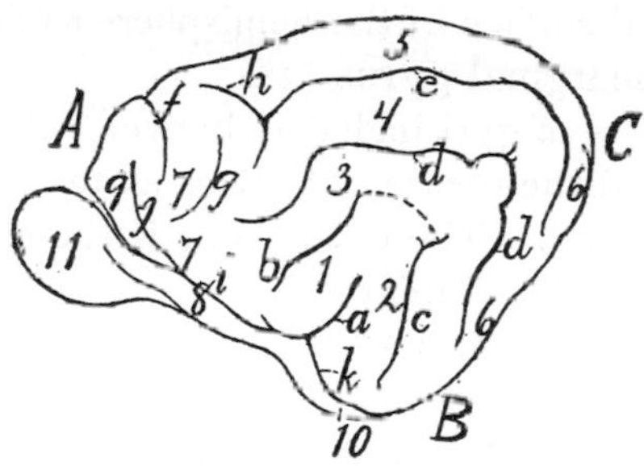

FIG. 145.—DIAGRAM OF THE SULCI AND GYRI ON THE LATERAL SURFACE OF THE HEMISPHERE.

A, frontal lobe; *B*, temporal lobe; *C*, occipital lobe. *a*, lateral fissure or fissure of Sylvius; *b*, sulcus anterior; *c*, sulcus posterior (the broken line connecting the ends of *a* and *b* serves to show how the first arch is completed to form the ectosylvian sulcus, as in the dog; *d*, sulcus suprasylvius; *e*, sulcus lateralis; *f*, sulcus cruciatus; *g*, sulcus coronalis; *h*, sulcus ansatus; *i*, sulcus rhinalis; *j*, sulcus præsylvius; *k*, sulcus rhinalis posterior. 1, anterior Sylvian gyrus; 2, posterior Sylvian gyrus; 3, gyrus ectosylvius; 4, gyrus suprasylvius; 5, gyrus marginalis; 6, gyrus compositus posterior; 7, sigmoid gyrus; 8, olfactory tract; 9, orbital gyrus; 10, lobus pyriformis; 11, olfactory bulb.

plete arch is not formed, but only the two sides of the arch, as two separate sulci (*b* and *c*). The one of these craniad of the fissure of Sylvius is the **sulcus anterior** (*b*); the other is the **sulcus posterior** (*c*). In the dog this arch is usually complete and the sulcus forming it is frequently known as the ectosylvian sulcus (**sulcus ectosylvius**).

The gyri included between the fissure of Sylvius on the one hand and the anterior and posterior sulci on the other are known as the **anterior** (1) and **posterior** (2) **Sylvian gyri.**

The second arch is formed by the **suprasylvian sulcus** (**sulcus suprasylvius**) (*d*). The gyrus between the anterior and posterior sulci ventrad and the suprasylvian sulcus dorsad is the **ectosylvian gyrus** (3) (because dorsad of the ectosylvian sulcus).

The third arched sulcus, next to the medial margin of the hemisphere, is variable: it forms the **lateral sulcus** (*e*). The gyrus lying between the suprasylvian and lateral sulci is the **suprasylvian gyrus** (4) (because dorsad of the suprasylvian sulcus). The lateral sulcus is sometimes broken into two (as in Fig. 137, *h*), the two ends overlapping so as to leave a small gyrus between the two ends.

The gyrus dorsomediad of the lateral sulcus, extending onto the medial surface of the hemisphere as far as the splenial sulcus, is the **marginal gyrus** (5).

The four sets of gyri included between these three sets of arched sulci and the fissure of Sylvius unite caudad and craniad to form single gyri. The caudal one is the **gyrus compositus posterior** (6). The cranial one (less regular than the caudal one) is the **sigmoid gyrus** (7). The latter curves about the cruciate sulcus (*f*) (described below).

In the cranial part of the lateral surface of the hemisphere are certain sulci and gyri which do not belong to the system above described. The **cruciate** sulcus (*f*) is a short transverse sulcus passing from the lateral surface of the hemisphere onto its medial surface, where it extends caudad about a centimeter. Curving around the lateral end of this, separated from it by part of the sigmoid gyrus, is the short **coronal sulcus** (*g*). Connected usually with the end of the lateral sulcus (*e*) and running nearly parallel with the cruciate sulcus is the short **sulcus ansatus** (*h*).

At its ventral end the fissure of Sylvius (*a*) joins a longitudinal groove passing craniad and caudad from the point of junction. That part which passes craniad is the **sulcus rhinalis** (*i*); it forms the dorsolateral boundary of the olfactory tract (8). Passing dorsocraniad from the sulcus rhinalis is a sulcus which separates a very small cranial lobe from the rest of the hemisphere; this is the **supraorbital** or **præsylvian sulcus** (*j*). The portion of the hemisphere craniad of this sulcus is the **orbital gyrus** (9).

The sulcus rhinalis (*i*) is continuous caudad with the

sulcus rhinalis posterior (or **sulcus postrhinalis**) (*k*). This extends caudad onto that portion of the hemisphere which faces the cerebellum. It forms the lateral boundary of a large elongated oval lobe lying at the side of the ventral floor of the midbrain and 'tween-brain. This lobe has been called **tractus postrhinalis** or **lobus pyriformis** (Fig. 145, 10; Fig. 138, *f*).

In addition to the sulci and gyri above mentioned, any given specimen will usually show a number of small inconstant sulci and gyri in various regions; these inconstant structures will not be here described.

On the medial surface of the hemisphere (Fig. 146), the following arrangement of sulci and gyri seems to be typical. Some distance from the dorsal margin a long sulcus runs parallel with the margin; this is the **sulcus splenialis** (*a*). The **marginal gyrus** (1) is dorsad of the splenial sulcus, passing onto the lateral surface of the hemisphere, where it is

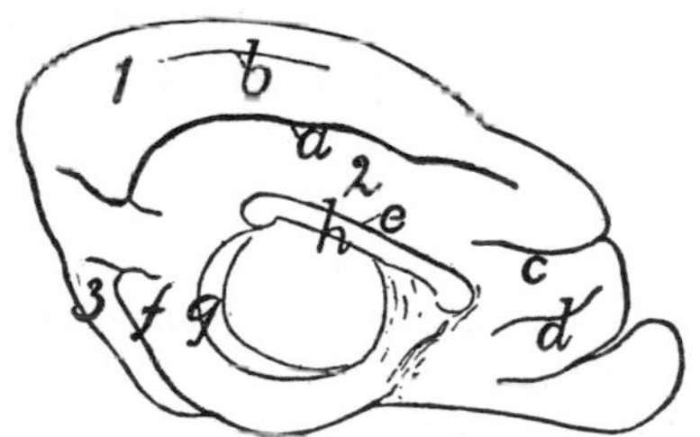

FIG. 146.—DIAGRAM OF THE SULCI AND GYRI ON THE MEDIAL SURFACE OF THE HEMISPHERE.

a, sulcus splenialis; *b*, sulcus marginalis; *c*, sulcus cruciatus; *d*, sulcus falcialis, *e*, sulcus supracallosalis; *f*, sulcus rhinalis posterior; *g*, hippocampal sulcus; *h*, corpus callosum. 1, gyrus marginalis; 2, gyrus fornicatus; 3, gyrus compositus posterior.

bounded by the lateral sulcus. The splenial sulcus extends onto the caudal surface of the hemisphere. A shallow **sulcus marginalis** (*b*) occurs frequently between the sulcus splenialis and the dorsal margin of the hemisphere. Cranioventrad of the cranial end of the splenial sulcus is that portion of the **sulcus cruciatus** (*c*) that lies on the medial surface of the hemisphere. Ventrad of this is a short shallow furrow which has been called the **sulcus falcialis** (*d*).

Immediately dorsad of the corpus callosum (*h*), separating its dorsal surface from a part of the hemisphere, is the

supracallosal or **callosal** sulcus (*e*). Between the supracallosal (*e*) and splenial (*a*) sulci is the **gyrus fornicatus** (2).

On the caudal surface of the hemisphere (that facing the cerebellum) appear the ends of the sulcus splenialis (*a*) and the sulcus rhinalis posterior (*f*). Hidden in the natural condition by the thalami and optic tract is the broad **hippocampal** sulcus (*g*), marking externally the course of the hippocampus.

A further extension of the surface of the cerebrum has taken place in connection with the sense of smell. A mass of gray matter, the **olfactory bulb** (Fig. 144, *a*), reckoned as a part of the cerebrum, is separated from the latter and lies against the cribriform plate of the ethmoid bone. From it the olfactory fibres pass through the perforations of the plate to the olfactory mucous membrane. The olfactory bulb contains a cavity, a part of the lateral ventricle.

The bulb lies against the ventral surface of the frontal lobe and projects craniad of it. It is connected to the cerebrum by a tract of fibres, the **olfactory tract** (Fig. 138, *a*), which is divisible into two roots, medial and lateral. The medial root comes from the medial surface of the frontal lobe, where it is continuous with a tract extending to the cranial end of the corpus callosum. The lateral root is traceable from an elevated gyrus-like portion of the cerebrum which lies at the side of the infundibulum and is known as the lobus pyriformis or tractus postrhinalis (Fig. 138, *f*). The lateral root is divisible into a medial white strand and a lateral gray strand.

That part of the brain comprising the olfactory bulb and the parts intimately related to it are frequently included under the term **rhinencephalon.**

In the triangular area between the two olfactory tracts and craniad of the optic chiasma appears a mass of gray matter, subdivided by a longitudinal fissure. This possesses numerous openings through which blood-vessels pass to the brain substance, and is thence known as the **anterior perforated substance** (**substantia perforata anterior**) (Fig. 138, *b*).

Internal Structures of the Cerebrum.—The cavity of each of the cerebral hemispheres is known as a **lateral ventricle.** The two lateral ventricles constitute the *first* and *second* of the ventricles of the brain, whence the application of the names *third* and *fourth* ventricles to the cavities of the 'tween-brain and hindbrain. The lateral ventricles do not grow at the same rate as the walls of the hemispheres, so that they remain comparatively small. The cavity of each ventricle is further reduced in size by the development on its floor of a large ridge-like thickening, the **corpus striatum** (Fig. 148, *f*).

The dorsal wall or roof of the lateral ventricle joins the thin roof of the third ventricle on each side along an oblique curved line (Fig. 141, 1) which follows the cranial or lateral border of the thalamus (Fig. 141, *t*). Along this line the thin roof of the brain is folded in together with the pia mater to form the **choroid plexus** of the **lateral ventricles** (**lamina chorioidea epithelialis**) (Fig. 148, *e*). When this is pulled out there is left a fissure, the "great transverse fissure of the cerebrum" (Fig. 141, 1). Just dorsad of the groove between the thalami there runs a tract of white fibres known as the **fornix** (Fig. 148, *a*). The two halves of the fornix separate at the cranial ends of the thalami and pass ventrad, forming thus the **pillars** of the **fornix** (Fig. 148, *b*; Fig. 143, *v*). Dorsad of the cranial end of the fornix the **corpus callosum** (Fig. 143, *p*) passes from one hemisphere to the other. Caudad of the pillars of the fornix, the lateral ventricles communicate with the third ventricle by way of the **interventricular foramen** (foramen of Monro).

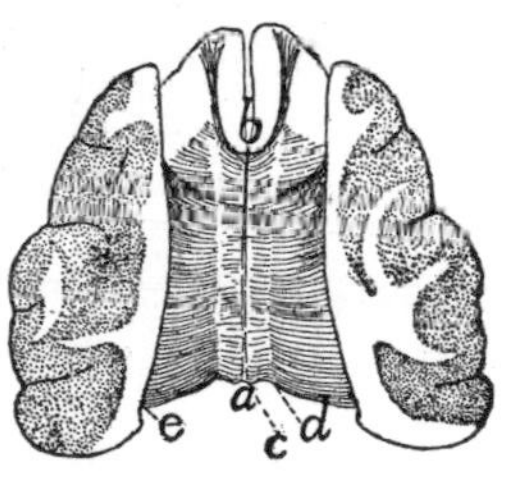

FIG. 147. — THE CORPUS CALLOSUM.

The dorsal portion of the hemispheres has been dissected away, then sliced off, showing the plate of transverse fibres forming the corpus callosum. *a*, splenium; *b*, genu; *c*, line marking the medial edge of the hemisphere; *d*, line marking the lateral boundary of the supracallosal sulcus; laterad of this line the corpus callosum lies in the substance of the hemispheres, which have been dissected away; *e*, line marking medial limit of cut surface.

The parts of the cerebrum may now be taken up in detail.

The **corpus callosum** (Fig. 147; Fig. 143, *p*; Figs. 149–152, *a*) is a broad transverse band of fibres forming a secondary connection between the medial walls of the two hemispheres, dorsad of the roof of the third ventricle. Its outer surface (Fig. 147) is exposed at the bottom of the fissure which separates the hemispheres. On each side it passes laterad, forming the roof of the lateral ventricle. Its cranial part lies dorsad of the corpus striatum, and its caudal part dorsad of the thalamus. Laterally its fibres radiate into the substance of the hemispheres. At its cranial end the corpus callosum bends ventrad and then caudad (Fig. 143). The part which turns to pass ventrad is the **genu** (Fig. 143, *q*) or knee, while the part which projects caudad is the **rostrum** (*r*). The caudal border of the corpus callosum is also thickened and turned ventrad and is called the **splenium** (Fig. 143, *s*); it lies dorsad of the cranial corpora quadrigemina (*z*).

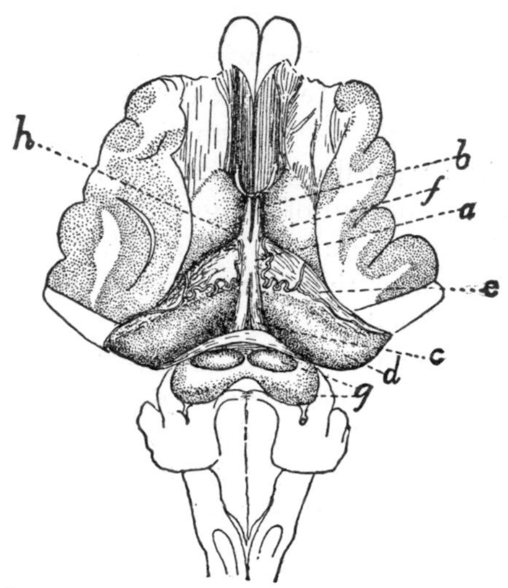

FIG. 148.—FORNIX, HIPPOCAMPUS, AND CORPUS STRIATUM.

The dorsal portion of the hemispheres has been dissected away and the corpus callosum removed. *a*, fornix; *b*, columns or pillars of the fornix; *c*, crura of the fornix; *d*, hippocampus; *e*, choroid plexus of the lateral ventricles overlying the fimbria (the choroid plexus shows an artery). *f*, corpus striatum; *g*, corpora quadrigemina; *h*, position of the interventricular foramen (foramen of Monro).

The caudal half of the ventral surface of the corpus callosum is united with the fornix (Fig. 143, *u*).

The **fornix** (Fig. 148, *a*; Fig. 143, *u*, *v*; Figs. 150–152, *b*) consists of an arched tract of longitudinal fibres near the medial border of each hemisphere, ventrad of the corpus callosum. Each tract begins in the mammillary bodies, and passes dorsad, the two converging until they run side by side, forming a cylindrical dorsoventral bundle known as the columns or pillars of the fornix (Fig. 143, *v*; Fig. 150, *e*), which cross the anterior commissure (Fig. 143, *c*; Fig. 150, *f*) caudad of the latter. Caudad of the pillars of the fornix, between these and the thalamus, lies on each side the interventricular foramen or foramen of Monro, a small opening which connects the lateral ventricles with the third ventricle. Dorsad of the foramen the fornix turns caudad, the two fibre-tracts of each hemisphere lying side by side and closely connected (Fig. 148, *a*), forming thus another secondary union between the medial surfaces of the two hemispheres. This portion of the fornix is the **corpus** or **body** (Fig. 148, *a*); it lies dorsad of the roof of the third ventricle and passes to the splenium (Fig. 143, *s*) of the corpus callosum, and its dorsal surface unites with the ventral surface of the latter (Fig. 143). Caudad the two halves of the fornix diverge, forming the **crura** of the fornix (Fig. 148, *c*); these and the body are continuous laterally with the **hippocampus** (Fig. 148, *d*) and the **fimbria** (Fig. 148, beneath *e*).

The **anterior commissure** (Fig. 143, *c*; Fig. 150, *f*) is a transverse band of white fibres which stretches from one hemisphere to the other about half way between the interventricular foramen or foramen of Monro and the floor of the third ventricle, and just craniad of the pillars of the fornix. This tract of fibres is developed in the original wall of the third ventricle, so that it does not form a *secondary* connection between the halves of the cerebrum, as do the fornix and corpus callosum. It lies dorsad of the lamina terminalis (Fig. 143, *d*) and is continuous with it.

The **septum pellucidum** (Fig. 143, *t*) is a vertical partition which separates the lateral ventricles and fills the interval between the corpus callosum dorsad and the fornix ventrad. It is triangular and translucent. It is formed from the medial walls of the two hemispheres and therefore is made up of two laminæ which embrace between them a space which originally was a part of the fissure separating the hemispheres. This space has been called the fifth ventricle.

The **hippocampus** (Fig. 148, *d*; Fig. 152, *d*) is an elongated rounded elevation of the floor of the lateral ventricle. It is continuous mediad with the fornix (Fig. 148, *a*) and extends thence along the inferior horn of the lateral ventricle to its end in the temporal lobe. It is somewhat narrower at its lateral end. It is thus curved into a semicircle in conformity

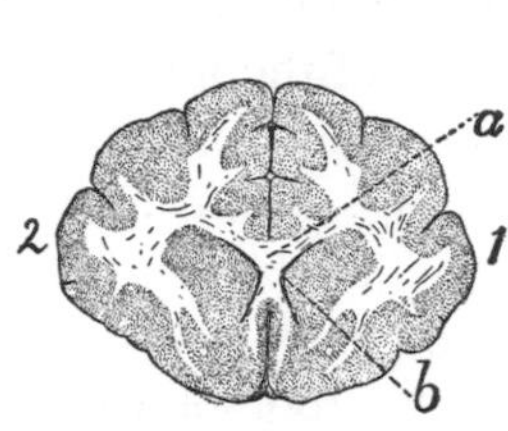

FIG. 149.—CAUDAL SURFACE OF TRANSVERSE SECTION OF BRAIN THROUGH THE GENU OF THE CORPUS CALLOSUM.

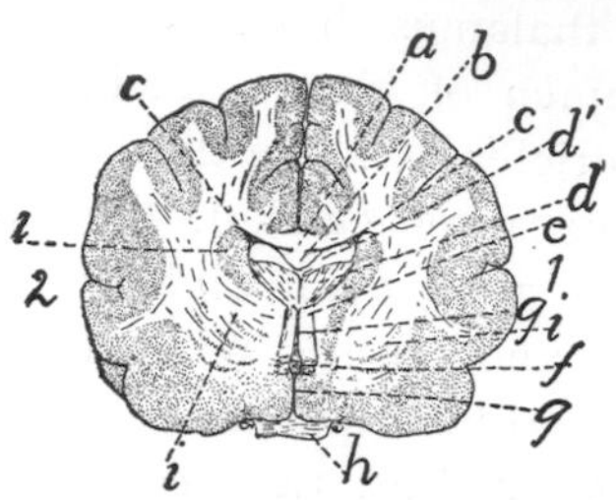

FIG. 150.—CAUDAL SURFACE OF TRANSVERSE SECTION OF BRAIN THROUGH THE OPTIC CHIASMA AND THE REGION OF THE INTERVENTRICULAR FORAMEN (FORAMEN OF MONRO).

Fig. 149.—Gray matter dotted; white matter with a few lines. 1, right hemisphere; 2, left hemisphere. *a*, corpus callosum, section through genu and rostrum; *b*, cavity of lateral ventricles.

Fig. 150.—1, right hemisphere; 2, left hemisphere. *a*, corpus callosum; *b*, fornix (cut); *c*, cavity of lateral ventricles; *d*, fimbria (*d'*, cut surface; *d*, caudal uncut surface of the part that curves ventrad); *e*, pillars of fornix; *f*, anterior commissure; *g*, parts of third ventricle; *h*, optic chiasma; *i*, parts of corpus striatum.

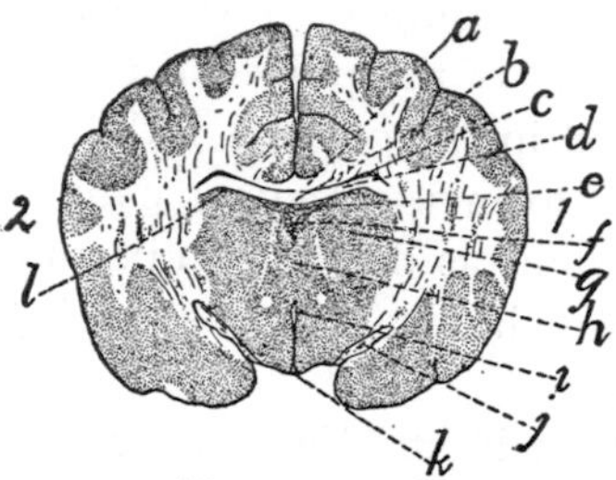

FIG. 151.—CAUDAL SURFACE OF TRANSVERSE SECTION OF THE BRAIN THROUGH THE TUBER CINEREUM AND INFUNDIBULUM, CRANIAD OF THE HYPOPHYSIS.

a, corpus callosum; *b*, fornix (continuous at the sides with the hippocampus); *c*, cavity of lateral ventricles; *d*, hippocampus; *e*, choroid plexus of the third ventricle (roof of the diencephalon); *f*, dorsal part of cavity of the third ventricle; *g*, section of thalamus; *h*, massa intermedia of the thalami, dividing the third ventricle into a dorsal (*f*) and a ventral (*i*) portion; *i*, ventral part of third ventricle; *j*, part of optic tracts; *k*, thin wall of infundibulum, with part of cavity of third ventricle; *l*, line separating roof of thalamus (diencephalon) from floor of hemispheres (telencephalon).

with the inferior horn of the ventricle. Its dorsal surface is convex and looks into the lateral ventricle; its ventral surface is concave and rests upon the thalamus and the optic tract.

Along the craniolateral edge of the hippocampus is a broad, clearly marked fibre-tract, the **fimbria**; this runs parallel to the choroid plexus of the lateral ventricle and beneath it, and is continuous at its medial end with the fornix.

The **corpus striatum** (Fig. 148, *f*; Fig. 141, *y*; Fig. 150, *i*) is a fusiform or ovoid elevation of the floor of the lateral ventricle. One of its narrow ends lies about opposite the middle

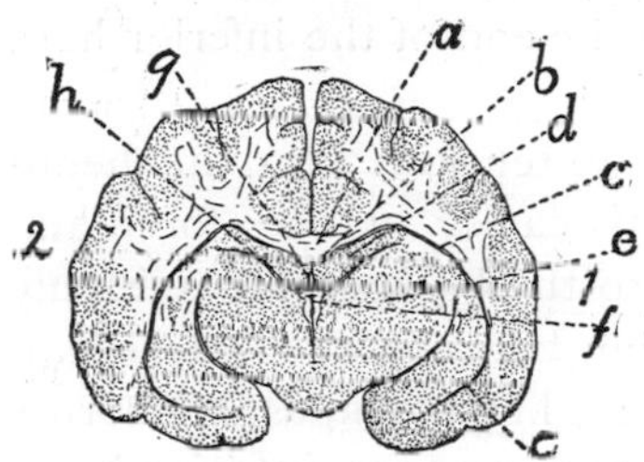

FIG. 152. — CAUDAL SURFACE OF TRANSVERSE SECTION OF THE BRAIN THROUGH THE PINEAL BODY AND THALAMI.

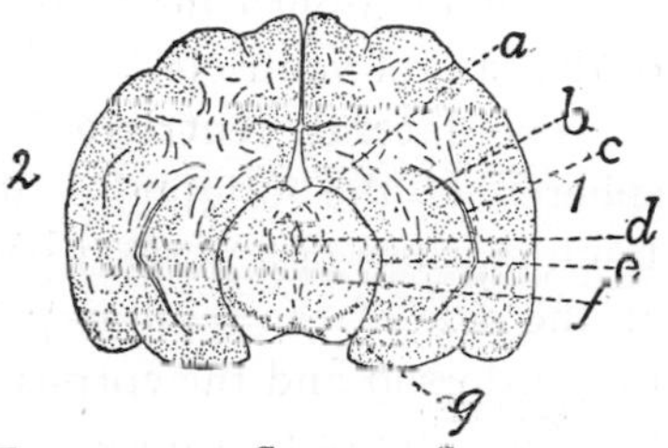

FIG. 153. — CAUDAL SURFACE OF TRANSVERSE SECTION OF THE BRAIN THROUGH THE CRANIAL PAIR OF CORPORA QUADRIGEMINA.

Fig. 152.—*a*, corpus callosum; *b*, fornix; *c*, inferior horn of lateral ventricles; *d*, hippocampus; *e*, thalamus; *f*, third ventricle; *g*, pineal body; *h*, space between the floor of the hemisphere (hippocampus) and roof of the 'tween-brain (thalamus).

Fig. 153.—*a*, cranial corpora quadrigemina; *b*, hippocampus; *c*, part of inferior horn of lateral ventricle; *d*, aqueductus cerebri (aqueduct of Sylvius); *e*, space between the outer surface of the midbrain and the lower surface of the hemisphere; *f*, cross-section of midbrain; *g*, pedunculi cerebri.

of the thalamus (Fig. 141, *t*) and it extends thence obliquely mediad nearly parallel with the thalamus. In the groove between it and the thalamus is the choroid plexus of the lateral ventricles (Fig. 148, *e*). Internally the corpus striatum is made up of several layers of different texture (Fig. 150, *i*), whence its name.

The **choroid plexus** of the lateral ventricles (**lamina chorioidea epithelialis**) (Fig. 148, *e*).—The line of junction of the roof of the third ventricle (i.e., the choroid plexus of the third ventricle) and the cerebral hemispheres is along the lateral (or cranial) border of the thalamus (Fig. 141, *t*). Along this line (Fig. 141, 1) the brain-wall remains very thin and becomes closely associated with the pia mater, so that on the removal of the pia there is left the "transverse fissure" which leads into the lateral ventricle. In an early stage, before the cerebrum has grown far caudad, the fissure is exposed in dorsal view, but after the hemispheres have covered the thalami the fissure appears to be in the lower face of the hemisphere. Through this fissure the pia mater extends upward into the lateral ventricles as a fold separated from the ventricle by the thin brain-wall. This fold is vascular and is known as the choroid plexus of the lateral ventricle (Fig. 148, *e*). It is a fringe-like fold lying on the fimbria and extending from the foramen of Monro (at *h*) nearly to the end of the inferior horn of the lateral ventricle.

The **lateral ventricles** are the extensions into the hemispheres of the originally unpaired cavity of the forebrain. Each consists of a portion parallel to the basis cranii and lying at the side of the septum pellucidum between the corpus callosum dorsad and the corpus striatum, hippocampus, and fornix ventrad, and of two horns, an **anterior** and an **inferior** horn. The inferior horn (Fig. 152, *c*) is a narrow cleft, crescent-shaped in cross-section, which follows the dorsal surface of the hippocampus (Fig. 148, *d*; Fig. 152, *d*) along the temporal lobe to its end almost against the tuber cinereum. It thus passes first caudad and then ventrad and finally mediad. The choroid plexus and hippocampus project into it from its floor. The **anterior** horn extends ventrad and then slightly caudad in the frontal lobe, following the corpus striatum (Fig. 148, *f*), on which it lies.

The **interventricular foramen** (or **foramen of Monro**).—If the choroid plexus of the lateral ventricle (Fig. 148, *e*) is followed to its medial end, it is found to pass through a foramen (at *h*) in which it becomes continuous with the opposite plexus or roof of the third ventricle. This foramen leads from one lateral ventricle to the other and is connected ventrally by a median opening with the third ventricle. It is thus Y-shaped or T-shaped and is the interventricular foramen (or foramen of Monro). The foramen lies opposite the middle of the corpus striatum and caudad of the pillars of the fornix.

Membranes of the Brain.—The membranes of the brain are the **dura mater**, the **arachnoid,** and the **pia mater.**

The dura mater is a strong fibrous membrane lining the cranial cavity and covering the brain. It is strongly attached to the projections of the base of the skull and to the tentorium. It dips between the cerebral hemispheres and olfactory bulbs, forming the **falx cerebri.** It likewise dips between the cerebrum and the cerebellum, covering both surfaces of the bony tentorium. The dura mater does not pass into the fissures or sulci of the surface of the brain. It becomes continuous with the sheath of the cranial nerves as they leave the skull. It is continuous with the dura mater of the spinal cord.

The arachnoid and pia mater are essentially similar to the same structures on the spinal cord. The pia mater dips into the fissures and sulci of the brain and blood vessels course in this membrane.

II. THE PERIPHERAL NERVOUS SYSTEM.

1. **Cranial Nerves. Nervi cerebrales.**—I. N. OLFACTORIUS.—The fasciculi of the olfactory nerves arise from the olfactory bulb (Fig. 144, *a*) and pass through the foramina of the cribriform plate, upon which the bulb lies, to be distributed to the olfactory mucous membrane of the nose.

II. N. OPTICUS.—The second nerve or optic (Fig. 138, *II*) arises from the optic chiasma (Fig. 138, *c*), passes through the optic foramen, and extends in an S-shaped curve to the eyeball. Its course is craniodorsad. It pierces the sclerotic and choroid coats of the eye and spreads out into the retina.

III. N. OCULOMOTORIUS.—The third or oculomotor nerve arises (Fig. 138, *III*) from the pedunculus cerebri and passes into the orbit through the orbital fissure. It passes between the lateral and superior recti, sends a large branch to the superior rectus and levator palpebræ superioris, supplies the medial rectus and the retractor oculi, passes laterad of the optic nerve, supplies the inferior rectus, and sends a long branch to the inferior oblique (Fig. 166, *f*). The triangular reddish **ciliary** (or ophthalmic) **ganglion,** about two millimeters in diameter, is directly attached to the inferior oblique branch at its origin. It receives a delicate sensory filament from the ophthalmic nerve. From the ciliary ganglion proceed two **short ciliary nerves** which pass along each side of the optic nerve to the eyeball. These nerves penetrate the sclerotic at the sides of the eyeball to be distributed to the ball.

IV. N. TROCHLEARIS.—The fourth nerve, the trochlearis (or patheticus), arises from the lateral border of the velum medullare anterius, as already described (Fig. 141, *n*). It passes craniad, emerges through the orbital fissure in company with the oculomotor, abducens, and ophthalmic, passes dorsad of the superior rectus muscle, and reaches (Fig. 154, *l*) the caudal border of the belly of the superior oblique muscle near its middle. It supplies only the superior oblique.

V. N. TRIGEMINUS.—The fifth nerve, the trigeminus (or trifacial) arises (Fig. 138, *V*) by two roots, a large sensory and a small motor root (4), as already described (p. 347). One of these, the motor (4), is smaller and more ventral; the other, the sensory root, is larger and dorsal. The dorsal root soon enlarges to form a large ganglion, the **semilunar** (or Gasserian) **ganglion** (Fig. 138, *k*), from which three branches diverge. One branch is joined by the ventral root (4), which passes over the ventral surface of the semilunar ganglion; and the nerve thus formed is the **mandibular** division (1) of the fifth nerve. Of the other two branches from the ganglion, the middle and longest is the **maxillary** nerve (2), and the smallest is the **ophthalmic** (3). The mandibular nerve is thus mixed, motor and sensory, while the others are sensory.

1. **N. ophthalmicus.**—The ophthalmic or first division of the fifth nerve arises from the semilunar (or Gasserian) ganglion. It passes out of the cranial cavity and into the orbit by way of the orbital fissure, in company with the third, fourth, and sixth nerves and with the extension of the carotid (arterial) plexus.

It passes between the superior and medial recti along with the third nerve, crosses dorsad of the optic nerve, and divides into **infratrochlear** and **ethmoidal** branches. In the orbital fissure it gives off the **frontal** nerve, and while crossing the optic it gives off the **long ciliary** nerve.

a. **N. frontalis.**—The frontal nerve passes along the lateral border of the superior oblique muscle and then laterad of the pulley to near the middle of the supraorbital crest of the frontal bone. Here it passes out of the orbit and is distributed to the integument of the upper eyelid and the adjacent region at the side of the nose.

b. **N. infratrochlearis.**—The infratrochlear nerve passes between the superior rectus and the superior oblique in the first part of its course. It then passes ventrad of the superior oblique and ventrad of the pulley to be distributed to the integument of the upper eyelid near the inner angle.

c. **N. ethmoidalis.**—The ethmoidal nerve passes along with the ethmoidal artery through the ethmoidal foramen (or foramina) in the orbital plate of the frontal bone. It is finally distributed to the mucosa of the nose and to the cartilage and integument of the snout.

d. **N. ciliaris longus.**—The long ciliary nerve arises from the ophthalmic and passes along the optic nerve to be distributed to the eyeball. It divides into several branches before penetrating the sclerotic.

One or two small communicating branches to the **ciliary ganglion** are given off at about the same point as the long ciliary nerve. (For a description of this ganglion see the account of the oculomotor nerve, page 369.)

2. **N. maxillaris.**—The maxillary nerve, the second division of N. trigeminus, rises from the semilunar (Gasserian) ganglion and leaves the skull by the foramen rotundum. It is the sensory nerve of the palate, upper teeth and upper lip, and of part of the forehead and cheek.

On leaving the foramen the maxillary nerve divides into three branches, the two **infraorbital** nerves (Fig. 154, *f*) and the **sphenopalatine** (Fig. 154, *g*). Two smaller branches are likewise given off either within or just outside of the foramen, the **lachrymal** nerve (Fig. 154, *j*) and the **zygomatic** (subcutaneus malæ) (Fig. 154, *i*).

a. **N. lachrymalis** (Fig. 154, *j*; Fig. 155, *m*).—The lachrymal nerve passes along the periorbita to the lachrymal gland (Fig. 154, 11), to which it gives branches. It then continues caudad of the zygomatic process of the temporal to the integument; here it turns caudad and is distributed to the integument in the region between the eye and the external ear (Fig. 155, *m*). It anastomoses with the zygomatic branch of the seventh nerve (Fig. 155, *h*).

b. **N. zygomaticus** (subcutaneus malæ) (Fig. 154, *i*).—This arises with the preceding and follows it for some distance. It passes through a foramen in the frontal process of the malar bone and is distributed to the lower eyelid and adjacent integument.

c. **Nn. infraorbitales** (Fig. 154, *f*; Fig. 155, *l*).—The infraorbital nerves are two of nearly equal size. They pass through the orbit ventrad of the eyeball to the infraorbital canal. On their course each divides once or twice and each divides again in the infraorbital foramen, so that about eight branches emerge from the infraorbital foramen and diverge to the integument and whiskers of the upper lip and to the side and wing of the nose (Fig. 155, *l*). In the infraorbital canal, and before reaching it, branches are given to the molar teeth, and a branch continues in the bone to the canine, incisor, and premolar teeth.

d. **N. sphenopalatinus** (Fig. 154, *g*).—The sphenopalatine nerve turns mediad from the infraorbitals, directing its course toward the sphenopalatine foramen. Before reaching this it gives off the **greater palatine** nerve (**N. palatinus major**), which enters the posterior palatine canal and passes to the hard palate. The sphenopalatine then usually divides into two branches which pass along side by side to enter the **sphenopalatine ganglion.** This is a large elongated triangular ganglion lying on the dorsal surface of the external pterygoid muscle, just laterad of the sphenopalatine foramen.

The following nerves are connected with the sphenopalatine ganglion:

a. **N. palatinus minor.**—This leaves the craniolateral angle of the ganglion and passes to the soft palate.

b. **N. nasalis posterior.**—The posterior nasal nerve enters the nasal cavity by the sphenopalatine foramen and is distributed to the mucosa of the ventral and middle parts of the nasal cavity.

c. **N. canalis pterygoidii** (Vidian Nerve).—This is a large nerve which leaves the caudal angle of the sphenopalatine ganglion and passes caudad. It enters the orbital fissure, lying in a groove on its ventral wall (the cranial end of this groove is sometimes converted into a canal). The groove ends caudally in a foramen which pierces the sphenoid bone between the wing and the body and lies just mediad of the foramen rotundum. The groove and foramen constitute the pterygoid canal (from which the nerve is named). After emerging from the pterygoid canal onto the ventral surface of the basisphenoid the nerve enters the tympanic bulla along with the Eustachian tube, lying on the medial side of the latter. Just after entering, on reaching the internal carotid artery, it divides into two. One of these, **N. petrosus superficialis major** (p. 375), passes into the hiatus facialis of the petrous bone and joins the facial nerve. The other, **N. petrosus profundus**, accompanies the internal carotid artery caudad, turning therefore out of the bulla and passing caudad along its medial side; it finally joins the superior cervical ganglion of the sympathetic system.

3. **N. mandibularis.**—The third division of the fifth, the mandibular nerve, takes origin by a strong root from the semilunar (or Gasserian) ganglion, and receives also after separating from the ganglion the smaller ventral root (portio minor) of the fifth nerve. The root from the ganglion is sensory; the smaller root is motor, so that the mandibular nerve is both sensory and motor. The nerve passes through the foramen ovale, and sends off at once the following branches:

a. **N. auriculotemporalis** (Figs. 154 and 155, *n*).—This passes dorsad between the cartilaginous auditory meatus and the zygomatic process of the temporal bone (Fig. 154, *n*), emerges at the caudal border of the masseter muscle (Fig. 155, *n*), and divides into two chief branches. One, the **auricular** branch, passes along the cranial side of the external ear and is distributed to its integument. The other, the **temporal** branch, passes along the zygomatic arch, gives branches to the temporal muscle and to the skin, follows the zygomatic arch almost to the angle of the mouth, and anastomoses with the superior buccal branch of the facial (Fig. 155, *k*).

b. **N. temporalis profundus.**—One or more large branches passing mediad of the zygomatic arch to the temporal muscle.

c. **N. massetericus.**—The masseteric nerve passes dorsocraniad to the masseter muscle.

d. **N. pterygoideus.**—One or more pterygoid branches pass to the pterygoid muscles. A small twig from the nerve to the internal pterygoid passes into the tympanic cavity and supplies the tensor tympani muscle.

e. **N. buccinatorius** (Fig. 154, *e*).—This passes craniad along the dorsolateral surface of the pterygoid muscles (Fig. 154, 8) to the angle of the mouth. Here it divides into branches to the masseter muscle, the mucosa of the mouth, and to the lips.

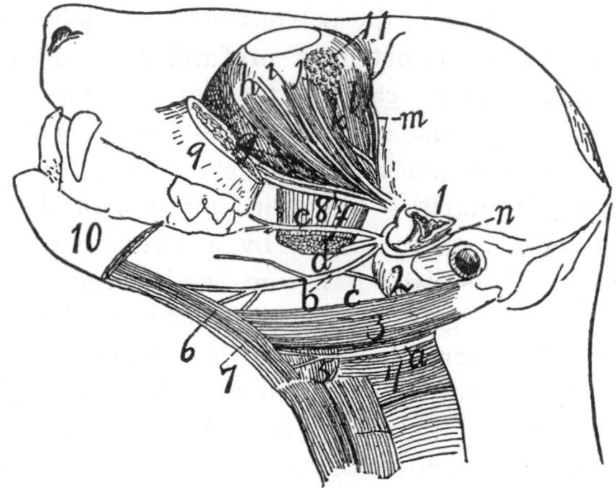

FIG. 154.—DISSECTION SHOWING A NUMBER OF THE CRANIAL NERVES.

The mandible and zygomatic arch have been cut and removed; the temporal and internal pterygoid muscles are also removed. *a*, N. hypoglossus; *b*, N. lingualis; *c*, N. chorda tympani; *d*, N. alveolaris inferior (cut); *e*, N. buccinatorius; *f*, Nn. infraorbitales; *g*, N. sphenopalatinus; *h*, branch of N. oculomotorius; *i*, N. zygomaticus; *j*, N. lachrymalis; *k*, N. abducens; *l*, N. trochlearis; *m*, N. frontalis; *n*, N. auriculotemporalis. 1, cut end of zygomatic process of temporal; 2, tympanic bulla; 3, M. digastricus; 4, M. constrictor pharyngis medius; 5, M. hyoglossus; 6, M. genioglossus; 7, M. geniohyoideus; 8, M. pterygoideus externus (cut); 9, cut cranial end of zygomatic arch; 10, mandible (cut); 11, lachrymal gland.

After giving off the above branches the mandibular nerve passes three or four millimeters laterad along the root of the zygomatic process of the temporal bone, and divides into two large branches, the **inferior alveolar** (or dental) nerve (*d*) and the **lingual** nerve (*b*).

f. **N. alveolaris inferior** (Fig. 154, *d*).—This passes toward the mandibular foramen, but before reaching it gives off a branch to the mylohyoid and digastric muscles. It then enters the foramen, passes through the mandibular canal, and gives numerous **inferior dental** branches to the teeth. At the mental foramen (or foramina) it passes out of the canal and divides into several **mental** nerves, to the chin, lower lip, and mucosa of the lower jaw.

g. **N. lingualis** (Fig. 154, *b*).—The lingual nerve passes between the internal and external pterygoid muscles, and two or three millimeters from its origin it receives the **chorda tympani** nerve (*c*), a communicating branch from the facial (see page 376). It passes onto the ventral surface of the external pterygoid, thence onto the side of the tongue, beneath the mylohyoid. On the side of the tongue it divides into branches which enter the tongue and are distributed to its mucous membrane. One branch passes to the mucosa of the pharynx. Just before entering the tongue a branch is given off to the sublingual and submaxillary glands.

VI. N. ABDUCENS.—The sixth nerve, the abducens, arises from the medulla, as already described (Fig. 138, *VI*, and page 347). It passes into the orbit through the orbital fissure, then extends obliquely cranioventrad along the medial surface of the lateral rectus muscle (Fig. 154, *k*). At about the middle of the length of the muscle it divides into two or three branches which enter at once into the lateral rectus and supply it.

VII. N. FACIALIS (Fig. 155).—The seventh or facial nerve arises from the trapezium at the caudal margin of the pons, craniad of the origin of the eighth nerve, as described in the account of the brain (Fig. 138, *VII*). It passes into the internal auditory meatus, traverses the facial canal through the petrous bone, and emerges at the stylomastoid foramen.

Within the facial canal the nerve bears an enlargement, the **ganglion geniculi.** It gives off within the canal a branch to the stapedius muscle, and the **superficial petrosal** and **chorda tympani** nerves.

The **superficial petrosal** (N. petrosus superficialis major) nerve passes into the hiatus facialis, through the canal which forms its continuation, and joins the sphenopalatine ganglion (p. 373).

The **chorda tympani** is given off two or three millimeters before the emergence of the facial at the stylomastoid foramen. It passes into the tympanic cavity, extends across it between

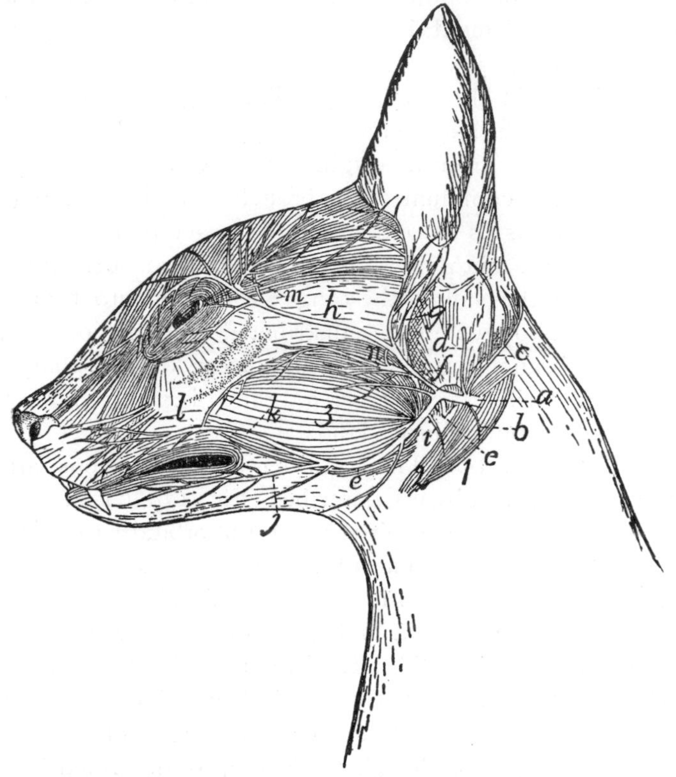

FIG. 155.—SUPERFICIAL NERVES OF THE FACE.

a, N. facialis; *b*, branch to digastric; *c*, N. auricularis posterior; *d*, branch to inside of ear; *e*, ventral ramus; *f*, dorsal ramus; *g*, temporal nerve; *h*, zygomatic nerve; *i*, nerve to stylohyoid muscle; *j*, inferior buccal nerve; *k*, superior buccal nerve; *l*, infraorbital branches of fifth nerve; *m*, lachrymal branches of fifth nerve; *n*, auriculotemporal branches of fifth nerve. 1, M. digastricus; 2, M. stylohyoideus; 3, M. masseter.

the malleus and incus, passing close against the tensor tympani muscle, and leaves it (by a small cleft, the canal of Huguier) between the bulla and the squamous portion of the temporal. It then passes craniad (Fig. 154, *c*), ventrad of the root of the zygomatic process of the temporal, and joins the lingual nerve (Fig. 154, *b*) (branch of the third division of the fifth nerve).

On emerging from the stylomastoid foramen the facial nerve (Fig. 155, *a*) gives off at once a small branch (*b*) to the digastric muscle (1), and a larger branch, **N. auricularis posterior** (*c*), which passes dorsocaudad about the base of the ear, supplying some of its muscles. Another small branch (*d*) pierces the cartilaginous external ear and is distributed to its inner surface. The facial nerve then curves craniad about the proximal part of the cartilaginous external ear, and divides five or six millimeters from its emergence into two main branches, which may be designated as the **dorsal** (*f*) and **ventral** (*e*) rami. A third small branch may also rise from the point of union of the two; it is usually, however, a twig from the dorsal ramus, and passes to M. submentalis.

The dorsal ramus (*f*) sends two or three small branches to the cheek (including the one just mentioned), and divides into the **temporal** (*g*) and the **zygomatic** (*h*) branches. The former (*g*) passes along the cranial margin of the external ear, supplying the superficial muscles, and extends into the temporal region, where it lies deeper than the terminal branches of the lachrymal nerve (*m*) (from the fifth cranial). The **zygomatic** branch (*h*) passes across the malar bone to the caudal angle of the eye, sends branches into both eyelids, anastomoses with twigs from the lachrymal branch (*m*) of the fifth nerve, and passes along the medial side of the eye to the lateral surface of the nose, where it ramifies.

The ventral ramus (*e*) gives off a minute branch (*i*) to the stylohyoid muscle (2), then proceeds toward the angle of the mouth and divides into **superior** (*k*) and **inferior** (*j*) buccal branches, the former to the muscles of the upper lip and the contiguous regions, the latter to those of the lower lip and chin.

The seventh nerve thus supplies most of the muscles of the head except those of mastication, and of these it supplies the digastric.

VIII. N. ACUSTICUS.—The eighth or auditory nerve takes origin (Fig. 138, *VIII*) from the floor of the fourth ventricle.

as before described (page 347). It passes into the internal auditory meatus, divides into auditory and vestibular portions and is distributed to the internal ear within the petrous bone.

IX. N. GLOSSOPHARYNGEUS (Fig. 156, *a* and page 347).—Shortly after its origin (Fig. 138, *IX*) from the side of the medulla the ninth or glossopharyngeus nerve bears a small enlargement on its trunk, the **ganglion superius.** It passes through the jugular foramen with the tenth and eleventh nerves and at its exit shows a second enlargement, the **ganglion petrosum,** connected by fine fibres with the ganglion nodosum (Fig. 156, *d*) of the vagus. It then (Fig. 156, *a*) passes craniad over the surface of the tympanic bulla (15) and mediad of the digastric muscle. Continuing mediad of the carotid artery it divides, near the cranial cornu of the hyoid, into two parts: 1. to the muscles and mucosa of the pharynx; 2. to the tongue, where it is the special nerve of taste but supplies a small branch to the stylopharyngeus muscle.

X. N. VAGUS.—The vagus nerve arises from the side of the medulla in the manner described under The Brain (page 346 and Fig. 138, *X*). It passes through the jugular foramen along with the glossopharyngeal and accessory nerves.

Cervical Portion of the Vagus (Fig. 156, *d*, *d'*).—In the jugular foramen, or just before entering it, it presents a ganglionic enlargement, the **ganglion jugulare** (or "ganglion of the root"), and just beyond the foramen it forms a second ganglion, the **ganglion nodosum** (*d*) (or "ganglion of the trunk"), which lies dorsocaudad of the superior cervical sympathetic ganglion (*e*). The ganglia of the vagus and sympathetic are closely united by connective tissue, and that portion of the vagus craniad of the ganglion nodosum is interconnected by a network of nerve fibres with the sympathetic (*e*), hypoglossal (*b*), and accessory (*c*) nerves and with the pharyngeal plexus. From the ganglion nodosum the vagus (*d'*) passes caudad at the side of the common carotid artery where it is closely bound up with the sympathetic trunk. Just before entering the thorax the two separate, the larger vagus lying ventrad of the sympathetic. (In rare cases the two are distinctly separated throughout their length.)

The vagus sends branches to the outer ear, to muscles of the pharynx and larynx, and to the œsophagus, heart, lungs and abdominal viscera.

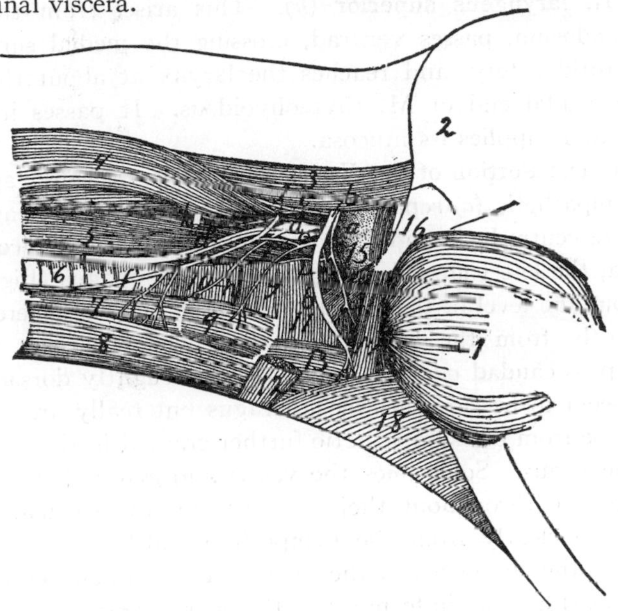

FIG. 156. — GLOSSOPHARYNGEAL, HYPOGLOSSAL, VAGUS, SYMPATHETIC, AND FIRST CERVICAL NERVES IN THE NECK.

a, N. glossopharyngeus; *b*, N. hypoglossus; *c*, N. accessorius; *d*, ganglion nodosum of vagus nerve; *d'*, N. vagus; *e*, ganglion cervicale superius of sympathetic; *f*, ramus descendens of N. hypoglossus (united with first cervical); *g*, branch to M. thyrohyoid from ramus descendens of N. hypoglossus; *h*, N. laryngeus superior of N. vagus; *i*, united vagus and sympathetic nerves; *j*, first cervical nerve; *k*, second cervical nerve; *l*, N. pharyngeus from vagus. 1, M. masseter; 2, outline of external ear; 3, M. splenius; 4, M. levator scapulæ ventralis; 5, M. longus capitis; 6, trachea; 7, M. sternothyreoideus; 8, M. sternohyoideus; 9, M. thyreohyoideus; 10, M. constrictor pharyngis inferior; 11, M. constrictor pharyngis medius; 12, cut end of M. stylohyoideus; 13, M. hyoglossus; 14, M. stylopharyngeus; 15, bulla tympani; 16, M. jugulohyoideus; 17, M. styloglossus; 18, M. mylohyoideus.

Branches of the vagus in the cervical region (Fig. 156).

a. **N. auricularis.**—This leaves the ganglion jugulare, passes through the petrous bone to the facial canal, leaves the skull by the stylomastoid foramen along with the facial nerve, and is distributed to the external ear.

b. **N. pharyngeus** (*l*).—This leaves the vagus craniad of the ganglion nodosum, passes ventrad, sends a small communicating branch to N. laryngeus superior (*h*), and is distributed to the pharyngeal muscles and cranial part of the œsophagus.

c. **N. laryngeus superior** (*h*).—This arises from the ganglion nodosum, passes ventrad, crossing the medial surface of the carotid artery, and reaches the larynx at about the level of the caudal end of M. thyreohyoideus. It passes into the larynx and supplies its mucosa.

Thoracic Portion of the Vagus (Fig. 157).—As the vagus (*b*) and sympathetic (*c*) separate to enter the thorax, the vagus (*b*) lies more ventrad, the right vagus along the lateral surface of the trachea, the left vagus along that of the œsophagus (Fig. 157). At about the level of the first rib or further craniad there arise, apparently from the vagus, the two slender **cardiac nerves** which pass caudad close to the vagus and slightly dorsad of it. They seem to be branches of the vagus but really are not, for they arise from the sympathetic further craniad in the neck and join the vagus. Sometimes the vagus and sympathetic trunks are separate throughout their courses and the cardiac nerves then arise clearly from the sympathetic, although the vagus supplies other branches to the heart. The cardiac nerves pass to the heart and aid in forming on the heart a network known as the **cardiac plexus** (*k*).

The vagus usually receives also, at about the level of the first rib, one or two communicating branches from the middle cervical ganglion (*d*) of the sympathetic. It then passes to the roots of the lungs, crossing the lateral surface of the aortic arch on the left side and the medial surface of the azygos vein on the right side. As it crosses the aortic arch the left vagus gives off **N. laryngeus inferior** (*j*) or recurrent laryngeal. This curves around the caudal side of the aortic arch to the lateral surface of the trachea (*o*), then extends craniad into the neck region on the lateral and ventral surfaces of the trachea. There it passes to the dorsolateral side of the trachea, reaches the larynx, which it penetrates between the cricoid and thyroid cartilages and supplies the muscles of the larynx. It anastomoses with the superior laryngeal.

The *right* inferior laryngeal nerve is given off from the right vagus much further craniad than the left; it curves around

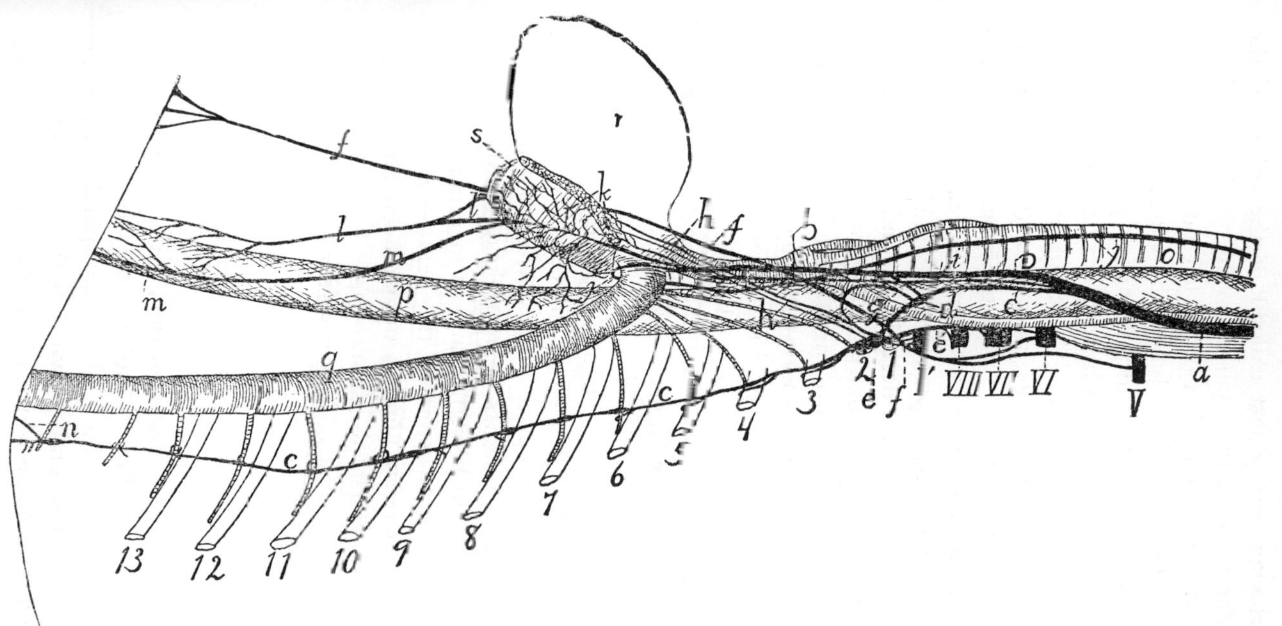

FIG. 157.—SYMPATHETIC, VAGUS, AND PHRENIC NERVES IN THE NECK AND THORAX.

1–13, the thirteen ribs (cut); *V–VIII*, the fifth to eighth cervical nerves (cut); *I'*, first thoracic nerve (cut). *a*, combined trunk of vagus and sympathetic; *b*, vagus; *c*, sympathetic; *d*, middle cervical ganglion of sympathetic; *e*, inferior cervical ganglion; *e'*, communicating branch to sixth, seventh, and eighth cervical nerves; *f*, phrenic nerve; *g*, loop of sympathetic about subclavian artery, between the middle and inferior cervical ganglia; *h*, cardiac branches from the inferior cervical ganglion; *i*, cardiac branch passing from sympathetic along with vagus to heart; *j*, inferior laryngeal nerve; *k*, pulmonary and cardiac plexus; *l*, ventral œsophageal branch of vagus; *l'*, similar branch from the opposite side; *m*, dorsal œsophageal branch of vagus; *n*, great splanchnic nerve; *o*, trachea; *p*, œsophagus; *q*, aorta; *r*, heart; *s*, root of lung.

the right subclavian artery just caudad of the origin of the internal mammary artery, then passes to the trachea, and has a course and distribution like that of the left side.

On reaching the root of the lungs the vagus divides into numerous branches which form the **pulmonary plexus** (*k*) over the roots of the lungs, and extends onto the basis of the heart as the **cardiac plexus.** From these plexuses numerous branches pass to the heart, lungs, pulmonary artery, pericardium, etc. The cardiac branches from the sympathetic, mentioned above, are also connected with the cardiac plexus.

Caudad of the pulmonary plexus the vagus is continued on each side as two trunks, a **dorsal** (*m*) and a **ventral** (*l*) which pass along the œsophagus (*p*) and give branches to it. The ventral branches of the two vagi (*l* and *l'*) unite a little caudad of the root of the lung, and the single trunk passes into the abdominal cavity on the ventral surface of the œsophagus. The dorsal branches unite farther back, near the diaphragm, and the single trunk (*m*) enters the abdominal cavity on the dorsal surface of the œsophagus. Both divisions give fine nerves to the œsophagus.

Abdominal Portion of the Vagus (Fig. 164, page 412).—After passing through the diaphragm the ventral division (Fig. 164, *l*) reaches the lesser curvature of the stomach (1), over which it ramifies, some branches being traceable almost to the pylorus. The network of branches thus formed is the **anterior gastric plexus.** Some twigs from the ventral division pass transversely across the cranial end of the stomach and join the plexus formed by the dorsal division.

The dorsal division (*m*) of the vagus reaches the greater curvature of the stomach, where it ramifies, forming the **posterior gastric plexus.** Branches from this anastomose with the anterior gastric plexus and with the cœliac plexus of the sympathetic (*e*).

XI. N. ACCESSORIUS.—The accessory (or spinal accessory) nerve arises (Fig. 138, *XI*) by numerous rootlets from the lateral surface of the medulla and of the spinal cord as far caudad as the fifth to seventh cervical nerve. These spinal rootlets join to form a nerve which enters the cranium through the foramen magnum. After receiving the rootlets from the medulla, it leaves the cranial cavity by the jugular foramen along with the vagus and glossopharyngeal. Just outside the foramen (Fig. 156, *c*) many fine branches interconnect it with the vagus, sympathetic, and hypoglossal and form the **pharyngeal plexus.** It then turns laterad and caudad (Fig. 158, 1) and pierces the cleidomastoid muscle (*d*), to which it gives small branches. It then divides: one branch enters the sternomastoid muscle; the other passes caudad along the dorsal border of the levator scapulæ ventralis, sends branches to the clavotrapezius, and may be traced to the acromiotrapezius and spinotrapezius, which it supplies.

XII. N. HYPOGLOSSUS (Fig. 156, *b*).—The twelfth or hypoglossal nerve arises from the ventral side of the medulla (Fig. 138, *XII*), as previously described. It emerges from the skull through the hypoglossal canal. At first it passes ventrad, then gradually turns craniad, following thus a curved course and passing successively laterad of the vagus and sympathetic nerves (Fig. 156, *d*, *e*), the common carotid artery, and the cranial cornu of the hyoid bone. A short distance from its origin the nerve gives off a **ramus descendens** (Fig. 156, *f*), which receives a communicating branch from the first cervical nerve (*j*), and divides into two branches, one (*g*) to the thyrohyoid muscle (9), the other to the sternohyoid (8) and sternothyroid muscles (7). The main nerve passes beneath the mylohyoid muscle into the tongue, at first following the lingual artery, then laterad of it, then crossing it again. It sends branches to all the muscles of the tongue, and may be traced to its tip.

Just outside of the jugular foramen the hypoglossal nerve is involved in the pharyngeal plexus with which the vagus, sympathetic, and accessory nerves are also connected.

2. **Spinal Nerves.**—The origin and general features of the spinal nerves have been described in connection with the account of the spinal cord (page 337). A description of their peripheral distribution will now be given.

A. CERVICAL NERVES.—There are eight pairs of cervical nerves. The first leaves the vertebral canal through the atlantal foramen. The second passes out between the arches of the atlas and axis, not through a special intervertebral foramen, so that its ganglion lies among the muscles of the back of the neck. The others emerge through the intervertebral foramina, the eighth one from between the last cervical and first thoracic vertebræ.

Dorsal Rami (Rami posteriores).—The dorsal ramus of the first nerve (N. suboccipitalis) supplies the short dorsal muscles

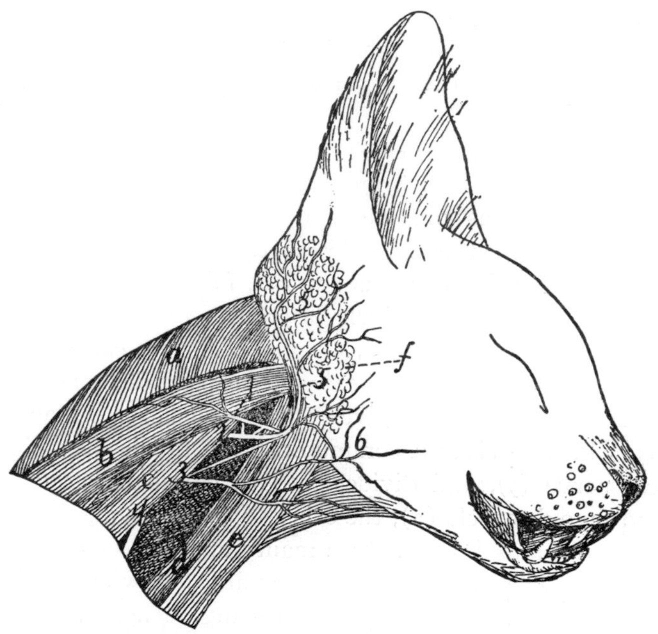

FIG. 158. —SUPERFICIAL NERVES OF THE NECK.

M. clavotrapezius has been partly removed. 1, N. accessorius; 2–4, ventral rami of second to fourth cervical nerves; 5, N. auricularis magnus; 6, N. cutaneus colli. *a*, M. clavotrapezius (cut); *b*, M. splenius; *c*, M. levator scapulæ ventralis; *d*, M. cleidomastoideus; *e*, M. sternomastoideus; *f*, parotid gland.

which move the head and connect the atlas and skull. In the second nerve the dorsal ramus is much larger, forming **N. occipitalis major.** It sends small branches to the muscles about its origin, then turns craniad on the surface of the obliquus superior muscle, passes through the biventer cervicis and splenius, joins a small branch from the third nerve, and reaches the dorsal surface of the back of the head. It passes craniad, lying beneath the levator auris longus, emerges from between the two divisions of this muscle, and supplies the skin and cutaneous muscles between the two external ears. The dorsal rami of the other cervical nerves supply muscles and integument on the back of the neck.

Ventral Rami (**rami anteriores**).—These pass ventrad between the transverse processes of the vertebræ, except in the case of the **first** nerve (Fig. 156, *j*). This passes ventrad from the atlantal foramen along the groove for the vertebral artery, through the notch in the wing of the atlas, and across the lateral surface of the longus capitis muscle (5). Here it sends a branch caudad to join the second cervical (*k*), then crosses the vagus (*d′*) and sympathetic and the carotid artery, giving off communicating branches to the vagus and sympathetic, and uniting with a branch of the descending ramus of the hypoglossal (*f*). At the lateral surface of the larynx it turns caudad, following the lateral border of the sternothyroid muscle (7), and is distributed to the sternohyoid (8) and sternothyroid (7).

The ventral ramus of the **second** nerve (Fig. 158, 2) receives a branch from that of the first nerve, passes laterad between the levator scapulæ ventralis (*c*) and the cleidomastoid (*d*), receives a communicating branch from the third cervical (3), sends a branch to N. accessorius (1) and numerous small nerves into the sternomastoid (*e*) and cleidomastoid (*d*), then turns craniad and divides into **N. auricularis magnus** (5) and **N. cutaneus colli** (6).

N. auricularis magnus (5), the great auricular nerve, passes dorsocraniad across the lateral surface of the sternomastoid (*e*) to the lateral and caudal surface of the external ear and parotid gland (*f*), where it ramifies. The **cutaneus colli** (6) is the smaller, ventral, division of the second nerve; it may receive also an accession from the third. It passes to the integument over the ventral part of M. masseter and ventrad of that muscle.

The **third** nerve (Fig. 158, 3) communicates with the second and supplies the levator scapulæ ventralis (*c*), cleidomastoid (*d*), sternomastoid (*e*), longus capitis, and other muscles of this region and aids in forming the cutaneus colli (6). The **fourth**

(4) and **fifth** are distributed to the muscles and integument of the sides of the neck. A branch of the fourth supplies the integument in the hollow of the shoulder, and one from the fifth follows the vena cephalica and supplies the integument over the shoulder. The fifth by sending a branch to aid in forming the phrenic nerve (Fig. 157, *f*) may be considered to enter partly into the brachial plexus.

Owing to the intercommunicating branches between the ventral roots of the first five cervical nerves, these are sometimes considered as forming a loose plexus which receives the name **cervical plexus.**

The sixth, seventh, and eighth cervical nerves (with a part of the fifth) become interconnected with each other and with the first thoracic to form the **brachial plexus.**

The Brachial Plexus (Fig. 159).—The brachial plexus is formed by the ventral rami of the fifth, sixth, seventh, and eighth cervical nerves and the first thoracic. Of the fifth cervical only a small part enters into the plexus, forming part of the phrenic nerve. The formation of the plexus is due to the union of the different nerves by means of strong connecting branches or **ansæ.** The plexus lies in the axilla, along with the axillary artery and vein; all its component nerves pass laterad in front of the first rib. Its branches supply the arm and shoulder.

The precise arrangement of the different strands is somewhat variable. The plexus is commonly made up in approximately the following manner (Fig. 159). From the **fifth** cervical nerve (*V*) a small branch joins a similar one from the sixth to form the phrenic nerve (*a*); the remainder of the fifth does not enter into the plexus. From the **sixth** cervical (*VI*) arise parts of the phrenic nerve (*a*), the suprascapular (*b*), the cranial one of the three subscapular nerves (*c*), the axillary (*d*), and the musculocutaneus (*f*). The sixth also gives off close to its origin a nerve (*b'*) which passes to the inner surface of the levator scapulæ and ramifies over the surface, supplying this muscle and extending to the rhomboideus, which it also innervates. The **seventh** cervical (*VII*) is the largest nerve entering into the plexus; it furnishes parts of one or both of the anterior thoracic nerves (*k* and *n*), of the posterior thoracic (*m*), the three subscapular nerves (*c*, *e*, and *i*), the axillary (*d*), musculocutaneus (*f*), radial (*h*), and median (*g*) nerves. The **eighth** cervical (*VIII*) supplies parts of one

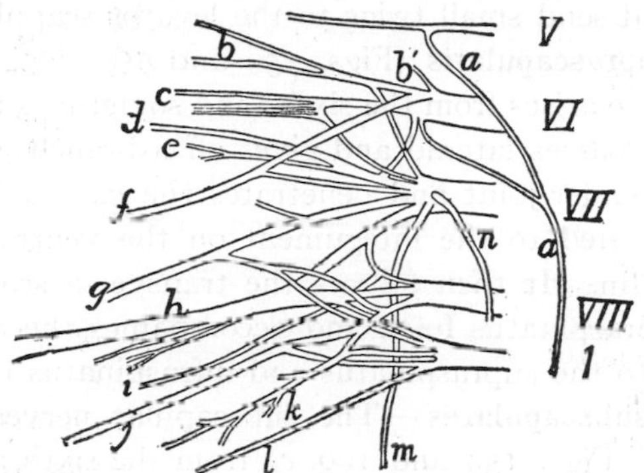

FIG. 159.—DIAGRAM OF THE RIGHT BRACHIAL PLEXUS.

V, *VI*, *VII*, *VIII*, the fifth to eighth cervical nerves. 1, the first thoracic nerve. *a*, phrenic nerve; *b*, suprascapular; *b'*, nerve to serratus anterior and levator scapulæ muscles; *c*, first or cranial subscapular nerve; *d*, axillary nerve; *e*, second subscapular; *f*, musculocutaneous; *g*, median; *h*, radial; *i*, third subscapular; *j*, ulnar; *k*, second anterior thoracic; *l*, medial cutaneous; *m*, posterior thoracic; *n*, first anterior thoracic.

of the anterior thoracic nerves (*k*), the caudal one of the subscapular nerves (*i*), the radial (*h*), median (*g*), and ulnar (*j*) nerves. The **first thoracic** (1) curves craniad, so as to leave the thorax on the cranial side of the first rib; it supplies the median cutaneous nerve (*l*) and parts of the radial (*h*), ulnar (*j*), and median (*g*) nerves; sometimes also a part of one (*k*) of the anterior thoracic nerves.

The following are the nerves which arise from the brachial plexus:

A. **Nerves of the Shoulder and Breast** (Fig. 160).

1. **Nn. thoracici anteriores.**—There are two anterior thoracic nerves. One (Fig. 160, *h*, Fig. 159, *n*) arises from the seventh cervical and passes to the pectoral muscles (9) along with the anterior thoracic artery. The other (Fig. 159, *k*; Fig. 160, *q* and *r*) arises usually by two roots, one from the eighth cervical, one from the first thoracic; it passes along with the long thoracic artery to be distributed to the pectoralis muscles (Fig. 160, 8) and sometimes also to the latissimus dorsi (7).

2. **N. thoracicus posterior.**—The posterior or long thoracic nerve (external respiratory) (Fig. 159, *m*) arises from the seventh cervical near its beginning. It pierces the scalenus and then passes caudad on the outer surface of the serratus anterior to supply it and send small twigs to the levator scapulæ.

3. **N. suprascapularis** (Figs. 159 and 160, *b*).—The suprascapular nerve arises from the sixth (and sometimes the seventh) cervical. It passes laterad and gives off a branch which passes over the shoulder-joint and penetrates the clavodeltoid muscle to be distributed to the integument on the ventral surface of the upper arm. It then follows the transversa scapulæ artery into the supraspinatus fossa and accompanies the artery to be distributed to the supraspinatus and infraspinatus muscles.

4. **Nn. subscapulares.**—The subscapular nerves are three: 1. a cranial (Figs. 159 and 160, *c*) from the sixth and seventh cervical to the subscapular muscle; 2. a middle (Fig. 159, *e*) from the seventh principally to the teres major, the thoracodorsal nerve of man; 3. a caudal (Fig. 159, *i*) from the seventh and eighth cervical to the latissimus dorsi. Their points of origin from the plexus vary.

5. **N. axillaris** (or **circumflexus**) (Fig. 159, *d*).—The axillary nerve arises from the sixth and seventh cervicals, passes toward the shoulder-joint, then follows the posterior circumflex artery ventrad of the long head of the triceps to be distributed to the spinodeltoid, acromiodeltoid and teres minor. A branch continues to the clavobrachial, which it supplies.

B. **The Phrenic Nerve** (Fig. 157, *f*, page 381).

6. **N. phrenicus.**—The phrenic nerve (internal respiratory) arises by the junction of two slender branches, one each from the fifth and sixth cervical nerves (Fig. 159, *a*). (It is said to receive sometimes a branch from the fourth.) It passes caudad into the thorax on the ventral surface of the subclavian artery in company with the vagus and then runs at the side of the inferior and superior venæ cavæ, to reach the diaphragm of which it is the motor nerve.

C. **Nerves of the Arm.**

7. **N. musculocutaneus** (Fig. 160, *d*).—The musculocutaneous nerve or external cutaneous arises from the ventral

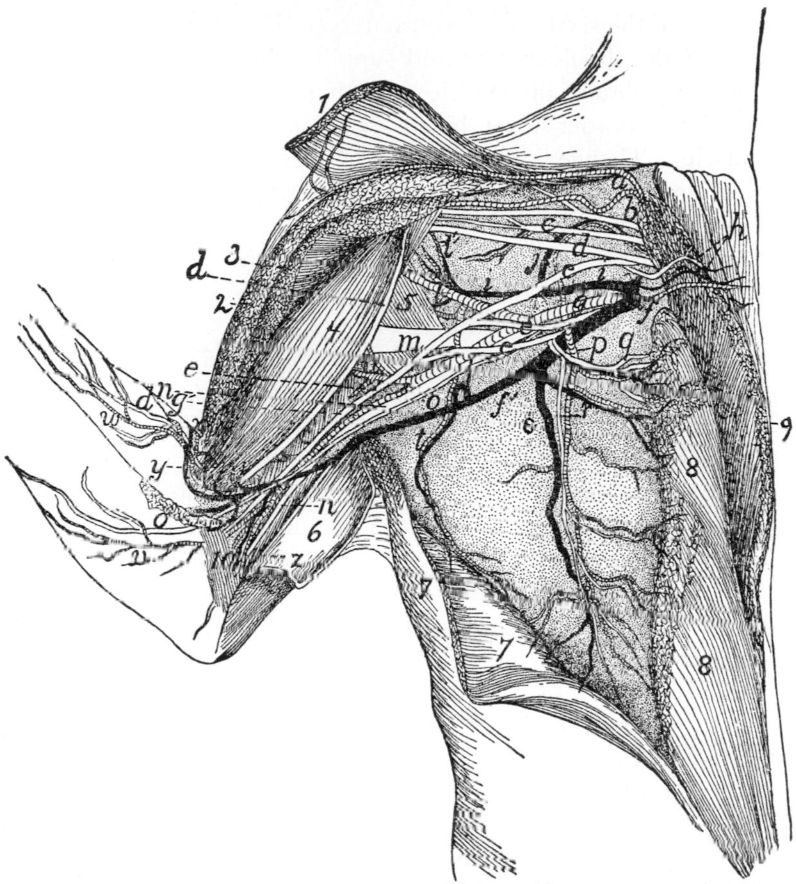

FIG. 160.—BLOOD-VESSELS AND THE MORE VENTRAL NERVES OF THE AXILLA, VENTRAL VIEW.

The pectoral and clavobrachial muscles have been cut and laid aside, their ends being shown; only a part of the nerves are exhibited. 1, M. clavobrachialis; 2, cut end of M. pectoralis major; 3, cut end of M. pectoralis minor; 4, M. biceps; 5, M. teres major; 6, M. epitrochlearis, partly cut and turned back; 7, M. latissimus dorsi, partly cut; 8, M. pectoralis minor; 9, M. pectoralis major; 10, short portion of caput mediale of M. triceps brachii. *a*, branches of the thyrocervical axis to clavobrachial and clavotrapezius muscles; *b*, suprascapular nerve; *c*, first subscapular nerve; *d*, musculocutaneous nerve; *e*, median nerve; *f*, V. axillaris; *g*, A. axillaris; *h*, first anterior thoracic nerve, accompanied by the anterior thoracic artery and vein; *i*, V. subscapularis; *j*, large muscular branch (to subscapular muscle) of the subscapular vein and brachial artery; *l*, A. subscapularis; *l'*, A. circumflexa humeri anterior; *m*, radial nerve; *n*, ulnar nerve; *o*, medial cutaneous nerve; *p*, A. thoracica longa; *q*, *r*, second anterior thoracic nerve; *s*, V. thoracica longa; *t*, A. and V. thoracicodorsalis; *u*, A. pofunda brachii; *v*, branch of brachial artery accompanying medial cutaneous nerve; *w*, branch of A. collateralis radialis superior; *x*, A. collateralis radialis superior; *y*, V. mediana cubiti; *z*, A. collateralis ulnaris.

surface of the sixth and seventh nerves (Fig. 159, *f*). It passes toward the shoulder-joint and supplies the biceps (Fig. 160, 4) and coracobrachialis muscles. It then passes distad, resting on the dorsal border of the biceps (4), and supplies the brachialis muscle. Thence it passes dorsad of the biceps to the lateral side, and reaches the integument by passing between the clavo-brachialis and pectoantibrachialis muscles near the elbow; it is then distributed to the skin on the radial side of the ventral surface of the forearm, as far as the wrist (Fig. 130, *h*, page 319).

8. **N. cutaneus medialis** (Fig. 160, *o*).—The medial (or internal) cutaneous nerve rises from the first thoracic. It passes distad along the medial side of the biceps, and at the junction of the second and third thirds of the upper arm reaches the integument by passing between the epitrochlearis and pectoantibrachialis muscles. It then curves spirally about the dorsal border of the forearm and is distributed to the integument of the forearm on the ulnar side, extending nearly to the wrist.

9. **N. medianus** (Fig. 160, *e*).—The median nerve is formed by the junction of three branches, one each from the seventh and eighth cervical with the brachial artery (*g*) passing between them, and one from the first thoracic nerve. It accompanies the brachial artery (*g*) lying on its medial side, and passes with it through the supracondyloid foramen; here it is connected by a branch to the musculocutaneous nerve. It passes into the forearm (Fig 161, *b*), lying at first beneath the pronator teres (5). Here it gives branches to the pronator teres and flexor muscles (flexor carpi radialis, palmaris longus, five heads of the flexor profundus digitorum, but *not* to the flexor carpi ulnaris). Continuing along the forearm, lying on the flexor carpi radialis, it sends a **posterior interosseous** nerve to the pronator quadratus muscle and branches to the deep and superficial divisions of the flexor sublimis digitorum. It thus supplies the **flexor** and **pronator** muscles (except the flexor carpi ulnaris). It then passes into the palm beneath the transverse ligament and gives rise to three principal branches. The first of these supplies the integument of the thumb, sending a branch on either side of it; and onto the radial side of the

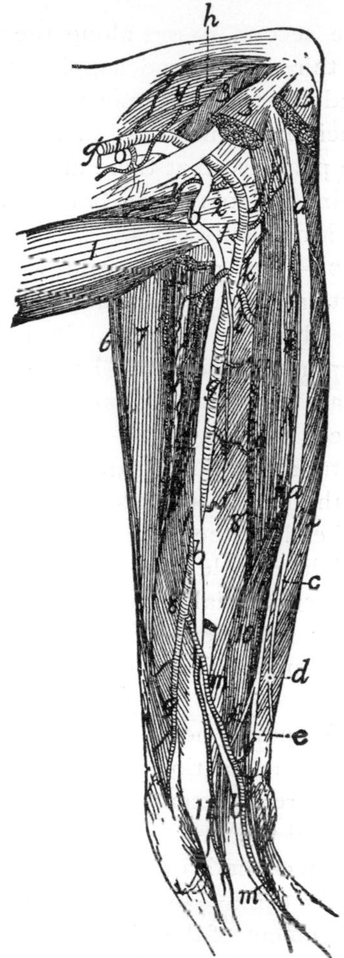

FIG. 161.—NERVES AND ARTERIES OF THE FOREARM, SEEN FROM THE FLEXOR SIDE.

Mm. palmaris longus, flexor carpi radialis, flexor carpi ulnaris, and the third and fourth heads of M. flexor profundus digitorum have been removed; also part of the pronator teres. 1, M. biceps; 2, conjoined tendon of M. brachialis and M. clavobrachialis; 3, short portion of caput mediale of M. triceps; 4, intermediate portion of caput mediale of M. triceps brachii; 5, cut ends of M. pronator teres; 6, M. brachioradialis; 7, M. extensor carpi radialis longus and brevis; 8, fifth head of M. flexor profundus digitorum; 9, second head of M. flexor profundus digitorum; 10, radial part of M. flexor sublimis digitorum; 11, common tendon of M. flexor profundus digitorum; 12, first head of M. flexor profundus digitorum; 13, cut origin of M. flexor carpi ulnaris. *a*, ulnar nerve; *b*, median nerve; *c*, dorsal cutaneous branch of the ulnar nerve; *d*, palmar branch of ulnar nerve; *e*, deep palmar branch; *f*, superficial palmar branch; **g′**, A. brachialis; *g*, A. radialis; *h*, A. collateralis ulnaris superior; *i*, A. radialis recurrens; *j*, A. ulnaris recurrens; *k*, A. ulnaris; *l*, A. interossea anterior; *m*, large branch of A. radialis, joining A. ulnaris.

second digit. The second passes along the contiguous sides of the second and third digits and supplies their integument. The third passes along the contiguous sides of the third and fourth digits to their integument. Each sends twigs into the trilobed pad in the palm, so that there are thus seven terminal branches in the palm. From these, branches (probably) pass to the three radial Mm. lumbricales.

10. **N. radialis.**—The radial (or musculospiral) nerve is formed by the junction of branches from the seventh and eighth cervical and first thoracic nerves. It immediately sends branches to the epitrochlearis, long head of the triceps, and long and intermediate portions of the medial head of the triceps. It then passes between the long and intermediate portions of the medial head of the triceps, following the profunda brachii artery, and curves about the humerus to its cranial side. It supplies there the lateral head of the triceps and the anconeus, and, lying on the brachialis muscle, divides into a superficial and a deep branch. The superficial branch is the **superficial radial nerve** (Fig. 130, *g*); the deep one forms the **dorsal** (or posterior) **interosseous nerve.** The former is sensory and the latter motor.

The **superficial radial** nerve (Fig. 130, *g*, page 319) becomes cutaneous at the junction of the second and third thirds of the upper arm, where it emerges from between the lateral head of the triceps and the brachialis muscle. It then follows the course of the vena cephalica (*c*) to the wrist and follows the dorsal tributary of the same vein onto the dorsum of the hand. It supplies the integument of the distal part of the ventral surface of the upper arm and that along the forearm. On the hand it is distributed to the dorsal surface in the same manner as the median nerve on the ventral surface, i.e. to the integument of the thumb on both sides and to that of the medial side of the second digit; to that of the contiguous sides of the second and third digits and of the contiguous sides of the third and fourth digits. There are thus seven terminal branches, one for each of these regions.

The **dorsal interosseous** nerve follows the brachialis muscle and passes onto the forearm between it and the extensor carpi radialis longus. It supplies the **supinator** and **extensor** muscles of the forearm (brachioradialis, supinator, extensor carpi radialis longus, extensor carpi radialis brevis, extensor communis digitorum, extensor digitorum lateralis, extensor indicis, extensor brevis pollicis). The dorsal interosseous and radial nerves thus supply all the extensor muscles of the forearm and upper arm and the supinators (modified extensors).

11. **N. ulnaris** (Fig. 160, *n*).—The ulnar nerve arises from the eighth cervical and first thoracic and accompanies the brachial artery (*g*) and median nerve (*e*) through the upper arm. It does not pass through the supracondyloid foramen, but curves over the dorsal end of the medial epicondyle of the humerus within the short division of the medial head of the triceps, and reaches the dorsal border of the forearm. In the forearm (Fig. 161, *a*) it lies beneath the flexor carpi ulnaris. It supplies muscular branches to the flexor carpi ulnaris and the first or ulnar head of the flexor profundus digitorum. Near the middle of the forearm it divides into two branches, **dorsal cutaneous** (*c*) and **palmar** (*d*).

The **dorsal cutaneous** branch (*c*) curves about the ulnar side of the wrist to the dorsum of the hand and divides into twigs which supply the dorsal part of the ulnar side of the fifth digit and of the contiguous sides of the fourth and fifth. The **palmar branch** (*d*) sends a twig to the integument on the flexor surface of the arm near the wrist, and then divides into deep palmar (*e*) and superficial palmar (*f*) branches.

The **superficial palmar branch** (*f*) passes into the palm and supplies the ventral portion of the integument on the ulnar side of the fifth digit, and on the contiguous sides of the fifth and fourth.

The **deep palmar branch** (*e*) passes into the palm, beneath the ligament of the pisiform bone. Just distad of the pisiform bone it curves toward the radial side and breaks up into a number of small branches which are distributed to the short muscles in the palm.

B. THORACIC NERVES.

Dorsal Rami.—The dorsal rami of the thoracic nerves are

small and supply the muscles and integument of the back. Each gives off a branch directly dorsad to the spinal muscles, and a lateral branch which reaches the integument some distance from the middle line.

Ventral Rami.—The ventral ramus of the first thoracic nerve enters into the brachial plexus, as already described. The ventral rami of the other thoracic nerves form the **intercostal nerves.** Each of these passes ventrolaterad, lying close to the caudal border of a rib, in company with the intercostal artery. Branches are given to the intercostal muscles, and at about the middle of the length of the rib a large lateral branch is given off, which passes to the more superficial muscles of the thoracic wall (serrati posteriores, obliquus externus, etc.), its main branches running dorsad and ventrad. The main intercostal nerve extends ventrad to the transversus costarum and rectus abdominis, supplying these muscles.

C. LUMBAR NERVES.—There are seven lumbar nerves, one passing from the vertebral canal caudad of each lumbar vertebra.

Dorsal Rami.—The dorsal rami are similar to those of the thoracic region, sending one branch dorsad to the muscles of the vertebral column, another dorsolaterad to reach the integument at about the lateral border of the longissimus dorsi. The dorsal rami are somewhat smaller caudad.

Ventral Rami.—The last four lumbar nerves are interconnected to form the **lumbar** or **lumbosacral plexus.** The first three are distinct, and will therefore be described separately.

The first three lumbar nerves are directed strongly caudad (as well as ventrad), so that on leaving the intervertebral foramen they pass ventrad of the transverse process of the vertebra immediately succeeding. Each communicates with the sympathetic system and gives off near its origin branches to the muscles on the ventral side of the vertebræ,—the first to the crus of the diaphragm, the second and third (Fig. 162, *II* and *III*) to the quadratus lumborum and psoas muscles. Each divides three to five centimeters from its origin into a **lateral** and a **medial** branch, the first having a more cranial, the latter a more caudal course. The first three nerves of the cat are represented in man by the iliohypogastric and the ilioinguinal nerves. There seems no good ground for applying these names to two of the three in the cat, in preference to the third, so that we shall speak of these nerves in the cat as simply the first, second, and third lumbar nerves.

1. The first lumbar nerve arises from the intervertebral foramen caudad of the first lumbar vertebra. Its lateral division passes between the transversus and obliquus internus muscles, then between the obliquus internus and externus. At about the middle of the abdomen it pierces the obliquus externus and is distributed to the integument of the middle of the ventral surface of the abdomen. The medial division passes between the obliquus internus and transversus, crosses the lateral division of the second (lying mediad of it), and extends to the rectus abdominis, which it supplies.

2. The second lumbar nerve (Fig. 162, *a*) divides, like the others, into two branches. The lateral branch pierces the muscles of the abdominal wall at the lateral border of the longissimus dorsi and passes, lying just beneath the integument, ventrocaudad nearly to the pubis. It supplies the integument of the caudal half of the abdomen and of the fold between the thigh and abdomen. The medial branch passes at first almost directly caudad, lying on the medial surface of the transversus abdominis; it curves gradually ventrad, lying in the substance of the transversus, and reaches the rectus abdominis three or four centimeters craniad of the pubis.

3. The third lumbar nerve (*b*) is not united with the fourth, as in many animals, but remains distinct. It divides one or two centimeters from its origin. The lateral branch passes caudad to the outer surface of the abdominal muscles, and extends, lying just beneath the integument, to that portion of the abdominal wall which is partly covered by the thigh. The medial branch passes caudad on the lateral surface of the iliopsoas muscle, follows the iliolumbar artery for a short distance, and gives branches to the caudal part of the transversus and rectus abdominis muscles.

The Lumbar Plexus (Fig. 162).—The fourth, fifth, sixth, and seventh lumbar nerves are interconnected by short branches, forming thus the **lumbar plexus.** They are also connected with the sacral plexus, so that the two are often considered together as the **lumbosacral plexus** (Fig. 162). In some other animals the first three lumbar nerves form also a part of the plexus; but they are not connected with it in the cat.

The fourth lumbar nerve forms the genitofemoral (*c*) and part of the lateral cutaneous (*d*) nerves, and is connected by a short strand with the fifth. The fifth aids in forming the lateral cutaneous (*d*) and femoral (*f*) nerves, and is connected by a short branch with the sixth. The sixth lumbar is large; it forms the major part of the femoral (*f*) and a large part of the obturator nerve (*g*), and sends a large connecting branch caudad to join the seventh and thus pass into the sacral plexus. The seventh passes caudad to join the sacral plexus and aid in forming the great sciatic nerve (*h*); by its connection with the sixth it aids in forming also the obturator nerve (*g*).

4. **N. genitofemoralis** (or N. lumboinguinalis) (*c*, *c'*, *c''*).—This is a direct continuation of the fourth lumbar nerve. Its medial branch (*c''*) passes along the medial surface of the iliopsoas (8) and the psoas minor (9) to the external iliac artery, accompanies this, lying on the ventral surface, from its origin to the point where it gives off the profunda femoris, then accompanies the latter artery and passes onto that branch of it that spreads out under the integument of the ventral pelvic region. It crosses the spermatic cord and ramifies in the skin of the proximal part of the medial side of the thigh. The lateral branch of the genitofemoralis (*c'*) pierces the psoas minor (9), appearing on its ventral surface opposite the fifth lumbar vertebra. It passes caudad on the ventral surface of this muscle, crosses the iliolumbar artery, then turns caudolaterad, passes through the abdominal wall, and is distributed to the craniomedial surface of the thigh and to the adjacent abdominal wall.

This nerve is variable in origin and in distribution. Its lateral branch is sometimes lacking.

5. **N. cutaneus femoris lateralis** (*d*).—The lateral cutaneous nerve arises from the connecting strand between the fourth

and fifth nerves, most of its fibres coming from the fifth. It passes caudoventrad between the iliopsoas and psoas minor and accompanies the iliolumbar artery across the ventral surface of the iliopsoas. It pierces the abdominal wall in company with the artery and passes onto the cranial border of the thigh. Its terminal branches are distributed to the integument along with the branches of the iliolumbar artery,—supplying the lateral surface of the femur and extending as far as the knee.

6. **N. femoralis** (*f*).—The femoral is a large nerve which rises by strong roots from the fifth and sixth lumbar nerves. It gives branches to the iliopsoas (8) and passes through that muscle to its ventral surface. It leaves the abdominal cavity lying on the ventral surface of the iliopsoas, and at the point where it pierces the abdominal wall it divides into three (or four) branches. One (or two) of these pass to the sartorius muscle. Another passes between the rectus femoris and vastus medialis muscles, and divides into numerous branches which supply these muscles and the vastus intermedius.

The third branch of the femoral is **N. saphenus** or the **long saphenous** nerve (Fig. 127, *g*, page 310). This passes distad along with the femoral artery and vein, giving a few twigs to the integument. Where the long saphenous artery (*f*) separates from the femoral artery the nerve follows the former and passes with it along the medial side of the lower leg. At the knee and in the lower leg it gives off a number of cutaneous branches, and finally divides just distad of the middle of the lower leg into two main branches. Both of these pass to the concavity of the ankle-joint and divide into fine branches, which form a sort of plexus on the ankle and dorsal surface of the foot; branches from this can be traced almost to the toes.

7. **N. obturatorius** (Fig. 162, *g*).—The obturator nerve arises from the connecting band between the sixth and seventh nerves. It lies at first laterad, then dorsad, of the common iliac vein, and passes almost directly caudad to the cranial border of M. obturator internus (15). Here it turns sharply laterad about the pubis, and passes through the obturator foramen. It gives twigs to the obturator externus muscle, and

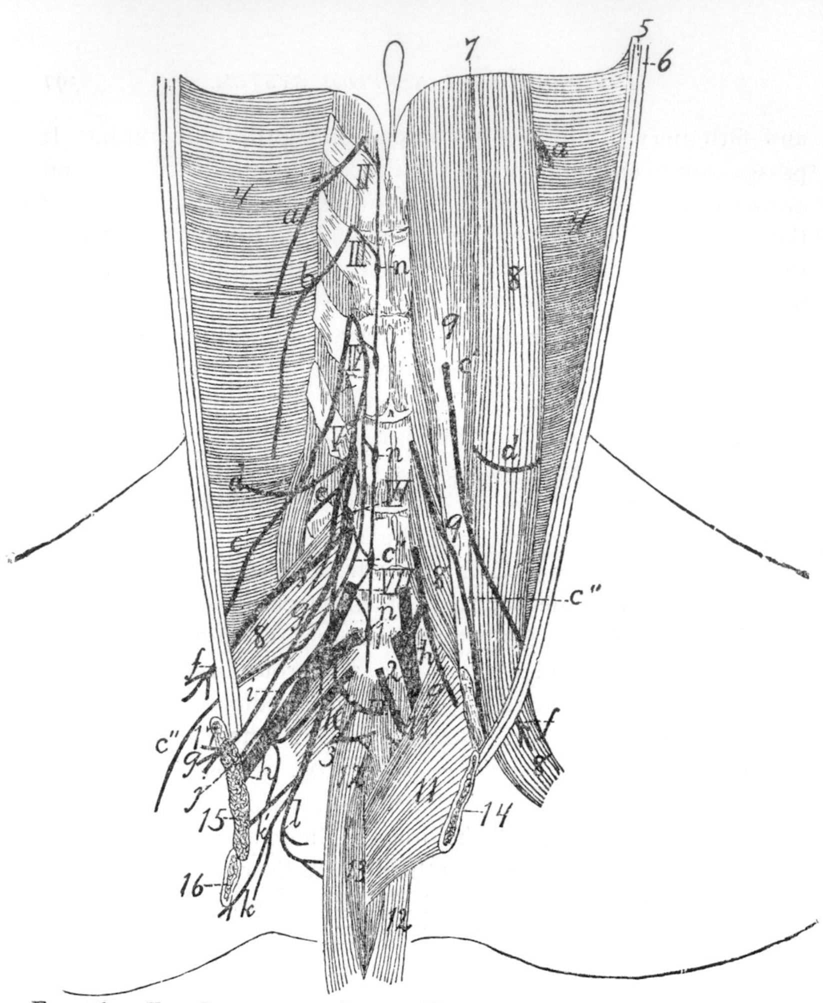

Fig. 162.—The Lumbar and Sacral Nerves, as seen in a View of the Dorsal Wall of the Abdominal Cavity, after Removal of the Viscera.

On the right side the iliopsoas, psoas minor, and quadratus lumborum have been removed. The symphysis pubis has been split and the two parts divaricated, to show the pelvic cavity; on the right side parts of the innominate bones and the levator ani and coccygeus muscles have been removed. *II–VII*, second to seventh lumbar nerves; 1–3, first to third sacral nerves. *a*, second lumbar nerve; *b*, lateral and medial branches of third lumbar nerve; *c*, N. genitofemoralis (*c'*, its lateral branch; *c''*, its medial branch); *d*, N. cutaneus femoralis lateralis; *e*, muscular branch of N. femoralis; *f*, N. femoralis; *g*, N. obturatorius; *h*, N. ischiadicus or great sciatic nerve; *i*, N. gluteus superior; *j*, N. gluteus inferior; *k*, N. cutaneus femoris posterior; *l*, N. pudendus; *m*, N. hemorrhoidalis inferior; *n*, part of the sympathetic (incompletely shown, merely to indicate connections with the spinal nerves); 4, M. transversus abdominis; 5, 6, cut edges of M. obliquus internus and externus; 7, dorsal border of the diaphragm; 8, M. iliopsoas (mostly removed on the right side); 9, M. psoas minor; 10, M. pyriformis; 11, M. levator ani; 11', M. ilio-caudalis; 12, M. flexor caudæ longus; 13, M. flexor caudæ brevis; 14, edge of pubic symphysis; 15, cut end of M. obturator internus; 16, cut ramus of ischium; 17, cut ramus of pubis.

divides into several branches, which innervate the adductor femoris, adductor longus, pectineus, and gracilis.

D. SACRAL NERVES AND SACRAL PLEXUS (Fig. 162).—A large band passes caudad from the sixth and seventh lumbar nerves to connect with the sacral nerves; this constitutes the so-called **lumbosacral cord.** The sacral nerves are three in number. Their dorsal rami pass dorsad out of the two posterior sacral foramina and the foramen caudad of the sacrum, to the muscles and skin dorsad of the sacrum. The ventral rami pass from the two anterior sacral foramina and from the foramen between the last sacral and first caudal vertebræ. The first is the largest; it joins the lumbosacral cord to form the great sciatic nerve (N. ischiadicus) (*h*) and the superior (*i*) and inferior (*j*) gluteal, and sends a branch caudad to connect with the second sacral. The second and third sacral nerves are small; they unite with the connecting branch from the first to form a network from which arises the pudendus (*l*), cutaneus femoris posterior (*k*), hemorrhoidalis inferior (*m*), and a small branch to the great sciatic (*h*).

The nerves arising from the sacral plexus are the following:

1. **N. gluteus superior** (Fig. 162, *i*; Fig. 163, *j*).—The superior gluteal nerve arises from the lumbosacral cord and the first sacral nerve; it passes dorsad in the notch between sacrum and ilium, caudolaterad of the first anterior sacral foramen, curves over the dorsal border of the ilium between the gluteus medius and pyriformis muscles (Fig. 163, 7), passes between the gemellus superior (6) and gluteus minimus (5) and ventrad of the latter, and reaches the medial surface of the tensor fasciæ latæ, which it innervates. In its course it sends branches to the gluteus medius, gluteus minimus (5), and gemellus superior.

2. **N. gluteus inferior** (Fig. 162, *j*; Fig. 163, *i*).—A small nerve from the lumbosacral cord and the first sacral nerve. It passes dorsocaudad, lying on the dorsal surface of the great sciatic nerve (Fig. 162, *h*). After leaving the pelvis by the great sciatic notch it divides beneath the pyriformis (Fig. 163, 7) into two branches; one goes to M. caudofemoralis (4), the other to M. gluteus maximus (3).

3. **N. ischiadicus** (Fig. 162, *h*; Fig. 163, *a*).—The **great sciatic** nerve, the largest nerve in the body, arises from the lumbosacral cord (formed chiefly by the sixth and seventh lumbar nerves), the first sacral nerve and a small branch from the second sacral. It passes caudodorsad and leaves the pelvis by passing across the great sciatic notch, between M. pyriformis and M. gemellus superior. It passes across the tendon of M. obturator internus (Fig. 163, 9) near the insertion, and here sends caudad a large muscular branch (*b*) beneath the biceps. This branch innervates the biceps, semitendinosus (17) and semimembranosus (16). Other twigs in this region pass to the quadratus femoris (10) and tenuissimus. The great sciatic nerve (*a*) now passes across the quadratus femoris (10), adductor femoris (15), and semimembranosus (16), lying beneath the biceps femoris. It thus enters the popliteal space and approaches the popliteal artery and vein. Here it gives off one or two small muscular branches to the distal part of the biceps, and sends a slender branch, **N. suralis** (*c*), along the medial surface of the biceps to the lateral surface of the lateral head of M. gastrocnemius (20). The sural nerve (*c*) becomes cutaneous at the distal (ventral) border of the biceps, and divides three or four centimeters proximad of the ankle into two branches. One passes over the tendon of Achilles (27) to the proximal end of the calcaneus and ramifies in this region. The other passes onto the lateral surface of the foot, and supplies the integument in this region over the tarsus and part of the metatarsus.

The great sciatic nerve now divides in the popliteal space into the **peroneus communis** (*d*) and the **tibialis** (*e*).

a. **N. peroneus communis** (*d*).—This is the more lateral of the two divisions of the great sciatic nerve. It passes along the medial surface of the biceps to the lateral surface of the lateral head of M. gastrocnemius (20), where it extends to a point just distad of the head of the fibula. Here it passes beneath that part of the gastrocnemius which has origin on the fascia of the shank, passes between the soleus and peroneus longus (21), then between the peroneus longus and peroneus tertius. It gives off a number of small muscular branches,

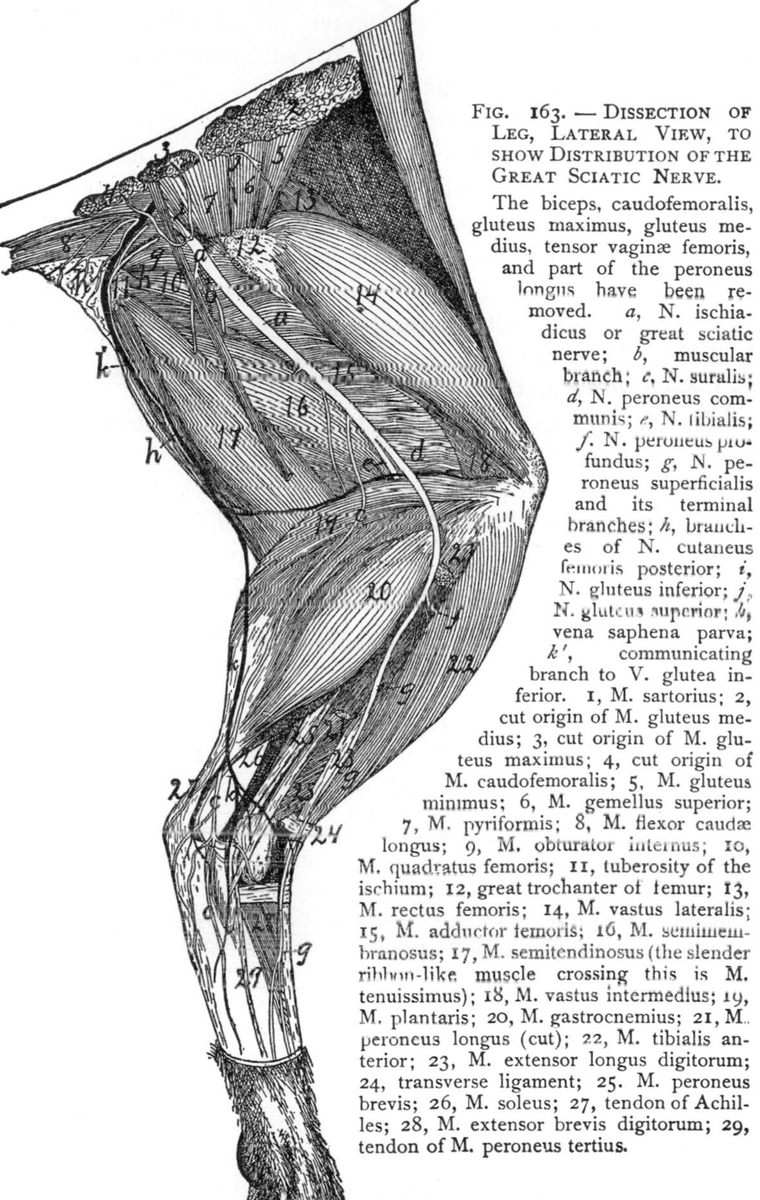

FIG. 163. — DISSECTION OF LEG, LATERAL VIEW, TO SHOW DISTRIBUTION OF THE GREAT SCIATIC NERVE.

The biceps, caudofemoralis, gluteus maximus, gluteus medius, tensor vaginæ femoris, and part of the peroneus longus have been removed. *a*, N. ischiadicus or great sciatic nerve; *b*, muscular branch; *c*, N. suralis; *d*, N. peroneus communis; *e*, N. tibialis; *f*, N. peroneus profundus; *g*, N. peroneus superficialis and its terminal branches; *h*, branches of N. cutaneus femoris posterior; *i*, N. gluteus inferior; *j*, N. gluteus superior; *k*, vena saphena parva; *k'*, communicating branch to V. glutea inferior. 1, M. sartorius; 2, cut origin of M. gluteus medius; 3, cut origin of M. gluteus maximus; 4, cut origin of M. caudofemoralis; 5, M. gluteus minimus; 6, M. gemellus superior; 7, M. pyriformis; 8, M. flexor caudæ longus; 9, M. obturator internus; 10, M. quadratus femoris; 11, tuberosity of the ischium; 12, great trochanter of femur; 13, M. rectus femoris; 14, M. vastus lateralis; 15, M. adductor femoris; 16, M. semimembranosus; 17, M. semitendinosus (the slender ribbon-like muscle crossing this is M. tenuissimus); 18, M. vastus intermedius; 19, M. plantaris; 20, M. gastrocnemius; 21, M. peroneus longus (cut); 22, M. tibialis anterior; 23, M. extensor longus digitorum; 24, transverse ligament; 25. M. peroneus brevis; 26, M. soleus; 27, tendon of Achilles; 28, M. extensor brevis digitorum; 29, tendon of M. peroneus tertius.

then divides two or three centimeters distad of the head of the fibula into two main branches, **N. peroneus superficialis** (*g*) and **N. peroneus profundus** (*f*).

(1) **N. peroneus superficialis** (*g*).—The superficial peroneal nerve passes distad between the peroneus longus and peroneus tertius and supplies them. Near the ankle it becomes superficial, crosses the transverse ligaments which bind down the tendons of the extensor longus (23) and tibialis anterior (22) in the concavity of the ankle and reaches the dorsum of the foot. After giving off two or three minute twigs to the ankle it divides into four parts which pass distad and subdivide so as to send a nerve to each side of each toe.

(2) **N. peroneus profundus** (*f*).—The deep peroneal nerve passes between the tibialis anterior and extensor longus digitorum muscles, which it innervates, and passes distad with the tibialis anterior artery, lying on the inner surface of the tibialis anterior muscle. It passes onto the dorsum of the foot, lying on the inner surface of the tendon of the tibialis anterior muscle. On the tarsus it divides into two branches. The lateral branch passes into the extensor brevis digitorum, while the medial one extends in the dorsal groove between metatarsals four and five to the toes; here it divides into two nerves which supply the contiguous sides of digits four and five. The deep peroneal supplies anterior tibial and dorsal foot muscles.

b. **N. tibialis** (*e*).—The tibial nerve passes distad parallel with the peroneal nerve, but mediad of it. It passes first between the lateral and medial heads of the gastrocnemius, giving off muscular branches to them and to the popliteus, plantaris and soleus, then between the plantaris and the medial head of the gastrocnemius, to the space between the plantaris and flexor longus hallucis, where it passes distad. It gives off, in the region just described, muscular branches to the flexor longus digitorum, flexor longus hallucis, and tibialis posterior. Below the middle of the lower leg the nerve becomes superficial (Fig. 127, *i*, page 310), lying on the ventral surface of the flexor longus hallucis. In the depression between the heel and the medial malleolus it passes to the plantar surface of the tarsus, sends a small branch to the plantar surface of the heel, and divides into two branches, the **medial** and the **lateral plantar** nerves.

(1) **N. plantaris medialis.**—The medial plantar nerve passes along the medial border of the flexor brevis digitorum and divides into two branches. One passes to the medial (second) digit, supplying both sides; the other supplies the third digit in the same way. Both send branches to the fibrous pad on the sole of the foot.

(2) **N. plantaris lateralis.**—The lateral plantar nerve passes laterad across the tendon of the flexor longus digitorum to its lateral edge. At about the proximal end of the metatarsi it divides into two branches. The lateral branch passes distad to the ventral surface of the fifth digit. The medial branch passes beneath the tendon of the flexor longus digitorum and transversely across the interossei; it divides into numerous nerves which innervate the interossei and other short muscles of the sole of the foot.

4. **N. pudendus** (Fig. 162, *l*; Fig. 112, 8, page 265).—This arises (Fig. 162, *l*) from the sacral plexus caudad of the great sciatic nerve. It has two roots, one from the second sacral, one from the third, and it may also receive a small accession from the great sciatic nerve (*h*) three or four centimeters caudad of the origin of the latter. It passes at first dorsolaterad, laterad of the coccygeus muscle, then curves mediad toward the anus. It divides into two branches: one passes to the base of the penis, sends twigs into the compressor urethræ muscle, and passes onto the dorsal surface of the penis. This branch is **N. dorsalis penis**; it extends with the artery of the same name to the glans. The second branch of N. pudendus (**N. hemorrhoidalis medius**) passes to the anus and innervates the muscles and other structures about the caudal end of the rectum. In the female, branches of N. pudendus supply the urogenital sinus and adjacent structures (Fig. 112, 8).

5. **N. cutaneus femoris posterior** (Fig. 162, *k*; Fig. 163, *h*).—This arises from the sacral plexus, its roots coming chiefly from the second and third sacral nerves, and passes caudodorsad, at first in close connection with N. pudendus. It then accompanies the posterior gluteal artery and vein, sends

branches (perineal nerves) into the fat at the sides of the anus, and branches onto the lateral surface of the biceps muscle. One of the latter follows the communicating vein (Fig. 163, *k'*) from V. saphena parva, and may be traced as far distad as the popliteal space.

6. **N. hemorrhoidalis inferior** (or **posterior**) (Fig. 162, *m*). —This arises by two roots, from the second and third sacral nerves, and passes with the inferior hemorrhoidal artery ventrad across the lateral surface of the rectum to the urethra. Here it divides into two parts: one passes craniad to the bladder, the other caudad onto the ventrolateral surface of the rectum.

A small nerve passes from the sacral plexus, especially from the third sacral nerve, into M. levator ani (Fig. 162, 11). Another small nerve from the same region passes to M. coccygeus, and a third to the proximal end of M. tenuissimus.

E. NERVES OF THE TAIL. COCCYGEAL NERVES.—From the intervertebral foramina of the first seven or eight caudal vertebræ spinal nerves of the usual type are given off. The dorsal rami innervate the dorsal muscles of the tail. The ventral rami are interconnected with each other and with the last sacral nerve by a longitudinal cord; they innervate the muscles and integument of the ventral side of the tail.

3. The Sympathetic Nervous System. Systema nervorum sympatheticum.

The sympathetic system consists of those ganglia, nerves and plexuses through which afferent and efferent fibres are supplied for the heart and other viscera, for the glands and for the smooth muscle of the blood vessels, hair follicles and other organs. The relations of its parts to one another and to the central nervous system are not revealed by a study of its gross anatomy but have been made clear by advances in our knowledge of its minute anatomy and its physiology, subjects the details of which lie beyond the scope of this book. These relationships are shown diagrammatically in Fig. 164a, which should be studied in connection with the literature cited in the preface to this edition. For preliminary orientation the minute structures in Fig. 164a may be ignored and the following anatomical constituents of the sympathetic system recognized.

A. Outline of Gross Structures.

1. **The sympathetic trunks** (Figs. 157, 164, 164a) lie one on either side of the bodies of the vertebræ from the base of the skull to the tail. Each consists of a series of ganglia (**chain ganglia**) (Fig. 164a, *M*, *N*, *O*, *P*) united by nerve cords. The ganglia are connected to the thoracic and first four lumbar spinal nerves by white and gray rami communicantes (Fig. 163a, *F*, *G*; Fig. 164a, *23′*, *23″*, *24′*, *24″*), and to the cervical, last lumbar and sacral spinal nerves by gray rami only (Fig. 164a, *23*).

2. **The collateral ganglia** (Fig. 164a, *G*, *H*, *I*) which lie along the abdominal aorta and its branches, and which are connected to the trunks by nerves (Fig. 163a, *J*; Fig. 164a, *18*, *20*, *21*) and supply nerves to the viscera (Fig. 163a, *6*, *7*; Fig. 164a, *10*, *19′*, *19″*).

3. **The terminal ganglia** (Fig. 164a, *A*, *B*, *C*, *D*, *E*, *F*) on or near all the viscera. These ganglia are connected with the central nervous system through the third, seventh, ninth, tenth and eleventh cranial nerves and the second and third sacral spinal nerves (Fig. 164a, *1*, *3*, *7*, *10*, *22*) but not directly with the sympathetic trunk.

4. Numerous complicated nerve plexuses (Fig. 157, *k*; Fig. 164, *e*, *g*, *h*, *l*, *m*; Fig. 164a, *J*, *K*, *L*) to be described later.

B. Outline of Minute Structure.

In its minute structure the sympathetic system shows afferent fibres (Fig. 163a, *7*, *8*) which conduct impulses from the viscera, glands, blood vessels and skin to the central nervous system (**visceral afferent fibres**); and other fibres which conduct impulses outward from the central nervous system to the structures mentioned in the first paragraph, **efferent fibres** (Fig. 163a, *2*, *5*). The efferent neurons only are shown in Fig. 164a. In this efferent portion of the sympathetic nervous system outgoing impulses are conducted through chains of two neurons, a proximal neuron with its cell body in the central nervous system, and a distal with its cell body in either a chain, collateral or terminal ganglion. The fibres of the proximal neurons are known as **pre-**

ganglionic (Fig. 164a, *1, 3, 7, 10, 18, 20, 21, 22*); those of the distal neurons as **postganglionic** (Fig. 164a, *11, 13, 14, 15, 17, 19, 19′, 19″*).

Two anatomical-physiological subdivisions of the efferent sympathetic nervous system may be recognized: 1. The **craniosacral subdivision** (Fig. 164a, heavy lines) with the cell bodies of its proximal neurons in the brain or in the sacral portion of the spinal cord and the cell bodies of its distal neurons in terminal ganglia; 2. The **thoracicolumbar subdivision** (Fig. 164a, light lines) with the cell bodies of its proximal neurons in the intermediolateral column of the thoracicolumbar region of the spinal cord and the cell bodies of its distal neurons in the sympathetic trunk or in collateral ganglia.

1. **Minute Structure of the Thoracicolumbar Subdivision.**—The preganglionic fibres pass from cells of origin in the intermediolateral cell column (Fig. 163a, *1*; Fig. 164a, *25, 25′, 25″*) of the spinal cord through all the thoracic spinal nerves and the first three or four lumbar nerves (Fig. 164a) and then through the white rami communicantes (Fig. 163a, *F*; Fig. 164a, *24, 24′, 24″, 24‴*) to the sympathetic trunk. They either terminate in the ganglia of the trunk or pass through the trunk to end in collateral ganglia. In the trunk ganglia the preganglionic neurons synapse with the postganglionic neurons, from which postganglionic fibres then pass either to the viscera or by way of the gray rami communicantes (Fig. 163a, *G*; Fig. 164a, *23′, 23″*) and branches of the spinal nerves to the skin and blood vessels (Fig. 163a, *D*, *E*). In the collateral ganglia the preganglionic neurons synapse with postganglionic neurons which supply the viscera (Fig. 163a, *5*; Fig. 164a, *G*, *H*, *I*).

2. **Minute Structure of the Craniosacral Portion.**—The preganglionic fibres pass by way of cranial nerves *III*, *VII*, *IX*, *X* and *XI* and the second and third sacral spinal nerves directly to the terminal ganglia, without synapsing in the sympathetic trunk (Fig. 164a, *1, 3, 7, 10, 22*). In these ganglia the preganglionic neurons synapse with the cells of the distal neurons (Fig. 164a, *A*, *B*, *C*, *D*, *E*, *F*) from which short postganglionic fibres pass to the parts innervated.

All major structures supplied by the sympathetic system thus receive a double innervation, one set of fibres from the craniosacral portion and one from the thoracicolumbar portion. The two usually produce antagonistic physiological activities in the organs supplied.

The afferent neurons of the sympathetic system, not included in Fig. 164a, should be thought of as having fibres which accompany the efferent fibres, bound up in the same nerves (Fig. 163a,

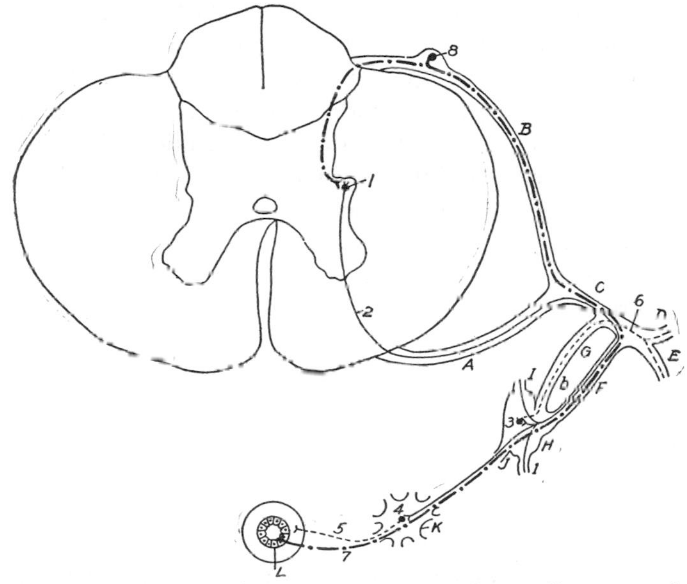

FIG. 163a.—DIAGRAMMATIC SECTION THROUGH THE SPINAL CORD AND A SPINAL NERVE IN THE THORACIC REGION TO ILLUSTRATE THE FIBRES ASSOCIATED WITH THE SYMPATHETIC NERVOUS SYSTEM IN A TYPICAL SPINAL NERVE.

Solid light line indicates a preganglionic neuron; broken light line indicates a postganglionic neuron; heavy dash and dot line indicates a visceral afferent neuron.

A, ventral root; *B*, dorsal root; *C*, spinal nerve trunk; *D*, dorsal ramus; *E*, ventral ramus; *F*, white ramus communicans; *G*, gray ramus communicans; *H*, chain ganglion; *I*, sympathetic trunk; *J*, splanchnic nerve; *K*, collateral ganglion; *L*, viscus. 1, cell body in intermediolateral cell column; 2, preganglionic fibre (to simplify the diagram only one fibre is shown). In the chain ganglion the four possibilities of the course of such fibres is illustrated; 3, synapse in chain ganglion; 4, synapse in collateral ganglion; 5, postganglionic neuron to viscera; 6, postganglionic neuron to sweat glands, blood vessel wall, or muscle of hair follicle; 7, visceral afferent fibre; 8, cell body of visceral afferent neuron in spinal (dorsal root) ganglion.

7). Their cell bodies (Fig. 163a, *8*) in the cerebrospinal ganglia send processes into the central nervous system and fibres (Fig. 163a, *7*) from the parts innervated pass to them without interruption.

C. Description of Parts by Regions.

1. **The Thoracicolumbar Subdivision.**—The trunk and ganglia for each region of the body will be described separately.

a. **Cervical Portion** (Fig. 156 and 157; 164a).—The sympathetic trunk begins caudad of the tympanic bulla with the large **superior cervical ganglion (G. cervicale superius)** (Fig. 156, *e*; Fig. 164a, *M*), which lies on the cranioventral side of the ganglion nodosum (Fig. 156, *a*) of the vagus nerve. From this ganglion the trunk passes caudad, closely bound up with the vagus nerve (Fig. 157, *a*) and in close connection with the common carotid artery and internal jugular vein. This entire group of structures lies in the chink between the trachea and œsophagus (Fig. 156, *i* and 6). A few centimeters craniad of the first rib the vagus and sympathetic trunks separate, and just craniad of the first rib the sympathetic trunk usually has the **middle cervical ganglion** (sometimes lacking) (Fig. 157, *d*; Fig. 164a, *N*) associated with it. Caudad of the middle cervical ganglion the sympathetic trunk divides into two portions; a larger dorsal which passes dorsocaudad and joins the **stellate ganglion** (Fig. 157, *e*; Fig. 164a, *O*), which lies at the head of the first rib and on the lateral surface of the longus colli muscle; and a ventral branch (Fig. 157, *g*) which is smaller and passes laterad, crosses the medial and caudal surfaces of the subclavian artery, and joins the stellate ganglion.

Through the white rami communicantes (Fig. 164a, *24*, *24'*) of the first four thoracic spinal nerves, the sympathetic trunk receives preganglionic fibres which pass craniad to end in the superior cervical ganglion. From the superior cervical ganglion pass the following postganglionic fibres: 1. Fibres to join the first three or four cervical spinal nerves (gray rami communicantes) (Fig. 164a, *M* and *23*); 2. Fibres which follow the blood vessels into the head to furnish the thoracicolumbar innervation in that region (Fig. 164a, *11*). Most of these fibres follow the internal carotid artery (Fig. 164a, *g*) on which they form the **carotid plexus** (Fig. 164a, *12*). Fibres of this type reach the intrinsic eye-muscles and the glands of the head. Particularly important is the **deep petrosal nerve** (N. petrosus profundus) (page 372), which forms part of the **Vidian nerve** (page 372); 3. Many smaller branches which have been identified by Ranson and Billingsley (see Preface) and listed as follows: *a.* To superior thyroid artery; *b.* to ganglion nodosum separately or with the superior laryngeal branch of the vagus just after it leaves the ganglion nodosum; *c.* branches to hypoglossal nerve; *d.* branch to glossopharyngeal nerve (identified in only a few instances); *e.* pharyngeal branches which pass over the carotid artery to the pharynx; *f.* to external carotid artery and probably through this to the parotid gland; 4. **superior cardiac nerve** (Fig. 164a, *13*) which usually accompanies the vagus to reach the heart, but may be lacking.

The **middle cervical ganglion** (Fig. 157, *d* and Fig. 164a, *N*) sends postganglionic fibres through the gray rami communicantes (Fig. 164a, *23*) to the fifth and sixth cervical spinal nerves and sometimes to the fourth, and others to form the **middle cardiac nerve** (Fig. 164a, *14*) which accompanies the vagus to the heart. From the inferior cervical ganglion which is fused with the first three thoracic ganglia to form the **stellate ganglion** (Fig. 157, *e* and Fig. 164a, *O*) postganglionic fibres pass to the last two cervical spinal nerves and to form the **inferior cardiac nerve** (Fig. 157, *h*; Fig. 164a, *15*) which passes caudad, joins the vagus and reaches the heart.

b. **Thoracic Portion.**—This portion of the trunk begins at the caudal end of the stellate ganglion (Fig. 157, *c* and Fig. 164a). It lies at first on the lateral surface of the longus colli muscles, then on the lateral surface of the bodies of the vertebræ and passes through the diaphragm laterad of the crus. There is typically a ganglion for each spinal nerve, but in the cat the first three are fused with the inferior cervical ganglion to form the stellate ganglion. Each receives preganglionic neurons through white rami (Fig. 164a, *24*, *24'*, *24"*) from the corresponding spinal nerve and gives postganglionic neurons through the gray rami (Fig. 164a, *23'*, *23"*) to the same nerve. From the first thoracic ganglion (fused as part of the stellate ganglion) may arise a **cardiac nerve** which joins the vagus to reach the heart. Fibres from the first four thoracic ganglia pass to the root of the lung (Fig. 164a, *17*) and with fibres from the vagus form the **pulmonary plexus.** Preganglionic fibres pass through the fifth to the ninth ganglia and unite in the formation of the **greater splanchnic nerve** (N. splanchnicus major) (Fig. 157, *n*; Fig. 164, *b*; Fig. 164a, *18*) which passes ventrocaudad and pierces the diaphragm to reach the **cœliac ganglion** (Fig. 164, *d* and Fig. 164a, *G*). From the remainder of the thoracic ganglia similar fibres unite to form the **lesser splanchnic nerve** (Fig. 164, *d*; Fig. 164a, *20*) which passes to the **cœliac** and **superior mesenteric ganglia** (Fig. 164, *d* and *f* and Fig. 164a, *G* and *H*), where they synapse.

c. **Abdominal Portion.**—The sympathetic trunk enters the abdominal cavity at the side of the crus of the diaphragm and dorsad of the greater splanchnic nerve (Fig. 164, *a* and *b*). In their course through the abdomen the two trunks lie at first some distance apart on the bodies of the vertebræ, but they gradually approach each other. As they pass caudad they become medial and deep to the psoas minor and then to the psoas major muscles. The trunks become smaller as they are traced into the pelvis and are lost as the caudal region is reached. The ganglia of the abdominal portion of the trunks correspond in number and position to the lumbar and sacral spinal nerves. These ganglia send gray rami to all the spinal nerves in the region (Fig. 164a, *23″*) but receive preganglionic fibres through white rami from the first three or four lumbar nerves only (Fig. 164a, *24″*). Some of the latter synapse at the level at which they join the trunk and others pass caudad to a lower level within the trunk before they synapse. Other preganglionic fibres (Fig. 164a, *21*) from the first four lumbar nerves will be described in connection with the abdominal plexuses and ganglia following the account of the craniosacral subdivision of the sympathetic system.

2. **The Craniosacral Subdivision of the Sympathetic Nervous System.**—This is associated with the nerves listed in the preliminary outline of the system (page 405). The preganglionic fibres of the oculomotor nerve originate in the Edinger-Westphal nucleus in the mesencephalon (Fig. 164a, *2*) and are carried through the branch of the nerve which innervates the inferior oblique muscle. The fibres synapse in the **ciliary ganglion**

(Fig. 164a, *1* and *A*, and page 369). The chorda tympani branch of the facial nerve (page 376), which joins the lingual branch of the trigeminal nerve (page 375), carries preganglionic fibres which originate in the **superior salivatory nucleus** in the pons (Fig. 164a, *6*). These synapse in the submaxillary and sublingual ganglia from which postganglionics pass to the glands of the same name (Fig. 164a, *3*, *4*, *C*, *D*, *d*, *e*). Another small branch from the facial nerve, the **greater superficial petrosal** (N. petrosus superficialis major) (page 373), passes to the **sphenopalatine ganglion** (Fig. 164a, *B*) to synapse there with postganglionic neurons which pass to the lachrymal gland and to glands in the palate.

The innervation of the parotid gland in the cat is difficult to dissect. It comes by way of preganglionic fibres from the glossopharyngeal nerve (page 378) which originate in the **inferior salivatory nucleus** (Fig. 164a, *8*). These fibres synapse in the **otic ganglion** (Fig. 164a, *E*), located close to the mandibular division of the trigeminal nerve (page 373), and postganglionic fibres accompany the auriculotemporal nerve (page 373) to reach the gland. The **vagus nerve** (Fig. 164a, *10*) carries preganglionic fibres to all the thoracic viscera and to the abdominal viscera as far caudad as the splenic flexure of the colon. The preganglionic fibres of the vagus are accompanied by those of the spinal accessory nerve, the fibres originating in the **dorsal motor nucleus** of cranial nerves *X* and *XI* (Fig. 164a, *9*). The first fibres for the thoracic viscera arising from the vagus trunk are cardiac nerves (Fig. 157; Fig. 164a, *16*; and page 380). These are accompanied by the superior, middle and inferior cardiac nerves from the sympathetic trunk (page 409 and Fig. 164a, *13*, *14*, *15*), with which they form the **cardiac plexus** (Fig. 157, *k*). The cardiac fibres from the vagus synapse in terminal ganglia on the heart wall (Fig. 164a, *F*). Fibres also pass from the thoracic portion of the vagus trunk to the lungs and œsophagus (page 382). The fibres of the sacral spinal nerves pass directly through the sympathetic ganglia to reach the pelvic viscera on which they synapse in terminal ganglia (Fig. 164a).

3. Sympathetic Plexuses and Collateral and Chain Ganglia

in the Abdomen.—The vagus fibres enter the abdomen on the dorsal and ventral surfaces of the œsophagus (page 382). The fibres on the ventral surface pass to the lesser curvature of the stomach and there form the anterior gastric plexus (page 382). Those on the dorsal surface form the posterior gastric plexus on the greater curvature (page 382). Fibres from the latter plexus anastomose with the cœliac plexus (Fig. 164a, *J*).

The greater and lesser splanchnic nerves (Fig. 164a, *18*,

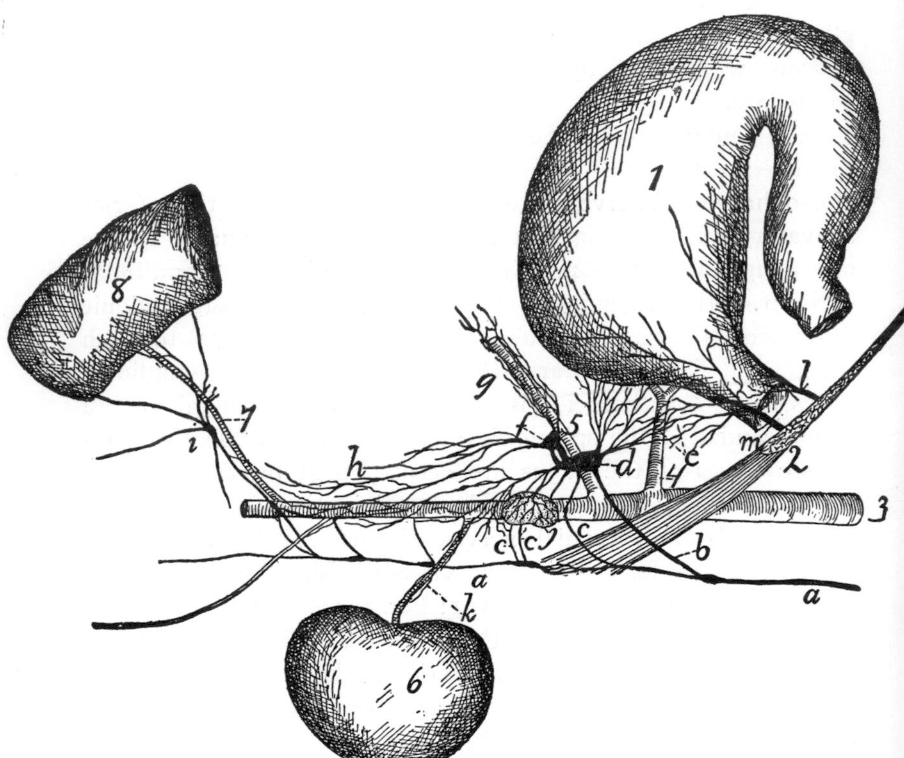

FIG. 164.—SYMPATHETIC AND VAGUS IN THE ABDOMEN (SOMEWHAT SCHEMATIC).

1, stomach; 2, crus and cut edge of diaphragm; 3, aorta; 4, cœliac artery; 5, superior mesenteric artery; 6, kidney, 7, inferior mesenteric artery; 8, large intestine. *a*, main trunk of sympathetic; *b*, great splanchnic nerve; *c*, lesser splanchnic nerves; *d*, cœliac (or semilunar) ganglion; *e*, cœliac plexus; *f*, superior mesenteric ganglion; *g*, superior mesenteric plexus, following the artery; *h*, aortic plexus; *i*, inferior mesenteric ganglion and plexus; *j*, suprarenal plexus on suprarenal body; *k*, renal plexus following renal artery; *l*, ventral œsophageal branch of vagus, forming anterior gastric plexus; *m*. dorsal œsophageal branch of vagus, forming posterior gastric plexus.

20) pass ventrad to join the **cœliac** and **superior mesenteric ganglia** (Fig. 164 *d*, *f*; Fig. 164a, *G*, *H*), which lie just caudad of the cœliac artery and close to the lateral surface of the superior mesenteric artery. The two ganglia are connected by nerve trunks. The preganglionic fibres carried to these ganglia by the splanchnic nerves synapse in the ganglia and postganglionic fibres from the ganglia accompany fibres from the vagus to supply the surrounding abdominal viscera, and form on the vessels the **cœliac and superior mesenteric plexuses** (Fig. 164, *e*, *f*; Fig. 164a, *J*, *K*). These fibres follow closely the arteries of the same name, form plexuses over their surfaces and pass with them to the organs that they supply. Fibres following the branches of the cœliac artery, for instance, form the **hepatic plexus, splenic plexus,** etc. A plexus is formed on the suprarenal body (**suprarenal plexus**) (Fig. 164, *j*) and the **renal plexus** (Fig. 164, *k*) to the kidney follows the renal artery. Fibres following the branches of the superior mesenteric artery have the same name as the artery that they follow.

A plexus, largely made up of fibres from the cœliac and superior mesenteric plexuses, passes caudad on the aorta and is known as the **aortic plexus** (Fig. 164, *h*). It receives fibres from the sympathetic trunk in the upper lumbar region (thoracico-lumbar fibres) (Fig. 164, *n* and Fig. 164a, *21*) and leads to various plexuses in the pelvic cavity. These plexuses follow the arteries, as the **vesical plexus, spermatic plexus,** etc. One of the chief of them in the region is the **inferior mesenteric plexus** (Fig. 164, *i*; and Fig. 164a, *L*) which lies on the inferior mesenteric artery and is associated with the **inferior mesenteric ganglion** (Fig. 164, *i*; Fig. 164a, *I*). Postganglionic fibres from the inferior mesenteric ganglion which follow the aorta into the pelvis constitute the **hypogastric nerve.**

FIG. 164a.—DIAGRAM OF EFFERENT FIBRES OF SYMPATHETIC NERVOUS SYSTEM.

Heavy lines indicate craniosacral fibres, light lines thoracicolumbar fibres. Preganglionic fibres are shown by solid lines, postganglionic fibres by broken lines. Collateral ganglia with heavy outlines, terminal ganglia with light outlines.

a, intrinsic eye-muscles; *b*, lachrymal gland; *c*, palatine glands; *d*, sublingual gland; *e*, submaxillary gland; *f*, parotid gland; *g*, carotid artery; *h*, trachea; *i*, heart; *j*, right lung; *k*, diaphragm; *l*, liver; *m*, stomach; *n*, spleen; *o*, pancreas; *p*, adrenal gland; *q*, kidney; *r*, small intestine; *s*, ascending colon; *t*, transverse colon; *u*, descending colon; *v*, urinary bladder; *w*, prostate gland; *x*, testis; *y*, vas deferens. *A*, ciliary ganglion; *B*, sphenopalatine ganglion; *C*, sublingual ganglion; *D*, submaxillary ganglion; *E*, otic ganglion; *F*, terminal ganglia; *G*, cœliac ganglion; *H*, superior mesenteric ganglion; *I*, inferior mesenteric ganglion; *J*, fibres of cœliac plexus; *K*, fibres of superior mesenteric plexus; *L*, fibres of inferior mesenteric plexus; *M*, superior cervical ganglion; *N*, middle cervical ganglion; *O*, stellate ganglion; *P*, chain ganglia. *1*, oculomotor nerve; *2*, Edinger-Westphal nucleus; *3*, facial nerve; *4*, chorda tympani nerve; *5*, greater superficial petrosal nerve; *6*, superior salivatory nucleus; *7*, glossopharyngeal nerve; *8*, inferior salivatory nucleus; *9*, dorsal efferent nucleus of nerves *X* and *XI*; *10*, vagus nerve; *11*, postganglionic thoracicolumbar fibres; *12*, carotid plexus; *13*, superior cardiac nerve; *14*, middle cardiac nerve; *15*, inferior cardiac nerve; *16*, cardiac branch from vagus; *17*, pulmonary fibres; *18*, greater splanchnic nerve; *19*, *19'*, *19''*, postganglionic fibres from cœliac, superior mesenteric and inferior mesenteric ganglia; *20*, lesser splanchnic nerve; *21*, preganglionic lumbar fibres to inferior mesenteric ganglion; *22*, sacral branches to pelvic viscera; *23*, *23'*, *23''*, gray rami communicantes; *24*, *24'*, *24''*, *24'''*, white rami communicantes; *25*, *25'*, *25''*, intermediolateral cell groups.

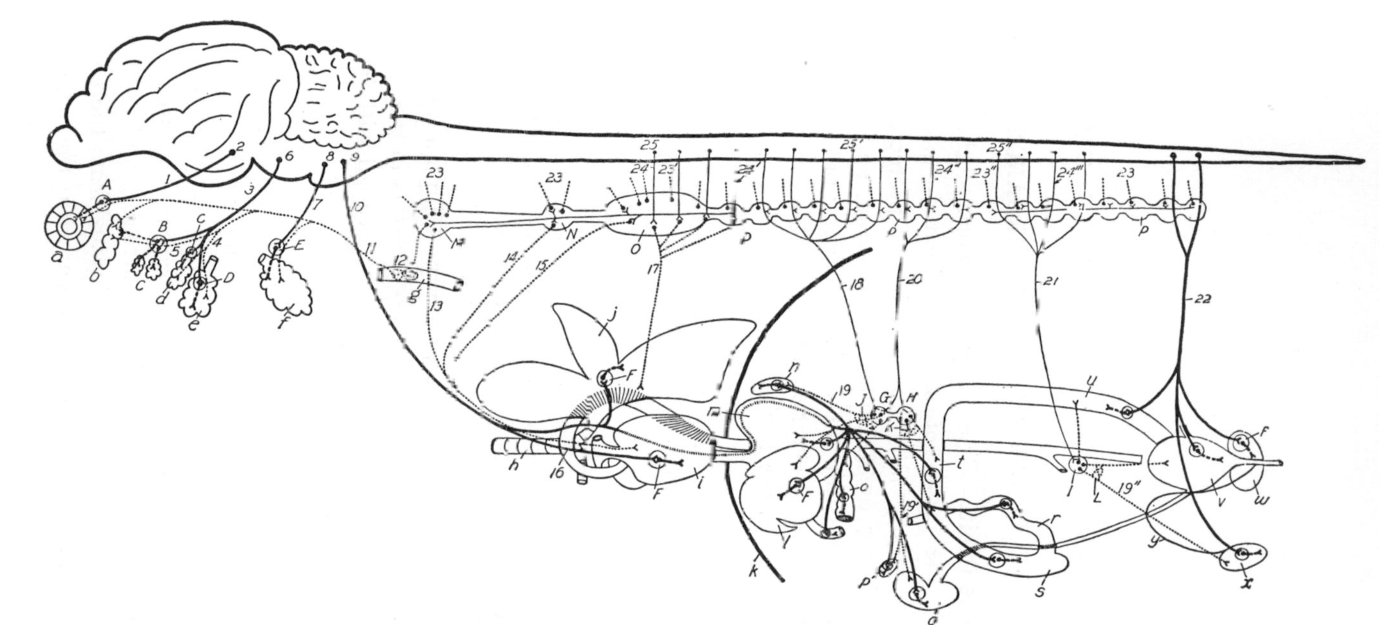

FIG. 164a.—DIAGRAM OF EFFERENT FIBRES OF SYMPATHETIC NERVOUS SYSTEM.

SENSE-ORGANS AND INTEGUMENT.

I. THE ORGAN OF SIGHT. ORGANON VISUS.

1. **The Orbit.**—The bony framework of the orbital fossa, in which the organ of sight is situated, has already been described (page 53). The orbit is not protected by bone on all sides, being open caudad and ventrad, and partly laterad. The structures within the orbit are further protected and separated from other structures by a very thin, tough, transparent membranous sac, the **periorbita,** which surrounds them almost completely and nearly fills the orbit. The periorbita forms a conical sac with the apex of the cone directed caudoventrad and attached about the optic foramen and orbital fissure. The base of the cone is attached about the margin of the orbital fossa,—to the supraorbital margin of the frontal, to the maxillary and malar bones, and to the orbital ligament, connecting the frontal process of the malar with the zygomatic process of the frontal. The periorbita is partly separated from the walls of the orbital fossa by masses of fat. It comes in contact, aside from the bones, with the temporal and pterygoid muscles, and with nerves and blood-vessels in the orbit.

The sac thus formed encloses the eyeball with its muscles and glands (Fig. 166), as well as a mass of fat in which these are imbedded. The periorbita and its contents are freely movable with relation to surrounding structures.

2. **The Eyelids. Palpebræ.**—The eyelids are two thin folds which protect the eye. Externally they are covered with hair; internally by the thin membranous **conjunctiva.** The eyelids contain the **Meibomian** or **tarsal** glands, arranged in short rows passing perpendicularly inward from the edge of the lids; these may sometimes be seen with the naked eye as

broad yellowish lines. They secrete a substance which prevents the adhesion of the edges of the two lids. On the edge of each eyelid, three to four millimeters from the medial angle of the eye, is one of the openings of the lachrymal canals.

At the medial angle of the eye is the large **nictitating membrane (membrana nictitans)**, or "third eyelid," corresponding to the plica semilunaris of man. In the cat this is large and may cover the whole surface of the eye. It is supported (Fig. 165) by a broad central strip of cartilage (*a*), passing from its edge to its inner angle, and the inner end of this cartilage is surrounded, on the medial (concave) side of the membrane, by the large lobulated **Harderian** glands (*b*).

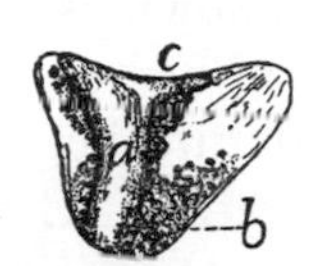

FIG. 165. — INNER SURFACE OF MEMBRANA NICTITANS, showing the supporting cartilage and Harderian glands. *a*, supporting cartilage; *b*, Harderian glands; *c*, outer edge.

The **conjunctiva** is the thin membrane covering the inner surface of the lids, the outer surface of the eyeball, and both surfaces of the nictitating membrane.

The muscles of the eyelids are **M. orbicularis oculi,** already described (page 98), and **M. levator palpebræ superioris,** described below.

3. **Lachrymal Apparatus.**—The **lachrymal gland** is a large reddish gland, not lobulated externally, which lies on the surface of the eyeball just beneath the lateral angle of the eye. The gland is situated immediately craniad of, and in contact with, the zygomatic process of the frontal bone (Fig. 154, 11, page 374). It is flat and about one centimeter in diameter. The ducts which pass from the gland to the eye are not visible to the naked eye. The fluid secreted by the gland collects at the medial angle of the eye and passes into the two openings of the lachrymal canals, one of which is found on the pigmented edge of each lid, three or four millimeters from the medial angle of the eye. The canals passing from these openings soon unite to form the **nasolachrymal duct,** which passes through the lachrymal bone, along the medial surface of the maxillary, to open into the nasal cavity ventrad of the ventral concha of the nose.

4. **Muscles of the Orbit** (Fig. 166).—Within the orbit are eleven muscles, ten connected with the eyeball, and one, M. levator palpebræ superioris, with the upper eyelid.

Of the ten muscles of the eyeball, eight are straight muscles, passing from an origin about the inner end of the orbit directly distad; the other two have an oblique direction. Four of the straight muscles are larger and are known as the **Mm. recti** (*b*, *c*, *d*); these are distinguished according to their position as **lateral** (*c*), **medial, superior** (*d*), and **inferior** (*b*). The four smaller straight muscles constitute together **M. retractor oculi** (*e*). The two oblique muscles are known as **Mm. obliqui** and are distinguished according to their position as **inferior** (*a*) and **superior.**

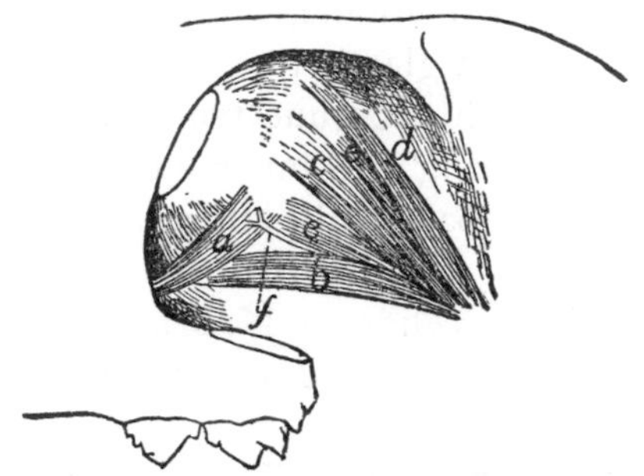

FIG. 166.—MUSCLES OF THE EYEBALL, LATERAL VIEW.

a, M. obliquus inferior; *b*, M. rectus inferior; *c*, M. rectus lateralis; *d*, M. rectus superior; *e*, parts of M. retractor oculi; *f*, the oculomotor nerve.

Mm. recti (*b*, *c*, *d*).—The four recti muscles arise from the bone about the optic foramen and pass toward the eyeball. They are inserted by thin, flat tendons along a line which separates the darker caudal part of the sclerotic from the white zone of the sclerotic which borders the cornea,—the line of insertion of the four tendons forming thus a circle about the eyeball. The rectus superior (*d*) is partly covered by M. levator palpebræ superioris. The tendon of the rectus inferior (*b*) is crossed by M. obliquus inferior (*a*). The recti muscles are all innervated by the oculomotor (third) nerve (*f*), except the lateral (*c*), which is supplied by the abducens (sixth) nerve.

M. retractor oculi (*e*).—The retractor oculi arises about the optic foramen and divides into four heads which lie nearer the eyeball than the recti and are therefore partly covered by the latter. They alternate with the recti and are inserted into the eyeball at about its equator, except the inferior division, which is inserted on a line with the recti. They are supplied by the oculomotor nerve.

M. obliquus inferior (*a*).—The inferior oblique arises from the maxillary bone just laterad of the lachrymal bone and curves over the ventral side of the eyeball along the lines of insertion of the recti (crossing the tendon of the rectus inferior, *b*) to the ventral edge of the tendon of the lateral rectus (*c*), where it is inserted. It rotates the eyeball and is supplied by the third nerve (*f*).

M. obliquus superior.—The superior oblique takes origin from the cranial border of the optic foramen, passes dorso-craniad, and ends in a small rounded tendon which passes through a fibrous pulley-ring. This ring is situated near the rim of the orbit, one or two centimeters craniad of the zygomatic process of the frontal bone, and is attached to the wall of the orbit by two fibrous bands. After passing through the pulley-ring the tendon turns and passes laterocaudad; it becomes much expanded, passes caudad of the superior rectus, and is inserted into the eyeball along the caudal margin of the insertion of the superior rectus tendon. The superior oblique is supplied by the trochlear (fourth) nerve.

M. levator palpebræ superioris.—This is a small thin muscle which takes origin on the wall of the optic foramen close to the rectus superior, passes over the outer surface of the rectus superior and beneath the lachrymal gland, and forms a thin tendon which is inserted into the margin of the upper eyelid. It is innervated by the oculomotor.

5. **The Eyeball.**—The eyeball is approximately spherical in form, but the cranial surface has a slightly greater curvature than the caudal portion, so that the eye appears slightly pointed at the cranial (free) surface. The large cylindrical **optic nerve** (Fig. 167, *a*) enters the eyeball at nearly the centre of the caudal half of the eye. On the outer surface is seen the transparent **cornea** (*c*), covering the free surface of the eye, and the opaque **sclerotic** (*b*), covering the remainder of the ball.

Through the cornea can be seen the yellow curtain-like **iris,** with an opening in its centre, the **pupil.**

Coats of the Eye (Fig. 167).—The outer coat of the eyeball is formed by the **sclerotic** (or sclera) (*b*) and the **cornea** (*c*). The sclerotic is the whitish opaque portion covering the caudal three-fourths of the eye. It forms a tough sac serving as a protection for the structures within. The cornea (*c*) is the circular transparent portion of the outer coat, covering the free surface of the eye; it is a direct continuation of the sclerotic. Just before passing into the cornea the sclerotic is much thickened, forming a broad white zone (*b'*) about the eyeball near its equator. To this zone, at its caudal margin, are attached the rectus muscles of the eyeball. The sclerotic has many pigment-cells on its inner surface, giving it a brownish appearance and forming the **lamina fusca.**

The **cornea** (*c*) is transparent and more strongly curved than the sclerotic. It is thicker than most of the sclerotic coat, but not so thick as the white zone of the latter.

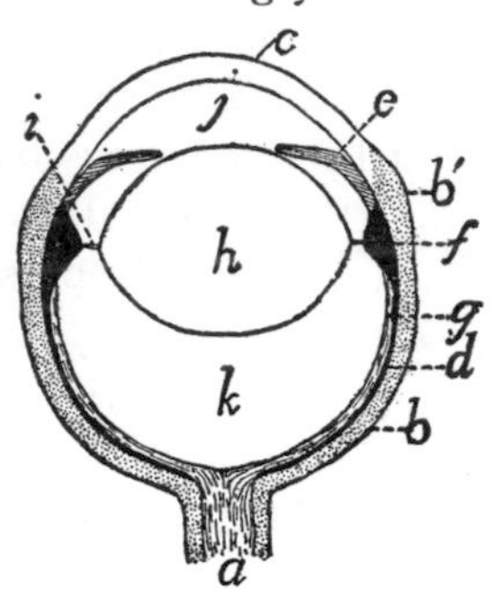

FIG. 167. — DIAGRAM OF A SECTION OF THE EYE.

a, optic nerve; *b*, sclerotic (*b'*, thickened "white zone"); *c*, cornea; *d*, choroid; *e*, iris; *f*, ciliary body; *g*, retina; *h*, crystalline lens; *i*, zonula ciliaris; *j*, anterior chamber of eye; *k*, vitreous humor.

Within the sclerotic is the second coat of the eye, formed by the **choroid** (*d*) and the **iris** (*e*). The choroid (*d*) is a vascular layer, and contains much pigment, giving it a dark color. It lines the inner surface of the sclerotic, but does not cover the inner surface of the cornea. At the white zone of the sclerotic it is thrown into a large number (about seventy) of meridional folds, the plicæ ciliares or ciliary folds, which together constitute the so-called **ciliary body** (**corpus ciliare**) (*f*). This forms a circular zone on the inner surface of the white zone of the sclerotic, and is continuous with the **iris** (*e*). The choroid coat is furnished in certain parts of its area with a layer of cells containing crystals, which give it a brilliant color, forming the **tapetum.** The color of the tapetum is a metallic yellowish blue or green; it is this layer which causes the cat's eye to "shine" in the dark.

The **iris** (*e*) is a continuation of the choroid. It projects inward from the white zone of the sclerotic, forming a circular curtain lying some distance behind the cornea, and perforated by an opening, the **pupil.** The iris is usually yellow in color on its outer surface, darkly pigmented within. The pupii varies normally in size and form according to the amount of light to which the eye is subjected. In a cat killed with chloroform the pupil is very large and circular; in the living animal it is elliptical with the long axis dorsoventral, or when much contracted it is a mere dorsoventral slit.

The inner coat of the eye is formed by the **retina** (*g*). This is the part of the eye which is sensitive to light; it is formed by an expansion of the optic nerve (*a*). In a preserved eye it is usually soft and opaque, and may be seen to line the caudal half of the inner surface, extending apparently to the ciliary body. Here it seems to end as a free margin, the **ora serrata**; it really becomes thin and passes onto the surface of the ciliary body, forming the **ciliary portion** of the retina, and onto the inner surface of the iris, where it forms the uvea. Near the centre of the retina the entrance of the optic nerve is marked by a small round spot, the **blind spot.**

The **Crystalline Lens** (*h*).—The lens is a biconvex transparent body situated within the eye a little in front of the ciliary body and just behind the iris. It is more strongly convex in front than behind. The lens is surrounded by a thin transparent sac, the **capsule** of the lens (capsula lentis). The capsule of the lens is attached all around the equator of the lens by fibrous bands to the ciliary body, this attachment forming the **zonula ciliaris** (or zonula Zinni) (*i*), by which the lens is suspended.

Chambers of the Eye.—The lens (*h*) and zonula ciliaris (*i*) form a partition dividing the eye into two parts. The cavity in front of the lens contains a fluid, the **aqueous humor.** This cavity is partly subdivided by the iris into the *anterior* and *posterior chambers* of the eye.

The part of the eye lying behind the lens is much larger

than the part in front of the lens. It is lined chiefly by the retina, its front boundary being the lens. It contains a jelly-like substance, the **vitreous humor** (or vitreous body, **corpus vitreum**).

II. THE EAR. ORGANON AUDITUS.

The ear of the cat, like that of man, is composed of three parts, the external, middle, and internal ear.

The **external** ear is limited internally by the tympanic membrane.

The **middle** ear extends from the tympanic membrane to the fenestra cochleæ and fenestra vestibuli. It contains the bones of the ear, and is connected with the pharynx by the Eustachian tube.

The **internal** ear is wholly contained within the petrous bone, and on the surface of the membrane lining its cavities are distributed the branches of the auditory (eighth) nerve.

The External Ear.

The external ear consists of an expanded portion, the **auricle** (**auricula**) or pinna, and of a canal leading from the auricle to the tympanic membrane, known as the **external auditory meatus.** The concave surface of the auricle is directed craniolaterad, and its edges form the dorsal and lateral boundaries of the auditory opening. From the bottom of the cavity which it partly encloses, the external auditory meatus passes medioventrad.

The auricle (Fig. 168) is composed of a thin curved plate of cartilage (**cartilago auriculæ**), to which numerous muscles are attached and which is covered on both sides by integument intimately attached to the cartilage. Distad the edges of the cartilage form a free border (*b*); proximad the plate is rolled together in such a way that its edges (*g* and *h*) overlap on the craniomedial side, thus enclosing a tube or funnel (*e*) (concha) which forms the enlarged outer portion of the auditory passage.

Within the cavity of the auricle, on its medial surface, somewhat below the level of the lowest portion of the margin of the auditory opening is seen a very prominent pedunculated process (*d*). This is really part of a transverse ridge, extending craniocaudad on the medial wall of the auricular cavity. This ridge is the **antihelix** (*d*); it divides the auricula into a distal and a proximal portion. The portion distad of the antihelix is the **scapha** (*a*); its surface is smooth except for two slight longitudinal ridges extending distad from near the two ends of the antihelix. That portion of the auricle that lies proximad of the antihelix forms a deep irregular cavity known as the **concha** (*e*). A deep furrow, corresponding to the antihelix, separates scapha from concha externally. The concha extends caudad as a deep, rounded pocket; externally this pocket forms a prominent convexity, the **eminentia conchæ** (*j*), on the caudal surface of the proximal portion of the external ear. Farther proximad the concha narrows like a funnel and becomes much compressed laterally, so that a section of its cavity forms a narrow craniocaudal slit.

The inner surface of the concha is marked by a number of very prominent ridges and projections. These are usually due to folds in the cartilage, so that external furrows and depressions correspond to the internal projections. The edges of these depressions serve for attachment of muscles (Fig. 169), by contraction of which the form of the concha is changed,—the folds of the cartilage thus serving as regions of greater flexibility.

Two or three centimeters proximad of its external opening the cartilage of the concha ends in a free edge which receives within itself the distal end of the cartilaginous external auditory meatus (*e'*). The two are united together by fibrous tissue. The cartilaginous auditory meatus (*e'*) extends as a nearly cylindrical tube mediad and slightly craniad to the tympanic membrane in the opening of the bulla tympani. This tube is lined with integument which continues over the tympanic membrane. The subcutaneous tissue of the tube contains the ceruminous glands, which secrete the ear-wax and open on the surface of the skin.

To understand the relations of the muscles of the external ear it is necessary to consider a little more fully the structure of the auricular cartilage (Fig. 168), especially as compared with the human ear. The ear of the cat differs from the human ear in the fact that the edges of the auricular cartilages are rolled together proximad so as to overlap. There is thus no gap between the tragus (*g*) and antitragus (*h*), as in man, but these two structures partly overlap.

The free edge (*b*) of the auricular cartilage corresponds partly to the **helix** of man. At its mediocranial angle the proximal part of the auricle is composed of muscle and integument only, so that the cartilage when isolated presents here a deep notch distad of which is a prominent projecting angle, the **spine** (*c*) of the helix, which serves for attachment of the adductor auris superior muscle (Fig. 169, 1). Proximad of the spine, separated from it by the deep notch, the cranial edge (*g*) of the auricular cartilage approaches the caudal edge (*h*), finally overlapping it, so that the cavity of the auricle is now completely surrounded. This overlapping portion of the cartilage is on the medial side of the cavity, and in the natural state is covered by muscles and integument, so as not to be apparent.

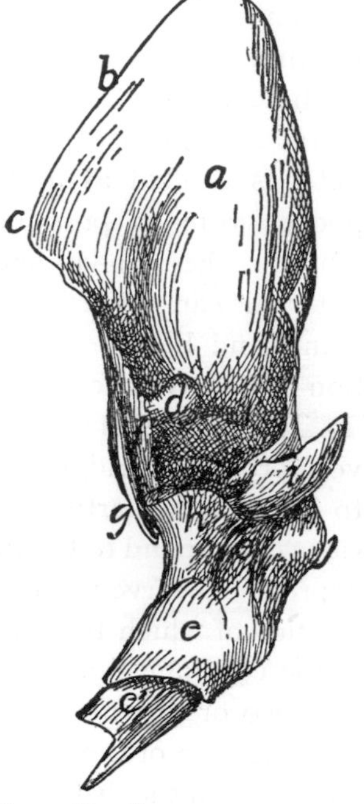

FIG. 168.—CARTILAGE OF THE EXTERNAL EAR, CRANIOMEDIAL VIEW.

a, scapha or pinna; *b*, helix, *c*, spine of the helix; *d*, antihelix, *e*, concha; *e'*, cartilaginous auditory meatus; *f*, crista helicis; *g*, tragus; *h*, antitragus; *i*, processus uncinatus; *j*, eminentia conchæ.

That portion of the cranial edge of the cartilage that overlaps the caudal edge forms a cartilaginous plate which projects proximad as a blunt point; this plate is the **tragus** (*g*). Along the inner edge of the tragus is a ridge which forms a continuation of the helix; this is the **crista helicis** (*f*). The portion of the caudal edge of the cartilage that is partly overlapped by the tragus is an irregular flat plate known as the **antitragus** (*h*). At its caudolateral margin the antitragus extends distad as a thin, pointed, cartilaginous spine, the **processus uncinatus** (*i*). This supports a sheet of integument which bears two longitudinal ridges projecting into the cavity of the ear, with a broad groove between them.

The Scutiform Cartilage.—Closely connected with the external ear, but not forming a part of it, is the scutiform cartilage. This lies in the temporal fossa, between the integument and the temporal muscle, just behind the orbit and beneath the craniomedial portion of the auricle (Fig. 63, 1, page 97). It is a narrow cartilage about two centimeters long, with its long axis craniocaudal. For the greater part of its length it forms a slender rod, from which a thin cartilaginous sheet extends a short distance laterad; at its caudal end the rod forks, the two arms extending nearly at right angles to the main portion. The scutiform cartilage serves for the origin or insertion of a number of the muscles of the ear.

Muscles of the External Ear (Fig. 169).—(*a*) The muscles connecting the cartilages of the external ear with other parts of the head have been described (page 96), excepting the tragicus lateralis (4). These muscles are the following: M. intermedius scutulorum (Fig. 63, *a*), M. frontoauricularis, M. levator auris longus (including the cervicoauricular) (Fig. 63, *g*, *g'*), M. auricularis superior (Fig. 63, *k*), M. abductor auris longus (Fig. 63, *m*), M. abductor auris brevis (Fig. 63, *l*), M. zygomaticus (Fig. 64, *d*), M. submentalis (Fig. 64, *c*), M. depressor conchæ (Fig. 64, *b*), M. frontoscutularis, M. adductor auris inferior (Fig. 63, *f*), and M. tragicus lateralis (Fig. 169, 4).

M. tragicus lateralis (Fig. 169, 4).—A band about seven millimeters wide, lying beneath the mass of fat about the ear and running ventrad lengthwise of the concha and close against it.

Origin (Fig. 96, *a*, page 229) on the caudal end of the mandibula, in the cavity found between the condyloid process and the angular process. The muscle passes dorsad and is *inserted* (Fig. 169, 4) on the caudal margin of the tragus and in the depression on the concha just caudad of the tragus.

Relations.—This muscle lies between the temporal muscle and the concha.

Action.—Pulls the ear ventrad and probably rotates it outward.

(*b*) The following three muscles connect the scutiform cartilage with other parts of the external ear.

M. rotator auris or **scutuloauricularis inferior.**—A flat craniocaudal band of fibres lying between the auricle and the temporal muscle.

Origin on the scutiform cartilage, just caudad of the insertion of the frontoscutularis, of which this muscle seems to be a continuation. The muscle passes caudad as a band seven or eight millimeters wide, curving about the medial surface of the auricle, and is inserted on the caudomedial surface of the eminentia conchæ.

Relations.—Lateral surface with the auricular cartilage; medial surface with the temporal muscle.

Action.—Rotates the external ear mediad and caudad.

M. adductor auris superior (Fig. 169, 1; Fig. 63, *f*). (Part of the auricularis anterior of man.)

Origin on the dorsal surface of the scutiform cartilage for its entire length. The fibres form a continuation of those of the frontoscutularis; they pass dorsocaudad and are *inserted* into the spina helicis or craniomedial margin of the auricular cartilage. This muscle lies in the fold of skin that connects the craniomedial angle of the auricular cartilage with the head, so that it is covered on both sides by integument.

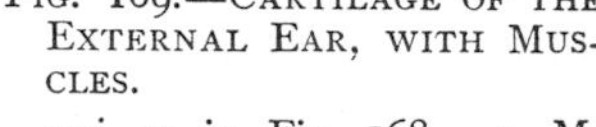

FIG. 169.—CARTILAGE OF THE EXTERNAL EAR, WITH MUSCLES.

a–i, as in Fig. 168. 1, M. adductor auris superior (cut); 2, M. adductor auris medius (cut); 3, M. helicis; 4, M. tragicus lateralis (cut); 5, 5′, M. tragicus medialis; 6, M. antitragicus; 7, M. adductor auris inferior (cut); 8, M. depressor conchæ (cut); 9, M. conchæus externus; 10, part of M. auricularis externus; 11, M. abductor auris longus (cut).

Action.—Draws the auricle craniad.

M. adductor auris medius (Fig. 169, 2). (Part of the

auricularis anterior of man.)—A very thin band of fibres eight to ten millimeters broad.

Origin on the middle two-thirds of the caudoventral edge of the scutiform cartilage. The fibres pass nearly ventrad and are *inserted* along the medial or caudal surface of the tragus.

Relations. — Outer surface with the auricular cartilage. Inner surface with the temporal muscle or with the pad of fat separating this from the auricle.

Action.—Pulls the concha dorsocraniad.

(*c*) The remainder of the muscles of the ear interconnect parts of the auricular cartilage.

M. transversus auriculæ (Fig. 63, *i*).—A band about six to eight millimeters wide, on the medial convex surface of the auricle, between the distal ends of M. levator auris longus (*g'*) and M. auricularis superior (*k*).

Origin on the medial surface of the concha, just proximad of the furrow which corresponds to the antihelix. The muscle bridges this furrow, passes distad about two centimeters, and is inserted on the auricular cartilage on a line which forms a caudal continuation of the line of insertion of the levator auris longus (*g'*).

Relations.—Outer surface with the levator auris longus (*g*, *g'*), the auricularis superior (*k*), and the integument; inner surface with the auricular cartilage.

Action.—Flexes the scapha mediad on the concha, thus enlarging the external opening of the concha.

M. auricularis externus (Fig. 169, 10; Fig. 64, *r*).—This consists of small scattered bands of interrupted fibres on the convex surface of the auricle, caudad of the transversus auriculæ. The largest of these bands runs parallel with the transversus auriculæ about five or six millimeters caudad of the latter. It has origin on the eminentia conchæ distad of the insertion of the abductor auris longus. Thence the fibres run distad five or six millimeters and are interrupted by an attachment to the cartilage. Distad the fibres begin again, and the muscle runs thence distad for about one centimeter, the distal end being attached to the cartilage.

Caudad of this, especially of its proximal portion, are one or two small bands of fibres usually running parallel with it, but unconnected with it and with each other. The extent and distribution of these bands varies, and the direction of fibres is also variable.

Relations.—Outer surface with the integument; inner surface with the auricular cartilage.

Action.—Flexes the auricular cartilage.

M. helicis (Fig. 169, 3; Fig. 64, *m*).—A muscle about two centimeters in length and five or six millimeters in width, on the inner surface of the ear, along its cranial margin.

Origin on the medial surface of the concha, just caudad of the proximal end of the tragus. The fibres pass distad to be inserted on the auricular cartilage at the caudal angle of the notch which lies beneath the cranial edge of the auricle, along with the caudal fibres of the adductor auris superior (1).

Relations.—Lateral surface with the integument; medial surface with the tragus.

Action.—Draws proximad the cranial margin of the auricle.

M. antitragicus (Fig. 169, 6; Fig. 64, *n*).—A small muscle about one centimeter in length and three millimeters in thickness, attached at one end to the caudal border of the antitragus. The fibres pass mediodistad and are inserted on the tragus, in common with the fibres of the tragicus medialis (Fig. 169, 5, 5′).

Relations.—Outer surface with the adductor auris inferior and the integument; inner surface with the cartilage.

Action.—Constricts the external auditory opening.

M. tragicus medialis (Fig. 169, 5, 5′).—A small, flat muscle, in two parts, on the medial surface of the concha.

Origin on the ventral end of the tragus. The cranial fibres form a thick nearly cylindrical bundle which extends proximad about one centimeter, and is inserted on the cranial surface of the concha just proximad of a deep fold in the cartilage. The caudal fibres form a thin sheet which spreads on the medial surface of the concha and is inserted on an obliquely proximodistal line on the medial surface of the concha, less than one centimeter from the free distal edge.

These two bundles are distinct except at their origin, and are sometimes considered as separate muscles.

Relations.—Outer surface with the tragicus lateralis (4) and the fat about the concha. Inner surface with the concha.

Action.—Flexes the concha.

Strauss-Durckheim describes under the name **cornetoconchæus** a small muscle bridging the deep groove caused by the folding of the medial surface of the concha, its proximal end being close to the insertion of the abductor auris brevis (page 100). This muscle was absent in all of the cases examined for its presence.

M. conchæus externus (Fig. 169, 9).—A quadrilateral muscle on the lateral surface of the concha. The cranial end of this muscle is attached to the concha a short distance distad of the antitragus along a dorsoventral line six to eight millimeters in length; the fibres pass thence caudodorsad a distance of about one centimeter, where they are again attached to the concha. The muscle thus bridges a shallow depression on the lateral surface of the concha.

Action.—Constricts the concha.

The Middle Ear.

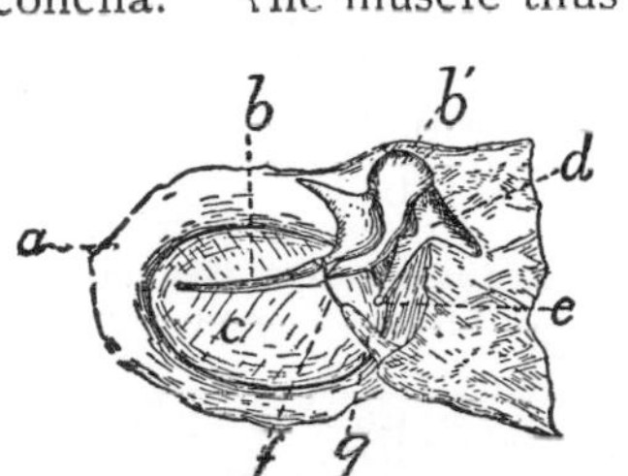

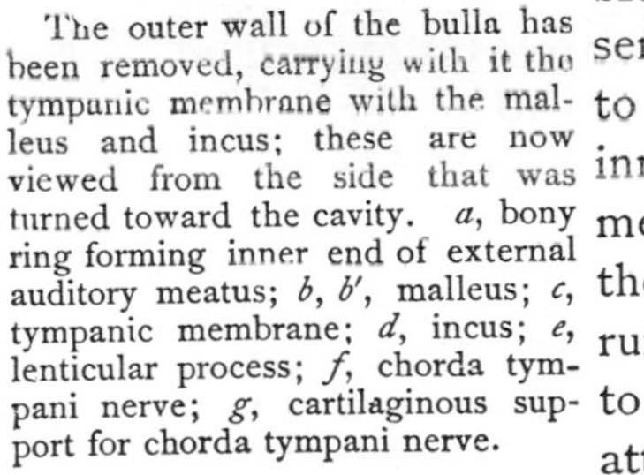

FIG. 170.—TYMPANIC MEMBRANE, VIEWED FROM THE INNER SIDE.

The outer wall of the bulla has been removed, carrying with it the tympanic membrane with the malleus and incus; these are now viewed from the side that was turned toward the cavity. *a*, bony ring forming inner end of external auditory meatus; *b*, *b'*, malleus; *c*, tympanic membrane; *d*, incus; *e*, lenticular process; *f*, chorda tympani nerve; *g*, cartilaginous support for chorda tympani nerve.

The middle ear is enclosed in a cavity within the tympanic bulla. Its outer boundary, as well as the inner boundary of the external ear, is formed by the **tympanic membrane** (Fig. 170, *c*.) This is a thin, semitransparent membrane attached to the bony ring (*a*) surrounding the inner end of the external auditory meatus. It is oval in outline. Across the dorsal third of its inner surface runs the handle of the malleus (*b*), to which the membrane is firmly attached and which by pulling on the membrane gives it the form of a cone instead of a flat surface. The apex of the cone is directed mediad.

The middle ear, or **cavum tympani,** is an ellipsoidal cavity situated in the tympanic bulla. On removing the medial wall of the bulla, a bony plate is seen separating its cavity into two chambers. This plate of bone extends in from the lateral wall of the bulla, forming a complete partition except at the dorso-caudal part, where a notch in the bone forms a free communication between the two chambers. The lateral chamber, or tympanum proper, contains the bones of the ear and is limited externally by the tympanic membrane. At its cranial end is seen the opening of the **tuba auditiva,** or **Eustachian tube.**

The tuba auditiva, or Eustachian tube, is a cartilaginous tube about one and a half to two centimeters long, passing from the nasopharynx to the middle ear and placing these two cavities in communication. The pharyngeal opening is at about the middle of the length of the nasopharynx, near the dorsal border of the lateral wall; it is a narrow slit two or three millimeters long. Thence the tube passes caudolaterad on the ventral surface of the sphenoid bone, and enters the tympanic cavity through the opening just laterad of the styliform process of the tympanic bulla. The tube has a thick, cartilaginous medial wall, while the lateral wall is thin and formed of connective tissue. The lumen of the tube is a curved slit in cross-section.

Bones of the Ear (ossicula auditus).—There are three small bones in the middle ear, the malleus (hammer) (Fig. 171, 1), incus (anvil) (Fig. 171, 2), and stapes (stirrup) (Fig. 172).

FIG. 171.—MALLEUS AND INCUS, UNITED IN THE NATURAL POSITION.

1, malleus; 2, incus. *a*, handle of malleus; *b*, neck; *c*, head; *d*, process for attachment of tendon of M. tensor tympani; *e*, wing-like plate and process of neck; *f*, *g*, the two processes of the incus.

The malleus (Fig. 171, 1) consists of a slender handle (*a*) with a small neck (*b*) attached at an angle to the caudal end of the handle. At the end of the neck is a rounded head (*c*) which articulates with the incus (2), and together with one part of the incus lies in a small fossa dorsad of the fenestra vestibuli. From the medial aspect of the neck extends a short process of bone (*d*) to which is attached the tendon of the tensor tympani muscle. One side of the neck is produced into a thin wing-like plate, bearing on its edge a pointed process (*e*).

The **incus** (Fig. 171, 2) bears much resemblance to a two-fanged molar tooth. It lies in the fossa with the head of the malleus. Its head or crown is directed craniad and has a concave surface which articulates with the head of the malleus. One of the fangs (*f*) extends caudad in the fossa above mentioned and is held in position by a ligament. The other fang (*g*) extends ventromediad and articulates with the head of the stapes. This fang terminates in a minute rounded tubercle known as the **lenticular process**; this in early stages of development is a separate bone, the **os lenticulare.**

The **stapes** (Fig. 172) has the form of a stirrup, and is the last in the chain of bones. The small end is termed the head (*a*), and the broader part the base (*b*). The head of the stapes articulates with one of the processes of the incus. The base of the stapes fits into the fenestra vestibuli of the petrous bone and completely closes it. The stapes is held in position by the stapedius muscle, which is attached to a minute process (*c*) near the head.

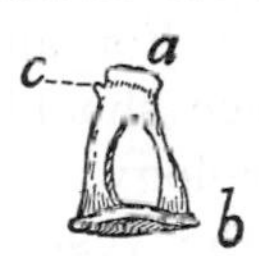

FIG. 172. STAPES. *a*, head; *b*, base; *c*, process for attachment of the stapedius muscle.

Thus the three bones of the midle ear form a chain which connects the medial surface of the tympanic membrane with the fenestra vestibuli. As the fenestra vestibuli forms a portion of the wall of the vestibule, the vibrations of the tympanic membrane are transmitted through the chain of bones to the fluid within the vestibule.

Muscles of the Middle Ear.

M. tensor tympani.—The tensor tympani muscle is a short conical muscle having origin in a small fossa (Fig. 25, *d*, p. 34) in the petrous bone dorsocraniad of the fenestra vestibuli. Its very short tendon passes laterad and is inserted into a projection (Fig. 171, *d*) on the neck of the malleus.

M. stapedius.—The stapedius muscle is a short muscle taking origin from a fossa (Fig. 25, *f*) in the lateral surface of the petrous bone caudad of that for the incus. It is inserted into the head of the stapes.

The Internal Ear (Fig. 173).

The internal ear or **labyrinth** is completely enclosed in the petrous bone. In the dry bone the internal ear communicates with the middle ear by the fenestra cochleæ and the fenestra vestibuli, which have been described in the account of the petrous bone (page 33). In the recent state the fenestra vestibuli is closed by the base of the stapes, while the fenestra cochleæ is covered by a delicate membrane,—so that the internal ear forms a closed cavity. It is possible to distinguish a **bony** labyrinth and a **membranous** labyrinth (Fig. 173), the former being the cavity in the petrous bone, while the latter is the real auditory organ, situated within the cavity. The membranous labyrinth repeats in general the form of the bony labyrinth, so that it will not be necessary to distinguish the two in our account of the main features of the structure. The auditory nerve is distributed to the membranous labyrinth. For an account of the minute structure of this organ reference should be made to a text-book of general histology or physiology.

The labyrinth (Fig. 173) consists of a cavity, the **vestibule** (*a*), and connected with this a coiled tube, the **cochlea** (*b*), and the three **semicircular canals** (*c*, *d*, and *e*).

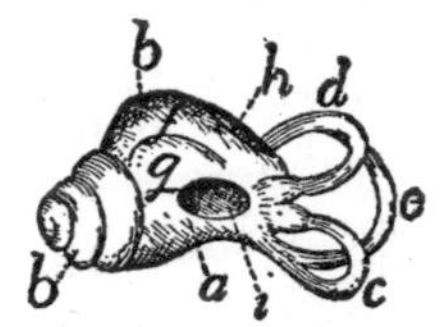

FIG. 173.—MEMBRANOUS LABYRINTH.

a, vestibule; *b*, cochlea; *c*, external semicircular canal; *d*, superior semicircular canal; *e*, posterior semicircular canal; *f*, scala tympani; *g*, scala vestibuli; *h*, fenestra cochleæ; *i*, fenestra vestibuli.

The **cochlea** (*b*) is situated in the promontory,—the rounded elevation of the petrous bone extending craniad from the fenestra cochleæ. It consists of a bony tube coiled spirally about a central column known as the **modiolus.** The coil has nearly the form of a snail's shell, and is somewhat more lengthened in the cat than in man. A plate of bone, the **lamina spiralis,** incompletely divides the cavity of the canal lengthwise into two parts, known as **scalæ** (*f* and *g*). One of these opens at the fenestra cochleæ (*h*) into the tympanic cavity (or would so open but for the thin membrane covering the fenestra); this is known as the **scala tympani** (*f*). The other scala is connected with the vestibule (*a*) and is known as the **scala vestibuli** (*g*).

The **vestibule** (*a*) is a pyramidal cavity situated mediad of the caudal end of the cochlea. It is connected with the scala vestibuli of the cochlea, and with the three semicircular canals.

The fenestra vestibuli (*i*) is an opening in its bony wall, filled in the recent state by the stapes. On the medial surface of the vestibule are a number of minute orifices through which the auditory nerve enters.

The **semicircular canals** (*c*, *d*, and *e*) are three curved tubes, each forming about two-thirds of a circle, and opening at both ends into the vestibule. They are imbedded in the petrous bone. The planes of the three tubes intersect nearly at right angles; from their position in man they have been named **external** (*c*), **superior** (*d*), and **posterior** (*e*). The external one (*c*) is nearly horizontal in position, and surrounds the curved fossa (Fig. 25, *f*) for the stapedius muscle, caudad of the fenestra vestibuli. The superior (Fig. 173, *d*) and posterior (*e*) are in nearly dorsoventral planes, but at right angles to each other. The superior (*d*) lies in the ridge forming the caudal boundary of the appendicular fossa. The posterior (*e*) is situated in a continuation caudad of the ridge which forms the dorsal boundary of the internal auditory meatus. One end of each canal is slightly enlarged to form an **ampulla.** The superior (*d*) and posterior (*e*) canals join at one end and enter the vestibule by a common opening. One end of the external canal (*c*) opens into the vestibule so close to one end of the posterior canal (*e*) that they appear to have a common opening, and this is commonly stated to be the case; according to Jayne, however, the openings are really separate. The two remaining ends (of the superior (*d*) and external (*c*) canals) also enter the vestibule separately, so that the three canals enter the vestibule by five openings.

III. THE OLFACTORY ORGAN. ORGANON OLFACTUS.

The olfactory organ consists of the olfactory mucous membrane, in the dorsocaudal part of the nasal cavity. The nasal cavity has been described in connection with the respiratory system.

IV. THE ORGAN OF TASTE. ORGANON GUSTUS.

The sense of taste is located in the mouth-cavity. Its proper organs are the so-called taste-buds, found especially in the mucosa on the papillæ of the tongue, the soft palate, the region of the epiglottis, etc. Their exact distribution in the cat has apparently not been worked out.

V. THE INTEGUMENT. INTEGUMENTUM COMMUNE.

The skin of the cat consists of the usual two layers, the outer **epidermis** and the inner fibrous **corium.** The skin is particularly thick and tough about the sides of the neck and face.

The skin is covered almost completely with fine soft hairs. Only the end of the nose, the pads on the soles of the feet, and the nipples are without hair. A number of long stiff sensory hairs (vibrissæ) are found on the upper lip, the cheek, and above the upper eyelid.

The pads on the soles of the feet are cushion-like projections of skin, composed largely of connective and elastic tissue and fat. There is one large pad for each foot, and in addition a small pad for each digit. The fore limb has besides a small conical pad which is situated almost exactly over the pisiform bone.

The **nails** are horny outgrowths of the epidermis, covering the distal phalanges.

The **muscles** of the skin are the cutaneus maximus and platysma; these have been described (page 93). The superficial facial muscles are differentiations of the skin-muscles.

PART II.

TABULAR SUMMARIES FOR REFERENCE AND REVIEW.

SUMMARY I.

OUTLINE OF ENTIRE SKELETON OF CAT.

I. Axial Skeleton

A. Head
- 1. Skull
  - *a.* Cranium
    - 1′. Frontal — 2
    - 2′. Parietal — 2
    - 3′. Temporal — 2
    - 4′. Occipital — 1
    - 5′. Interparietal — 1
    - 6′. Ethmoid — 1
    - 7′. Sphenoid — 1
  - *b.* Face
    - 1′. Premaxillary — 2
    - 2′. Maxillary — 2
    - 3′. Palatine — 2
    - 4′. Vomer — 1
    - 5′. Nasal — 2
    - 6′. Maxilloturbinal — 2
    - 7′. Lachrymal — 2
    - 8′. Malar or zygomatic — 2
    - 9′. Mandible — 1
- 2. Hyoid bones
  - *a.* Tympanohyal — 2
  - *b.* Stylohyal — 2
  - *c.* Epihyal — 2
  - *d.* Ceratohyal — 2
  - *e.* Basihyal — 1
  - *f.* Thyrohyal — 2

B. Trunk
- 1. Vertebral column
  - *a.* Cervical vertebræ — 7
  - *b.* Thoracic vertebræ — 13
  - *c.* Lumbar vertebræ — 7
  - *d.* Sacral vertebræ — 3
  - *e.* Caudal vertebræ—21-23
- 2. Thorax
  - *a.* Ribs — 26
  - *b.* Sternum — 1

II. Appendicular Skeleton

A. Thoracic appendage
- 1. Shoulder girdle
  - *a.* Scapula — 2
  - *b.* Clavicle — 2

2. Arm
   a. Humerus — 2

3. Forearm
   a. Radius — 2
   b. Ulna — 2

4. Hand
   a. Carpals
      1′. Scapholunar — 2
      2′. Cuneiform or triquetral — 2
      3′. Pisiform — 2
      4′. Greater multangular — 2
      5′. Lesser multangular — 2
      6′. Capitate — 2
      7′. Hamate — 2
   b. Metacarpals — 10
   c. Phalanges
      1′. Proximal — 10
      2′. Middle — 8
      3′. Distal — 10

B. Pelvic appendage

1. Pelvic girdle
   a. Innominate — 2

2. Leg
   a. Femur — 2
   b. Patella — 2
   c. Tibia — 2
   d. Fibula — 2

3. Foot
   a. Tarsals
      1′. Talus or astragulus — 2
      2′. Calcaneus — 2
      3′. Scaphoid or navicular — 2
      4′. Internal cuneiform — 2
      5′. Middle cuneiform — 2
      6′. Lateral cuneiform — 2
      7′. Cuboid — 2
   b. Metatarsals — 10
   c. Phalanges
      1′. Proximal — 8
      2′. Middle — 8
      3′. Distal — 8

SUMMARY II.

SKULL FORAMINA AND TRAVERSING STRUCTURES.

Foramen	Surrounding Bones	Traversing Structures
Infraorbital	Maxillary	Infraorbital branch of maxillary division of trigeminal nerve and infraorbital artery.
Anterior palatine	Maxillary and premaxillary	Nasopalatine branch of maxillary division of trigeminal nerve and nasal artery.
Sphenopalatine	Palatine	Sphenopalatine nerve and artery and posterior nasal nerve.
Posterior palatine canal	Palatine	Greater palatine nerve and descending palatine artery.
Olfactory foramina, cribriform plate of ethmoid	Ethmoid	Olfactory nerve.
Ethmoidal	Orbital plate of frontal bone	Ethmoid artery and ethmoid nerve from ophthalmic division of trigeminal nerve.
Optic	Orbitosphenoid	Optic nerve and ophthalmic artery.
Orbital fissure (or foramen lacerum anterius)	Alisphenoid and orbitosphenoid	Oculomotor, trochlear, abducens, and ophthalmic division of trigeminal nerve, and artery from carotid plexus to cranial cavity.
Rotundum	Alisphenoid	Maxillary division of trigeminal
Ovale	Alisphenoid	Mandibular division of trigeminal and middle meningeal artery.
Foramen lacerum or lacerum medius	Tympanic and basisphenoid	Internal carotid artery.
Internal auditory meatus	Petrous portion of temporal	Auditory nerve.
Facial canal	Temporal	Facial nerve (exit from cranial cavity).
Stylomastoid	Temporal	Facial nerve (exit from skull).
Jugular	Occipital and temporal	Glossopharyngeal, vagus, spinal accessory nerves and inferior cerebral vein.
Hypoglossal canal	Occipital	Hypoglossal nerve.
Foramen magnum	Occipital	Spinal cord; spinal roots of spinal accessory nerve; vertebral arteries.
Mandibular	Mandible	Inferior alveolar artery and nerve.
Mental	Mandible	Mental artery and nerves.

SUMMARY III.

MUSCLE INNERVATION.

The following chart summarizes the nerve supply of the important muscles of the body. In case an entire group of muscles is supplied by the same nerve the individual muscles are not listed. This outline may be followed during the course of muscle dissection but should not be considered as a substitute for the descriptive material on the distribution of the various nerves, the page references to which are inserted in it.

Muscle	Innervation
I. Muscles of the Head	
A. Facial muscles	Facial (p. 375).
B. Muscles of mastication	
1. Digastric	Small branch from facial (p. 377) and branch from inferior alveolar branch of mandibular division of trigeminal (p. 374).
2. Masseter	Masseteric branch of mandibular division of trigeminal (p. 374).
3. Temporalis	Deep temporal branch of mandibular division of trigeminal (p. 374) and temporal branch from auriculotemporal of mandibular division of trigeminal (p. 373).
4. External pterygoid	Pterygoid branch of mandibular division of trigeminal (p. 374).
5. Internal pterygoid	Pterygoid branch of mandibular division of trigeminal (p. 374).
C. External ear muscles	Facial (p. 375).

Muscle	Innervation
D. Muscles of orbit	
1. Levator palpebrae superioris	Oculomotor (p. 369).
2. Retractor oculi	Oculomotor (p. 369).
3. Superior, medial and inferior recti	Oculomotor (p. 369).
4. Inferior oblique	Oculomotor (p. 369).
5. Superior oblique	Trochlear (p. 370).
6. Lateral rectus	Abducens (p. 375).
E. Muscles of hyoid bone	
1. Stylohyoid	Facial (p. 375).
2. Geniohyoid	Hypoglossal (p. 383).
3. Jugulohyoid	Hypoglossal (p. 383).
4. Mylohyoid	Branch from inferior alveolar of mandibular division of trigeminal (p. 374).
5. Ceratohyoid	Hypoglossal (p. 383).
6. Thyrohyoid	Hypoglossal and branch from cervical 1 (p. 385).
F. Muscles of tongue	Hypoglossal (p. 383).
G. Muscles of soft palate	
1. Tensor veli palatini	Trigeminal.
2. Levator veli palatini	Spinal accessory through the pharyngeal plexus (p. 383).
H. Muscles of pharynx	
1. Glossopharyngeus	Glossopharyngeal and vagus through the pharyngeal plexus (pp. 378 and 383).
2. Constrictor pharyngeus superior	Glossopharyngeal and vagus through the pharyngeal plexus.
3. Constrictor pharyngeus medius	Glossopharyngeal and vagus through the pharyngeal plexus.
4. Constrictor pharyngeus inferior	Glossopharyngeal and vagus through the pharyngeal plexus.
5. Stylopharyngeus	Glossopharyngeal (p. 378).

MUSCLE	INNERVATION
III. Muscles of larynx	
1. Thyrohyoid	Hypoglossal (p. 383).
2. Sternothyroid	Hypoglossal (p. 383).
3. Muscles of outer and inner surfaces	Superior and inferior (recurrent) laryngeal branches of vagus (p. 380).
IV. Muscles of back	
A. Connect forelimb with back	
1. Trapezius	Spinal accessory (p. 382) and ventral rami of cervical 1–4 (p. 385).
2. Occipitoscapularis	Ventral ramus of cervical 4 (p. 385).
3. Rhomboideus	Ventral rami of spinal nerves in region of origin.
4. Cleidomastoideus	Spinal accessory (p. 382) and ventral rami of cervical 2–3 (p. 385).
5. Levator scapulae ventralis	Ventral ramus of cervical 3 (p. 385).
6. Latissimus dorsi	Anterior thoracic (p. 387) and caudal division of subscapular (p. 388).
7. Serratus anterior	Posterior thoracic (p. 388).
8. Levator scapulae	Ventral rami of cervical 3–4 (p. 385).
B. Interconnect parts of vertebral column	
1. Muscles except suboccipital group	Dorsal rami of spinal nerves in the region in which the muscle is found.
2. Suboccipital group	
a. Rectus capitis posterior major	All muscles of this group are supplied by the dorsal ramus of cervical 1, which is known as the suboccipital nerve (p. 384).
b. Rectus capitis posterior minor	
c. Rectus capitis posterior medius	
d. Obliquus capitis superior	
e. Obliquus capitis inferior	
V. Muscles of tail	Dorsal and ventral rami of spinal nerves of caudal region (p. 404).

Muscle	Innervation
VI. Muscles on ventral side of vertebral column	
A. Lumbar and thoracic regions	Ventral rami of thoracic and lumbar spinal nerves.
B. Cervical region	Ventral rami of cervical spinal nerves.
VII. Muscles of ventral side of neck	
1. Sternomastoid	Spinal accessory (p. 383) and ventral rami of cervical 1–3 (p. 385).
2. Sternohyoid	Hypoglossal (p. 383) and ventral ramus of cervical 1 (p. 385).
3. Sternothyroid	Hypoglossal (p. 383) and ventral ramus of cervical 1 (p. 385).
4. Scalenus	Ventral rami of cervical 1–6 (p. 385).
5. Longus capitis	Ventral ramus of cervical 3 (p. 385).
6. Rectus capitis anterior minor	Ventral rami of cervical 2–3.
7. Rectus capitis lateralis	Ventral rami of cervical 2–3.
8. Longus colli	Ventral rami of cervical 3 through thoracic 5 or 6.
VIII. Muscles of thorax	
A. Breast muscles	
1. Pectoralis	Anterior thoracic (p. 387).
B. Wall of thorax	All muscles of this region are supplied by branches from the intercostal nerves (p. 394).
IX. Diaphragm	Phrenic (p. 388).
X. Abdominal muscles	
1. Obliquus abdominis externus	Branches from intercostal nerves (p. 394) and from ventral rami of lumbars 1–3 (p. 394).

MUSCLE	INNERVATION
2. Obliquus abdominis internus	Branches from intercostal nerves (p. 394) and from ventral rami of lumbars 1–3 (p. 394).
3. Transversus abdominis	Ventral rami of lumbars 1–3 (p. 394).
4. Rectus abdominis	Ventral rami of lumbars 1–3 (p. 394).
XI. Muscles of shoulder	
A. Lateral surface	
1. Deltoideus	Axillary (p. 388).
2. Clavobrachial	Axillary (p. 388).
3. Supraspinatus	Suprascapular (p. 388).
4. Infraspinatus	Suprascapular (p. 388).
5. Teres minor	Axillary (p. 388).
B. Medial surface	
1. Subscapular	Subscapular (cranial division) (p. 388).
2. Teres major	Subscapular (middle division) (p. 388).
XII. Muscles of upper arm	
1. Coracobrachialis	Musculocutaneous (p. 388).
2. Epitrochlearis	Radial (p. 393).
3. Biceps brachii	Musculocutaneous (p. 388).
4. Brachialis	Musculocutaneous (p. 388).
5. Triceps brachii	Radial (p. 392).
6. Anconeus	Radial (p. 392).
XIII. Muscles of forearm	
A. Ulnar and dorsal side	Entire group by radial (p. 392).
B. Radial and ventral side	
1. Entire group except:	Median (p. 390).
a. Flexor carpi ulnaris	Ulnar (p. 393).
b. Sublimis digitorum, ulnar head of Flexor.	Ulnar (p. 393).

Muscle	Innervation
XIV. Muscles of hand	
A. Between tendons	
1. Lumbricales	Three on radial side by median (p. 390); one ulnar by ulnar (p. 393).
B. Of thumb	Median (p. 390).
C. Between metacarpals	
1. Interossei	Ulnar (p. 393).
D. Of index finger	Median (p. 390).
E. Of fifth digit	Ulnar (p. 393).
XV. Muscles of hip	
A. Lateral surface	
1. Tensor fasciæ latæ	Superior gluteal (p. 399).
2. Gluteus maximus	Inferior gluteal (p. 399).
3. Gluteus medius	Superior gluteal (p. 399).
4. Pyriformis	Superior gluteal (p. 399).
5. Gemellus superior	Superior gluteal (p. 399).
6. Gluteus minimus	Superior gluteal (p. 399).
7. Capsularis	Superior gluteal (p. 399).
8. Gemellus inferior	Branch from ventral ramus of lumbar 5.
9. Quadratus femoris	Sciatic (p. 400).
10. Obturator externus	Obturator (p. 397).
B. Medial surface	
1. Obturator internus	Branches from ventral rami of sacrals 1–3.
2. Iliopsoas	Psoas division by branches from ventral rami of lumbar nerves; iliacus by femoral (p. 397).

Muscle	Innervation
XVI. Muscles of thigh	
1. Biceps femoris	Sciatic (p. 400).
2. Tenuissimus	Sciatic (p. 400).
3. Caudofemoralis	Inferior gluteal (p. 399).
4. Semitendinosus	Sciatic (p. 400).
5. Semimembranosus	Sciatic (p. 400).
6. Sartorius	Femoral (p. 397).
7. Gracilis	Obturator (p. 397).
8. Adductor femoris	Obturator (p. 397).
9. Adductor longus	Obturator (p. 397).
10. Pectineus	Obturator (p. 397).
11. Quadriceps femoris	Femoral (p. 397).
XVII. Muscles of lower leg	
A. Ventral surface	Tibial (p. 402).
B. Dorsal surface	Deep peroneal (p. 402).
C. Lateral surface	Superficial peroneal (p. 402).
XVIII. Muscles of foot	
A. Dorsal surface	
1. Extensor brevis digitorum	Deep peroneal (p. 402).
B. Ventral surface or sole	
1. Flexor brevis digitorum	Medial plantar (p. 403).
2. Quadratus plantae	Lateral plantar (p. 403).
3. Lumbricales	Medial one by medial plantar (p. 403); remainder by lateral plantar (p. 403).
4. Interossei	Lateral plantar (p. 403).
5. Muscles of fifth digit	Lateral plantar (p. 403).
6. Muscles of tarsus	
a. Calcaneometatarsalis	Lateral plantar (p. 403).
b. Scaphocuneiformis	Lateral plantar (p. 403).

SUMMARY IV.

CRANIAL NERVE DISTRIBUTION.

NERVE	ORIGIN	EXIT	CHIEF BRANCHES	DISTRIBUTION
I	Olfactory bulb	Foramina of cribriform plate		Olfactory mucosa.
II	Optic chiasma	Optic foramen		Retina.
III	Cerebral peduncle	Orbital fissure		Levator palpebræ all recti muscles except lateral; retractor oculi; motor branch to ciliary ganglion; inferior oblique.
IV	Anterior medullary velum	Orbital fissure		Superior oblique.
V	Pons	Orbital fissure	Ophthalmic	
			1. Frontal	Integument of upper eyelid and surrounding region.
			2. Infratrochlear	Integument of lower eyelid and surrounding region.
			3. Ethmoidal	Mucosa of nose.
			4. Long ciliary	Eyeball.
		Foramen rotundum	Maxillary	
			1. Lachrymal	Lachrymal gland; integument between eye and external ear.
			2. Zygomatic	Integument over zygomatic arch.
			3. Infraorbital	Integument over upper lip and side of nose; teeth of upper jaw.
			4. Sphenopalatine	
			a. Greater palatine	Hard palate.
			b. Branches to sphenopalatine ganglion	Lesser palatine to soft palate; posterior nasal to nasal mucosa.

Nerve	Origin	Exit	Chief Branches	Distribution
		Foramen ovale	Mandibular 1. Auriculo-temporal	
			a. Auricular	Integument of external ear.
			b. Temporal	Temporalis muscle and integument over zygoma.
			2. Deep temporal	Temporalis muscle.
			3. Massetericus	Masseter muscle.
			4. Pterygoideus	External and internal pterygoid muscles; tensor tympani muscle.
			5. Buccinatorius	Mucosa of mouth and lips; masseter muscle.
			6. Inferior alveolar	
			a. Mylohyoid	Mylohyoid and digastric muscles.
			b. Inferior dental	Teeth of mandible.
			c. Mental	Integument of lower jaw and mucosa of lower lip.
			7. Lingual	Mucosa of tongue and pharynx (accompanied by chorda tympani of VII).
VI	Pons	Orbital fissure		Lateral rectus muscle.
VII	Pons	Internal auditory meatus	1. Superficial petrosal	To sphenopalatine ganglion.
			2. Chorda tympani	To mucosa of tongue (follows lingual of V).
			3. Posterior auricular	External ear muscles and to inner surface of external ear.
			4. Dorsal ramus	
			a. Temporal	Superficial muscles.
			b. Zygomatic	Superficial muscles.
			c. Small branch to submental muscle.	Submental muscle.
			5. Ventral ramus	
			a. Superior buccal	Muscles of upper lip.

Nerve	Origin	Exit	Chief Branches	Distribution
			b. Inferior buccal	Muscles of lower lip and chin.
			c. Branch to stylohyoid muscle	Stylohyoid muscle.
			6. Branch to stapedius muscle while nerve is in facial canal	Stapedius muscle.
VIII	Junction of pons and medulla	Internal auditory meatus	1. Cochlear portion	Cochlea.
			2. Vestibular portion	Vestibule and semi-circular canals.
IX	Medulla	Jugular foramen		Stylopharyngeal muscle; muscles and mucosa of pharynx (taste) through pharyngeal plexus.
X	Medulla	Jugular foramen	1. Auricular	External ear.
			2. Pharyngeal	Pharyngeal muscles and cranial end of œsophagus (through pharyngeal plexus).
			3. Superior laryngeal	Mucosa of larynx.
			4. Cardiac	Heart (through cardiac plexus).
			5. Inferior or recurrent laryngeal	Muscles of larynx.
			6. Pulmonary	Lungs (through pulmonary plexus).
			7. Dorsal and ventral branches on œsophagus through diaphragm	Abdominal viscera.
XI	Bulbar from medulla; spinal from spinal cord	Jugular foramen		Cleidomastoid, sternomastoid and trapezius muscles (joins the pharyngeal plexus).
XII	Medulla	Hypoglossal canal		Hyoid and tongue muscles.

SUMMARY V.

DISTRIBUTION OF NERVES FROM BRACHIAL PLEXUS.

Nerve	Formation	Branches	Distribution
Anterior thoracic	1. Anterior — C 7 2. Posterior — C 8–T 1		Pectoralis muscle. Pectoralis muscle; sometimes to latissimus dorsi.
Posterior thoracic	C 7		Serratus anterior muscle.
Suprascapular	C 6. Sometimes C 6–7		Integument over ventral surface of upper arm; supraspinatus and infraspinatus muscles.
Subscapular	1. Cranial — C 6–7 2. Middle — C 7 3. Caudal — C 7–8		Subscapularis muscle. Teres major muscle. Latissimus dorsi muscle.
Axillary	C 6–7		Spino- and acromiodeltoids; clavobrachial and teres minor muscles.
Phrenic	C 5–6		Diaphragm.
Musculocutaneous	C 6–7		Biceps, coracobrachialis and brachialis muscles; integument on radial side of ventral surface of forearm.
Medial cutaneous	T 1		Integument on ulnar side of forearm.
Median	C 7–8; T 1		All muscles on radial and ventral side of forearm except flex. carpi ulnaris and ulnar head of flex. profundus digitorum; integument of thumb and all the digits except ulnar side of fifth; muscles of hand: 1. Three radial lumbricales. 2. Muscles of thumb. 3. Muscles of index finger.

Nerve	Formation	Branches	Distribution
Radial	C 7–8; T 1		Epitrochlearis, anconeus and triceps brachii muscles.
		1. Superficial radial	Integument of distal part of ventral surface of upper arm and forearm; integument on dorsal surface of hand.
		2. Dorsal interosseous	Supinator and extensor muscles of forearm (all muscles of ulnar and dorsal side).
Ulnar	C 8; T 1		Flex. carpi ulnaris and ulnar head of flex. profundus digitorum muscles.
		1. Dorsal cutaneous	Integument of dorsal side of ulnar surface of fifth digit and contiguous sides of fourth and fifth digits.
		2. Palmar	Integument on flexor surface of forearm.
		a. Superficial palmar	Integument on ventral surface of ulnar side of fifth digit and contiguous sides of fourth and fifth digits.
		b. Deep palmar	Ulnar one of lumbricales and interossei muscles; muscles of fifth digit.

SUMMARY VI.

NERVES FROM LUMBAR PLEXUS.

Nerve	Formation	Branches	Distribution
Genitofemoral	L 4		Integument on ventral surface of pelvis; on proximal part of medial surface of thigh; on craniomedial surface of thigh and adjacent abdominal wall.
Lateral femoral cutaneous	L 4–5		Integument over lateral surface of femur.
Femoral	L 5–6		Branches to sartorius and quadriceps femoris muscles.
		Long saphenous	Integument along medial surface of lower leg and over dorsal surface of foot.
Obturator	L 6–7		Obturator externus, adductor femoris and longus, pectineus and gracilis muscles.

SUMMARY VII.

NERVES FROM SACRAL PLEXUS.

Nerve	Formation	Branches	Distribution
Superior gluteal	Lumbosacral cord (L 6–7) and S 1		Tensor fasciæ latæ, gluteus medius and minimus and gemellus superior muscles.
Inferior gluteal	Lumbrosacral cord and S 1		Caudofemoralis and gluteus maximus muscles.
Great sciatic (Ischiadicus)	Lumbosacral cord and S 1–2		Biceps femoris, tenuissimus semitendinosus, semimembranosus and quadratus femoris muscles.

Nerve	Formation	Branches	Distribution
		1. Sural	Integument over region of calcaneus and lateral surface of foot in region of tarsus and metatarsus.
		2. Common peroneal	
		a. Superficial peroneal	Lateral crural muscles and branches to four toes.
		b. Deep peroneal	Anterior crural muscles; extensor digitorum brevis muscle; branches to contiguous sides of fourth and fifth digits.
		3. Tibial	Posterior crural muscles (on ventral surface of lower leg).
		a. Medial plantar	Flexor brevis digitorum and medial lumbricales muscles; second and third digits and fibrous pad on sole of foot.
		b. Lateral plantar	Ventral surface of fifth digit; quadratus plantæ, three lateral lumbricales; muscles of fifth digit and of tarsus
Pudendal	S 2–3	1. Dorsalis penis	Dorsal surface of penis; compressor urethræ muscle; glans of penis.
		2. Medial hemorrhoidal	Muscles around caudal end of rectum; urogenital sinus, and adjacent structures in female.
Posterior femoral cutaneous	S 2–3		Integument over lateral surface of biceps femoris muscle.
Inferior Hemorrhoidal	S 2–3		Bladder and urethra.
Small branch	S 2–3		Levator ani muscle.
Small branch	S 2–3		Coccygeus muscle.

SUMMARY VIII.

ARTERIAL SYSTEM.

I. Thoracic Aorta
- A. Right and left coronary — to heart wall
- B. Innominate
  - 1. Mediastinal — to mediastinal contents
  - 2. Left common carotid
  - 3. Right common carotid. The two common carotid arteries have the same branches
    - *a.* Inferior thyroid — to thyroid, trachea and œsophagus
    - *b.* Superior thyroid — to thyroid gland and sternohyoid and thyroid muscles
      - 1′. Superior laryngeal to muscles of larynx.
    - *c.* Muscular branches — to muscles of dorsal side of neck
    - *d.* Occipital — to deep muscles of neck and to those of back of head
    - *e.* Internal carotid — to brain
    - *f.* Continues as the external carotid
      - 1′. Lingual — to hyoid and pharyngeal muscles and to tongue
      - 2′. Muscular — to digastric and hyoid muscles
      - 3′. External maxillary
        - *a′.* Submental — muscles on mandible
        - *b′.* Superior labial — to upper lip
        - *c′.* Inferior labial — to lower lip
      - 4′. Posterior auricular — to muscles and integument of external ear
        - *a′.* Anterior auricular — to cranial side of external ear
      - 5′. Superficial temporal — to masseter and temporalis muscles and to eyelids
        - *a′.* Auricular — to cranial surface of external ear
      - 6′. Internal maxillary is the continuation of the external carotid
        - *a′.* Inferior alveolar — enters mandibular foramen, supplying the teeth and emerging on chin as the mental artery
        - *b′.* Middle meningeal — to dura mater
        - *c′.* Branches from plexus to within the cranial cavity
          - 1″. Posterior communicating — joins the internal carotid
          - 2″. Middle cerebral — to brain
          - 3″. Anterior cerebral — to brain
        - *d′.* Branches from carotid plexus to the muscles of mastication
        - *e′.* Ophthalmic — to structures in orbit
          - 1″. Ethmoidal — to nasal cavity

f′. Lesser palatine — to soft palate
g′. Sphenopalatine — to mucosa of nose
1″. Descending palatine — to hard palate

4. Right subclavian
a. Vertebral — to muscles of back of neck
1′. Branches which unite to form anterior spinal
2′. The two vertebrals unite to form the Basilar artery
a′. Posterior inferior cerebellars — to cerebellum
b′. Posterior cerebrals — to cerebrum
c′. Pass into the formation of the circle of Willis (circulus arteriosus)
b. Internal mammary — mediastinal branches to mediastinal contents and supply to ventral thoracic and anterior part of ventral abdominal wall
c. Costocervical
1′. Superior intercostal — to first and second intercostal spaces
2′. Branch which divides into:
a′. Transverse colli — to scalenus, serratus anterior and rhomboidei muscles
b′. Deep cervical — to deep muscles of back
d. Thyrocervical
1′. Ascending cervical — to ventral neck muscles
2′. Becomes known as Transverse Scapular or Suprascapular artery
a′. Branches to lymphatic glands and to trapezius, levator scapulæ ventralis, splenius, occipitoscapularis and rhomboideus muscles
b′. Branch to subscapularis and supraspinatus muscles
c′. Branch to supraspinatus muscle
e. Laterad of the first rib the subclavian continues as the Axillary
1′. Anterior thoracic — to medial ends of the pectoral muscles
2′. Long thoracic — to middle portions of pectoral muscles and to latissimus dorsi muscle
3′. Divides into:
a′. Subscapular
1″. Thoracodorsal — to teres major, latissimus dorsi and epitrochlearis muscles
2″. Posterior humeral circumflex — to deltoid and long and lateral heads of triceps brachii muscles
b′. Brachial — continuation of the axillary into the arm beyond the region of the subscapular artery
1″. Anterior humeral circumflex — to head of humerus

2″. Deep brachial (follows the radial nerve) — to triceps, epitrochlearis and latissimus dorsi muscles
3″. Musculars
4″. Ulnar collateral — to structures in convexity of elbow
5″. Superior radial collateral — to pectoantibrachial and clavobrachial muscles; integument of forearm and dorsum of hand
6″. Radial — is continuation of brachial beyond the convexity of the elbow
a″. Radial recurrent — to structures in convexity of elbow on radial side; to brachialis, extensor carpi radialis and extensor digitorum communis muscles
b″. Ulnar recurrent — to structures in concavity of elbow on ulnar side; to pronator teres, proximal end of flexor carpi ulnaris and flexor profundus digitorum muscles
c″. Muscular branches
d″. Anterior interosseous — to muscles of forearm and to wrist
e″. Posterior interosseous — to muscles on dorsal surface of forearm
f″. Ulnar — to muscles on ulnar side of ventral surface of forearm
g″. Anastomosis with radial to form the *palmar arch*
1‴. Princeps pollicis and indicis to ulnar side of thumb and radial side of index finger
2‴. Palmar interossei — to dorsal and ventral surfaces of hand

C. Left subclavian — has the same plan of distribution as the right which has been outlined
D. Intercostals
E. Bronchials — may arise from the fourth intercostals
F. Œsophageals
G. Lumbars — usually one or two pairs arise anterior to the diaphragm

II. Abdominal Aorta
A. Cœliac
1. Hepatic
a. Gastroduodenal
1′. Pyloric — to pylorus and lesser curvature of stomach
2′. Superior pancreaticoduodenal — to pancreas and duodenum

- 3′. Right gastroepiploic — to greater curvature of stomach
- 2. Left gastric — to lesser curvature of stomach
  - *a.* Dorsal ventricular (may arise from cœliac) — to greater curvature of stomach near the cardiac end
- 3. Splenic — to spleen

B. Superior mesenteric
- 1. Inferior pancreaticoduodenal — to pancreas and duodenum
- 2. Middle colic — to transverse colon
- 3. Right colic — to ascending colon
- 4. Ileocolic — to ileocoecal junction
- 5. Intestinals — to small intestine

C. Adrenolumbalis — to adrenal and body wall

D. Renals — to kidneys
- 1. May give rise to Internal spermatic or ovarian

E. Internal spermatics or ovarians — to testes or ovaries.

F. Inferior mesenteric
- 1. Left colic — to descending colon
- 2. Superior hemorrhoidal — to rectum

G. Iliolumbars — to body wall

H. Lumbars — to body wall

I. External iliacs
- 1. Deep femoral
  - *a.* Inferior epigastric — to ventral body wall, passing forward in the rectus sheath
  - *b.* External spermatic — within the spermatic cord
  - *c.* Branches passing to bladder, urethra and medial surface of thigh
- 2. Continues into thigh where it is known as the *femoral*
  - *a.* Lateral femoral circumflex — to muscles on front of thigh
  - *b.* Muscular branches
  - *c.* Superior articular — to medial surface of knee-joint
  - *d.* Saphenous
    - 1′. Dorsal branch to dorsum of foot
    - 2′. Plantar branch to plantar surface of foot
  - *e.* Continues into popliteal space where it is known as the *popliteal*
    - 1′. Sural — to structures within and forming boundaries of the popliteal space
    - 2′. Posterior genicular — to knee-joint
    - 3′. Muscular — to muscles around popliteal space
    - 4′. Continues as *anterior tibial*
      - *a′.* Recurrent tibial — to knee-joint
      - *b′.* Muscular branches
      - *c′.* Superficial ramus — along leg and on to dorsal surface of foot
      - *d′.* Medial tarsals — to ankle-joint region
      - *e′.* Metatarsals

J. Hypogastrics or Internal iliacs
  1. Umbilical
    a. Superior vesical — to sides of bladder
    b. Inferior vesical — to neck of bladder and urethra
  2. Superior gluteal — to pelvic wall and hip muscles of medial side
  3. Middle hemorrhoidal
    a. Branch to urethra and prostate in male and corresponding uterine in female
    b. Branches to bladder, vagina, urogenital sinus and anus in female
    c. Branches to urethra, bulbourethral glands and penis (dorsalis penis artery) in male
  4. Inferior gluteal — accompanies the sciatic nerve into the thigh and supplies structures there

K. Middle sacral
  1. Lateral sacral — to structures within the sacrum and to muscles over its dorsal surface

SUMMARY IX.

VENOUS SYSTEM.

I. Superior Vena Cava

A. Azygos.
  1. Bronchials — from lungs
  2. Intercostals
  3. Œsophageals

B. Internal mammary — the two internal mammary veins unite in the formation of the sternal vein

C. Innominates. The right and left innominate veins unite in the formation of the superior vena cava. Each is formed by the union of the external jugular and subclavian vein
  1. External jugular
    a. Formed by the union of the anterior and posterior facial veins
      1′. Anterior facial
        a′. Begins as *frontal* vein — over the orbit
          1″. Receives the superior palpebral from the upper eyelid
        b′. Continuation of frontal along the cranial angle of the eye is known as the *angular*
          1″. External nasal — from side of nose
        c′. Angular continues over the malar bone to become known as the *anterior facial* vein

1″. Inferior palpebral — from lower eyelid
2″. Superior labial — from upper lip
3″. Deep facial — from beneath the masseter muscle
4″. Inferior labial — from lower lip
5″. Submental — from lymph nodes from side of neck
6″. Transverse — connects the two facial veins
  a″. Receives laryngeal veins from larynx

2′. Posterior facial
  a′. Superficial temporal — from lateral surface of head and face
    1″. Anterior auricular — from in front of external ear
  b′. Posterior auricular — from back of head posterior to external ear

b. Tributaries of external jugular vein
  1′. Transverse scapular — tributaries correspond to branches of artery of same name
    a′. Receives branch from vena cephalica humeri
  2′. Ascending cervical — follows corresponding artery from the thyreocervical axis
  3′. Internal jugular
    a′. Inferior cerebral vein from dural sinuses
    b′. Communicating branch from posterior facial
    c′. Occipital — from vertebral column (by atlantal foramen) and from back of head
    d′. The dural sinuses which largely drain into this vein through the inferior cerebral vein will be listed here
      1″. Superior sagittal — in falx cerebri
        a″. Receives great cerebral vein (vena cerebri magna)
        b″. Enters transverse sinus
      2″. Transverse sinus in dorsal border of tentorium
        a″. Enters into the formation of the inferior cerebral vein
      3″. Cavernous — on each side of hypophysis on body of sphenoid
      4″. Inferior petrosal — passes caudolateralward from the cavernous sinus. One branch enters into formation of inferior cerebral vein and other joins the vertebral sinus
      5″. Sinus of vertebral column — extends the entire length of the spinal cord on the ventral surface. Sends branches to inferior cerebral vein, intercostals and lumbar veins and receives veins from the spinal cord

2. Subclavian.
   a. Is the continuation of the axillary vein which parallels the axillary artery and has the same tributaries as the artery has branches. This set of veins constitutes the deep set of veins of the thoracic extremity
   b. Superficial veins of thoracic extremity.
      1′. Begin by veins on volar and dorsal surfaces of the hand which unite to form the vena cephalica, which passes to the elbow. This vein divides at the elbow into:
         a′. Vena mediana cubiti, which joins the brachial vein in the concavity of the elbow
         b′. Vena cephalica humeri — this passes through the upper arm and at the level of the acromiodeltoid muscle divides into:
            1″. Branch which joins the posterior humeral circumflex vein
            2″. Branch which joins the transverse scapular vein

II. INFERIOR VENA CAVA
A. Formed by the union of the common iliac veins which are formed by the union of the internal iliac and external iliac veins
   1. Internal iliac or hypogastric
      a. Tributaries correspond to branches of the artery of same name. The inferior gluteal vein receives a branch from the lesser saphenous vein
   2. External iliac
      a. Follows the corresponding artery in returning the blood from the pelvic extremity. Veins of pelvic extremity:
         1′. Deep set — accompany branches of popliteal and anterior tibial arteries and have same names as the branches of the arteries
         2′. Superficial set
            a′. Branches from the dorsum of the foot unite to form the great saphenous vein (vena saphena magna), which passes proximally on the medial surface of the leg to join the femoral vein
            b′. Branches from plantar surface of foot enter into the formation of the lesser saphenous vein (vena saphena parva), which passes proximally along the lateral surface of the leg to the popliteal space where it divides into two branches, one of which enters the popliteal vein while the other passes farther proximad to join the inferior gluteal vein

B. Tributaries
   1. Lumbars
   2. Iliolumbars
   3. Internal spermatics or ovarians — the left usually joins the left renal vein while the right joins the inferior vena cava direct

4. Renals
5. Adrenolumbalis
6. Phrenics
7. Hepatics — these return all blood from the liver which is carried there by the hepatic artery and portal vein
   a. Portal vein
      1′. Formed by union of superior mesenteric and gastrosplenic veins
      2′. Tributaries:
         a′. Pancreaticoduodenalis
         b′. Gastroepiploic — from greater curvature of stomach
         c′. Coronaria ventriculi — from lesser curvature of stomach
         d′. Gastrosplenic — receives branches from pancreas, stomach and spleen
         e′. Superior mesenteric — tributaries correspond to branches of superior mesenteric artery
            1″. Receives the inferior mesenteric, which has tributaries corresponding to the branches of the artery by the same name

INDEX

OF PARTS I AND II

DISSECTION *of the* CAT

PRACTICAL DIRECTIONS FOR THE DISSECTION OF THE CAT
AND THE STUDY OF ITS ANATOMY,
TO ACCOMPANY
Reighard and Jennings' *Anatomy of the Cat*
(Third Edition Revised by Rush Elliott)

BY
JACOB REIGHARD
AND
H. S. JENNINGS

REVISED
WITH THE ADDITION OF
A MANUAL OF REGIONAL DISSECTION
BY
RUSH ELLIOTT, PH.D.
*Professor of Anatomy, Department of Zoology,
and Dean, College of Arts and Sciences, Ohio University*

SECOND EDITION

HOLT, RINEHART AND WINSTON
New York · Chicago · San Francisco
Toronto · London

PRINTED IN THE
UNITED STATES OF AMERICA

PREFACE

In Reighard and Jennings' *Anatomy of the Cat* published in 1901, an appendix includes practical directions for the preparation of material and for dissection, with references to the essential literature.

The directions for dissection follow the "*system plan,*" by which each system of organs, the muscular system, the circulatory system etc., is dissected separately and more or less without reference to other systems. The student thus gains knowledge of the organ-systems of the cat as wholes and may readily compare them with those of other vertebrates, as in the study of comparative vertebrate anatomy.

Since 1901 an increasing number of pre-medical students have taken laboratory courses in cat anatomy as a preparation for the anatomical work of the medical school. When they reach the medical dissecting room they find another plan of dissection in use, the traditional "*regional plan*" of teachers of human anatomy, as distinguished from comparative anatomy. This involves the dissection of the body, region by region. All the structures of the arm, for instance, muscles, blood vessels and nerves, are dissected together and with little immediate reference to the system-wholes to which they belong. A student thus encounters blood vessels and nerves without necessarily learning, at the time, their relations in the systems of which they are parts. But he learns human anatomy in the form in which it is of most use in the daily work of the physician and surgeon.

For the medical school the regional plan has the further advantage that the student may complete his work in the dissecting room by the use of a single cadaver. The relative scarcity of material and the cost of preserving, preparing and storing it practically enforces the regional plan in medical schools.

Many teachers who use the *Anatomy of the Cat* in laboratory courses prefer a regional plan of dissection for the work of pre-medical students. One of them, Dr. Rush Elliott, had prepared a Manual of Dissection by the Regional Plan and had used it successfully for some years. He has now consented to revise and rearrange the practical directions of the Anatomy and to add to them his own manual. This booklet then, after discussing the more essential literature and describing methods of preparing the anatomical material, provides two sets of instructions for dissection; one is a Manual of Dissection by the System Plan, while the other is Dr. Elliott's Manual of Dissection by the Regional Plan.

By the use of the regional plan a single cat for each student may be made to serve for the entire course, whereas the system plan requires the use of several cats. There is an obvious economy in the use of the former plan.

Although the original authors of the *Anatomy* continue to believe that dissection by systems affords the better general preparation for the medical dissecting room they are glad that both plans are now available. They hope that the directions for dissection may prove convenient in use as a separate booklet and they are now published separately as well as in the same volume with the *Anatomy*.

J. R.

August, 1932.

CONTENTS

PART I. BOOKS

PART II. PREPARATION AND USE OF MATERIALS

PART III. MANUAL OF DISSECTION BY THE SYSTEM PLAN

PART IV. MANUAL OF DISSECTION BY THE REGIONAL PLAN

DIRECTIONS FOR DISSECTION OF THE CAT AND STUDY OF ITS ANATOMY

PART I. BOOKS

A. Books on Dissection and Anatomy of the Cat. — A copy of Jayne's *Mammalian Anatomy* should be in the laboratory for reference. Only the volume on the Bones of the Cat has been issued.

Wilder and Gage's *Anatomical Technology* will be found very useful for methods of work.

The plates of Strauss-Durckheim's *Anatomie du Chat* are exceedingly valuable for the bones and muscles, and should be in the laboratory if possible. Outline reproductions of these plates have been published by H. S. Williams (G. P. Putnam's Sons, New York, 1875). The use of both the original plates and the reproductions is made difficult by the antiquated nomenclature used for the structures figured.

Good brief descriptions of the various systems of the cat, of which that of the muscles is the most valuable, are given in Stromsten's revision of Davison's *Mammalian Anatomy* (P. Blakiston's Son and Co., Philadelphia).

Laboratory directions on the anatomy of the cat, particularly for courses in Comparative Anatomy in which the study of the cat serves as a part of the course, are given in Hyman's *A Laboratory Manual for Comparative Vertebrate Anatomy* (University of Chicago Press, 1922); Bigelow's *Directions for the Dissection of the Cat* (The Macmillan Co., New York); and in *A Laboratory Guide for the Dissection of the Cat* by Gorham and Tower (Chas. Scribner's Sons, New York, 1895). The last-named manual contains some excellent plates of the muscles.

Bibliographic details for the foregoing references are given in the Preface to the *Anatomy of the Cat*, page iii. Other references are to be found on page v, and to them should be added the papers of Ranson and Billingsley on "The Sympathetic Nervous System of the Cat" (Journal of Comparative Neurology, Vol. XXIX, No. 4, August 1918).

B. The Manuals of Dissection in this Book. — The following manuals on the dissection and study of the cat are not intended as a general treatise on methods of preservation and dissection, but attempt only to give the application of well-known methods to the dissection of the particular animal with which the book deals. General methods that are referred to, but not described, must be looked up, if unfamiliar, in the manuals of general methods.

In the Manuals of Dissection the order of study of the structures is usually not the same as the order in which they are described in the *Anatomy*, except in the case of the bones. This is of course due to the practical difficulties in dissection. The Manuals of Dissection give the *order of study*, or at least the order of dissection; of course after dissection the structures can be reviewed in the logical order given in the descriptions in the *Anatomy*. But in the first study and dissection, the student is to use the Manuals for the *order of work*, while using the *Anatomy* for the descriptions. In studying muscles, for example, by the use of either Manual, the student will follow the order of dissection given in the Manual, but as each muscle is dissected he will find, confirm, and study the description of that muscle given in the *Anatomy*. Other organs are studied in a similar manner.

Before commencing the study, read the portion of the Preface which explains the use of *terms of direction* (pp. vii–viii).

Note that the page on which each figure in the *Anatomy* is found is given in the List of Illustrations following the Table of Contents (pp. xix–xxii). Page numbers in this text refer to the *Anatomy of the Cat* when in roman type, to the pages of this book when in *italic* type.

PART II

PREPARATION AND USE OF MATERIALS

A. Preparation of Bones. — The bones will of course be studied from dried specimens. These may be prepared once for all and kept in the laboratory from year to year. A number of mounted skeletons of the cat should be at hand; these must be prepared by some one who has skill in such work.

Preparation of Separate Bones. — For preparing the separate bones the liquid-soap process recommended by Wilder and Gage (*Anatomical Technology*, p. 107) will be found most convenient. This is as follows: The skin and soft parts are removed as far as possible without injury to the bones.

Make the following "liquid-soap" mixture:

Soft water	2000 cc.
Strong ammonia	150 cc.
Nitrate of potash (saltpeter)	12 grams
Hard soap	75 grams

Heat these together till a homogeneous mixture is formed. Now immerse the bone or bones to be cleaned in a liquid composed of four parts water to one part of the above liquid-soap mixture. Boil forty minutes; pour off the liquid and renew it. Boil about half an hour longer; then remove soft parts with fingers, scalpel, and brush. The bones may be boiled as much longer in the mixture as is necessary to make the soft parts come away easily. If they are boiled too long, however, the epiphyses will separate from the bones. This is especially likely to occur in young skeletons, which must therefore not be boiled so long as the bones of an old cat.

Skeletons prepared in the following rough way are useful for many purposes. The entire body of the cat, or a single limb, is placed in the liquid-soap mixture (after partial removal of soft parts), and boiled till the muscles may be removed, but the ligaments, holding the bones together, remain. Clean thoroughly without removing the ligaments, and allow to dry. The bones are thus held together in their natural positions. Skeletons so prepared are not elegant, but are frequently useful.

Disarticulation of Skulls. — The bones of the skull may be separated as follows: Clean the skull in the liquid-soap mixture, as above described. Then fill the cranial cavity with dry rice, beans, corn, or some other seeds that swell much on imbibition of water. Cork up the foramen magnum, and place the skull for twelve to twenty-four hours in water. The swelling of the seeds will partially separate the bones at the sutures. The bones may then usually be separated completely by hand.

Entire skulls, and longitudinal sections, as represented in Fig. 43, p. 60, should be at hand.

B. Preparation and Preservation of Materials for Dissection. — The cat may be killed by placing it in a tight box or jar with a bit of cotton saturated with chloroform or ether. Illuminating gas serves as well and is cheaper. The cat is placed in a tight wooden box which is about 10 inches high, 15 inches long, and 8 inches wide, and has at one end a close-fitting hinged door with a square of window glass set in it. A piece of iron pipe with a stopcock attached is screwed into a hole bored in the other end. The pipe is connected to a gas outlet by rubber tubing. After the cat is placed in the box and the door closed, the stopcock is opened and the animal watched through the glass. Death usually occurs in about three minutes. Whatever method of killing is used, it is not necessary to bleed the specimen after killing. When the cat is dead, remove it to a tray, place it on its back, and tie the limbs loosely so that they will remain outspread.

Formalin is one of the most satisfactory and cheapest preservatives for anatomical material. It is, however, offensive to some workers, and sometimes causes an irritation of the skin and mucous membranes. A solution employing alcohol in its place may be used. This has the disadvantage of being more expensive, but furnishes excellent material for dissection.

Use of one of the following embalming fluids is recommended:

1. Formalin fluid. — Prepare a stock solution according to the following formula:

Glycerin (commercial)	4000 cc.
Formalin (commercial)	600 cc.
Phenol (commercial)	1070 cc.

At the time of embalming use 1 part of this solution diluted with 6 parts of water.

2. Formalin-free fluid. — Make a solution according to the following formula:

Glycerin (commercial)	535 cc.
Phenol (commercial)	535 cc.
95% alcohol (ethyl)	135 cc.
Water	2800 cc.

The embalming fluids and injection masses are usually introduced into the femoral artery. Expose the artery by an incision through the integument on the medial side of the thigh from the region of the pubic symphysis to the knee. Locate the femoral artery, introduce into it a canula directed toward the body, and tie it in place.

If the specimen that is to be embalmed is an adult of good size, about 300 to 400 cc. of either solution is required. If a syringe is used, the fluid should be injected slowly and carefully so as to avoid ruptures which may occur in the vessels in case of too rapid injection. Use of the gravity method for embalming is advantageous since the fluid penetrates the tissues more slowly and more thoroughly, and there is consequently less danger of vessel injury. Where time and space permit its use, this method is recommended. It consists in placing the fluid in a receptacle elevated about three feet above the specimen and allowing it to run to the canula and into the vessel through a rubber hose provided with a stopcock. About three hours' time is required, during which the specimen needs no attention. Where many cats are to be embalmed, the rubber tube may be attached to one end of a piece of iron pipe which is permanently fastened to a table edge or other support. The pipe is provided with five to ten lateral outlets, each of which bears two stopcocks for attachment of rubber tubes leading to canulas. With this device and a large-enough elevated reservoir, twenty cats may be embalmed at one time.

If the specimen is to be used for dissection of blood vessels, the arteries should be injected and this process should follow immediately upon the completion of embalming. Among many injection masses that may be used, the following is very satisfactory. Prepare a stock mixture for color according to the following formula:

Chrome yellow	1 volume
Glycerin (commercial)	1 volume
5% formalin or 95% alcohol (ethyl)	1 volume

Mix and allow to stand for some time. Filter through cheesecloth. At the time of injection prepare the following injection mass:

Dry starch	1 volume
5% formalin or 95% alcohol	$1\frac{1}{4}$ volumes
Color stock mixture	$1\frac{1}{4}$ volumes

The following mass is also in very common use. Mix together equal volumes of either vermilion or red lead, glycerin, and 5% formalin. Grind these together in a mortar, so as to break up all lumps; strain the resulting mixture through fine muslin. This color mixture may be preserved in a closed bottle till it is to be used. Then mix together one volume of dry starch, one and one-fourth volumes of 5% formalin, and one-fourth volume of the color mixture. See that no lumps are present.

Either mass is usually injected into the femoral artery with a metal syringe. Introduce the mixture slowly. It drives the fluid already injected into the veins, and the arteries are filled with the injection mass. Keep a close watch on the roof of the mouth during the injection and as soon as the injection mass begins to show in the arteries stop the injection, tie off the artery and remove the canula. Injection too long continued, particularly under pressure, may result in ruptured vessels.

The veins need not be injected, as they will be found to be filled with the embalming fluid, colored by the blood, so that they can be traced without great difficulty.

After injection with either embalming fluid, the specimen may be preserved by immersing it in either a 5% formalin solution, or in 70% alcohol. A more recent and more desirable method of preservation is the dry method, which dispenses with immersion and consists in keeping the specimen wrapped in strips of muslin previously soaked in either a 5% formalin solution, a 70% alcohol solution, or a 3% phenol solution. The phenol fluid is cheaper and leaves the material in better condition for dissection. When the specimen is not being used it should be kept in a closed container, as nearly air-tight as possible. Material preserved by the dry method remains in excellent condition for an indefinite period. The parts retain their pliability much better than when immersed, and their colors are so well retained that the different structures are more easily distinguishable.

If the regional plan of dissection is followed, one specimen suffices for the entire laboratory study. If the system plan is followed, the specimen used for the study of the muscles will serve also for the study of the spinal cord and brain. For the study of the viscera, blood vessels, and nerves, other specimens will have to be prepared. This may be done according to the directions given above.

C. GENERAL INSTRUCTIONS FOR DISSECTION. 1. *Muscles.* — A prime requisite for successful dissection of muscles is to clean them thoroughly. Fat, connective tissue, etc., is to be carefully but thoroughly cleared away from the surface of the muscles and from between them. Frequently when it seems impossible to distinguish the structures described, all difficulty will vanish as soon as the dissection is thoroughly cleaned.

In transecting a muscle, work under it completely from both edges (except in case of very wide muscles), then introduce the scissors or scalpel, and sever the muscle by a smooth clean cut. Unless otherwise directed, always leave the entire origin with one-half of the muscle, the entire insertion with the other half. Leave the nerve supply attached to the muscle when practicable to do so.

The student must be prepared to find in some specimens considerable variations from the conditions described. The descriptions attempt to give an account of the usual structures, but specimens showing no variations whatever are undoubtedly rare.

2. *Ligaments.* — It will usually not be practical for each student to make the dissections and preparations necessary for studying the ligaments. Rather should these be examined on demonstration preparations preserved in the laboratory. Such preparations may most easily be made by using *fresh* material, and dissecting away muscles and other tissues, leaving only the ligaments connecting the bones. The preparations are then preserved in one or two per cent formalin. It is difficult to prepare the ligaments satisfactorily on preserved material, because they do not stand out clearly from other tissues in such material, so that they are not easily distinguishable.

3. *Blood Vessels.* — The methods for the preparation of specimens for the dissection of the blood vessels have been given (*p. 5*).

In general the arteries and the veins will be traced together, as they tend to parallel each other in course and in name. It is an excellent plan to make a sketch of each vessel as it is dissected, showing its origin, branches, and name. This will be of great aid to the memory and will be of much assistance in reviewing the vessels. The sketches can later be combined into a well-ordered drawing. The description of each vessel must of course be studied as the vessel is dissected.

In tracing blood vessels *do not* grasp them between the forceps-blades, but handle them by taking hold with the forceps of the connective-tissue coats of the vessels. *Do not* use the scalpel, but *pull* away the connective tissue and fat with fine forceps, using two forceps or one forceps and the tracer.

Variations are especially common in blood vessels, and the student must not be surprised to find considerable deviation from the conditions described and figured in the text. These variations usually present nothing new in principle and are easily understood by comparing them with the structures described.

4. *Lymphatics.* — It will be found hardly practical to have each student make a dissection of the lymphatic system, and such parts of it as are to be studied may best be shown on a specimen prepared for demonstration purposes.

The thoracic duct and the receptaculum chyli may be demonstrated by the following well-known method: A lean cat is fed with milk about two hours before killing it. An egg may be beaten up with the milk to advantage. Kill the cat with chloroform, and inject the arteries with colored starch through the femoral, in the usual way. The thoracic duct, the receptaculum chyli, and the lymphatics leading to the receptaculum chyli will be colored white by the milk, and can therefore be easily followed. For this purpose the abdomen should be opened, and the left side of the thorax removed, as in the dissection of the blood vessels. The thoracic duct will be found at the left side of the aorta and may then be traced in both directions.

For a more complete study of the lymphatics they should be injected. This is done as follows: Make a glass canula with a small point, and leave the point sharp. Connect this to the syringe by means of a rubber tube. Use a saturated solution of soluble Prussian blue as injecting fluid. Employ a freshly killed animal.

For injecting the lymphatics of the limbs, make with some pointed instrument, as the tracer, a small hole in one of the pads on the sole of the foot. Introduce the point of the canula into this opening and inject the fluid. This will pass into the spaces in the connective tissue of the pad, which will swell up, and the colored fluid will pass from the connective-tissue spaces into the lymphatics. Pressure must be maintained with the syringe for a considerable time — fifteen minutes to a half-hour for a good injection of the main trunks of the lymphatics of the limbs. During injection the movement of the fluid should be facilitated by pressing and manipulating the limb with the hand, in such a way as will tend to drive the fluid proximad.

The lymphatics of the head may be injected in a similar manner, through a canula introduced into the upper and lower lip, or into the bare surface at the end of the nose.

The internal lymphatic vessels may be filled by injecting the lymphatic glands with which they are connected. This may conveniently be done as follows: Draw out to a fine point the tip of an ordinary pipette or medicine dropper. The point should be fine, but should taper rapidly in a conical fashion, so that when the point is inserted the part of the glass tube behind it will close the opening.

Fill the pipette with soluble Prussian blue; insert the point into the gland, and inject the fluid slowly. The lymphatic vessels passing from the glands will be filled. By injecting thus the large lymphatic gland ("pancreas Aselli") in the mesentery, the abdominal lymphatics, the receptaculum chyli, and the thoracic duct may be filled.

By using thin gelatin colored with Prussian blue as an injecting fluid, permanent preparations may be obtained; of course the process of injection is then less simple, and should be looked up in some manual of methods.

5. *Central and Peripheral Nervous Systems.*

a. Brain. — The brain will usually be found to be in an entirely satisfactory condition for study in any specimen injected with five per cent formalin or the glycerin and alcohol mixture. It may be a little swollen, but all parts are well preserved, and the white and gray matter are clearly marked off from each other. Either the specimen used for the muscles or that employed for the blood vessels may therefore be used, or if the brain was removed from the specimen employed for the viscera, that will be satisfactory.

The following directions for removing the brain are designed for specimens preserved as above. For removing the *fresh* brain the process is essentially similar, but as the brain is then very soft, care should be taken not to tear it. The fresh brain should be preserved in the alcohol-formalin mixture given below, and should be allowed to rest only on some soft substance, as absorbent cotton.

Remove the head from the body by cutting through the neck a little craniad of the first rib, if this has not already been done. Remove all skin, muscles, and other soft parts from the head and cervical vertebræ, as far as possible. Remove the structures in the orbit by cutting through the zygomatic arch at each end, and removing it. The lower jaw should also be removed, if this has not already been done. (If a fresh specimen is used, and the head is to be employed for other purposes, the brain can be removed without separating the head from the body, and without taking away the lower jaw and other structures on the ventral surface of the skull.)

Have at hand dissecting instruments and a dish containing alcohol and formalin in the following proportions by volume (Parker and Floyd's mixture):

95% alcohol	6 parts
2% formalin	2 parts

In the bottom of the dish should be placed a little absorbent cotton, to support the brain.

In removing the brain have at hand entire and dissected skulls and note the relations of parts on these as far as necessary before cutting the specimen.

With bone forceps make a small opening in the parietal bone so as to expose the dura mater, but do not cut through the dura mater. With some blunt instrument free the dura mater from the bone about the opening, and continue to cut away the bone until the dorsal and lateral faces of the cerebrum are fully exposed craniad of the tentorium. The olfactory bulbs (Fig. 137, *I*) should be exposed carefully and as fully as possible. Cut away the dorsal arch of the atlas and carefully insert the forceps in the foramen magnum and, working as before, remove the squamous portion of the occipital and the parietal bones as far as the tentorium and as far ventrad as possible. Leave the dura mater intact if possible. Free the surface of the tentorium from the dura mater, carefully separate slightly the cerebellum and cerebrum; insert the bone forceps (not too far) with the blades inclined from without ventromediad, and cut the tentorium on each side. Remove it slowly, cutting adhesions to the dura mater. That part of the dura mater which dips between the cerebral hemispheres is the falx cerebri. Cut the dura mater along both sides of the falx cerebri and remove it by turning it down at the sides and cutting it at the level of the cut edge of the bone. Remove it also from the cerebellum and notice how it dips down on both sides of the tentorium and in close contact with it. Cut the falx at the cranial end between the olfactory bulbs and cut the tentorial dura (cut its adhesions, but do not remove with it the pineal body). The falx and tentorial dura may then be removed.

Allow the head to hang sideways over the dish of alcohol-formalin in such a way that the brain will tend to fall out of the cranium. Free the olfactory bulbs from the bone. Then begin at the caudal end and tilt the brain out with the handle of a scalpel. In doing this note carefully and cut the cranial nerves. They should be left with central ends as long as possible, and those on the side which is uppermost should be cut first. In doing this refer to the foramina in the base of the skull and to Fig. 138. Take especial pains also not to break off the hypophysis, which is lodged in the sella turcica.

The brain falls out and rests with its dorsal surface on the cotton. Now remove the remainder of the dura mater, carefully cutting all adhesions to nerves. Remove also the pia mater, as far as that can be done without pulling off at the same time parts of the brain substance. Preserve the brain in the alcohol-formalin mixture.

b. Nerves. — In the dissection of nerves care must be exercised not to break the delicate branches. The connective-tissue sheath around the nerve should be removed by carefully pulling it away with forceps. Each nerve should be traced to its origin (as nearly as possible) and to its distribution. Each connection of the nerve should be maintained unless otherwise directed.

PART III

MANUAL OF DISSECTION BY THE SYSTEM PLAN

STUDY OF BONES

The bones should be studied in the order in which they are described in the body of the book. No further special directions for their study are necessary.

DISSECTION OF MUSCLES

(For the technique of dissection see p. 6)

I. The Skin-muscles (pp. 93–96, and Fig. 62)

These will perhaps not usually be dissected. If they are to be dissected, proceed as follows: Make a ventromedian longitudinal incision of the skin from the cranial end of the manubrium to a point opposite the crest of the ilium. Connect the cranial end of this incision with the middle of the lambdoidal ridge by a similar incision through the skin. Make another incision from the manubrium to the spinous process of the thirteenth thoracic vertebra. Connect the caudal end of the first incision by an oblique cut with the root of the tail. Make another incision from the convexity of the knee joint along the fold of skin which connects the hind limb and body, as far as the incision which leads to the root of the tail. Make an incision surrounding the base of the fore limb. Now reflect these flaps one at a time, working in general from the ventral side toward the dorsal middle line. Take great pains not to take up the thin skin-muscle with the skin. In this way all of one side of the body will be uncovered. The cutaneus maximus (Fig. 62, *b*) and a part of the platysma (Fig. 62, *a*) will be thus exposed. Read and verify the descriptions of these muscles (pp. 93–96). The cranial portion of the platysma cannot be seen at this stage, but should be dissected in connection with the muscles of the face.

II. Superficial Muscles of the Face and Head (pp. 96–107, and Figs. 63 and 64)

These will perhaps not usually be dissected by the student. They should be studied on a well-dissected laboratory preparation, if possible. If they are to be dissected, this should be done on a fresh specimen, if possible, as it is very difficult to dissect them on preserved material. Proceed as follows:

The skin should be removed with care from the sides and top of the face and head, without injury to the external ear.

1. The platysma (p. 95, and Fig. 62, *a*). Determine its cranial attachments.
2. The intermedius scutulorum (p. 96, and Fig. 63, *a*).
3. The corrugator supercilii medialis (Fig. 63, *b*).
4. The orbicularis oculi (Fig. 63, *c*; Fig. 64, *s*).
5. The corrugator supercilii lateralis (Fig. 64, *k*).
6. Notice the frontoauricularis if it exists.
7. The levator auris longus (Fig. 63, *g*, *g′*). Transect and reflect.
8. The auricularis superior (Fig. 63, *k*). Transect.
9. The abductor auris longus (Fig. 63, *m*). Transect.
10. The abductor auris brevis (Fig. 63, *l*). Transect.
11. The epicranius (Fig. 63, *h*, *h′*). In dissecting this muscle the intermedius scutulorum and corrugator supercilii medialis may be cut by an incision parallel to the middle line but a short distance to one side of it.
12. The zygomaticus (Fig. 64, *d*). This and the two following muscles may usually be best seen running beneath the fibers of the platysma, without reflecting the latter. If necessary, however, the platysma may be transected and reflected, though this can be done only with great difficulty.

13. The submentalis (Fig. 64, *c*).
14. The depressor conchæ (Fig. 64, *b*).

The zygomaticus, submentalis, and depressor conchæ should now be transected one or two centimeters from the external ear. The corrugatores supercilii lateralis and medialis may be cut across between the eye and the ear, and reflected. There are thus exposed:

15. The frontoscutularis. Transect near the scutiform cartilage.
16. The adductor auris inferior (Fig. 64, *o*). Transect near its insertion.

The external ear is now attached to the head only by the external auditory meatus and the tragicus lateralis muscle. Read the description of the latter (p. 418, and Fig. 67, *a*), find it beneath the fat which surrounds the proximal portion of the external ear, and cut it as far ventrad as possible. Now cut across the cartilaginous auditory meatus as near to the tympanic bone as possible, and remove the external ear, preserving it for future study. (The remainder of the muscles of the external ear may be studied in connection with the study of the auditory organ.)

17. The orbicularis oris (p. 105, and Fig. 64, *i*).
18. The zygomaticus minor, if it exists (p. 105, and Fig. 64, *e*).
19. The quadratus labii superioris (p. 105).
    a. The levator labii superioris proprius (Fig. 64, *f*).
    b. The levator labii superioris alæque nasi (Fig. 64, *g*).
20. The caninus (p. 106, and Fig. 64, *f′*).
21. The buccinator (p. 106).
22. The myrtiformis (p. 106, and Fig. 64, *h*).
23. The "moustachier" (p. 107).
24. The quadratus labii inferioris (p. 107).

III. Muscles of the Fore Limb

A. *Muscles connecting the Arm with the Body.* — If the skin-muscles have been dissected, as above, cut the cutaneus maximus near its insertion, and reflect it toward the median dorsal line; in this way remove it completely. Remove the platysma in the same way. The first layer of body-muscles is thus exposed.

If the skin-muscles are not to be dissected, they may be removed with the skin. If the skin has not yet been removed, proceed as follows:

Beginning at the cranial end of the manubrium make two incisions in the skin, one passing to the lambdoidal ridge and the other to the spinous process of the thirteenth thoracic vertebra. Raise the triangular flap thus formed, taking up the skin-muscles with it.

1. The trapezius group of muscles (pp. 115–117, and Fig. 68, *d, h,* and *j*) is now exposed and may be dissected. Begin with the spinotrapezius (Fig. 68, *j*). Read the description of the muscle, then raise its caudal border and work under it until its cranial border is reached and the middle of its inner surface is free. Then transect it, and reflect the two halves of the muscle toward the origin and insertion, clearing the fat, etc., from the inner surface of the muscle and the parts covered by it. Determine origin and insertion.

2. The acromiotrapezius (Fig. 68, *h*). Dissect in the same manner, being careful not to injure the broad thin tendon which connects the two muscles across the middle line.

3. The clavotrapezius (Fig. 68, *d*). Separate it carefully from the cleidomastoid (p. 120). Transect and reflect, as before.

4. The occipitoscapularis (Fig. 73, *a*, p. 149). Note the strong fascia which separates it from the deeper muscles of the neck. Be careful not to injure adjacent muscles in tracing it toward origin and insertion. Transect.

5. The rhomboideus (p. 119). Transect.

Recognize the levator scapulæ ventralis (Fig. 68, *f*), the sternomastoid (Fig. 68, *c*; Fig. 65, *g*), and the cleidomastoid (Fig. 65, *h*). Then dissect —

6. The levator scapulæ ventralis (Fig. 68, *f*). Its origin (Fig. 72, *c, c′*) cannot be seen at this stage and should be left until the cervical muscles are dissected. Be careful in transecting this muscle to separate it well from the cleidomastoid. Transect.

7. The cleidomastoid (Fig. 65, *h*). Its origin cannot be fully seen at this stage. Transect.

Make a midventral incision of the skin from the cranial end of the manubrium to a point opposite the crest of the ilium. From the caudal end of this incision make an incision to the root of the tail. From the cranial end of the incision in the ventral middle line make a cut around the base of the fore limb on its caudal side, thus connecting the ventral incision with the incision which passes between the manubrium and the thirteenth thoracic vertebra.

Make another incision from the convexity of the knee at the joint along the fold of the skin which connects the hind limb and body, to the incision which leads to the root of the tail.

Reflect the flaps thus formed so as to expose the body and flank, removing the skin-muscle with the skin.

8. The latissimus dorsi (p. 121, and Fig. 68, *m*). Dissect it up and transect it. Work carefully toward its insertion and note the origin from its outer surface in the axilla of a part of the cutaneus maximus, and at about the same place of a thin muscle, the epitrochlearis (p. 164, and Fig. 65, *r*), *without* determining the insertion of the latissimus.

9. Dissect the pectoralis group of muscles (Fig. 65, and p. 144), i.e., the pectoantibrachialis (Fig. 65, *m*), the pectoralis major (*l*), pectoralis minor (*o*), and xiphihumeralis (*p*).

Determine the border of each muscle before lifting it, then work it up at its middle, transect it, and work toward its ends, determining origin and insertion.

Refer constantly to the skeleton.

10. Then recognize the teres major (p. 163, and Fig. 75, *d*; Fig. 77, *c*) and the common insertion of the teres major and latissimus (Fig. 79, *d'*); find the bicipital arch (Fig. 65, *t'*) and determine its composition (p. 166).

11 and 12. The serratus anterior and levator scapulæ (Fig. 73, *h* and *i*, and p. 122). In order to expose the origin of these muscles, the external oblique muscle (Fig. 68, *p*) must be recognized, and that part of it which has its origin from the fourth to the ninth rib should be transected about an inch and a half from its origin and reflected.

The thoracic portion of the rectus abdominis (Fig. 73, *k*) and of the scalenus (Fig. 73, *f–f'''*) should also be recognized and then raised at their outer borders and displaced toward the median line. *No part* of any of these muscles should be removed or cut except as directed.

The serratus anterior and levator scapulæ should be transected and reflected to get at their origin and insertion.

B. *Muscles of the Arm* (p. 156). — The arm is thus removed from the body and the dissection may be continued on the separated arm.

13. The clavobrachial (Fig. 65, *k*, and p. 157). Its origin is best seen later. Dissect it up, but do not transect it.

Search now with great care for the coracobrachialis. Consult the figures (Fig. 79, *c*) and descriptions (p. 164), and be especially careful not to injure the long head of the muscle and its tendon.

14. Dissect the coracobrachialis (Fig. 77, *f*). Cut and reflect it.

15. The subscapularis (Fig. 77, *a*, and p. 161). Near its glenoid end, its glenoid and coracoid borders are separated by triangular intervals from the adjacent muscles. Transect the muscle by a line connecting the apices of these triangles. Carry an incision from the middle of this one to the middle of the vertebral border of the scapula, and reflect the muscle on both sides of this incision — thus determining its area of origin. Reflect the humeral end without injuring the capsule of the joint.

16. Dissect the supraspinatus (Fig. 75, *a*, and p. 159). Cut the strong fascia free from the border of the scapula and its spine. Then transect the muscle and reflect it, being careful not to injure the capsule of the joint.

17. The spinodeltoideus (Fig. 75, *e*, and p. 156). Find its two borders, beginning with the caudal one. In freeing the very short cranial border do not injure the acromiodeltoideus (Fig. 75, *f*). Transect and reflect the spinodeltoid.

18. The acromiodeltoideus (p. 157, and Fig. 75, *f*). Transect and reflect.

19. The infraspinatus (p. 160, and Fig. 75, *c*). Locate the borders in the region of the great scapular notch. It is difficult to separate the glenoid border from the adjacent teres minor (Fig. 80, *c*). The separation should be begun at the humerus. Transect the muscle at the great scapular notch and reflect. Be careful not to injure the teres minor (Fig. 80, *c*).

20. The teres major (p. 163, and Fig. 75, *d*; Fig. 77, *c*) should be cut near its junction with the latissimus dorsi (Fig. 77, *e*).

21. The teres minor (Fig. 80, *c*, and p. 161) need not be cut.

22. The epitrochlearis (p. 164, and Fig. 65, *r*).

23. The triceps (p. 166). (*a*) The long head of the triceps (Fig. 77, *i*; Fig. 75, *g*). Find first its medial border and separate it from the medial head. Note the union of its lateral surface with the dorsal border of the lateral head by strong fascia, and then cut the fascia.

(*b*) The lateral head (Fig. 75, *h*).

(*c*) The medial head (Fig. 79, *g*, *h*, and *j*).

24. The anconeus (p. 170, and Fig. 80, *l*).

25. The brachioradialis (p. 173, and Fig. 75, *k*). Reflect it carefully to its origin and insertion.

26. The biceps (Fig. 77, *g*, and p. 165). The capsule of the

shoulder joint may be opened in order to expose its origin. Its insertion cannot be seen at this stage.

27. The brachialis (Figs. 75 and 79, *i*, and p. 166). Work under it near its union with the clavobrachial; cut it at that point and reflect it.

28. Extensor carpi radialis longus (p. 173, and Fig. 75, *l*). Note the oblique tendon on the radial side of the wrist near the insertion of the brachioradialis. A second tendon passes beneath its distal border. This tendon may be separated into a deep and superficial portion. The latter may be traced proximad to its muscle, the extensor carpi radialis longus.

29. Extensor carpi radialis brevis (p. 174). Its tendon is the deeper of the two tendons seen when isolating the tendon of the extensor longus.

30. Extensor communis digitorum (p. 174, and Fig. 75, *m*).

31. Extensor lateralis digitorum (p. 175, and Fig. 75, *n*).

32. Extensor carpi ulnaris (p. 176, and Fig. 75, *o*).

33. Extensor indicis (p. 176, and Fig. 85, *c*).

34. Pronator teres (p. 179, and Fig. 77, *q*).

35. Flexor carpi radialis (p. 179, and Fig. 77, *r*). The tendon of the flexor carpi radialis should not be traced to its insertion until the deep muscles of the palm of the hand have been dissected.

36. Abductor brevis pollicis (p. 184, and Fig. 77, *w*).

37. Flexor carpi ulnaris (p. 180, and Fig. 77, *t*).

38. Palmaris longus (p. 179, and Fig. 77, *s*). In dissecting this muscle be careful not to injure the part of the flexor sublimis (Fig. 77, *x*) that rises from its surface (see flexor sublimis, p. 181). Cut the palmaris proximad of the origin of the flexor sublimis and reflect it.

39. Flexor sublimis digitorum (p. 181, and Fig. 77, *x*). Trace one or two of the tendons through the sheaths on the ventral surfaces of the first phalanges. Cut and reflect the radial portion.

40. Flexor profundus digitorum (p. 181, and Fig. 77, *u*). After recognizing the parts, cut through the tendons of the first and fifth parts and reflect them to determine their origin. Then cut through the common tendon so as to reflect the other three parts together. Trace one or two of the tendons to the distal end of the digit.

41. The supinator (p. 177, and Fig. 85, *b*).

42. The extensor brevis pollicis (p. 178, and Fig. 85, *a*).

43. Pronator quadratus (p. 183, and Fig. 87, *a*).

The insertion of the brachialis and clavobrachial (Fig. 87, *c*) and of the biceps (Fig. 87, *b*) should now be examined.

There remain to be dissected the small muscles of the palm of the hand. If these have been injured on the side dissected, the hand of the other side may be used.

44. The lumbricales (p. 184, and Fig. 88, *f*).

45. The flexor brevis pollicis (p. 184, and Fig. 89, *a*).

46. The adductor pollicis (p. 185, and Fig. 89, *b*).

47. The abductor digiti quinti (p. 185, and Fig. 89, *i*).

48. The flexor brevis digiti quinti (p. 186, and Fig. 89, *h*). Cut and reflect it.

49. The opponens digiti quinti (p. 186, and Fig. 89, *g*). Cut and reflect it.

50. The interossei (p. 185, and Fig. 89).

IV. Muscles of the Neck and the Deep Muscles of the Head

If the superficial muscles of the head have been dissected according to the directions above given (*p. 12*), the skin of the head and neck, and the external ear, will have been removed, and the specimen is ready for further study. The parotid and submaxillary glands (Fig. 65, 1 and 2) should be removed if this has not been done; also the lymphatic glands (Fig. 65, 3).

If the superficial muscles of the head have not been dissected and are not to be, remove the skin from the side of the neck, head, and face to the median dorsal line, removing the thin superficial muscles with the skin. Remove also the parotid, submaxillary, and lymphatic glands (Fig. 65, 1, 2, and 3), and cut through the ear-muscles and the cartilaginous auditory meatus (under direction) and remove the external ear. Clean fat, connective tissue, etc., from the surface of the muscles of the thorax, neck, and head; then dissect as follows:

1. The sternomastoid (p. 139, and Fig. 65, *g*). Transect and reflect it.

2. The cleidomastoid (p. 120, and Fig. 65, *h*). This has already been transected; examine now its origin.

Remove the large lymphatic gland beneath the sternomastoid and close to the tympanic bulla, and clean the surface of the muscles in this region.

3. The levator scapulæ ventralis (p. 120, and Fig. 72, *c*, *c′*, *c″*). This has already been cut; study now its origin.

4. The sternohyoid (p. 140, and Fig. 65, *e*). In raising it begin at the cranial end and take care not to injure the subjacent sternothyroid (Fig. 65, *g′*). Transect.

5. The sternothyroid (p. 141, and Fig. 65, *g′*). Transect.

6. The stylohyoid (p. 112, and Fig. 65, *d*). Transect.

7. The digastric (p. 107, and Fig. 65, *b*). Transect, and reflect completely, to the origin and insertion.

8. The mylohyoid (p. 114, and Fig. 65, *c*). Transect and reflect.

9. The geniohyoid (p. 113, and Fig. 67, *g*).

10. The jugulohyoid (p. 113, and Fig. 67, *b*).

(The extrinsic muscles of the tongue (p. 228, and Figs. 67 and 96) may be dissected at this point, if desired. (*a*) The styloglossus; (*b*) the genioglossus; (*c*) the hyoglossus. They need not be cut.)

11. The masseter (p. 108, and Fig. 65, *a*). Cut the superficial and middle layers near their insertions by incisions parallel to the border of the jaw. Cut the deep layer near its origin. Look for the origin of fibers of the temporal muscle from the inner surface of the middle layer.

12. The temporal (p. 110, and Fig. 63, *n*). Clean its outer surface completely. Cut the temporal fascia transversely and reflect it toward the insertion of the muscle, with the superficial portion of the muscle. Cut through the zygomatic arch at its two ends and remove it, dissecting the fibers of the temporal free from their origin on its inner surface. Then examine the insertion of the temporal.

(The muscles of the pharynx (p. 232) may be dissected at this point; for directions, *see p. 31*.)

13. The ceratohyoid (p. 115). To uncover this, the middle constrictor of the pharynx (Fig. 67, *j*) must be cut and reflected.

Cut free from the mandible on both sides, the mylohyoid, geniohyoid, genioglossus, and the mucosa of the floor of the mouth, so that the tongue and the floor of the mouth may be drawn ventrad and turned out of the way, exposing the roof of the mouth (as in Fig. 66, p. 112). Cut through one side of the pharynx near the ventral surface and turn the tongue toward the uncut side.

The roof of the mouth is thus exposed. Dissect next —

14. The pterygoid muscles (Fig. 66). Remove the mucosa of the roof of the mouth, especially at the sides of the soft palate, and the

two pterygoid muscles (p. 111) are exposed. The lower jaw may be removed on one side to get at their origin.

(The muscles of the soft palate (p. 230, and Fig. 66, *d* and *e*), and the superior constrictor of the pharynx (p. 233, and Fig. 66, *f*) may be observed at this point, if desired.)

V. Muscles of the Wall of the Thorax and of the Abdomen

1. The scalenus (p. 141, and Fig. 73, *f*–*f'''*). To trace its cervical portion, cut the trachea and œsophagus just craniad of the first rib, cut the pharynx and hyoid free from the ventral side of the head and neck, and remove the pharynx, larynx, œsophagus, and trachea (these should be preserved for future study of the larynx).

2. The transversus costarum (p. 150, and Fig. 73, *j*).

3. The serratus posterior superior (p. 148, and Fig. 73, *l*). Transect this at about the middle of the muscle-bundles, and reflect it in both directions.

4. The serratus posterior inferior (p. 148, and Fig. 73, *n*). Transect and reflect as in the last.

5. The external oblique (p. 153, and Fig. 68, *p*). Transect it by an incision parallel to its tendon of origin and about an inch from it, and reflect in both directions.

6. The internal oblique (p. 154, and Fig. 73, *o*). Transect and reflect as above.

7. The transversus (p. 155, and Fig. 69, *l*). Requires no further dissection.

8. The rectus abdominis (p. 155, and Fig. 73, *k*). Open its sheath by a longitudinal incision near the linea alba.

9. The external intercostals (p. 150, and Fig. 73, *m*; Fig. 69, *i*). To see these, remove the origins of the levator scapulæ and serratus anterior; also the serratus posterior superior.

10. The internal intercostals (p. 151, and Fig. 69, *k*). To uncover these, remove the external intercostals from between two or three pairs of ribs.

11. The transversus thoracis (p. 151). To see this muscle, which lies on the inner surface of the thoracic wall, it is necessary to cut through the ribs on one side one or two inches from the sternum, and open the thorax. The muscle can then be observed directly.

(The levatores costarum will be dissected later.)

VI. Muscles on the Ventral Side of the Vertebral Column in the Neck Region (Fig. 72)

Clean the surface of these muscles, removing pharynx, larynx, œsophagus, and trachea, if this has not been done.

1. Longus capitis (p. 142, and Fig. 72, *a*).
2. Longus colli (p. 144, and Fig. 72, *g'*, *g''*).
3. Levator scapulæ ventralis (p. 120, and Fig. 72, *c'*, *c''*). Observe its origin.
4. Rectus capitis anterior minor (p. 143, and Fig. 72, *b*). To see this, cut through on one side the longus capitis and one head of the levator scapulæ ventralis, and remove the proximal portions, as in Fig. 72.
5. Obliquus capitis superior (p. 136, and Fig. 72, *e*).
6. Rectus capitis lateralis (p. 143, and Fig. 72, *d*).

VII. Muscles of the Back (p. 123)

Remove what remains of the dorsal portion of the latissimus dorsi, serratus posterior superior, and serratus posterior inferior. See that the skin is removed completely to the dorsal middle line, or even for a little distance beyond it. There is thus exposed the lumbodorsal fascia (p. 126), covering the muscles of the back.

Cut the superficial layer of the lumbodorsal fascia (that from which the latissimus dorsi and obliquus externus abdominis have origin) by an incision parallel to the dorsal median line, and remove it. The muscles of the back are thus exposed (Fig. 69). Observe; in the lumbar region the longissimus dorsi (*f*, *f'*, *f''*); in the thoracic region the longissimus dorsi, the spinalis dorsi (*g*), and the iliocostal (*h*); in the cervical region the splenius (Fig. 73, *b*).

1. The longissimus dorsi (p. 126, and Fig. 69, *f*, *f'*, *f''*). Notice in the lumbar region the strong deep layer of the lumbodorsal fascia, by which this muscle is covered, and from the under side of which many of the fibers of the muscle take origin. Cut this fascia by an incision parallel to the dorsal median line and about two centimeters from it, from the level of the crest of the ilium as far craniad as the fascia can be cut without cutting into the muscle fibers (usually to about the level of the last rib). Reflect the medial division of the fascia to the middle line. Reflect the lateral division of the fascia until it passes into the muscle and cannot be farther reflected.

Observe then in the lumbar region the medial (Fig. 70, *a*) and lateral (Fig. 70, *b*) divisions of the longissimus dorsi, and the portion (*b′*) of the lateral division taking origin from the lumbodorsal fascia (*c*). Dissect apart some of the muscle fibers of the longissimus and observe their origin and insertion.

Trace the longissimus dorsi into the thoracic and cervical regions (Fig. 69, *f′*, *f″*), noting the separation from it on the dorsal side of the spinalis dorsi (Fig. 69, *g*); on the ventral side of the iliocostal (Fig. 69, *h*).

2. The extensor caudæ lateralis (p. 137, and Fig. 70, *f*). Uncover this by cutting the lumbodorsal fascia over the sacral region.

3. The iliocostalis (p. 128, and Fig. 69, *h*). Uncover this completely; note its connection with the longissimus dorsi at the caudal end. Dissect apart some of its muscle-bundles, to see origin and insertion.

4. The splenius (p. 131, and Fig. 73, *b*). Transect this by an incision beginning at its lateral border about four centimeters from the cranial end of the muscle and extending obliquely craniodorsad to the craniomedial angle of the muscle. Be careful not to injure the longissimus capitis (Fig. 73, *g*).

5. The longissimus capitis (p. 131, and Fig. 73, *g*). Transect.

6. The spinalis dorsi (p. 129, and Fig. 69, *g*). Separate some of its muscle-fiber bundles and trace to origin and insertion.

7. The biventer cervicis (p. 132, and Fig. 69, *a*). Raise its lateral border, turning it toward the middle line, and transect it near its caudal end.

8. The complexus (p. 133, and Fig. 69, *b*). Raise its medial border, and transect it near its cranial end.

9. The longus atlantis (p. 134, and Fig. 71, *f*).

10. The multifidus spinæ (p. 130, and Fig. 70, *d*). Remove a part of the longissimus dorsi in the lumbar region, and trace the course of the fibers of the multifidus spinæ. (If desired, the entire longissimus may be removed and the multifidus spinæ completely uncovered.)

11. The extensor caudæ medialis (p. 136, and Fig. 70, *e*).

12. The semispinalis cervicis (p. 133, and Fig. 71, *c*). Dissect apart some of its fiber-bundles to see origin and insertion.

13. The interspinales and intertransversarii (p. 131) may be seen in the region from which the longissimus dorsi was removed, by removing the bundles of the multifidus spinæ.

14. The rectus capitis posterior major (p. 134, and Fig. 71, *a*). Transect.

15. The obliquus superior (p. 136, and Fig. 71, *e*).

16. The obliquus capitis inferior (p. 136, and Fig. 71, *b*).

17. The rectus capitis posterior medius (p. 135). Transect.

18. The rectus capitis posterior minor (p. 135).

19. The levatores costarum (p. 150). Remove, in a part of the thoracic region, a portion of the iliocostal and longissimus dorsi, so as to expose the dorsal ends of the ribs. The levatores costarum will be seen as but slightly separated bundles continuous with the external intercostals.

VIII. Muscles of the Hind Limb (p. 186)

Remove the skin and superficial fascia from the lateral surface of the thigh. Examine the *fascia lata* (p. 186, and Fig. 68, *z*). Dissect:

1. The biceps femoris (p. 194, and Fig. 68, *t*). Work under its cranial and caudal borders. Find the tenuissimus (Fig. 90, *g*) passing obliquely beneath it and reaching its caudal border in its distal half. Transect the biceps without injuring the tenuissimus, and reflect its halves.

2. The tenuissimus (p. 195, and Fig. 90, *g*). Transect.

3. The caudofemoralis (p. 195, and Fig. 68, *s*). Transect.

4. The gluteus maximus (p. 187). Transect.

5. The sartorius (p. 197, and Fig. 68, *q*; Fig. 91, *a*). Transect.

6. The tensor fasciæ latæ (p. 187, and Fig. 68, *r*). Cut the fascia lata along the distal end of the muscle fibers and reflect the muscle.

7. The gluteus medius (p. 188, and Fig. 90, *b*). Work under it carefully, separating it from underlying muscles; cut it close to its tendon of insertion, and reflect it.

8. The pyriformis (p. 188, and Fig. 163, 7, p. 401). Cut and reflect it.

9. The gemellus superior (p. 189, and Fig. 163, 6). This and the next muscle will sometimes be found to be completely united. Transect.

10. The gluteus minimus (p. 189, and Fig. 163, 5). Transect.

11. The obturator internus (p. 192, and Fig. 90, *e*). Cut it at the dorsal border of the ischium in order to reflect it. The whole origin cannot be seen at this stage.

12. The gemellus inferior (p. 190).

13. The gracilis (p. 198, and Fig. 91, *b*). Transect.

14. The semitendinosus (p. 196, and Figs. 90 and 91, *j*; Fig. 92, *i*). Transect.

15. The semimembranosus (p. 196, and Figs. 90 and 91, *i*; Fig. 92, *h*, *h'*). Transect.

16. The adductor femoris (p. 198, and Figs. 90 and 91, *h*; Fig. 92, *g*). Transect.

17. The quadratus femoris (p. 191, and Fig. 90, *f*). Transect.

18. The obturator externus (p. 191).

19. The adductor longus (p. 199, and Fig. 92, *f*). This and the following will sometimes be found to be almost completely united. Transect.

20. The pectineus (p. 200, and Fig. 92, *e*). Transect.

21. The iliopsoas (p. 193, and Fig. 91, *c*; Fig. 92, *d*). Only its distal part, near the insertion, can be seen at present.

22. The capsularis (p. 190). Transect.

23. The quadriceps femoris (p. 201). Isolate the rectus femoris (Fig. 92, *b*) as far as its junction with the vastus lateralis; cut it at this point and reflect its proximal portion. Turn aside the distal end and find beneath it the transverse aponeurosis between the vastus medialis and the vastus lateralis, and covering the vastus intermedius. The vastus lateralis (Fig. 90, *d*) may be cut near the middle and dissected up from its origin in both directions; the vastus intermedius is thus exposed. The vastus medialis (Fig. 92, *c*) and the vastus intermedius need not be cut.

24. The gastrocnemius (p. 203, and Fig. 90, *m*; Fig. 91, *k*). It may be raised cautiously near its middle and divided. Care should be taken not to divide the underlying plantaris (Fig. 90, *l*). After noting the connection of the outer head with the plantaris, the latter may be divided and reflected, together with the outer head.

25. The plantaris (p. 205, and Figs. 90 and 91, *l*).

26. The flexor brevis digitorum (p. 212). In tracing its tendon note the three branches of the common plantar ligament which emerges from between the second and third tendons. The outer branch is inserted into the fascia covering the base of the fifth digit, while the other two spread out into the bilobed pad of the sole.

27. The soleus (p. 205, and Fig. 90, *o*). Cut and reflect.

28. The popliteus (p. 206, and Fig. 92, *k*). Cut very near the origin and reflect.

The three following deep muscles on the ventral surface of the shank are covered by the deep crural fascia (p. 206) which separates them from the overlying muscles. It should be removed.

29. The flexor longus hallucis (p. 207, and Fig. 91, *m*). Divide the muscle at its junction with the tendon. Open the canals on the astragalus and calcaneus and reflect the tendon, cutting the tendon of the flexor longus digitorum near its insertion and dividing at the middle the quadratus plantæ (p. 213) which may be found inserted into its ventral surface.

30. Flexor longus digitorum (p. 208, and Fig. 91, *n*). This may be divided very near its origin.

31. Tibialis posterior (p. 208, and Fig. 91, *o*). This may be divided near its tendon.

32. Peroneus longus (p. 209, and Fig. 90, *q*). The overlying tendons may be cut in tracing its insertion.

33. Peroneus brevis (p. 210, and Fig. 90, *s*).

34. Peroneus tertius (p. 210, and Fig. 90, *r*).

35. Extensor longus digitorum (p. 210, and Fig. 90, *p*).

36. Tibialis anterior (p. 211, and Fig. 90, *n*).

37. The extensor brevis digitorum (p. 212, and Fig. 90, *u*).

38. The quadratus plantæ (p. 213). It was cut in dissecting the flexor longus hallucis.

39. The lumbricales (p. 213).

40. The interossei (with the muscles of the fifth digit) (p. 214).

41. The tarsal muscles (p. 215). The overlying ligaments must be removed in order to expose the scaphocuneiform.

IX. The Diaphragm and the Muscles on the Ventral Side of the Vertebral Column in the Lumbar and Pelvic Regions

Remove the ventral and lateral walls of the thorax completely, as far back as the diaphragm — leaving only a ring attached to the margin of the diaphragm. Remove the abdominal walls in the same way, as far back as the pubis, leaving the diaphragm in position. Remove the thoracic viscera (the heart and lungs may be preserved for future study). Remove also the abdominal viscera as far back as the beginning of the pelvis, cutting the large intestine where it passes into the pelvis. The dorsal wall of the abdominal cavity should be cleared of fat, blood vessels, etc., without injury to the crura of the diaphragm.

1. The diaphragm (p. 151, and Fig. 74). Study by transmitted light, to see the tendons, etc.

2. The psoas minor (p. 139, and Fig. 162, 9, p. 398). Find its tendon and separate it from the iliopsoas (Fig. 162, 8) as far craniad as this can be done without tearing the fibers.

3. The iliopsoas (p. 193, and Fig. 162, 8). Find both portions; isolate them as far as it can be done.

4. The quadratus lumborum (p. 139). Free the lateral edge of the iliopsoas from the abdominal wall and turn the whole muscle mediad as far as possible. The bundles of the quadratus lumborum will be found beneath it, against the transverse processes of the lumbar vertebræ.

With a heavy cartilage knife separate the two innominate bones along the pelvic symphysis. This is easily done if the knife is inserted exactly into the line of junction of the two bones. Divaricate the edges some distance, so as to make a ventral opening into the pelvic cavity. If necessary, part of the innominate bone of one side may be removed to make the opening larger.

Find the thin sheet of fibers forming the levator ani muscle (Fig. 162, 11) at the side of the rectum, attached to the edge of the symphysis. Carefully free the rectum and urogenital organs from this and remove them as far as the anus, leaving the levator ani intact.

5. The iliocaudalis (p. 137, and Fig. 162, 11′).

6. The levator ani (p. 269, and Fig. 162, 11).

Remove with great care the levator ani and iliocaudalis of one side, by cutting first the attachment to the symphysis and the ilium, turning the muscle mediad, then cutting the attachment to the tail. There are thus exposed on the lateral wall of the pelvis the medial surface of the obturator internus, craniad of it the pyriformis, caudad of it the quadratus femoris. Dorsad of these is the abductor caudæ internus.

7. The abductor caudæ internus (p. 137).

On the ventral surface of the tail are exposed the following:

8. The flexor caudæ longus (p. 138, and Fig. 162, 12).

9. The flexor caudæ brevis (p. 138, and Fig. 162, 13).

X. Muscles of the Tail (p. 136)

By removing the skin of the tail, all the muscles of the tail are now easily seen.

1, 2, 3, 4, 5 — see Section IX, 5, 6, 7, 8, 9, above.

6. The abductor caudæ externus (p. 137, and Fig. 113, b; Fig. 70, *g*).
7. The extensor caudæ lateralis (p. 137, and Fig. 70, *f*).
8. The extensor caudæ medialis (p. 136, and Fig. 70, *e*).

THE VISCERA

Kill the specimen with chloroform and inject with the five per cent formalin, or the mixture of formalin and glycerin, as for the muscles. (It is an advantage if the preliminary examination of the viscera can be done in a perfectly fresh, uninjected specimen; such a specimen can be kept but a day or two, however. After one day's examination the skin may be removed and the specimen placed in two per cent formalin; it will usually be fairly well preserved by this, though the formalin is too strong to make the later dissection pleasant. The specimen cannot be preserved in this manner unless the skin is removed, and a sufficient quantity of formalin used.)

Preliminary Examination of the Viscera

(In this preliminary examination the descriptions in the text need not be read, except when this is specially directed.)

Wet the hair along a line from the symphysis of the jaw to the pubis. Part it and make a longitudinal incision through the skin along the line. Make a transverse incision of the skin five centimeters caudad of the xiphoid process and reflect the flaps. Incise the body wall from the last rib to the pelvis along the same line as above and also transversely. Reflect the flaps without injuring the ligaments of the bladder. Make an incision through the pectoral muscles between the first rib and the ventral attachment of the diaphragm and about one centimeter from the median line. Make a second incision of the muscles from the cranial end of the first incision along the angles of the ribs to near the dorsolateral attachment of the diaphragm. Cut the ribs and thoracic wall along these incisions with strong scissors; connect the two incisions at their caudal ends, and remove the lateral thoracic wall thus circumscribed. Note the thoracic and abdominal cavities, separated by the diaphragm.

Note the following viscera in their fresh condition:

A. In the abdominal cavity (without injuring anything)

1. The liver, dark red and lobed, in the cranial part of the cavity, lying against the diaphragm.

2. The gall bladder partly imbedded in the right median lobe.

3. Displacing the liver craniad, the stomach is seen dorsad of its left lobe. It may extend dorsad of the right lobe, its size depending on the degree of distension.

4. The duodenum, or first part of the small intestine, leaves the stomach at its right side craniad and makes a U-bend, the head of which is directed caudad; it then turns toward the middle line dorsad of the remaining part of the small intestine.

5. The great omentum is a thin fold of peritoneum with many bands of fat. It passes, like a curtain, from the great curvature of the stomach ventrad of the coils of the small intestine (ileum). It is tucked beneath the mass of coils at the sides and caudally, and folds of it extend between the individual coils. Turn it craniad and note —

6. The numerous coils of the third part of the small intestine or ileum. Turn these to one side and note —

7. The connection of the ileum with the duodenum across the middle line. An indefinite part of the intestine between the ileum and duodenum is called the jejunum, because in man it is found empty after death.

8. The passage of the ileum into the side of the large intestine which begins on the right side just caudad of the loops of the duodenum. The first part of the large intestine is the colon. It may be traced first toward the head (ascending colon), then sinistrocaudad (transverse colon) and then caudad (descending colon). The descending colon returns to the middle line and the large intestine then continues to the anus as the rectum.

The blind pouch of the colon which lies caudad of the opening of the ileum is the cæcum.

9. Turn the duodenum toward the left and note the pancreas, a light red, elongated organ which stretches along the greater curvature of the stomach and thence between the two lines of the duodenal U to its bottom.

10. The spleen, parallel to the gastric portion of the pancreas. It is deep red (darker than the pancreas and not so brown as the liver) and is held against the great curvature of the stomach by a part of the great omentum.

11. The kidneys, close against the dorsal body wall and in contact with the caudal part of the liver.

12. The bladder, in the median line at the caudal end of the cavity, held in place by the suspensory ligament, which passes to the midventral line, and by the lateral ligaments.

13. The mesenteric glands, large grayish-red glands one to four centimeters long, more numerous in the mesocolon.

14. In the female, lying against the ventral surface of the rectum, the uterus. It divides into two horns which diverge. Near the end of each horn the ovary.

15. The peritoneum. Study and understand the description of it (p. 218; Fig. 92*b*). Dissect some of it free from the body wall. (Trace the folds by aid of the diagram.)

B. In the thoracic cavity:

1. The lungs. Each is divided into lobes, three on the left, four on the right. The caudal right lobe pushes the mediastinum toward the left and thus lies in a pocket dorsocaudad of the heart and dorsad of the vena cava inferior.

2. The pleuræ. Each pleura is a membrane like the peritoneum. It covers the diaphragm and the thoracic walls and is reflected onto the lungs. Hence it is divided into costal and pulmonary portions. Read the description (p. 217; Fig. 92*a*, *D*, *F*) and trace their connection. Each pleura forms a closed sac.

3. The mediastinal septum (Fig. 92*a*, *G*) or median vertical portion formed by the apposition of the medial walls of the two pleural sacs. It divides the thorax into halves.

4. In the mediastinum or space between the halves of the mediastinal septum are seen —

a. Ventrally (i.e., in the anterior mediastinum), blood vessels and fat, and craniad the pink thymus gland. Read the description of the thymus (p. 254, and Fig. 107).

b. Dorsally (i.e., in the posterior mediastinum) the trachea (best seen craniad), the œsophagus (best seen caudad), and the aorta (Fig. 92*a*, *H'*).

c. In the middle (reckoning in a dorsoventral line) (i.e., in the middle mediastinum) the heart, with the inferior vena cava approaching it from the rear (Fig. 92*a*, *H*). Prick into the mediastinum and inflate it. Remove the thoracic wall opposite the one already removed, so as to stretch the mediastinum and show it more clearly. Expose the trachea beneath the caudal end of the sternomastoidei. Note the thyroid gland (Fig. 96, 6, p. 229). Insert a blowpipe, without injury to the thyroid, and inflate the lungs. Cut the sternum at its caudal end and turn it craniad, cutting the mediastinal septum and noting its double character.

Dissect the mediastinal septum from the thymus so as to expose this organ.

d. The pericardium, a relatively thick-walled sac, within which the heart lies (Fig. 92*a*, *B*, *C*). The pericardium is covered by the mediastinal septum on each side, but not dorsally and ventrally. Dissect the mediastinal septum from the pericardium. Prick and inflate the pericardium. Open it and expose the heart.

DISSECTION OF THE ALIMENTARY CANAL

Study and verify the descriptions of the organs as they are dissected.

I. Salivary glands (p. 223).

1. Keep the mouth open by a cork between the teeth. Find the papillæ upon which open the sublingual and submaxillary ducts (pp. 223 and 224); remove the mucosa and enlarge the opening and insert a black bristle into either duct. Trace the duct by the bristle as far as possible on the floor of the mouth.

2. Find the white ridge formed on the cheek by the parotid duct (p. 223). It is opposite the molar tooth, and at its cranial end the opening of the duct is seen. Enlarge the opening and insert a black bristle as far as possible.

3. Remove the skin and the skin-muscles from the side of the face, beginning at the caudal end and working craniad. At the cranial border of the parotid on the ventral side look carefully for the parotid duct with the bristle in it. The duct is then easily traced by the removal of the skin and muscles. Study the parotid gland (Fig. 131, 10, p. 322).

4. Remove the facial veins (Fig. 131, *b* and *c*) and lymphatic glands (Fig. 131, 12) covering the submaxillary gland (Fig. 131, 11) and clean its outer surface. Raise it and find the submaxillary duct

leaving its inner surface. Reflect the digastric and mylohyoid muscles and trace the duct to the oral mucosa. The remainder of its course is shown by the bristle on the inside of the mouth.

5. The sublingual gland is uncovered in dissecting the submaxillary. Its duct is seen by the side of the submaxillary. It may be pricked near the gland and a bristle passed to its opening.

6. The infraorbital gland. Expose it by removal of the zygomatic arch and masseter muscle. Find its duct by dissecting apart the lobules at its ventral end. Prick the duct and insert a bristle to find its inner opening.

7. The molar gland. Find it by raising the orbicularis oris of the lower lip. By raising its ventral border and dissecting between it and the mucosa the ducts may be found and perhaps pricked and bristles inserted.

II. The mouth cavity. Study the general description (p. 221); the lips and the cheek. Then remove the masseter muscle and the caudal part of the zygoma. Cut through the mandible between the first premolar and the canine tooth. Then disarticulate the mandible, cut the cheek and also the mylohyoid muscle and oral mucosa parallel to the medial border of the mandible, and remove the mandible with the parts thus left attached to it. The organs in the mouth cavity are thus left exposed and should be studied. To demonstrate the incisive ducts (p. 222) pass a bristle into them.

The teeth (p. 224). These should be studied on a skull in which the roots of the teeth have been laid bare by means of the bone forceps, as in Figs. 93 and 94.

The tongue (p. 220, and Fig. 95). Study its dorsal surface, the papillæ, etc. Then dissect its *muscles* (p. 228) from the ventral side. The stylohyoid, digastric, and mylohyoid muscles must be removed. Then dissect (*a*) the styloglossus (Fig. 96, *e*), (*b*) the genioglossus (Fig. 96, *f*), (*c*) the hyoglossus (Fig. 96, *h*). Make a transverse section of the tongue to see the intrinsic muscle fibers.

III. The thyroid gland (p. 254, and Fig. 96, 6). Clean the sternomastoid muscles. Cut their interdigitating portions along the median line and reflect them. Find the lateral lobe of the thyroid gland beneath the lateral borders of the sternohyoid muscles. Dissect it, being careful not to destroy the delicate isthmus.

IV. The pharynx (p. 231). Remove the large lymphatic gland between the atlantal transverse process and the larynx. Clean the outer surface of the pharynx. Dissect the muscles of the pharynx (p. 232) as follows:

(*a*) The inferior constrictor (Fig. 96, *k*).
(*b*) The middle constrictor (Fig. 96, *j*).
(*c*) The glossopharyngeus (Fig. 96, *i*).
(*d*) The stylopharyngeus (Fig. 96, *l*).

The superior constrictor cannot well be seen at this point; it will be examined later.

Disarticulate the cranial cornu of the hyoid from the bulla tympani and make an incision the length of the lateral wall of the pharynx so as to expose its cavity; study. Examine its opening into the mouth cavity and study the general description (p. 231). Find and study the soft palate (p. 230). Dissect the tensor and levator palatini muscles (p. 230, and Fig. 66, *d* and *e*, p. 112), using, if necessary, the specimen on which the other muscles were dissected. Then slit the soft palate lengthwise at one side of the median line to expose the nasopharynx (p. 231). Bring the choanæ into view by use of a bit of mirror glass. Pass a bristle into the nares and out at the choanæ. Pass a bristle through the Eustachian tube into the middle ear.

V. Œsophagus (p. 234). After completing the study of the pharynx, leave the larynx and lungs in position and by displacing them toward the right follow the œsophagus to its termination. Open it to see the folds of the mucosa.

VI. Cut through the duodenum at its distal end and through the duodenal mesentery so as to separate the stomach and duodenum, with the liver, pancreas, and spleen, from the remainder of the alimentary canal. Float the parts in a dish of water.

VII. Study the stomach (p. 234, and Fig. 97). Cut out the ventral wall of the stomach and wash it out, so as to study its cavity, and then continue the cut so as to expose the pyloric valve (p. 235).

VIII. Study the duodenum (p. 236). Cut away the ventral walls of the duodenum far enough to expose the ampulla of Vater.

IX. Study the liver (p. 239, and Figs. 100 and 101). Expose the hepatic duct of the left lateral lobe near its entrance into the lobe, and follow it so as to expose it fully. If necessary, prick it and inflate with blowpipe in order to follow it. Then expose the cystic duct and other hepatic ducts and follow them to or from the common bile duct. Trace the latter to the duodenum. If the air does not enter any duct readily, it may be made to do so by manipulating the duct so as to break up the precipitated bile which obstructs it.

X. Study the pancreas (p. 241, and Fig. 102). Expose the pancreatic duct near its entrance into the ampulla of Vater, by removing the peritoneum from the pancreas just caudad of the end of the common bile duct, and by dissecting apart the pancreatic lobules until the duct appears. (If possible, expose also the accessory duct in the same way on the ventral side of the pancreas, two centimeters caudoventrad of the ampulla of Vater. Prick and inflate. Trace its connection with the main duct. To demonstrate its opening pass a bristle through an opening in it into the duodenum.) (The pancreatic duct may be injected, if desired.)

XI. The ventral wall of the duodenum should now be removed. Cut out a small piece, clean its mucosa with a fine brush, and examine the villi with a lens. Demonstrate the coats of the duodenal wall by stripping them off with forceps.

XII. The ampulla of Vater (p. 236). Pass bristles through openings in the common bile duct and pancreatic duct into the duodenum through the ampulla. Slice away the duodenal wall parallel to the bristles until the bristles are exposed.

XIII. The spleen (p. 242, and Fig. 102).

XIV. Cut the mesentery from the small intestine and colon and slit them both lengthwise, but do not destroy the ileocolic valve. Wash and brush the mucous membrane clean and study the villi, solitary glands, and Peyer's patches. Study the ileocolic valve (Fig. 99) and open it to study its inner surface.

DISSECTION OF THE ORGANS OF RESPIRATION

I. The nasal cavity (p. 243). Review the description of the nasal cavity given under the Bones (p. 59). Study the cartilaginous framework that supports the external nose (p. 243); make a cross section of the framework near the end of the nose and verify the description (p. 244, and Fig. 103). Without injuring the larynx or tongue saw through the head in a vertical plane and a little to one side of the median line. (If desired, the brain may first be removed from the specimen and preserved for future study. For directions, see *p. 9*. The removal of the brain does not injure the head for the study of the nasal cavity; the skull may be sawn lengthwise in the same way as before.) Wash out the cut surfaces before examining. Find the ventral conchæ (p. 40), the labyrinths of the ethmoid (p. 43), the inferior meatus of the nose (p. 243), and by bristles the lachrymal duct or canal (p. 245). The lachrymal duct is conveniently found by passing bristles into the openings of the lachrymal canals. One of these is to be found on the border of each eyelid, two or three millimeters from the inner angle of the eye (see p. 417).

Cut the œsophagus and trachea at the point where the blowpipe was inserted into the trachea. Separate the tongue, hyoid, larynx, œsophagus, and first part of the trachea from the adjacent parts and remove them.

II. The larynx (p. 246). (1) Read the description, studying the cartilages (p. 247) on a preparation (Fig. 104). Then very carefully remove the pharynx and its constrictor muscles, the sternothyroid and remains of sternohyoid muscles, and (2) dissect the muscles of the larynx (p. 249, and Fig. 105). Dissect all those of one side first. The mucosa lining the vestibule and middle portions of the laryngeal cavity must be removed. After studying the muscles, remove the muscles and entire mucosa by scraping carefully with a dull but smooth scalpel, and study the cartilages (Fig. 104).

III. The trachea and lungs (p. 251, and Fig. 106). The distal end of the trachea and lungs may now be removed from the body with the heart. The lungs may be inflated with the bellows. The bronchi should then be exposed, cleaned, and followed as far as possible into the lungs. The heart should be preserved for future study.

DISSECTION OF THE UROGENITAL ORGANS

A. *Excretory Organs.*

1. Expose the kidney (p. 255, and Fig. 108) by removal of the peritoneum and the surrounding fat, taking care not to open the capsule of the kidney. In removing the fat from the cranial end do not injure the suprarenal body (p. 257), which should be studied.

2. Open the capsule of the kidney and slice away its ventral wall to expose the sinus. After dissecting the contents of the sinus open the pelvis and study the papilla. Pass a bristle from the pelvis into the ureter.

3. Make a median section of the kidney parallel to its ventral surface and study structure (Fig. 109).

4. Trace the ureter to the bladder, being careful not to injure the vas deferens. Study the bladder and its ligaments, structure of its wall, etc. Pass a bristle through the ureter into it and then open it to see the openings of the ureter. Trace the neck of the bladder to the pubis.

B. *Male Genital Organs.*

1. Study the external genital organs (p. 257).

2. Carefully remove the integument about the anus and expose the external sphincter ani muscle (p. 268, and Fig. 113, *i*). Trace it to its origin. Remove the integument of the scrotum and dissect the intercolumnar fascia, the levator scroti muscle (p. 271, and Fig. 113, *j*), the tunica vaginalis communis, and propria (p. 258).

3. The testis; the epididymis with great care, especially in uncovering the vasa efferentia; the vas deferens and spermatic cord (p. 259, and Figs. 110 and 111).

4. Follow the cord to the external inguinal ring (p. 259) and expose the ring. Dissect off from the inguinal canal in order: (*a*) the external oblique muscle; (*b*) the internal oblique muscle; (*c*) the transversus. In this way the cord is followed with its tunica communis and tunica propria to the internal inguinal ring.

5. Trace the vas deferens (p. 260, and Fig. 111) within the abdominal cavity as far as it can be seen dorsad of the neck of the bladder.

6. The penis (p. 262, and Figs. 111 and 113). Cut the skin along the dorsum of the penis and reflect. Dissect the ligamentum suspensorium penis. Then introduce a bristle into the urethra and remove the integument from the whole penis and identify the corpora cavernosa and corpus spongiosum and the urethra.

7. Remove the fat at the side of the rectum and find the levator ani muscle (p. 269, and Fig. 162, 11). Transect and reflect it. The internal sphincter ani (p. 269, and Fig. 113, *h*). Find the external opening of the anal gland (p. 239); slit and examine it.

8. Dissect the ischiocavernosus (p. 269) and bulbocavernosus (p. 271) muscles (Fig. 113, *l*), and find the bulbus of the corpus cavernosum beneath the former. Cut it free from the ischial ramus.

9. Clean the muscles from the pelvis on the side from which the crus penis is removed, and remove with bone forceps the body of

the pubis and the ramus of the ischium. Then trace the neck of the bladder to its junction with the vasa deferentia, and the urethra from that point to the external opening (Fig. 111). Study the compressor urethræ muscle (p. 271, and Fig. 113, *n*). Find Cowper's glands (p. 261) and the prostate gland (Fig. 113, 3, 4). Dissect the other muscles of the urogenital organs (pp. 268 to 273, and Fig. 113).

10. Slit the urethra on one side throughout its length and find the veru montanum (p. 261); the openings of the vasa deferentia (p. 261), by bristles passed into the urethra from them; the openings of the prostate gland and the openings of Cowper's glands.

11. Study the structure of the penis (p. 262) by making a cross section, and that of the glans by making a longitudinal section. Note, if possible, the os penis.

C. *Female Urogenital Organs* (p. 263, and Fig. 112). The kidney and its ducts and the bladder are like those of the male (p. 255), except the neck of the bladder, which will be seen in dissecting the uterus and vagina.

a. Without cutting anything examine —

1. The ovaries (p. 264); the ligaments of the ovary (p. 264, and Fig. 112).

2. The uterine tube. Its ostium (p. 264).

3. The body of the uterus (p. 266) as far as exposed.

4. The cornu of the uterus.

5. The broad and round ligaments of the uterus (p. 266).

6. Slit open one Fallopian tube, cornu, and body of the uterus as far as the junction of the divisions of the body of the uterus.

b. Remove the ventral wall of the pelvis on one side only and find the vagina and urogenital sinus (p. 267). The levator ani muscle (p. 269, and Fig. 162, 11) must be cut and reflected.

1. Note the constrictor vestibuli, caudovaginalis, and urethralis muscles (p. 272, and Fig. 114).

2. Introduce a probe from the uterus into the vagina and feel with the finger for the hard cervix uteri (p. 266). Then open the vagina on the side, but do not cut the os uteri (p. 266).

3. Examine the cervix uteri and os uteri (p. 266).

4. Introduce a probe through the neck of the bladder and note its emergence into the urogenital sinus.

5. Find the end of the clitoris (p. 267), and its prepuce, and then dissect the integument carefully from about the external opening of

the urogenital sinus and note an external sphincter of the sinus (M. levator vulvæ) (p. 272, and Fig. 114), equivalent to the levator scroti in the male and continuous with the external sphincter ani.

6. Find (if possible) the corpora cavernosa of the clitoris (p. 267) and the ischiocavernosi muscles (p. 269).

DISSECTION OF THE CIRCULATORY SYSTEM

I. The Heart (p. 274, and Figs. 115–117)

Use the heart from the specimen dissected for the muscles, or from the specimen on which the viscera were studied.

1. Study the outside (p. 275, and Figs. 115 and 116), and learn to recognize all parts. Find the pulmonary veins (p. 275, and Fig. 116, *g*, *h*, *i*) and cut them, thus separating the heart from the lungs.

2. The pericardium (p. 279; Fig. 92*a*, *A*, *B*). In a specimen the thoracic contents of which have not been injured, dissect the mediastinal septum from the pericardial sac and remove fat about the great blood vessels so as to expose them all fully. Study their relations. Prick and inflate the pericardium. Slit it lengthwise over the ventricles and reflect it so as to expose its contents. Study the attachment of serous and fibrous layers to the heart and their relation to one another.

3. In dissecting the heart follow the course of the blood, studying each cavity with the aid of the descriptions (pp. 275–279) as you proceed. Dissect as follows:

a. Remove the dorsal wall of the right auricle (p. 275) and of its appendage except that part of it to which the venæ cavæ are attached.

b. Introduce the probe from the right auricle into the right ventricle, and feel with the probe the line along which the ventricular wall joins the septum. Cut along this line so as to turn back the ventricular wall as a flap, which remains attached at the base of the ventricle.

c. Introduce a probe through the conus arteriosus into the pulmonary artery and cut along the probe.

d. Remove the dorsal wall of the left auricle and its appendage, *but do not* remove that part to which the pulmonary veins are attached.

e. Make a longitudinal incision beginning at the apex and divaricate the lips of the cut as you pass toward the base, thus avoiding injury to the lateral flap of the bicuspid valve. Without injury to the flap or the columnæ carneæ, remove the heart wall at the sides of this incision near the base of the ventricle, as much as necessary to expose the cavity.

f. Pass a probe into the aorta. Introduce scissors behind the septal flap of the bicuspid valve and slit the aorta without injury to the bicuspid valve.

II. Dissection of the Blood Vessels

(For the technique of dissection see p. 7)

Preparation and Injection. — A new specimen must be prepared for the dissection of the blood vessels. The same specimen may be used, if necessary, for the dissection of the peripheral nervous system — one side being used for the blood vessels, the other for the nerves — but it is much better to use separate specimens for the two systems. Directions for injection are given on *page 5*.

Directions for Dissecting the Blood Vessels. — Make a median longitudinal incision through the skin from the symphysis of the jaw to the caudal end of the xiphoid process. About three or four centimeters caudad of the cranial end of the sternum make an incision at nearly right angles to this, passing from the first incision on the ventral side of the left arm about to the elbow. Reflect the flaps of skin, so as to uncover the left side of the thorax and the under surface of the arm, exposing the pectoral muscles. Isolate and transect the pectoral muscles one at a time, cutting each near its thoracic attachment. (The muscles (p. 145) should be reviewed at the same time.) In this way the nerves and blood vessels of the axilla are exposed (Fig. 122, p. 295).

Find the axillary artery and vein (Fig. 122, *f* and *g*) emerging from the thorax just craniad of the first rib, along with the nerves of the brachial plexus. Remove connective tissue, etc., so that the vessels and nerves are well isolated as they pass out of the thorax. Take great pains not to puncture the vessels, particularly the veins.

Then remove the left side of the thorax by cutting through the first rib near its sternal end and then near its dorsal end, without injury to the vessels and nerves; cut the other ribs in the same way, and take out the thoracic wall.

Now find with tracer and forceps the great blood vessels leaving the cranial end of the heart (see Fig. 118). Take the greatest pains not to injure them. Find the aorta and aortic arch (p. 281); the left subclavian artery (p. 283) (continuous with the axillary); the innominate artery (p. 282), and the beginnings of its three branches (see Fig. 115). Find also the superior vena cava, the innominate veins, and the subclavian vein, continuous with the axillary vein.

I. Study the smaller branches of the thoracic aorta (p. 283, and Fig. 118) — the intercostals, the bronchial and œsophageal arteries, and the first pair of lumbar arteries. (The coronary arteries will be examined later.)

II. Dissect the subclavian and its branches (p. 290) as follows:

1. The internal mammary (p. 292). Follow it onto the ventral wall of the abdomen. Follow the vein at the same time (p. 318).

2. The vertebral artery (p. 291). Find its beginning, but do not trace it at present.

3. The costocervical axis (p. 292). Find its beginning, and trace the superior intercostal branch some distance. The other branches are not to be followed at present.

4. The thyrocervical axis (p. 293). Find its beginning, but do not trace it at present.

5. The axillary artery (continuation of the subclavian) (p. 294). Follow its branches, tracing at the same time the axillary vein (p. 318). (Consult Fig. 122.) In tracing the blood vessels separate the muscles, but do not cut them except where absolutely necessary. (The muscles should be reviewed as the vessels are traced.)

The following notes may be of assistance in following the different branches:

(*a*) The anterior thoracic was probably cut in dissecting the pectoral muscles; it may be found, but its distal end is probably cut off.

(*b*) The long thoracic is easily followed.

(*c*) The subscapular. Follow the main artery before dissecting its branches. Where the subscapular disappears between the long head of the triceps, the latissimus dorsi, and the scapula, it may be traced and found again as follows: Remove the skin from the outer side of the shoulder — taking great pains to remove *only* the skin and not to injure the vena cephalica (p. 319), a large vein that lies just beneath the skin on the lateral surface of the shoulder, coming from the elbow. The branches of the subscapular will be found appearing on the lateral surface of the arm in the angle between the spino-trapezius, the long head of the triceps, and the infraspinatus. The distal branches may then be followed.

(*d*) The posterior circumflex (p. 296) may be traced distad in a similar manner, by seeking it beneath the caudal border of the spinotrapezius. (Do not injure the vena cephalica.)

(*e*) The other branches of the brachial artery and vein present no difficulty till we come to the collateralis radialis superior (Fig. 122, *x*). This must be traced with great care, along with the vena mediana cubiti (p. 319, and Fig. 122, *y*). Remove the skin from the extensor side of the forearm, taking great pains not to remove anything more than the skin. The artery and vein lie beneath the skin and should be traced to the hand (see Fig. 130).

Along with the collateral radial artery trace the vena cephalica (p. 319, and Fig. 130, *a* and *c*). Follow it across the shoulder, noting the branch to the posterior circumflex vein.

The remainder of the blood vessels of the arm present no special difficulty (see Figs. 123 and 124).

Make a diagram of the subclavian artery, as far as dissected.

III. Remove the skin from the sides of the neck, exposing the sternomastoid muscles and the external jugular veins crossing them (see Fig. 131). Clean the surface of the sternomastoid muscles, without injuring the vein; separate the two muscles caudad, and cut each close to the attachment to the sternum. Find the sternohyoid and sternothyroid muscles, and cut them close to their attachment to the first rib. Uncover the right side of the thorax in the same way as the left, cut the ribs without injury to the nerves and vessels of the right axilla, cut the internal mammary artery and vein (after tying the latter), and thus remove the sternum with nearly the entire thoracic wall.

The blood vessels of the thorax may now be more completely exposed. (If the nerves are to be dissected on the same specimen, find the phrenic, vagus, and sympathetic nerves (Fig. 157), and take the greatest pains not to injure them.)

1. The coronary arteries and the veins of the heart (pp. 281 and 316).

2. The superior vena cava (p. 316). Find its branches. Trace the azygos as far back as the diaphragm without dissecting it at all.

Find the division of the innominate (p. 318) into subclavian and external jugular.

Trace next —

3. The external jugular (p. 319). Remove the skin from the

side of the face and trace its branches (Fig. 131). The internal jugular, vena facialis profunda, the submentalis, and the deep terminal branches of the posterior facial cannot be followed at this time; veins shown on Fig. 131 should all be found, however.

4. Trace the thyrocervical axis and its branches (p. 293). Add them to your diagram of the subclavian.

5. Follow the common carotid artery (p. 283) and internal jugular vein (p. 320). Find the division of the common carotid into its terminal branches and then dissect its lateral branches and those of the internal jugular (see Fig. 119).

6. The external carotid (p. 285, and Fig. 119). Follow its branches with the exception of the internal maxillary.

7. The internal maxillary (p. 287). Find its inferior alveolar branch first and follow it by cutting away with bone forceps the ventral border of the lower jaw. To follow its other branches and those of the carotid plexus, remove the zygomatic arch, cut the temporal, masseter, and pterygoid muscles, and cut the mandible behind the incisor teeth and remove it. The branches which pass into the skull are not to be followed at present. The posterior facial vein (p. 323), the vena facialis profunda (p. 323), and the submental vein (p. 323) may be followed at the same time.

8. The internal carotid (p. 285). Follow it to the point where it enters the cranium.

9. Trace the other branches of the costocervical axis (p. 292). To do this, cut the arteries and nerves of the axilla on the side on which they have been dissected, allowing the arm to fall backward. Then trace the branches of the costocervical axis with tracer, scalpel, and bone forceps, taking care not to injure the vertebral artery. Add these branches to your diagram of the subclavian.

10. The vertebral artery (p. 291). Trace it to the foramen transversarium of the sixth cervical vertebra. Then with bone forceps follow it to the atlas and into the atlantal foramen. Add this to your diagram of the subclavian.

11. The basilar artery (p. 291) and the other arteries of the brain (p. 289) are best studied on a preparation similar to that shown in Fig. 121. To obtain such a preparation, it is only necessary to remove the brain (for directions, see *p. 9*) of a specimen in which the arteries have been injected.

12. Veins of the brain and dura mater (p. 324). These can be

worked out only with much difficulty, except on specimens injected with gelatin. The skull must be chipped away and the veins followed without destroying them.

13. Trace the pulmonary veins (p. 315) (filled with red injection) and the pulmonary artery (p. 280).

IV. Vessels in the abdominal cavity.

1. Open the abdominal cavity; find the superior mesenteric vein (p. 326, and Fig. 132) in the duodenal mesentery near the border of the pancreas. Inject this in both directions with white starch and then dissect the portal vein and its tributaries without injuring any of the structures in the abdomen (p. 326, and Fig. 132).

2. Follow the inferior vena cava (p. 325) from the heart to the diaphragm and then follow it to its tributaries in the abdominal cavity.

3. Dissect the branches of the abdominal aorta (p. 301) and of the inferior vena cava (Fig. 126). Make diagrams of the vessels dissected and review as far as necessary the viscera concerned.

V. The external iliac and its branches (vessels of the hind limbs) (pp. 309 and 329, and Figs. 127, 128, and 163).

Follow the branches of the external iliac arteries and the corresponding veins in the same manner as the vessels of the arm were traced, cutting the muscles only so far as absolutely necessary. Make diagrams of the vessels dissected.

Make a diagram (*a*) of the arterial system as a whole; (*b*) of the venous system as a whole.

THE LYMPHATIC SYSTEM (p. 330)

As it is usually best for the teacher to demonstrate the lymphatic system on specimens especially prepared for the purpose, no directions are here given for its dissection by individual students. For methods of preparing demonstration specimens, see *p. 8*.

DISSECTION OF THE NERVOUS SYSTEM

(*For the technique of dissection see p. 11*)

I. The Spinal Cord (p. 335)

Use the specimen on which the muscles were dissected. (Or if the peripheral nerves are not to be dissected on the specimen used for the blood vessels, that may be employed.)

Make a dorsal median incision of the skin, from the back of the head to root of the tail. Reflect the skin for one or two inches on each side of the incision and cut away the muscles covering the neural arches of the vertebræ from the third cervical to the seventh or eighth thoracic inclusive.

Remove with bone forceps the neural arch of one of the last cervical vertebræ and find the spinal nerve emerging from the intervertebral foramen. Isolate the nerve for a short distance, then proceed craniad, removing the neural arches on one side and isolating the nerves until the third has been uncovered. The ganglion of the second nerve should be sought among the muscles on the dorsal surface between the atlas and axis, and after it has been isolated the arch of the axis may be removed. (The nerve may be found beneath the clavotrapezius and traced to the ganglion.)

The ganglion of the second nerve should be isolated in or near the atlantal foramen, the muscles to which it passes turned aside, and the arch of the atlas removed. Having thus uncovered the first two or more spinal ganglia, proceed caudad, removing the vertebral arches, until the whole cord and its nerves are exposed. Then —

1. Study the cord, enlargements, filum terminale, etc. (p. 335, and Figs. 133 and 136).

2. Slit open and reflect the dura mater (p. 337) for an inch or two.

3. Demonstrate the arachnoid by pulling it off with forceps.

4. Reflect the pia mater in the same way as the dura mater.

5. Study the fissures and grooves of the cord.

6. Cut across the cord with fine scissors at the point where it is freed from its membranes and examine the section. Note the arrangement of gray and white matter and the fissures and grooves, particularly the anterior or ventral. Demonstrate the central canal with the blowpipe.

7. Study the origin of the spinal nerves (p. 337). Count them. Direction of exit? With fine scissors, carefully clean one in the thoracic region from dura mater and connective tissue and study dorsal and ventral roots and ganglion (see Fig. 135). Then follow it and find its dorsal ramus and ventral ramus and the communicating branch of the latter with the sympathetic system. Do not trace the perpheral branches of the nerve at present.

II. The Brain (p. 339)

Directions for the removal of the brain are given on *page 9*. These should be carefully followed.

Study of the Brain. — In the study of the brain, demonstration specimens are to be used as much as or more than your own specimen. See everything on a demonstration preparation before attempting to expose it in your own specimen.

I. Examine the brain of a shark or of a frog. Cranial nerves may be neglected, but the divisions of the brain should be recognized in dorsal and ventral views and in longitudinal sections, and sketched.

II. Read the general description of the cat's brain (pp. 339–343), using your own specimen and a longitudinal section. Cut nothing on your own specimen except when especially directed to do so. Study the cavities on a preparation. Compare the diagrams (Figs. 139 and 140) and the figures of the brain.

III. Study the individual parts as follows. To avoid errors make constant reference to preparations and figures.

1. The medulla (p. 344, and Figs. 138 and 141). Use your own specimen and a preparation and dissect out carefully the cranial nerves on your own specimen.

2. The cerebellum (p. 347). Study it entire, then to expose the fourth ventricle (p. 349) slice away with a very sharp scalpel one-half of the cerebellum by making a median longitudinal incision and then horizontal incisions.

3. The pons (p. 347).

4. The mesencephalon (p. 351, and Figs. 141 and 142). Study it first in a preparation. Then study the floor on your own specimen; origin of third nerves.

5. The diencephalon (Figs. 141 and 142). Study the roof and thalami and the pineal body on a preparation and on a longitudinal section; the floor on your specimen.

6. The telencephalon (p. 357). (Note that only *one* side of this is to be dissected.)

a. Study it externally; sulci and gyri (Figs. 145 and 146).

b. Examine a preparation showing the corpus callosum (Fig. 147). Then slice away with a very sharp scalpel the top of *one* hemisphere nearly to the corpus callosum (see the preparation). Expose the corpus callosum on this side to its cranial and caudal borders, by *tearing* away the brain substance at its side and above it.

c. Raise the corpus callosum at the side and remove it, thus exposing the lateral ventricle in which note the septum pellucidum and fornix, the corpus striatum, and choroid plexus of the lateral ventricle (Fig. 148). (These are to be exposed on *one* side only, the other being left intact.)

d. Expose the anterior and inferior horns of the ventricle and find the hippocampus, the fimbria, caudal part of the fornix, the foramen of Monro, the anterior commissure. See all these also on a preparation (Fig. 148).

e. Remove the occipital and parietal portions of the cerebrum, on the side already dissected, so as to expose the roof of the third ventricle and the midbrain in your specimen, and note the pineal body, choroid plexus of third ventricle, and structures on the roof of the midbrain (Fig. 141).

f. Remove the choroid plexus or roof of the third ventricle and study again the thalami (Fig. 141).

g. Make a longitudinal section of the brain, in the following manner: Use a very sharp large scalpel, or a razor point. Have this wet with the alcohol mixture at the time of using. Place the brain ventral surface down on a sheet of cork or a block of soft wood, the long axis of the brain coinciding with the direction of grain of the wood. Holding the brain firmly with one hand, place the wet knife between the hemispheres with its edge resting on the corpus callosum. See that it is in the median plane and parallel with the long axis of the brain. See also that it is not inclined to one side or the other, else you will not cut a median section throughout. The point of the knife should just reach the cork or wood between the olfactory bulbs. Now draw the knife caudad, keeping its point against the cork: the brain will thus be divided.

If the section is not exactly median, observe the amount of divergence by placing the two halves together and finding the median ventral line. Then on the half that has *too much* slice away thin shavings until the cavities are exposed, showing the section to be median. Compare with a demonstration section or Fig. 143. Draw the section and compare with a section of shark's brain (see Fig. 143).

h. Study a series of transverse sections, identifying parts. Observe especially in these sections the fornix, corpus callosum, and ventricles, and the distribution of white and gray matter (see Figs. 149–153).

III. Peripheral Nervous System

(There are some advantages in dissecting the eye with its muscles before dissecting the nerves, as a knowledge of the eye muscles is presupposed for dissecting some of the cranial nerves. For directions on the eye, see *p. 50.*)

A new specimen should be used, if possible, for the peripheral nervous system, though that used for the blood vessels can be employed, at considerable disadvantage.

Prepare as for the blood vessels. The arteries should be injected with red starch, to aid in tracing the nerves.

1. *The Cranial Nerves* (p. 369) *and Sympathetic System* (p. 404)

1. Reflect the skin covering the sternomastoid muscle, and make a longitudinal incision of the muscle so as to expose the carotid artery. Lying along the artery find the combined trunk of the sympathetic and vagus nerves. Follow the vagus (p. 378) first craniad; transect the muscles as necessity arises, and find its ganglion nodosum and at the same time locate the superior cervical ganglion of the sympathetic nerve (p. 408, and Fig. 156; Fig. 164*a*, *A*). Then find the hypoglossal nerve (Fig. 156, *b*), passing outside of the carotid artery to the tongue, and the accessory (Fig. 156, *c*), passing to the trapezius. Cut and reflect the digastric muscle and find the small glossopharyngeal nerve (Fig. 156, *a*), passing to the surface of the bulla and then beneath the carotid artery.

2. Follow the vagus (p. 378) caudad to its termination. To do this it is necessary to remove one side of the thorax, as in dissecting the blood vessels. Do not injure the nerves of the axilla, nor the phrenic or sympathetic nerves. For the vagus in the thorax, compare Fig. 157. Find the branches of the nerve; in dissecting them, pull on them to make them tense. They are then more easily visible. To dissect the abdominal portion of the vagus, open the abdominal cavity, and compare Fig. 164 (p. 412).

3. Dissect the sympathetic (p. 404), following it and its branches to the pelvic region (Figs. 156, 157, and 164).

4. The hypoglossal (p. 383, and Fig. 156, *b*).

5. The glossopharyngeal (p. 378, and Fig. 156, *a*).

6. The accessory nerve (p. 382, and Fig. 156, *c*; Fig. 158, 1).

Cut away a portion of the tympanic bulla and the base of the skull, sufficient to follow these nerves in the jugular foramen, to the brain.

7. Locate the stylomastoid foramen and pick away overlying tissue until the facial nerve is found emerging, and then follow its branches to their distribution (p. 375, and Fig. 155).

8. Expose the ventral surface of the pterygoid muscles just mediad of the angle of the jaw. Divide and reflect them, and the mandibular division of the fifth nerve (p. 373, and Fig. 154) will be found dorsad of them and of the internal maxillary artery. The chorda tympani (p. 375) passes ventrad of the artery to join the lingual. Follow out (1) the lingual branch (p. 375) (with the chorda tympani), and (2) the inferior alveolar (p. 375) by cutting away the ventral border of the mandible. Then cut the mandible near the canine tooth, and pull it to one side, and follow out the muscular branches of the mandibular nerve.

9. Remove the mandible and find the maxillary nerve (p. 371) emerging from the foramen rotundum. Follow its branches and find the sphenopalatine ganglion (p. 372).

10. Remove the zygoma so as to expose the whole ventral aspect of the orbit. Carefully pick away the fat in the orbit without injuring any nerves, so as to expose the four recti muscles and the inferior oblique (see p. 418, and Fig. 166). Find the abducens nerve (p. 375, and Fig. 154), entering the dorsal edge of the lateral rectus, and follow it back. Look on the inner surface of the inferior rectus for the branch of the third nerve (p. 369) which supplies it. Find the branch of this nerve which runs to the inferior oblique muscle, and on it the ciliary ganglion; find the branches to the ciliary ganglion from the ophthalmic nerve and follow them (p. 371). Follow also the short ciliary nerves (p. 370) to the eyeball.

11. Trace the third nerve (p. 369) to its foramen of exit and find its branches. Where it passes between the superior and lateral recti, find the ophthalmic nerve (p. 370) by its side and trace its branches.

12. Find the fourth nerve (p. 370), passing outside of the lateral rectus at its origin and entering the superior oblique.

13. Follow the third, fourth, fifth, and sixth nerves into the skull by chipping away the bone and removing the dura. Note the semi-

lunar or Gasserian ganglion (p. 370, and Fig. 138, *k*) and the origin of the fifth nerve from it, and the relation of the ventral root of the fifth nerve to the mandibular nerve.

2. *Spinal Nerves*

The spinal nerves may be dissected on the same side used for dissecting the cranial nerves. (If an undissected specimen is used, remove the skin from the side of the neck, and cut the sternomastoid, sternohyoid, and sternothyroid muscles, as directed for the vagus and sympathetic.)

Cervical Nerves (p. 383). — The ventral rami of the cervical nerves are to be sought as they pass out between the bundles of the scalenus, or between the scalenus and longus capitis, in the neck. This region has already been uncovered in dissecting the vagus and sympathetic (Fig. 156). Dissect first the *second* cervical (p. 385). Find its ventral ramus as it emerges between the levator scapulæ ventralis and cleidomastoid (Fig. 158, 2), and follow its branches — the auricularis magnus (5) and cutaneus colli (6). Find its *dorsal* ramus, the great occipital nerve (p. 384), by reflecting the clavotrapezius muscle; the nerve will be found emerging from the underlying muscles close to the craniomedial angle of the clavotrapezius, near its origin. Trace the nerve in both directions.

The ventral ramus of the first cervical (p. 385) will be found emerging from beneath the wing of the atlas, a little distance craniad of the second (Fig. 156, *j*). Trace it. To find its short dorsal ramus, the suboccipital nerve (p. 384), it is necessary to dissect apart the muscles on the dorsal side of the atlas till the nerve is found passing from the atlantal foramen.

Dissect the third, fourth, and fifth nerves (p. 385, and Fig. 158).

Brachial Plexus (pp. 386, 448, and Figs. 159 and 160). — The brachial plexus has been partly uncovered in dissecting the vagus and sympathetic. (If a new specimen or the opposite side is used, reflect the skin from the ventral surface of the thorax and arm, and cut the pectoral muscles, thus uncovering the vessels and nerves of the axilla.) Reflect the skin from the ventral surface of the upper arm. (Do not use scalpel, but tear the skin from the muscles. In this way the nerves will be seen passing to the skin, while if the scalpel were used the nerves might be cut.)

Tie the axillary vein or its two branches in two places, and cut the vein between the knots. Leave the arteries as guides for dissection, but remove the veins. Now clean thoroughly the nerves forming the brachial plexus as they pass from the thorax or neck. Be careful not to injure any of the fine nerves or the interconnections of the nerves in doing this. Find and distinguish clearly the fifth, sixth, seventh, and eighth cervical nerves and the first thoracic, as they emerge from the neck or thorax. (Compare Fig. 159 and Fig. 157, *V–VIII* and *I′*.)

Follow out the branches of the plexus, noting the origin and distribution of each branch, in order to determine its name. To follow the phrenic (p. 388, and Fig. 157, *f*), remove a portion of the thoracic wall. In following the other branches of the plexus, pull back the skin wherever an exposure is to be made, and separate the muscles. The epitrochlearis may be cut near the elbow, and the clavobrachial near the shoulder. In following the interosseous branches of the median nerve the fifth head of the flexor profundus, and the extensor brevis pollicis, may be cut. As a rule it will not be necessary to cut other muscles.

Thoracic and Lumbar Nerves. — One or two of the thoracic nerves (p. 393) should be dissected from the outside by finding the intercostal nerve along the caudal border of one of the ribs and tracing it in both directions. The nerve may be exposed by removing the external muscles covering the rib, and cutting the external intercostal muscles. The dorsal ramus should be traced after the ventral ramus has been studied.

The first lumbar nerve (p. 395) should be dissected in the same way.

The other lumbar and sacral nerves (pp. 395–400; p. 450) are best dissected from within.

The alimentary canal and its appendages should be removed from the abdomen, leaving only five or six centimeters of the caudal end of the rectum. The kidneys and urogenital organs may be left, to be removed during dissection. (Compare Fig. 162.)

Turn one of the kidneys to the other side, and find the second lumbar nerve (Fig. 162, *a*) appearing at the lateral border of the iliopsoas muscle. Trace it to its origin; trace it also distad, following both branches. It will be necessary to trace the nerves through the abdominal wall, then find them from the outside, and follow them to their distribution.

The third nerve (Fig. 163, *b*) may be found by dissecting apart the fiber-bundles of the iliopsoas and psoas minor, and following in the same way. The kidneys, ureters, vena cava, and aorta may be removed as occasion arises.

The remainder of the lumbar nerves may be found in order, in a similar manner. Follow the saphenous nerve and its branches (p. 397) by removing the integument from the medial side of the leg (see Fig. 127, p. 310). To dissect the sacral nerves (p. 399) separate the innominate bones at the pubic symphysis and divaricate them. Find the nerves arising from the sacral plexus, by cutting the levator ani muscle. After N. hemorrhoidalis inferior and N. pudendus have been traced, the rectum and urogenital organs may be removed, taking great care not to remove more than is necessary. To dissect the great sciatic nerve (p. 400, and Fig. 163), separate the biceps and caudofemoralis near their proximal ends and find the large nerve-trunk (*a*). Then lift the biceps away from the nerve, cut that muscle near its middle, and reflect it. The nerve may now be followed to its terminal branches; during the process cut the muscles only when absolutely necessary. The inferior gluteal nerve (*i*) will be found on the dorsal surface of the great sciatic; by cutting the caudofemoralis and gluteus maximus muscles near their insertions and turning them back, the distribution of the nerve may be followed. The superior gluteal (*j*) will be found at the cranial margin of the pyriformis by reflecting the gluteus medius in the same way; the tensor fasciæ latæ may also be cut.

DISSECTION OF THE SENSE ORGANS

I. The Eye (p. 417)

Use any specimen on which one side of the head has been left intact. Remove the head from the body by cutting through the neck a little craniad of the first rib.

Study the eye externally. Observe the eyelids, the conjunctiva, nictitating membrane with its cartilage, and the Harderian gland (Fig. 165); the two openings of the lachrymal duct, the Meibomian glands if possible.

Remove the zygomatic arch and expose the orbit and the structures which it contains. Study the periorbita (p. 416), and find the lachrymal gland (p. 417).

Study the muscles of the eyeball (p. 418, and Fig. 166). The lateral rectus on the lateral surface will perhaps be first found, and its tendon traced beneath the inferior oblique. Use great care not to injure the levator palpebræ superioris.

After studying the muscles, find the optic nerve. Cut it and the muscles, and remove the eyeball for further study.

The Eyeball (p. 419, and Fig. 167). — For an examination of the eye it is well to have both a fresh specimen and one hardened in formalin or alcohol. The hardened specimen is more essential, however. An eye from one of the specimens used in dissection is usually satisfactory. All accessory portions should be trimmed from the eyeball, leaving only the spherical ball with a short stalk formed by the optic nerve.

Observe such features of the eye as can be seen externally: the optic nerves, sclerotic, cornea, iris, and pupil. This should be done on a fresh specimen, if one is at hand. The changes in size and form of the pupil can be observed in the living cat by changing it from a light to a dark place and *vice versa.*

Dissection. — Examine the internal structures on a preparation. Then with fine scissors and forceps remove from the eye about one-fourth of the wall, in the form of a quadrant having one point at the optic nerve, the other at the center of the cornea. The coats of the eye can then be studied on the piece removed, while the other structures will be visible within the eyeball. No special directions are necessary for observation of the structures described, unless it be the capsule of the lens and the zonula ciliaris. The capsule of the lens may be demonstrated by tearing a bit of it off with fine forceps. The zonula ciliaris is easily seen by divaricating the edges of the cut made in removing the quadrant, so as to stretch the fine fibers of which the zonula is formed.

II. The Ear (p. 422)

(The muscles of the external ear are of little practical importance, and will doubtless usually be omitted.)

(1) The external ear. Read the description of the external ear (p. 422), verifying it by examination and comparison of an ear still covered with integument, in the natural condition, and of a preparation of the isolated cartilages of the ear (Fig. 168). The latter may be obtained by dissecting the skin and muscles from a fresh ear.

(2) The scutiform cartilage (p. 425) should be observed in the natural position, and as isolated.

(3) The muscles of the external ear (p. 425, and Fig. 169). Those connecting the external ear with other parts of the head have been studied in connection with the facial muscles. The remainder will be studied on an external ear removed according to the directions given on page *12*.

Remove the integument from the convex surface of the auricle, sufficiently to expose the entire extent of the muscles.

1. The rotator auris. Transect.
2. The adductor auris superior (Fig. 169, 1).
3. The adductor auris medius (2).
4. The transversus auriculæ (Fig. 63, *i*, p. 97).
5. The auricularis externus (Fig. 169, 10).
6. The helicis (Fig. 169, 3). To expose this it will be necessary to remove the integument from along the cranial border of the inner surface of the auricle.
7. The antitragicus (Fig. 169, 6). Remove the integument further if necessary.
8. The tragicus medialis (Fig. 169, 5, 5′).
9. The conchæus externus (Fig. 169, 9).

(4) Remove the tympanic bulla and petrous bone from the rest of the skull, by the use of bone forceps and scalpel. Trim away all soft tissue (including the cartilaginous auditory meatus), and all other bony parts from these, but leave them uninjured.

(5) Find the Eustachian tube and study it (p. 430).

(6) Study specimens of the bones of the middle ear (p. 430, and Figs. 171 and 172).

(7) The middle ear should be studied on a demonstration preparation, then dissected as follows:

Remove with bone forceps the medial side of the tympanic bulla (the entotympanic). Note the two cavities within the bulla, with the shelf separating them. Observe the fenestra cochleæ. Now remove with the forceps the shelf, first breaking through the middle part, then removing the rest with care. Remove part also of the membranous lining of the cavity, till the inner surface of the tympanic membrane, with the malleus crossing it, is visible. Observe the tensor tympani muscle (p. 431) attached to the malleus by its small tendon. Next, with bone forceps, fracture the thick, bony portion uniting the caudal end of the petrous with the caudal part of the ring of bone surrounding the external auditory meatus. These two parts may then be separated with the fingers, leaving the petrous bone on one side, the meatus, tympanum, and malleus on the other (Fig. 170). The head of the malleus may then be observed, with the incus attached to it. Note also the stapes, in the fenestra vestibuli, with the stapedius muscle (p. 431) attached to it.

(8) The internal ear (p. 431). Note the fenestra vestibuli and fenestra cochleæ and the promontory (p. 34). Study the cochlea and vestibule on a demonstration preparation, and compare with Fig. 173. Then remove the wall of the promontory and find the cochlea. Open the vestibule and find as many of the openings of the semicircular canals as possible. Study the semicircular canals on demonstration preparations, consulting Fig. 173. The semicircular canals may, if desired, be exposed on your own specimen, by cutting away the surface of the bone in places indicated in the description (p. 433), and inserting fine bristles (those from the sensory hairs on the face of the cat are excellent for this purpose).

The membranous labyrinth (Fig. 173) may be isolated by decalcifying the petrous bone with ten per cent nitric acid, then dissecting out the labyrinth. This is an operation of considerable delicacy, but at least one or two specimens for demonstration should, if possible, be prepared thus and kept in the laboratory.

PART IV

MANUAL OF DISSECTION BY THE REGIONAL PLAN

THE BACK

In order that the student may more readily locate the important bony landmarks which serve for the attachment of muscles that he will encounter, he should first make a thorough study of the vertebral column (pp. 1–16), the skull as a whole (pp. 49–57), and the scapula (pp. 62–64).

Make an incision through the skin from the level of the lambdoidal ridge to the root of the tail and remove the skin from the mid-dorsal to the mid-lateral line on both sides. Follow the general directions given for muscle dissection (*p. 6*) and make a careful study of the following muscles on the right side of the body:

1. Trapezius (pp. 115–118, and Fig. 68, *j*, *h*, and *d*). Separate into its subdivisions and reflect from its origin. Observe the spinal accessory nerve on the under surface of the muscle. It passes through the cleidomastoid and is joined by several of the anterior spinal nerves of the cervical region (forming the subtrapezial plexus of man).

2. Rhomboideus (p. 119). Transect.

3. Occipitoscapularis (p. 118, and Fig. 73, *a*). Transect. Note its delicate nerve supply from the fourth cervical nerve.

4. Levator scapulae ventralis (p. 120, and Fig. 68, *f*; Fig. 65, *i*; Fig. 72, *c*). The origin of the muscle cannot be seen at this time. Carefully separate from the cleidomastoid and transect.

5. Cleidomastoid (p. 120, and Fig. 65, *h*). Transect.

6. Splenius (p. 131, and Fig. 73, *b*). Cut at its insertion and reflect medialward.

7. Longissimus capitis (p. 131, and Fig. 73, *g*; Fig. 69, *e*). Note that this muscle is a cranial continuation of the longissimus dorsi (Fig. 69, *f''*) which will be observed later.

8. Biventer cervicis (p. 132, and Fig. 69, *a*). Cut at the origin and insertion and reflect medialward. It will remain attached to the splenius by the connective tissue between the two.

9. Complexus (p. 133, and Fig. 69, *b*). Is part of a muscle which will be noted later. Transect.

10. Latissimus dorsi (p. 121, and Fig. 68, *m*; Fig. 65, *q*; Fig. 77, *e*). Do not try to determine the insertion at this time. Transect.

11. Serratus posterior superior (p. 148, and Fig. 73, *l*). Cut from its origin and reflect.

12. Serratus posterior inferior (p. 148, and Fig. 73, *n*). Cut from its origin and reflect.

13. Longissimus dorsi (p. 126, and Fig. 69, *f*, *f'*, and *f''*). This muscle is covered in the lumbar region by the lumbodorsal fascia, which may be removed by making an incision parallel with the midline and about one inch from it and reflecting medially. Trace the muscle into the thoracic and cervical regions, noting the spinalis dorsi (Fig. 69, *g*) separating from it dorsally and the iliocostalis (Fig. 69, *h*) ventrally.

14. Extensor caudae lateralis (p. 137, and Fig. 70, *f*). This muscle may be exposed by removing the lumbodorsal fascia over the sacral region.

15. Iliocostalis (p. 128, and Fig. 69, *h*). The continuity of this muscle with the longissimus dorsi has been observed.

16. Longissimus capitis (p. 131, and Fig. 73, *g*; Fig. 69, *e*). This muscle was previously studied. Its connection with the longissimus dorsi should be noted at this time.

17. Spinalis dorsi (p. 129, and Fig. 69, *g*). This muscle is found medial to the longissimus dorsi. Trace the origin and insertion of the fibers.

18. Biventer cervicis and complexus have been seen.

19. Longus atlantis (p. 134, and Fig. 71, *f*).

20. Multifidus spinæ (p. 130, and Fig. 70, *d*). The fibers of this muscle may be seen by removing the longissimus dorsi from the lumbar region.

21. Extensor caudæ medialis (p. 136, and Fig. 70, *e*).

22. Semispinalis cervicis (p. 133, and Fig. 71, *c*).

23. Interspinales (p. 131). Is to be noted in the lumbar region where the longissimus dorsi has been removed.

24. Intertransversales (p. 131). Remove the fibers of the multifidus spinæ in the lumbar region to expose the intertransversales. The relations are the same in the other regions.

25. Rectus capitis posterior major (p. 134, and Fig. 71, *a*). Transect.

26. Obliquus capitis superior (p. 136, and Fig. 71, *e*). Transect.

27. Obliquus capitis inferior (p. 136, and Fig. 71, *b*).

28. Rectus capitis posterior medius (p. 135, and Fig. 71, *d*). Transect.

29. Rectus capitis posterior minor (p. 135). This is a very small muscle and lies beneath the rectus capitis posterior medius.

The last five muscles named are known as the suboccipital muscles. Their nerve supply may be noted to come from the dorsal ramus of the first cervical nerve, known as the suboccipital nerve (p. 384). The nerve may be seen between the obliquus superior, obliquus inferior and the rectus medius.

30. Levatores costarum (p. 150). The bundles of muscle forming this group may be seen in the thoracic region after the removal of the iliocostalis and longissimus dorsi muscles, thus exposing the dorsal ends of the ribs. The fibers of these muscles are continuous with those of the external intercostals.

During the course of dissection of the muscles of the back it will have been noted that the nerves supplying them are arranged segmentally. The branches to all muscles except those which attach to the anterior extremity are dorsal rami of the nerves of the various regions (pp. 384; 393–394; and 404).

SPINAL CORD AND SPINAL NERVES

Preparatory to opening the vertebral canal, remove all muscles on both sides of the back. Review again the structure of the vertebral column and study all joints and ligaments associated with it (pp. 16–18). Cut away the neural arches by clipping through the pedicles with the bone clippers. Do not cut too deep at first, else the spinal nerves in the intervertebral canals may be cut. Make the following study of the spinal cord:

1. The blood supply of the cord (p. 291).
2. The membranes covering the cord (p. 337). Slit open and reflect the dura. Demonstrate the arachnoid by pulling it with the forceps. The pia mater is closely adherent to the cord.
3. Study the entire cord for enlargements, sulci, and fissures (pp. 335–337). Note particularly the cauda equina and the filum terminale.
4. Note the plan of origin of a spinal nerve (pp. 337–339). Note the spinal ganglion in connection with the dorsal root. Trace the spinal nerve laterally and note its division into dorsal and ventral rami. The dura mater may be traced laterad over the nerve roots on to the formation of the nerve trunk.

Demonstrate the posterior and middle scalene muscles (p. 141). Cut away the articular processes of the cervical vertebræ so as to expose the trunks of the cervical and first thoracic nerves. Remove the dorsal portion of the transverse processes of the cervical vertebræ to expose the vertebral artery and vein (pp. 291 and 325). Trace the vertebral artery through the atlantal groove and foramen into the foramen magnum.

Follow the course of the external jugular vein (p. 319) along the neck and ligate it at its entrance into the thoracic wall.

BRACHIAL PLEXUS

Remove the integument from the ventral body wall from the caudal region of the head to the thigh.

Dissect the following muscles preparatory to the study of the brachial plexus:

1. Pectoralis group (p. 145). Reflect from their origin.
a. Pectoantibrachialis (p. 145, and Fig. 65, *m*).
b. Pectoralis major (p. 145, and Fig. 65, *l* and *l'*).
c. Pectoralis minor (p. 146, and Fig. 65, *o*).
d. Xiphihumeralis (p. 147, and Fig. 65, *q*).

2. Latissimus dorsi (p. 121, and Fig. 68, *m*; Fig. 65, *q*; Fig. 77, *e*). The origin of this muscle has been observed. Follow it now to its insertion and note its relation to the pectoralis at that point.

3. Review the cleidomastoid.

4. Sternomastoid (p. 139, and Fig. 65, *g*; Fig. 68, *c*). On its outer surface the external jugular vein may be seen, but it is not to be dissected at this time.

5. Serratus magnus or anterior (p. 122, and Fig. 73, *i*).

6. Levator scapulæ (p. 123, and Fig. 73, *h*). This muscle is continuous with the serratus anterior.

Note branches from the anterior cervical nerves which come from behind the caudal border of the cleidomastoid muscle and from the cervical plexus. Observe:

1. Great auricular nerve (p. 385, and Fig. 158, 5) passing to the region over the parotid gland.

2. Cutaneous colli (p. 385, and Fig. 158, 6) passing to the skin over the neck region.

Trace the spinal accessory nerve (p. 382) through this region in its course to supply the trapezius muscle (p. 383, and Fig. 156, *b*). Note those branches of the cervical nerves which join the spinal accessory and pass with it to the cleidomastoid and trapezius muscles. Identify the origin of the phrenic nerve (p. 388, and Fig. 159, *a*).

The axillary artery and vein and the nerves of the brachial plexus are now to be studied. Note the origin, course, and branches of the axillary artery (p. 294, and Fig. 122, *g*). Study the axillary vein (p. 318, and Fig. 122) as it accompanies the artery of the same name. The tributaries of the vein correspond in name and course to the branches of the artery.

Study the formation of the brachial plexus and the distribution of the nerves which originate from it (pp. 386 and 448, and Fig. 159; Fig. 160). Note the following:

1. Origin of plexus.
2. Formation of trunks.
3. Formation of cords.

4. Branches from cords and the distribution of those passing to the muscles which have already been dissected. The distribution into the arm will be followed later.

a. Anterior thoracics (p. 387) from cervicals 7–8 and thoracic 1.
b. Posterior thoracics (p. 388) from cervical 7.
c. Suprascapular (p. 388) from cervicals 6–7.
d. Subscapular (p. 388) from cervicals 6–7.
e. Axillary (p. 388) from cervicals 6–7.
f. Phrenic (p. 388) from cervicals 5–6.
g. Musculocutaneous (p. 388) from cervicals 6–7.
h. Medial cutaneous (p. 390) from thoracic 1.
i. Median (p. 390) from cervicals 7–8 and thoracic 1.
j. Radial (p. 392) from cervicals 7–8 and thoracic 1.
k. Ulnar (p. 393) from cervical 8 and thoracic 1.

Cut the spinal cord across between the fourth and fifth cervical segments and also between the first and second thoracic segments. Divide the segment of the cord thus isolated into halves by a longitudinal incision through the course of the dorsal fissure. Remove the right half of this segment of the cord with its attached nerve roots Bisect the muscles that still attach the right anterior extremity to the body wall and remove the appendage with the attached brachial plexus. Preserve the appendage for a later dissection.

Observe the cut surface of the spinal cord for the plan of structure of its cross section (p. 336, and Fig. 134; Fig. 135).

BRAIN AND CRANIAL CAVITY

Remove the skin from the head region, being careful not to injure any of the blood vessels which are superficial in position. Note the following vessels and then ligate them:

1. Occipital artery (p. 285, and Fig. 119, *f*).
2. Posterior auricular artery (p. 287, and Fig. 119, *o*).
3. Superficial temporal artery (p. 287, and Fig. 119, *p*; Fig. 120, *h*).
4. Veins of the same name accompany the arteries. Observe these at this time.

Study the origin of the occipitofrontalis muscle and remove it (p. 101). Study the intermedius scutulorum (p. 96, and Fig. 63, *a*) and the corrugator supercilii medialis (p. 97, and Fig. 63, *b*) and reflect both from the midline. By use of the bone forceps very carefully remove the skull cap. If the specimen has been preserved for some time the dura mater may be somewhat drawn away from the cranial bones. Be cautious in cutting so as not to destroy the cranial meninges. Special care will be required to avoid injury to the brain and its meninges during the removal of the tentorium cerebelli (pp. 36 and 58) formed by the parietal bones. Follow closely the directions given on *page 9* for removal of the brain.

Study the dura mater of the brain (p. 368). Note the venous sinuses associated with it (pp. 324–325):

1. Superior sagittal in the dorsal part of the falx cerebri.
2. Transverse.
3. Cavernous.
4. Inferior petrosal.

Study the arterial supply of the dura mater. This is furnished largely by the middle meningeal branch from the internal maxillary, which enters the cranial cavity through the foramen ovale (p. 289).

Remove the neural arches from the first three or four cervical vertebræ if this has not already been done. Cut the first four cervical nerves on both sides at their origin from the cord and raise the cord from the floor of the vertebral canal. Raise the brain in the region of the medulla and carefully work it loose from the floor of the cranial cavity. Cut the cranial nerves so that enough of each root remains attached to the brain to identify its origin, while the remainder of the trunk within the cranial cavity may be used to trace the nerve to the foramen of exit from the cranial cavity. After cutting the olfactory nerves as near their cranial exit as possible, remove the brain and preserve it for future study by keeping it moist with the phenol solution.

Complete the study of the dura mater and its venous sinuses. Note the structure of the arachnoid and pia mater of the brain (p. 368). Observe the floor of the skull for the following structures (p. 57, and Fig. 42):

1. Cribriform plate.
2. Optic foramina.
3. Sella turcica.
4. Posterior fossa in which the pons and medulla are found.
5. Lateral and temporal fossæ for the temporal lobes of the brain.

Note the foramina of the cranial cavity together with the structures passing through them:

1. Foramina of cribriform plate (p. 43) transmitting the olfactory nerve (p. 369).

2. Optic (p. 29) transmitting the optic nerve (p. 369).

3. Orbital fissure (p. 27) transmitting the oculomotor (p. 369), trochlear (p. 370), ophthalmic division of the trigeminal (p. 370) and abducens (p. 375) nerves and an arterial branch from the carotid plexus to the cranial cavity (p. 289, 3).

4. Foramen rotundum (p. 27) transmitting the maxillary division of the trigeminal nerve (p. 371).

5. Foramen ovale (p. 27) transmitting the mandibular division of the trigeminal nerve (p. 373) and the middle meningeal artery (p. 289).

6. Foramen lacerum (p. 26) transmitting the internal carotid artery (p. 285).

7. Internal auditory meatus (p. 35) transmitting the facial (p. 375) and auditory (p. 377) nerves.

8. Jugular foramen (p. 24) transmitting the glossopharyngeal (p. 378), vagus (p. 378) and spinal accessory (p. 382) nerves, and the internal jugular vein (p. 320).

9. Hypoglossal canal (p. 24) transmitting the hypoglossal nerve (p. 383).

Study the blood supply on the ventral surface of the brain (p. 291, and Fig. 121). Note the formation of the basilar artery (p. 291) on the ventral surface of the medulla by the union of the two vertebral arteries (p. 291), and the formation of the arterial circle of Willis. Trace especially the cerebral arteries and note the areas of their distribution.

Read the general description of the brain (pp. 339–343, and Fig. 137; Fig. 138; Fig. 144). Make a detailed study of each division as outlined below:

1. Medulla oblongata (p. 344, and Fig. 138; Fig. 141). Identify all structures listed in the description and the origin of all cranial nerves associated with this division.

2. Cerebellum (p. 347).

3. Pons (p. 347). Identify all cranial nerves from this division.

4. Mesencephalon (p. 351, and Fig. 141; Fig. 142). To expose the roof of this division, the cerebral hemispheres must be carefully separated in the occipital lobe region. The origin of the third and fourth cranial nerves should be observed.

5. The floor of the diencephalon may be studied at this time (p. 352, and Fig. 138; Fig. 142). Identify the optic tracts, optic chiasma, optic nerves, pituitary body (the infundibulum will still be in place), and the mammillary bodies.

6. Study the external surface of the cerebral hemispheres (p. 357, and Fig. 145; Fig. 144). Separate the two hemispheres slightly and note that they are connected by the corpus callosum (p. 357, and Fig. 143 *p*). Divide the brain into lateral halves by an incision following the longitudinal fissure. Study the midsagittal section and identify all structures found on it (p. 356, and Fig. 143). On the left half of the brain remove the roof of the ventricular system and make a thorough study of it from above, as illustrated in Fig. 139. On the right half of the brain observe its structure as illustrated in Fig. 140.

Use the right half of the brain for the preparation of transverse sections through the levels listed below and make a thorough study of each:

1. Cephalic to optic chiasma (Fig. 149).
2. Through optic chiasma (Fig. 150).
3. Through infundibulum (Fig. 151).
4. Through pineal body (Fig. 152).
5. Through the caudal pair of the corpora quadrigemina or inferior colliculi (Fig. 153).

THORACIC WALL AND THORACIC VISCERA

Clean the fat and connective tissue from the muscles of the neck and thoracic regions preparatory to the dissection of these regions. Dissect as follows:

1. Sternomastoid (p. 139, and Fig. 65, *g*). This was previously seen. Transect and reflect. Do not disturb the salivary glands at this time.

2. Cleidomastoid (p. 120, and Fig. 65, *h*). Review again and note particularly its origin. Observe the relation of the hypoglossal nerve (p. 383, and Fig. 156, *b*) to this and the sternomastoid.

3. Levator scapulæ ventralis (p. 120, and Fig. 72, *c*, *c′*, and *c″*). Note the origin at this time.

4. Sternohyoid (p. 140, and Fig. 65, *e*). Beginning at its cephalic end separate from underlying structures. Beneath its lateral edge note the thyroid gland, which is not to be disturbed.

5. Sternothyroid (p. 141, and Fig. 65, *g′*). Transect.

The pectoralis group of muscles has been dissected. These are now to be reviewed and removed from their origin. Dissect the remaining muscles associated with the thoracic wall:

1. Scalenus (p. 141, and Fig. 73, *f–f‴*). The cervical portion will be studied later.

2. Transversus costarum (p. 150, and Fig. 73, *j*).

3. Serratus posterior superior (p. 148, and Fig. 73, *l*) and serratus posterior inferior (p. 148, and Fig. 73, *n*) have been studied and separated from their origin. Review.

4. The attachment of the external abdominal oblique (p. 153, and Fig. 68, *p*) to the ribs may be observed at this time. Do not disturb.

5. Select one intercostal space and make a complete study of its contents:

a. External intercostal muscle (p. 150, and Fig. 73, *m*; Fig. 69, *i*). Remove this muscle, being very careful not to disturb other structures.

b. Trace the complete course of an intercostal nerve (p. 394). Note that it follows the caudal border of the anterior one of the two ribs.

c. Intercostal artery (p. 283) and intercostal vein (p. 316).

d. Internal intercostal muscle (p. 151, and Fig. 69, *k*).

Make a longitudinal incision through the thoracic wall about 1.5 cm. from the midline on the left side of the sternum and from the region of the diaphragm through the first rib, being especially careful not to injure any structures anterior to the first rib. Make lateral incisions from this incision to the dorsal body wall, following the intercostal spaces anterior to the diaphragm. Cut the left ribs near their attachment to the vertebral column, but do not cut the muscles. Turn the flap thus prepared to the right and note:

1. The thoracic cavity (p. 217).

2. The left lung and its lobes (p. 253, and Fig. 106).

3. Reflection of the pleura on the left side (p. 217, and Fig. 92*a*, *D*, *F*):

a. Parietal pleura.

b. Pulmonary pleura.

c. Mediastinal septum (p. 218, and Fig. 92*a*, *G*). Note that this divides the thoracic cavity into lateral halves. Note boundaries and contents of mediastinum.

4. Position of heart (p. 274).

5. Position of trachea (p. 251).
6. Position of œsophagus (p. 234).
7. Aorta (p. 281).
8. Left phrenic nerve (p. 388).
9. Internal mammary artery (p. 292, and Fig. 118, *h*), and internal mammary vein (p. 318, and Fig. 129, *g*). Trace the artery to its origin and the vein to its termination.

Turn the ribs and muscles of the right side of the thoracic wall dorsad as was done on the left side. Trace the internal mammary artery and vein throughout their entire course, determining the branches of the artery and the tributaries of the vein (pp. 292 and 318). Note:

1. Right lung and pleural sac (p. 252, and Fig. 106).
2. Inferior vena cava (p. 325, and Fig. 129, *c*). Note only its course at this time. Its tributaries will be observed later.

SYMPATHETIC TRUNK, VAGUS AND PHRENIC NERVES

Study the thyroid gland (p. 254, and Fig. 96, 6). Note its lobes with the connecting isthmus, but do not disturb it at this time. Its blood and nerve supplies will be studied later. Note again that this gland is beneath the lateral edge of the sternohyoid muscle.

Following the dissection of the muscles on the ventral surface of the neck, the ventral surface of the trachea and associated structures should be observed. Laterad of the trachea on either side is a connective-tissue sheath, the carotid sheath, which contains important vessels and nerves of the neck region. Open this sheath on the right side to expose:

1. Common carotid artery (p. 283, and Fig. 115, *l* and *m*; Fig. 119, *a*).
2. Vagus nerve (p. 378, and Fig. 156, *d* and *d'*). Just caudad of the tympanic bulla the ganglion nodosum (p. 378, and Fig. 156, *d*) of this nerve is to be observed.
3. Sympathetic trunk (p. 406, and Fig. 156, *i*). In close connection with the ganglion nodosum of the vagus, note the superior cervical ganglion (Fig. 156, *e*) of the sympathetic trunk.
4. Internal jugular vein (p. 320, and Fig. 118, 2; Fig. 119, *b*). Trace this vein at this time to its connection with the external jugular vein.

5. In the region of the ganglion nodosum, note the glossopharyngeal (p. 378, and Fig. 156, *a*), spinal accessory (p. 382, and Fig. 156, *c*), and hypoglossal nerves (p. 383, and Fig. 156, *b*).

Trace the vagus and sympathetic trunks caudad through the cervical region to where they separate cephalad of the first rib. Make a thorough study of the cervical and thoracic course of the vagus. Note:

1. Pharyngeal branch (p. 379, and Fig. 156, *e*). This has its origin immediately cephalad of the ganglion nodosum.

2. Superior laryngeal nerve (p. 380, and Fig. 156, *h*). Trace to the larynx at this time.

3. Trace the vagus along the lateral surface of the trachea and into the thorax caudal to the root of the lung and along the lateral surface of the pericardium (p. 380, and Fig. 157).

4. Inferior or recurrent laryngeal branch (p. 380, and Fig. 157, *j*). Note the difference in the origin of this branch on the two sides. Trace craniad to the larynx.

5. Cardiac nerves (p. 380, and Fig. 157, *i*). Note whether these are entirely from the vagus or if some fibers do not come from the sympathetic trunk (superior, middle, and inferior cardiac nerves) (pp. 409, 411; Fig. 164*a*, 13, 14, 15).

6. Pulmonary plexus (p. 382, and Fig. 157, *k*).

7. Division of each vagus caudal to the pulmonary plexus into dorsal and ventral trunks and the division of the trunks from each nerve dorsad and ventrad of the œsophagus in the formation of the single trunks (p. 382, and Fig. 157, *l*, *m*, and *p*). From these two trunks fine branches may be noted passing to the œsophagus.

8. Trace the dorsal and ventral trunks to where they pass through the diaphragm on the dorsal and ventral surfaces of the œsophagus.

The origin of the phrenic nerve is to be reviewed (p. 388). Note its close relation to the vagus and then the separation of the two at the root of the lung. Trace to its distribution to the diaphragm.

Trace the sympathetic trunk caudad from the superior cervical ganglion (p. 409, and Fig. 157; Fig. 164*a*, *M*). Cranial to the subclavian artery note the small middle cervical ganglion (Fig. 157, *d*; Fig. 164*a*, *M*), the division of the trunk to pass around the subclavian artery, and the union of the two trunks again at the head of the first rib in the inferior cervical ganglion (p. 409, and Fig. 157, *e*). Note:

1. Branches from the superior cervical ganglion to the first three cervical nerves (p. 408).

2. Branches from the superior ganglion passing into the head region (p. 408).

3. Branches from the superior ganglion to join the vagus, the fibers passing to the pharynx, larynx, and the heart, the latter forming the superior cardiac nerve (p. 409).

4. Branches from the middle ganglion to the fourth, fifth, and sixth cervical nerves and accompanying the vagus to the heart, the latter fibers forming the middle cardiac nerve (p. 409).

5. Branches from the inferior cervical ganglion join the seventh and eighth cervical nerves and pass with the vagus to the heart, forming the inferior cardiac nerve (p. 409).

Trace the sympathetic trunk throughout its entire thoracic course. Note:

1. Thoracic ganglia (Fig. 164*a*, *P*).
2. Gray rami communicantes (Fig. 163*a*, *G*; Fig. 164*a*, 23, 23′, 23″).
3. White rami communicantes (Fig. 163*a*, *F*; Fig. 164*a*, 24, 24′, 24″).
4. Pulmonary fibers to pulmonary plexus (Fig. 164*a*, 17).
5. Greater splanchnic nerves (p. 406, and Fig. 157, *n*; Fig. 164*a*, 18).
6. Lesser splanchnic nerves (p. 407, and Fig. 164, *c*; Fig. 164*a*, 20).

VENOUS SYSTEM: THORACIC PORTION

Observe the thymus gland (p. 254, and Fig. 107, *d*). In adult cats it is largely degenerated. Note the pericardium (pp. 279–280; Fig. 92*a*, *A*, *C*), observing its connection with the diaphragm and with the heart. Remove the thymus. Open the pericardium by making a midventral incision and note its division into visceral and parietal portions. Trace the parietal portion from its reflection over the roots of the large vessels, then remove it and find:

1. Heart (p. 274, and Fig. 115). Note its division into right and left auricles and ventricles.

2. Large vessels connecting with the heart and the portion of the heart with which each connects:

a. Pulmonary artery (p. 280, and Fig. 115, *f*).
b. Aorta (p. 281, and Fig. 115, *g*).
c. Ligamentum arteriosum (p. 280). Of what is it the remains?
d. Pulmonary veins (p. 315). Trace from the lungs. How many from each lung?

e. Inferior vena cava (p. 325, and Fig. 126, *a*) and the superior vena cava (p. 316, and Fig. 129, *b*). Note the relations of these two trunks as they enter the heart.

Trace the tributaries of the superior vena cava (p. 316, and Fig. 129, *b*; being careful not to injure any accompanying arteries. Note the relations of the arteries to the veins. Observe the following tributaries of the superior vena cava (p. 316):

1. Azygos (p. 316, and Fig. 129, *d*).

a. Note its entrance into the thorax through the diaphragm. The abdominal origin of this vessel will be noted later.

b. Tributaries:

1′. Intercostal veins. 2′. Bronchial veins. 3′. Œsophageal veins.

2. Sternal vein (p. 318). This vein is formed by the union of the two internal mammary veins. Note the relations of these veins to the arteries of the same name (p. 292).

3. Innominate veins (p. 318, and Fig. 129, *m*; Fig. 115, *p*). Note the following tributaries:

a. Vertebral (p. 318, and Fig. 129, *i*).

b. Costocervical (p. 318). This vessel usually unites with the vertebral, the two joining to enter the innominate as a single trunk.

c. Subclavian (p. 318). This vessel continues from the axilla and joins the innominate at about the level of the first rib. It may be seen uniting with the external jugular in the formation of the superior vena cava.

d. External jugular (p. 319, and Fig. 131; Fig. 65, 5). The cervical course of this vessel has been observed. It receives the internal jugular (p. 320) which was found to be within the carotid sheath, and the left vein receives the thoracic duct (p. 320). The course of this duct should be noted at this time.

ARTERIAL SYSTEM: THORACIC AND CERVICAL PORTIONS

Trace the aorta (p. 281, and Fig. 115, *g*; Fig. 118, *a*) from its origin from the left ventricle. Follow the entire thoracic course of the vessel. Note the following branches:

1. Coronary arteries to the heart (p. 281, and Fig. 118, *p*).

2. Innominate (p. 282, and Fig. 115, *j*; Fig. 118, *b*). Note and follow the branches which arise from this vessel:

a. Mediastinal (p. 282, and Fig. 118, *m*).
b. Left common carotid (p. 282, and Fig. 115, *l*).
c. Right common carotid (p. 282, and Fig. 115, *m*).
d. Right subclavian (p. 282, and Fig. 115, *n*).
3. Left subclavian (p. 283, and Fig. 115, *k*; Fig. 118, *c*).
4. Intercostals (p. 283, and Fig. 118, *n*).
5. Bronchials (p. 283). Note carefully the origin of each.
6. Œsophageals (p. 283, and Fig. 118, *o*).
7. Lumbars (p. 283). One or two pairs may be seen arising craniad of the diaphragm.

Note again the origin of each subclavian artery (p. 290) and trace each to its exit from the thorax. In the axilla it becomes known as the axillary artery and has been seen. Trace the branches arising from the artery:

1. Vertebral (p. 290, and Fig. 118, *g′*). The course of this vessel was previously noted.
2. Internal mammary (pp. 290 and 292, and Fig. 118, *h*). The sternal course was seen.
3. Costocervical axis (pp. 290 and 292, and Fig. 118, *g*).
4. Thyrocervical axis (pp. 290 and 293, and Fig. 118, *j*).

Follow the course of the common carotid artery (p. 283, and Fig. 115, *e*; Fig. 119, *a*). The relations of this vessel as it passes through the carotid sheath in the cervical region were seen. Note the following branches:

1. Inferior thyroid (p. 283).
2. Superior thyroid (p. 284, and Fig. 119, *c*).
3. Occipital (p. 285, and Fig. 119, *f*). This was previously seen on the back of the skull. Note its complete course at this time.
4. Division into the internal (p. 285, and Fig. 119, *g*) and external carotids (p. 285, and Fig. 119, *m*). The internal carotid has been seen as it enters the foramen lacerum and takes part in the formation of the arterial circle of Willis. The external carotid will be studied in connection with the dissection of the head.

HEART

With the heart still in position in the thorax, note:

1. Blood supply (p. 281, and Fig. 115; Fig. 118).
2. Venous return from heart wall:

a. Vena cordis magna (pp. 315–316, and Fig. 118, 3).

b. Smaller veins of heart (p. 315).

3. Review the larger arteries and veins which connect with the heart.

Cut the main vascular trunks a short distance from the heart, and carefully remove the heart from the thorax. Study both the dorsal and ventral surfaces (p. 276, and Fig. 115; Fig. 116). Slit open the right auricle (p. 275), wash it out and note:

1. Auricular appendage (Fig. 115, *c*).
2. Entrance of the superior vena cava (Fig. 116, *e*) and the inferior vena cava (Fig. 116, *d*).
3. Musculi pectinati.
4. Coronary sinus.
5. Valve of coronary sinus.
6. Coronary veins entering the coronary sinus.
7. Fossa ovalis. Significance?
8. Auriculoventricular opening.

Study the left auricle in a similar manner (p. 279, and Fig. 115, *d*. Fig. 116, *b*). Observe:

1. Openings of pulmonary veins (Fig. 116, *g*, *h*, and *i*).
2. Auricular appendage.
3. Auriculoventricular opening.

Make a longitudinal incision in the ventral wall of the right ventricle and prolong it into the pulmonary artery. Make another incision from the right ventricle into the right auricle. Note the following within the right ventricle (p. 277, and Fig. 117):

1. Conus arteriosus (Fig. 115, *e*; Fig. 117, *f*).
2. Muscular trabeculæ (Fig. 117, *a*).
3. Tricuspid valve (Fig. 117, *d*, *d'*, and *d''*).
4. Chordæ tendineæ (Fig. 117, *c*).
5. Columnæ carneæ (Fig. 117, *b*).
6. Pulmonary semilunar valves (Fig. 117, *g*) and pulmonary sinuses.
7. Note the thickness of the ventricular wall and compare with that on the left side.

In a similar manner open the left ventricle (p. 279, and Fig. 115, *b*) and note:

1. Bicuspid valve.
2. Chordæ tendineæ.
3. Columnæ carneæ.
4. Thickness of muscular wall.

5. Aortic semilunar valves.
6. Sinuses of Valsalva.

Study of the thoracic portion of the respiratory and digestive systems will be deferred until that of the cranial portions has been completed. In that way their continuity may be better observed.

HEAD AND FACE

Make a detailed study of the skull (pp. 21–49). Review the skull as a whole (pp. 49–61).

The skin and skin muscles have been removed. The superficial muscles of the head and face probably will not be dissected by the student, but if they are to be studied, he should follow the outline given below:

1. Intermedius scutulorum (p. 96, and Fig. 63, *a*). This was reflected from the midline.
2. Corrugator supercilii medialis (p. 97, and Fig. 63, *b*). This was reflected from the midline during the opening of the cranial cavity.
3. Orbicularis oculi (p. 98, and Fig. 63, *c*).
4. Corrugator supercilii lateralis (p. 98, and Fig. 63, *d*; Fig. 64, *k*).
5. Frontoauricularis (p. 99) if present.
6. Levator auris longus (p. 99, and Fig. 63, *g* and *g'*). Transect and reflect.
7. Auricularis superior (p. 100, and Fig. 63, *k*). Transect.
8. Abductor auris longus (p. 100, and Fig. 63, *m*; Fig. 64, *q*).
9. Abductor auris brevis (p. 100, and Fig. 63, *l*). Transect.
10. The epicranius or occipitofrontalis (p. 101) has been studied and removed preparatory to the opening of the cranial cavity.
11. Zygomaticus (p. 101, and Fig. 64, *d*). This may still be seen if the platysma has been carefully removed.
12. Submentalis (p. 103, and Fig. 64, *c*).
13. Depressor conchæ (p. 103, and Fig. 64, *b*). Reflect this muscle and the two previously studied muscles from near their attachment to the external ear. This will expose:
14. Frontoscutularis (p. 104, and Fig. 63, *o*). Transect near the scutiform cartilage.
15. Adductor auris inferior (p. 104, and Fig. 64, *o*). Transect near its origin.

The foregoing muscles of the external ear are those which attach it to the head. The remainder of the external ear muscles will not be studied.

16. Orbicularis oris (p. 105, and Fig. 64, *i*).

17. Zygomaticus minor (p. 105, and Fig. 64, *e*). This muscle may not be present.

18. Quadratus labii superioris (p. 105, and Fig. 63, *p* and *q*; Fig. 64, *f* and *g*).

19. Caninus (p. 106, and Fig. 64, *f′*).

20. Buccinator (p. 106).

21. Myrtiformis (p. 106, and Fig. 64, *h*).

22. "Moustachier" (p. 107).

23. Quadratus labii inferioris (p. 107).

These small superficial muscles of the head may now be removed and the connective tissue cleaned away from the deeper structures to expose them as illustrated in Fig. 155 and Fig. 131. Identify the masseter muscle (p. 108, and Fig. 65; Fig. 66, *a*), parotid gland (p. 223, and Fig. 65, 1; Fig. 131, 10) and the submaxillary gland (p. 223, and Fig. 65, 2; Fig. 131, 11). At the cranial border of the parotid observe the following from above downward:

1. Anterior auricular artery (p. 287, and Fig. 131, *u*) and vein (p. 324, and Fig. 131, *n*).

2. Superficial temporal artery (p. 287, and Fig. 119, *p*; Fig. 120, *h*) and vein (p. 324, and Fig. 131, *m*).

3. Zygomatic nerve (p. 372, and Fig. 154, *i*).

4. Parotid duct (p. 223) embedded in the fascia of the masseter muscle. This may be traced craniad over the masseter to where it turns inward to enter the mouth cavity.

5. Ventral ramus of the facial nerve (p. 377, and Fig. 155, *e*) emerging from the cranial border of the submaxillary gland.

6. Anterior facial vein (p. 321, and Fig. 131, *c*). This may be traced cranially to the inner angle of the eye where it is seen to be formed by the union of the frontal and external nasal veins. Observe its tributaries:

a. Superior palpebral.

b. Inferior palpebral.

c. Superior labial.

d. Deep facial.

e. Inferior labial.

f. Submental.

7. Trace the anterior facial vein caudad to where it joins the posterior facial in the formation of the external jugular (p. 319, and Fig. 65, 5; Fig. 131, *a*). Along the course of the vein two large lymph nodes may be seen. Do not confuse these with the salivary glands.

8. The auriculotemporal branch of the fifth nerve (p. 373, and Fig. 154; Fig. 155) may be noted sending a branch to the parotid gland (p. 223).

Remove the lymph nodes from along the anterior facial vein. Note the external maxillary artery (p. 286, and Fig. 119, *j*). After passing ventral to the anterior facial vein it emerges from between the masseter and digastric muscles.

Beginning at the junction of the anterior and posterior facial veins, remove the parotid gland from the posterior facial vein (p. 323, and Fig. 131, *b*), and trace the vein dorsally to its formation. The posterior facial vein should then be cut and the entire gland removed. Remove the fascia from the lateral surface of the submaxillary gland and loosen the gland from all surrounding structures, being careful not to cut anything on its medial surface where the following may be noted:

1. Sublingual gland (p. 224).

2. Artery to the gland from the external maxillary artery. Fine nerve fibers may be seen accompanying this vessel.

3. The duct of the submaxillary gland passing dorsad of the digastric and mylohyoid muscles.

After the removal of the parotid there may be noted ventrad and caudad of the external ear:

1. Facial nerve (p. 375, and Fig. 155) emerging from the stylomastoid foramen and giving the following branches:

a. Posterior auricular (Fig. 155, *c*).

b. Branch to inside of ear (Fig. 155, *d*).

c. Branch to digastric muscle (Fig. 155, *b*).

d. Division into dorsal and ventral rami (Fig. 155, *e* and *f*). Trace the dorsal ramus forward and note its division into temporal and zygomatic branches. These have been noted.

2. External carotid artery (p. 285, and Fig. 119, *m*) passing cephalad medial to the digastric muscle (p. 285, and Fig. 119, *m*). After displacing the digastric muscle ventrad and observing the lingual nerve (p. 375, and Fig. 154, *b*), trace the following branches from external carotid:

a. The external maxillary which is given off at the dorsolateral border of the digastric muscle (p. 286, and Fig. 119, *j*). Trace this ventromedially to where it emerges from between the masseter and digastric muscles, and note its division into inferior and superior labial branches (Fig. 119, *k* and *l*). Note the branch to the submaxillary and sublingual glands.

b. Posterior auricular (p. 287, and Fig. 119, *o*). Note its anterior auricular branch.

c. Superficial temporal (p. 287, and Fig. 119, *p*; Fig. 120, *h*).

1′. Branch to masseter muscle.

2′. Auricular branch to cranial surface of the external ear.

3′. The main trunk continues in a cranial direction, accompanying the superficial temporal vein.

d. The external carotid continues craniad as the internal maxillary, which turns caudad at the caudal end of the mandible and goes deep at the caudal border of the dorsal surface of the masseter muscle.

3. Auriculotemporal branch from the mandibular division of the fifth nerve (p. 373, and Fig. 154; Fig. 155, *n*) passing dorsad between the auricula and the zygomatic process of the temporal bone, emerging at the caudal border of the masseter muscle. Branches:

a. Auricular.

b. Temporal.

c. Small branches were previously noted to pass from this nerve to the parotid gland.

Study the stylohyoid muscle (p. 112, and Fig. 65, *d*) and remove it from its origin, leaving it attached at its insertion. Study the digastric (p. 107, and Fig. 65, *b*), bisect it in the middle, and reflect. This exposes the mylohyoid muscle (p. 114, and Fig. 65, *c*). Observe:

1. Hypoglossal nerve (p. 383, and Fig. 156, *b*) passing with the lingual artery (p. 286, and Fig. 119, *i*; Fig. 120, *d*), the two passing deep to the mylohyoid muscle.

2. Submaxillary and sublingual ducts, the two passing together to disappear beneath the mylohyoid.

3. The submental branch of the external maxillary artery (p. 286) passing along the dorsal surface of the digastric muscle.

Study the masseter muscle (p. 108, and Fig. 65; Fig. 66, *a*) and then carefully remove it, leaving all nerves and blood vessels encountered undisturbed. During the process of removal of the muscle, note its nerve supply (p. 374).

Remove the zygomatic arch, thus exposing the temporalis muscle (p. 110, and Fig. 63, *n*). Carefully remove the fascia from its surface and make a study of its origin, insertion, and blood supply. Bisect near its insertion and remove the coronoid and condyloid processes of the mandible. Note the mandibular articulation (p. 61) and the insertion of the pterygoid muscles (p. 111, and Fig. 66, *b* and *c*).

Clean the outer surface of the mandible to expose the mental foramen and mental nerve (p. 375). Origin of the nerve? Bisect the anterior facial vein at the region where it crosses the mandible, and cut the mandible through caudal to the canine tooth. Separate the mylohyoid muscle from its insertion on the mandible, and turn to the right the portion of the mandible which has been cut loose (Fig. 154; Fig. 120). Note:

1. Inferior alveolar artery (p. 287, and Fig. 120, *j*) and nerve (p. 375, and Fig. 154, *d*) entering the mandibular foramen. What is the origin of each?

2. Internal maxillary artery (p. 287, and Fig. 119, *n*; Fig. 120, *i*) dorsal to the pterygoid muscles. Trace its following branches:

a. Inferior alveolar entering the mandibular foramen.

b. Middle meningeal entering the foramen ovale.

c. Branches to the carotid plexus which is formed around the maxillary division of the trigeminal nerve where it leaves the foramen rotundum. Note its branches:

1′. Ophthalmic.
2′. Lesser palatine.
3′. Sphenopalatine.
4′. Infraorbital. This vessel follows the infraorbital nerve into the floor of the orbit.

Observe the maxillary (p. 371) and mandibular divisions (p. 373) of the trigeminal nerve (Fig. 154). Note the following branches:

1. Maxillary (p. 371).

a. Infraorbital (Fig. 154, *f*; Fig. 155, *l*). Two large trunks accompanied by the infraorbital artery.

b. Lachrymal (Fig. 154, *j*; Fig. 155, *m*). A small nerve which enters the dorsolateral angle of the orbit.

c. Zygomatic (Fig. 154, *i*). This may be noted accompanying the lachrymal for some distance.

d. Sphenopalatine (Fig. 154, *g*).

2. Mandibular (p. 373).

a. Auriculotemporal (Fig. 154; Fig. 155, *n*). This passes dorsad between the auditory meatus and the zygomatic process of the temporal bone.

b. Deep temporal.

c. Massetericus.

d. Pterygoideus.

e. Buccinatorius (Fig. 154, *e*).

f. The main trunk of the nerve now divides into:

1′. Inferior alveolar (p. 375, and Fig. 154, *d*) which enters the mandibular foramen. This has been noted. Observe that before it enters the mandibular foramen small branches pass from it to the digastric and mylohyoid muscles.

2′. Lingual (p. 375, and Fig. 154, *b*). This nerve passes between the external and internal pterygoid muscles, and then ventrad of the external pterygoid to reach the tongue. Note that near its origin it is joined by the chorda tympani nerve from the facial (p. 376). Study the complete course of the chorda tympani. What is its significance? Observe medial to the lingual nerve the ducts of the submaxillary and sublingual glands. Note nerve fibers passing from the lingual nerve to follow these ducts caudad to reach the glands. Significance?

THE ORBIT AND ITS CONTENTS

Cut the malar bone at its articulation with the temporal, and remove the portions of the frontal and sphenoid bones which form the medial wall of the orbit, thus exposing the orbit and its contents. Note:

1. Bony make-up of the orbit on the articulated skeleton (p. 53).

2. Eyelids or palpebræ (p. 416). Note:

a. Conjunctiva.

b. Meibomian glands.

c. Nictitating membrane with supporting cartilage and Harderian glands.

d. Oribicularis oculi muscle.

e. Levator palpebræ superioris muscle.

3. Lachrymal gland (p. 417, and Fig. 154, 11) at the lateral angle of the eye.

4. Openings of lachrymal ducts on each eyelid near medial angle.

5. Lachrymal nerve to the lachrymal gland (p. 371, and Fig. 154, *j*; Fig. 155, *m*).

6. Periorbita (p. 416). This is a tough membranous sac surrounding the contents of the orbit and separating them from other structures. Separate it from its enclosed structures, being careful not to destroy or disturb any of the relations of these structures. Remove the lachrymal gland and separate the levator palpebræ muscle from its origin, leaving it attached at its insertion. Note:

a. Extrinsic eye muscles (p. 418).

1′. Superior and inferior obliques.

2′. Four recti.

3′. Retractor oculi.

b. Frontal nerve (p. 370) passing along the lateral border of the superior oblique muscle, after entering the orbit dorsad of the superior rectus.

c. Ophthalmic artery and vein (p. 289, and Fig. 120, *n*).

d. Trochlear nerve (p. 370) entering the orbit dorsad of the superior rectus and distributed to the superior oblique. As it enters the orbit it is immediately medial to the frontal branch of the trigeminal nerve.

e. Oculomotor nerve (p. 369) enters the orbit between the superior and lateral recti muscles and immediately sends a branch to the medial rectus and retractor oculi. The main trunk of the nerve passes laterad above the optic nerve, supplies the inferior rectus, and sends a branch to the inferior oblique (Fig. 166, *f*). The branch to the inferior oblique is connected with the ciliary ganglion (pp. 369, 410); which is to be noted. Short ciliary nerves (p. 369) pass from this ganglion to the eyeball. Significance of the ganglion and short ciliary nerves?

f. Abducens nerve (p. 375, and Fig. 154, *k*) enters the orbit laterad of the superior rectus and dorsad of the lateral rectus. It supplies the lateral rectus.

g. Ethmoidal nerve (p. 371) enters the orbit ventral to the superior rectus, between it and the lateral rectus, passing ventrad of the superior rectus and dorsal to the optic nerve. It passes in a craniomedial direction dorsal to the internal rectus and ventral to the superior oblique to enter the ethmoidal foramen. Note the long ciliary branches from this nerve which pass to the eyeball in company with the optic nerve (p. 371).

h. Infraorbital nerve (p. 372, and Fig. 154, *f*; Fig. 155, *l*) passes along the floor of the orbit to enter the infraorbital foramen, through which it passes to reach the face. Note the branches from this nerve on the face.

i. Infratrochlear nerve (p. 371) passes between the superior rectus and superior oblique muscles and then ventral to the superior oblique to reach the upper eyelid near its medial angle.

Cut the extrinsic eye muscles from their origin and remove the eyeball from the orbit with its muscles attached. Study the relations of the muscles, noting their origin and insertion. Remove the muscles from the eyeball and bisect it sagitally by cutting through the entire eyeball from the optic nerve to the center of the cornea. Place the bisected eye in a pan of water, and note:

1. Coats of eyeball (p. 420, and Fig. 167).
2. Chambers of eye (p. 421, and Fig. 167).
3. Lens (p. 421).

After the removal of the eye the sphenopalatine ganglion may be noted (pp. 372, 411; Fig. 164*a*, *B*). Note the nerves associated with it, and determine the significance of each.

MIDDLE AND INNER EAR

With a small chisel or bone forceps remove the roof from the internal auditory meatus and facial canal in the petrous portion of the temporal bone, following the course of the facial (p. 375) and auditory (p. 377) nerves. Observe the geniculate ganglion (p. 375) associated with the facial nerve while it is within the facial canal. Careful dissection may reveal the origin of the superficial petrosal and chorda tympani nerves (p. 375). The peripheral distribution of these nerves has been noted. Identify the vestibular and auditory portions of the auditory nerve. Remove the roof of the tympanic cavity. Note the inner surface of the tympanic membrane and the malleus connected with it, the tensor tympani muscle (p. 431) attached to the malleus by a small tendon, and observe other contents of the tympanic cavity. Note the stapes articulating in the fenestra vestibuli and the stapedius muscle (p. 431) attached to it.

Note the fenestra vestibuli, fenestra cochleæ, and the promontory (p. 34). Remove the wall of the promontory and find the cochlea. Open the vestibule and find as many of the openings of the semicircular canals as possible.

MOUTH CAVITY AND ITS CONTENTS

Place the specimen on its back and proceed as follows:

1. Review the stylohyoid and digastric muscles (pp. 112 and 107).

2. Observe the transverse vein (p. 321, and Fig. 131, *d*).

3. Review the mylohyoid muscle (p. 114). This was cut from its attachment to the mandible and reflected to its origin.

4. Observe the geniohyoid muscle (p. 113) immediately dorsad of the mylohyoid.

5. Hypoglossal nerve (p. 383, and Fig. 156, *b*) is to be noted passing in a cranial direction lateral to the external carotid artery. It passes ventral to the styloglossus and turns laterad to supply the hyoglossus muscle.

6. Extrinsic tongue muscles are to be identified but not dissected (p. 228):

a. Genioglossus (Fig. 96, *f*).

b. Hyoglossus (Fig. 96, *h*).

c. Styloglossus (Fig. 96, *e*). The external carotid artery passes over the lateral surface of the caudal portion of this muscle.

7. Lingual artery (p. 386, and Fig. 119, *i*; Fig. 120, *d*) is to be noted passing craniad from the external carotid artery dorsal and medial to the hyoglossus muscle.

Disarticulate the mandible and cut the cheek from it, together with the muscles that attach to it and have been studied. Remove the mandible, leaving the mouth cavity exposed for study. Study the teeth in the mandible and in the upper jaw (p. 224). Proceed with a study of the contents of the mouth cavity:

1. Tongue (p. 226, and Fig. 95). Observe its shape and nature of its epithelium. Note its attachment to the floor of the mouth by the frenulum linguæ. Note the papillæ (p. 227), their types and the distribution of each. Study the intrinsic tongue muscles (p. 229).

2. Hard and soft palate (p. 230).

3. Isthmus faucium. Locate the openings of the ducts from the salivary glands (p. 222).

RESPIRATORY AND DIGESTIVE SYSTEMS

Preparatory to the study of the pharynx, note the following muscles connected with the hyoid bone:

1. Stylohyoid (p. 112, and Fig. 65, *d*). This muscle has been studied and reflected from its origin.

2. Review the digastric (p. 107, and Fig. 65, *b*). This has been transected and reflected.

3. Mylohyoid (p. 114, and Fig. 65, *c*). This has been reflected from its insertion on the mandible.

4. Geniohyoid (p. 113, and Fig. 67, *g*).

5. Jugulohyoid (p. 113, and Fig. 67, *b*).

Disarticulate the hyoid bone from the tympanic bulla and turn it medially. Clean the connective tissue from the pharyngeal muscles as in Fig. 66, and without destroying nerves or blood vessels dissect as follows:

1. Constrictor pharyngis superior (p. 233, and Fig. 66, *f*).
2. Constrictor pharyngis medius (p. 233, and Fig. 96, *j*).
3. Constrictor pharyngis inferior (p. 232, and Fig. 96, *k*).
4. Glossopharyngeus (p. 232, and Fig. 96, *i*).

Observe nerves to the preceding muscles from the pharyngeal branch of the vagus nerve (p. 379) and from the glossopharyngeal through the pharyngeal plexus.

Make a longitudinal incision through the entire length of the lateral wall of the pharynx, thus exposing its cavity, which is continuous cephalad with the oral and nasal cavities and caudad with the cavities of the larynx and œsophagus. Observe:

1. Nature of cavity (p. 231).

2. Division into oral pharynx, nasopharynx, and pharynx proper.

3. Continuation of the nasopharynx cranially through the choanæ with the nasal cavities. Pass a probe from the nasopharynx into the openings of the Eustachian tubes. Note that the nasopharynx is separated from the oral pharynx by the soft palate (p. 229). Dissect the tensor and levator veli palatini muscles (p. 230, and Fig. 66, *d* and *e*).

4. Pillars of fauces in which lie the pharyngeal tonsils (p. 230).

5. Epiglottis (p. 246).

Remove about 1.5 cm. of the anterior end of the snout by making a transverse section with the saw through the bones of that region, and study the structure of the nasal cavities (p. 243).

Review the course of the vagus nerve in the neck region and observe again its superior and inferior laryngeal branches to the larynx (p. 380, and Fig. 157).

Separate the larynx with the attached hyoid bone from the pharynx and remove the larynx, trachea, bronchi, and lungs from the body, and note:

1. Larynx (p. 246, and Fig. 104).

a. Epiglottis.

b. Vestibule.

c. True vocal folds.

d. False vocal folds.

e. Ventriculus.

f. Glottis.

g. Muscles. These should be carefully dissected and then removed and a study made of the cartilaginous skeleton of the larynx.

1′. Thyrohyoid (p. 249, and Fig. 96, *p*).

2′. Cricothyroid (p. 249, and Fig. 96, *n*). Remove these two muscles on the left side to expose the cricothyroid and thyrohyoid membranes.

3′. Cut away the caudal two-thirds of the left half of the thyroid cartilage, disarticulate from the cricoid cartilage, and remove. This will expose:

a′. Thyroarytenoid muscle (p. 251, and Fig. 105, *d*).

b′. Lateral cricoarytenoid (p. 251, and Fig. 105, *c*).

4′. Arytenoid (p. 250, and Fig. 105, *a*).

5′. Posterior cricoarytenoid (p. 249, and Fig. 105, *b*).

2. Trachea (p. 251, and Fig. 105, 5; Fig. 106, *a*).

3. Bronchi (p. 252, and Fig. 106). Note the plan of division within each lung. Eparterial and hyparterial branches within the right lung.

4. Lungs (p. 252, and Fig. 106). Note the lobes and the differences between the right and left lung.

Trace the œsophagus (p. 234) from its pharyngeal end to its exit from the thoracic cavity through the œsophageal opening in the diaphragm.

1. Observe its course in relation to the vertebral column.

2. Review its nerve and blood supply.

3. Make a transverse section through the wall of the œsophagus to note:

a. Cavity.

b. Mucosa.

c. Submucosa.

d. Muscular layers.

VENTRAL MUSCLES OF CERVICAL REGION

Remove the œsophagus to expose the muscles of the ventral side of the cervical region. Clean the connective tissue from the muscles, and note the following:

1. Longus capitis (p. 142, and Fig. 72, *a*).
2. Longus colli (p. 144, and Fig. 72, *g* and *g''*).
3. Levator scapulæ ventralis (p. 120, and Fig. 72, *c* and *c''*). Note the origin at this time; the insertion has been noted.
4. Rectus capitis anterior minor (p. 143, and Fig. 72, *b*). To note, cut through on one side of the longus capitis and one head of the levator scapulæ ventralis and remove the proximal portions on the right side, as in Fig. 72.
5. Obliquus capitis superior (p. 136, and Fig. 72, *e*).
6. Rectus capitis lateralis (p. 143, and Fig. 72, *d*).

ABDOMINAL WALL

The integument has been removed from the abdominal wall. Carefully remove the connective tissue from the muscles of the body wall, noting the anterior and lateral cutaneous branches from the spinal nerves of this region. Note the following:

1. Inferior epigastric artery (p. 309) passing cranially on the ventral surface of the rectus abdominis muscle. If the specimen is not well injected, it may not be visible at this time.
2. Structure of abdominal wall.

a. Linea alba. Significance?

b. External oblique muscle (p. 153, and Fig. 68, *p*). Transect by an incision parallel to the tendons of origin and about an inch from its attachment. Reflect in both directions.

c. Internal oblique muscle (p. 154, and Fig. 73, *o*). Transect and reflect in the same manner as the external muscle.

d. Transversus abdominis (p. 155, and Fig. 69, *l*).

e. Rectus abdominis (p. 155, and Fig. 73, *k*). Open the rectus sheath by a longitudinal incision paralleling the linea alba throughout its length and about 1 cm. from it. Study the rectus muscle and other contents of the rectus sheath.

Open the abdominal cavity by cutting through the rectus muscle along the line of incision already made through the outer layer of its sheath. Make lateral incisions on each side from the anterior end of the longitudinal incision to the dorsal body wall, following the caudal border of the costal margin. Turn the flaps thus produced laterad to expose the abdominal cavity and its contents.

PRELIMINARY SURVEY OF ABDOMINAL VISCERA

Make a preliminary survey of the viscera, and by carefully moving parts locate the various organs. Read about the peritoneum (p. 218; Fig. 92*b*) and make a study of its reflection, noting all folds, ligaments, etc., described for it. Note:

1. Division into parietal and visceral portions.
2. Ligamentum teres of liver.
3. Lesser omentum consisting of duodenohepatic and gastrohepatic ligaments.
4. Greater omentum (p. 219). Note that it covers most of the viscera as a sheet. Free it from the underlying viscera and note its attachments:
   a. Greater curvature of stomach.
   b. Spleen.
   c. Dorsal body wall. Relation to transverse colon and pancreas.
5. Coronary ligament.
6. Triangular ligament.
7. Mesentery.
8. Mesocolon.
9. Mesorectum.
10. Suspensory and lateral ligaments of bladder.
11. Broad and round ligaments of uterus and ligament of ovary in the female.
12. Division of the peritoneal cavity into the greater and lesser cavities, the communication between the two being by the foramen of Winslow (epiploic foramen).

Make a complete study of the diaphragm (p. 151). Note its form and position, its attachments, and its muscular and tendinous portions. Identify the openings in it and the structures traversing it.

1. Aortic opening.
2. Vena caval opening.
3. Œsophageal opening. The dorsal and ventral branches of the

two vagus nerves enter the abdomen on the dorsal and ventral surfaces of the œsophagus.

Make the following general visceral observations:

1. Liver (p. 239, and Fig. 100; Fig. 101). Note its division into lobes.

a. Right median or cystic and right lateral lobes.

b. Left median and left lateral lobes.

c. Caudate or Spigelian lobe.

2. Stomach (p. 234, and Fig. 97). Note the form and position.

a. Cardiac and pyloric ends.

b. Greater and lesser curvatures.

c. Fundus.

d. Peritoneal connections.

1′. Greater omentum along the greater curvature.

2′. Lesser omentum along the lesser curvature.

3′. Gastrohepatic ligament.

4′. Gastroduodenal ligament.

5′. Gastrolienal ligament.

3. Spleen (p. 242, and Fig. 102, *e*). Note its size, form, position, and attachments.

a. Relation to greater omentum.

b. Gastrolienal ligament.

4. Pancreas (p. 241, and Fig. 102, *a*). Note:

a. Its lobulated structure.

b. Relation to the greater omentum.

c. Relation to stomach, duodenum, and spleen.

5. Intestine.

a. Small intestine (p. 236). In studying this structure, be careful not to disturb its blood supply.

1′. Note its division into duodenum, jejunum, and ileum, and particularly the course and relations of the duodenum.

b. Large intestine (p. 237). Note its division into the colon and rectum, and the further division of the colon into the ascending, transverse, and descending portions.

1′. Note the cæcum at the beginning of the colon (p. 238, and Fig. 98, *c*).

2′. The muscles associated with the rectum and anus will be considered with the urogenital system.

6. Urinary bladder (p. 256, and Fig. 111, *a*). Note its peritoneal relations and the suspensory and lateral ligaments.

7. Kidneys (p. 255). Do not disturb their peritoneal coverings at this time.

8. Female reproductive system (p. 263).

a. Ovaries and their ligaments.

b. Oviducts.

c. Uterus.

d. Broad and round ligaments of the uterus.

ABDOMINAL SYMPATHETIC NERVOUS SYSTEM

The portion of the sympathetic nervous system associated with the abdominal portion of the digestive system is to be studied at this time, preparatory to a more thorough study of the abdominal viscera. Turn the entire intestine and the stomach to the right side of the specimen (to the dissectors left) and observe:

1. Left kidney.
2. Left suprarenal body.
3. Greater curvature of the stomach.

Carefully tease away the peritoneum on the left side between the stomach and the suprarenal body and expose:

1. Superior mesenteric plexus (p. 413, and Fig. 164, *g*; Fig. 164*a*, *K*) and ganglion (p. 413, and Fig. 164, *f*; Fig. 164*a*, *H*) lying upon the superior mesenteric artery (p. 303, and Fig. 126, *d*; Fig. 164, 5).

2. Left cœliac (semilunar) ganglion and plexus (p. 413, and Fig. 164, *d*; Fig. 164*a*, *G*) on the superior mesenteric artery. It is usually considered that there are two cœliac ganglia, a right and a left, but the two are so closely fused that only one can be distinguished.

From the cœliac ganglion follow the great splanchnic nerve (pp. 410, 412; and Fig. 164, *b*; Fig. 164*a*, 18) to where it passes through the diaphragm. Follow other branches from the same ganglion to the sympathetic trunk and determine how many of these trunks are present. These latter trunks are the lesser splanchnic nerves (pp. 410, 412; and Fig. 164, *c*; Fig. 164*a*, 20). Trace branches from the cœliac ganglion to the surrounding viscera. These nerves constitute the cœliac or solar plexus (p. 413, and Fig. 164, *e*; Fig. 164*a*, *J*), and each nerve may be distinguished according to the organ to which it passes, as the hepatic plexus, the renal plexus, the suprarenal plexus, the gastric plexus, etc. (pp. 382; 413). Distinguish as many of these as possible, and note that they follow the blood vessels to the organs that they supply.

In the posterior part of the mesocolon (p. 219) locate the inferior mesenteric artery (p. 306, and Fig. 126, *i*; Fig. 164, 7) and, by carefully teasing away the peritoneum, note:

1. Inferior mesenteric ganglion (p. 413, and Fig. 164, *i*; 164*a*, *I*) and the inferior mesenteric plexus (p. 413, and Fig. 164*a*, *L*).

Transect the adrenolumbalis artery and vein (p. 304, and Fig. 126, *e*, and p. 326; Fig. 126, *s*) opposite the anterior end of the left kidney. Cut through the parietal peritoneum lateral to the kidney, being careful not to destroy the ureter or any blood vessels. Loosen the kidney from the body wall, turn it to the right and tease away the connective tissue between the aorta and the psoas minor muscle (p. 139, and Fig. 162, 9) to expose the abdominal portion of the sympathetic trunk (p. 410, and Fig. 164). Trace the trunk caudad from the diaphragm as far as exposed, noting the ganglia, the connections with the spinal nerves, and the branches to the viscera. The remainder of the trunk will be traced later.

HEPATIC PORTAL SYSTEM

The portal system of circulation can be best demonstrated on a freshly killed specimen. But it should also be dissected on the specimen now being used. Locate the following vessels:

1. Portal vein (p. 326, and Fig. 132, *a*). Note its course in the lesser omentum, where it is accompanied by the bile duct and the hepatic artery. Note its formation near the pyloric end of the stomach by the union of the superior mesenteric and gastrosplenic veins.

2. Superior mesenteric vein and its tributaries from the small intestine (p. 328, and Fig. 132, *b*).

3. Inferior mesenteric vein and its tributaries from the large intestine (p. 328, and Fig. 132, *j*). It usually enters the superior mesenteric vein.

4. Coronaria ventriculi (p. 326, and Fig. 132, *f*) from the lesser curvature of the stomach. It will usually be found to enter the portal vein direct.

5. Pancreaticoduodenal vein (p. 326, and Fig. 132, *d*).

6. Gastrosplenic vein (p. 327, and Fig. 132, *c*). Note the tributaries which unite in its formation and its course to the union with the superior mesenteric in the formation of the portal vein.

ABDOMINAL AORTA AND INFERIOR VENA CAVA

In the study of the arteries be very careful not to destroy any accompanying veins. Note the entrance of the aorta through the aortic opening in the diaphragm. Trace it throughout its entire abdominal course. Note the aortic plexus of nerves and the aortic lymph nodes. Observe each branch from the aorta, its divisions and the structures supplied by each (p. 301, and Fig. 126):

1. Cœliac (p. 301, and Fig. 125).

a. Splenic branch to spleen.

b. Left gastric to stomach.

c. Hepatic. The main trunk passes in the lesser omentum with the portal vein and bile duct. Note its branches:

1′. Pyloric.

2′. Superior pancreaticoduodenal.

3′. Right gastroepiploic.

2. Superior mesenteric (p. 303, and Fig. 126, *d*).

a. Inferior pancreaticoduodenal.

b. Right colic.

c. Middle colic.

d. Ileocolic.

e. Intestinal branches to the small intestine.

f. Note the mesenteric lymph nodes within the mesentery alongside the arteries to the intestine.

3. Adrenolumbalis (p. 304, and Fig. 126, *e*).

a. Phrenic (p. 304, and Fig. 126, *f*). This branch may arise from the cœliac. Trace to the posterior surface of the diaphragm.

4. Renals (p. 304, and Fig. 126, *g*). A branch to the suprarenal and the spermatic artery may arise from this vessel. Observe these trunks if present.

5. Internal spermatic or ovarians (p. 304, and Fig. 126, *h*).

6. Inferior mesenteric (p. 306, and Fig. 126, *j*).

a. Left colic.

b. Superior hemorrhoidal.

7. Iliolumbars (p. 306, and Fig. 126, *j*).

8. External iliacs (p. 307, and Fig. 126, *k*). Observe their exit from the abdomen through the ventral body wall. Their branches will be noted later.

9. Lumbars (p. 306).

10. Internal iliacs or hypogastrics (p. 307, and Fig. 126, *l*).

a. Umbilical (Fig. 126, *n*). Note its superior and inferior vesical branches to the bladder.

b. Superior gluteal (Fig. 126, *p*).

c. Middle hemorrhoidal (Fig. 126, *r*).

d. Inferior gluteal (Fig. 126, *q*).

11. Middle sacral (p. 309, and Fig. 126, *o*).

Fine nerve strands may be traced along with these arterial branches. They are sympathetic branches from the aortic plexus and are passing to the viscera to furnish their nerve supply.

Trace the inferior vena cava (p. 325, and Fig. 126, *a*; Fig. 129, *c*) from its origin in the pelvis to its exit through the vena caval opening in the diaphragm. Note its formation by the union of the two common iliac veins and its tributaries:

1. Common iliac veins (p. 328, and Fig. 126, *w*). The left one of these two veins usually receives the medial sacral vein. Note the formation of the two common iliac veins by the union of the external and internal iliacs on each side.
2. Lumbars.
3. Spermatics or ovarians (Fig. 126, *u*). The left spermatic or ovarian usually joins the left renal while the right enters the inferior vena cava direct.
4. Renals.
5. Adrenolumbalis (Fig. 126, *s*).
6. Hepatics. These vessels enter the vena cava as it passes through the liver substance.
7. Phrenics enter the vena cava as it passes through the diaphragm.

Compare the branches of the abdominal aorta with the tributaries of the inferior vena cava and note the differences. Account for these.

ABDOMINAL PORTION OF DIGESTIVE SYSTEM

Note the entrance of the œsophagus into the abdominal cavity through the œsophageal opening in the diaphragm. After a short course it connects with the cardiac end of the stomach. Note the vagus nerve trunks and trace these on to the greater and lesser curvatures of the stomach.

In the free edge of the lesser omentum locate the common bile duct (p. 241, and Fig. 101, *i*) accompanying the portal vein and hepatic artery. Note:

1. Cystic duct from gall bladder (Fig. 101, *g*).

2. Hepatic ducts (Fig. 101, *h*).

3. Entrance of the common bile duct into the wall of the duodenum. Note whether or not it is joined by the pancreatic duct before it enters the duodenal wall.

Observe the nature, form, and position of the pancreas (p. 241, and Fig. 102, *a*). Tease away the gland from around the duct and note its formation and course. Look for accessory pancreatic ducts.

Note the form, position, and visceral relations of the spleen (p. 242, and Fig. 102, *e*). Remove it from the abdomen.

Ligate the rectum at its cranial end, cut the duodenum about three centimeters from its junction with the stomach, and remove the entire intestine by cutting the suspending peritoneal folds near their attachments to the intestine. The rectum and anal canal will be studied during the dissection of the urogenital system. Carefully examine the entire intestine (pp. 236–239):

1. Measure its entire length and compare with the body length of the animal.

2. Slit it open throughout its entire length and wash out its contents. Examine the inner surface by the aid of a hand lens and try to delimit the three divisions of the small intestine.

3. Study the cross section of the intestinal wall, and note:

a. Inner mucosa. In the small intestine this is thrown into minute elevations, the villi.

b. Submucosa.

c. Inner circular muscle fibers.

d. Outer longitudinal muscle fibers.

e. Serous (peritoneal) coverings.

4. Observe the nature of the ileocœcal valve (p. 237, and Fig. 99, *g*).

5. The wall of the large intestine is much like that of the small, except that it has no villi.

Remove the stomach (p. 234, and Fig. 97) by transecting the oesophagus near the cardiac orifice and cutting the lesser omentum along its attachment to the lesser curvature. Slit open the stomach along the greater curvature and wash out its contents. Observe:

1. Structure of wall.

2. Pyloric valve (p. 235) guarding the opening from the pylorus of the stomach to the duodenum.

Review the ligaments which hold the liver in place.

1. Coronary (p. 221).
2. Ligamentum teres or round ligament (p. 220).
3. Triangular (p. 221).
4. Lesser omentum (p. 220).

Remove the liver (p. 239) by cutting the above ligaments, and carefully study:

1. Lobe structure (Fig. 100; Fig. 101).
2. Duct system (Fig. 101). This has been studied. Review it.
3. Arterial supply and venous drainage. Review.
4. Peritoneal and visceral relations.

FORMATION OF AZYGOS VEIN AND THORACIC DUCT

The thoracic course and connections of these vessels have been noted, but should be reviewed at this time.

Observe the formation of the azygos vein (p. 316) by the union of a few small trunks in the lumbar region and its exit from the abdomen between the crura of the diaphragm.

Various groups of lymph glands have been noted in the abdomen. These are drained by the thoracic duct (p. 333). Observe its formation and abdominal exit between the crura of the diaphragm.

UROGENITAL SYSTEM

A. Excretory System.

Remove the peritoneum and fat from either kidney (p. 255, and Fig. 108), being careful not to open the capsule of the kidney or to destroy the connections of the ureter. Note the kidney:

1. Shape and size.
2. Relative position of the two kidneys. Is one anterior to the other?
3. Peritoneal relations.
4. Capsule.
5. Hilus. In connection with this, note the following vessels which enter it:

a. Renal artery.

b. Renal vein.

c. Ureter.

Open the capsule of the kidney and cut away some of the kidney substance parallel to the ventral surface to observe:

1. Sinus. What is its relation to the hilus?
2. Pelvis. Probe through this into the ureter.
3. Papilla.

Make a transverse section of the kidney and note the cortical and medullary layers.

The connection of the ureter with the pelvis of the kidney has been noted. Trace the complete course of the ureter (p. 256) from the hilus of the kidney to the bladder. Note its relations to all surrounding structures and its entrance into the bladder. If the specimen is a male, be careful not to injure the vas deferens.

Study the urinary bladder (p. 256):

1. Form and position.
2. Neck. Trace to the pelvis.
3. Peritoneal relations and ligaments.
4. Urinary bladder. Pass a bristle through the ureter into the bladder, then open the bladder and note the internal openings of the ureters.

B. Male Genital Organs.

Each student should study the reproductive organs of both a male and a female specimen. After dissecting the one in his own specimen, he should make a temporary exchange of specimens with another student so as to study the other in a specimen already dissected.

Study the external genital organs of the male (p. 257). Carefully remove the integument about the anus and expose the external sphincter ani muscle (p. 268, and Fig. 113, *i*). Trace to its origin. Remove the scrotal integument, if this has not been done, and dissect the coverings of the testis (p. 258).

1. Intercolumnar or cremasteric fascia.
2. Levator scroti or cremasteric muscle.
3. Tunica vaginalis communis.
4. Tunica vaginalis propria.

The testis is now exposed (p. 259, and Fig. 110). Note the epididymis, the vas deferens, and the spermatic cord. Trace the spermatic cord to the external inguinal ring (p. 259) and expose the ring. Dissect off, in order, the external abdominal oblique (p. 153), the internal abdominal oblique (p. 154), and the transversus abdominis (p. 155) muscles, and trace the spermatic cord with the tunica vaginalis communis and tunica propria to the internal inguinal ring (p. 259).

Determine the structures present in the spermatic cord besides the vas deferens (p. 258). Trace the vas deferens (p. 260, and Fig. 111) within the abdominal cavity as far as it can be seen dorsal to the neck of the bladder. Note its relations to the bladder and to the ureter.

Cut the skin along the dorsal surface of the penis and reflect it. Dissect the suspensory ligament of the penis (p. 262). Pass a bristle through the urethra from its external opening and remove the integument from the entire penis. Identify the corpora cavernosa and the corpus spongiosum and urethra (p. 262).

Remove any fat from the side of the rectum and find the levator ani muscle (p. 269, and Fig. 162, 11). Transect and reflect. Sphincter ani internus (p. 269, and Fig. 113, *h*). Dissect the ischiocavernosus (p. 269, and Fig. 113, *m*) and bulbocavernosus (p. 271, and Fig. 113, *l*) muscles, and beneath the ischiocavernosus find the bulb of the corpus cavernosum penis. Cut the bulb from the ramus of the ischium on one side.

Clean the muscles from the pelvis on the side from which the bulb of the penis is removed, and use the bone forceps to remove the body of the pubis and ischial ramus. Trace the neck of the bladder to its junction with the vas deferens and the urethra from that point to the external opening (Fig. 111). Find Cowper's glands (p. 261, and Fig. 111, *i*), and the prostate gland (p. 261, and Fig. 111, *g*). The other small muscles associated with the urogenital system (p. 268, and Fig. 113) may now be dissected, but they are so small that their dissection should usually be omitted.

Slit the urethra on one side throughout its entire length and find:

1. The openings of the two vasa deferentia with the veru montanum (p. 261) between them.
2. Openings of the prostate gland.
3. Openings of Cowper's glands.

Study further the structure of the penis (p. 262) by making cross sections through the body and a longitudinal section through the glans.

C. Female Genital Organs.

Without any dissection observe:

1. Ovaries (p. 264) and their ligaments (p. 264, and Fig. 112).

2. Uterine tube and its ostium (p. 264).
3. Uterus (p. 266, and Fig. 112, *f* and *i*).
a. Cornua.
b. Body. Observe it as far as exposed at present.
c. Broad and round ligaments (p. 266).

Remove the ventral wall of the pelvis on one side and find the vagina and urogenital sinus (p. 267). The levator ani muscle (p. 269, and Fig. 162, 11) must be cut and reflected. Note the constrictor vestibuli, caudovaginalis, and urethralis muscles (p. 272, and Fig. 114).

Introduce a probe from the uterus into the vagina and feel the hard cervix uteri (p. 266). Open the vagina on one side, being careful not to cut the os uteri (p. 266). Examine the cervix uteri and the os uteri (p. 266).

Pass a probe through the bladder and note that it emerges into the urogenital sinus. Find the end of the clitoris (p. 267) and its prepuce, and then dissect the integument carefully from around the urogenital sinus. Note the external sphincter muscle of the sinus, the levator vulvæ muscle (p. 272, and Fig. 114), which is equivalent to the levator scroti or cremasteric muscle in the male and is continuous with the sphincter ani externus. Locate the corpora cavernosa of the clitoris (p. 267) and the ischiocavernosus muscles (p. 269).

SYMPATHETIC TRUNK AND SPINAL NERVES

Use the side of the specimen which has not been disturbed in the dissection of the urogenital organs, and carefully remove both kidneys, if this has not already been done. Study and carefully remove the psoas minor muscle (p. 139, and Fig. 162, 9) and the iliopsoas (p. 193, and Fig. 162, 8; Fig. 91, *c*). During the removal of the fibers of these muscles, be careful not to injure the many nerves which are present in the region. Note the quadratus lumborum (p. 139, and Fig. 162). This need not be removed.

Find each of the following nerves and follow it to its origin and to its distribution, when possible to do so:

1. Lumbar one (p. 395).
2. Lumbar two (p. 395).
3. Lumbar three (p. 395).
4. Lumbar plexus (p. 395, and Fig. 162). Note the nerves which

enter into the formation of the plexus and trace the following branches which arise from it:

a. Genitofemoral (Fig. 162, *c*, *c'*, and *c''*).

b. Lateral femoral cutaneous (Fig. 162, *d*).

c. Femoral (Fig. 162, *f*).

d. Obturator (Fig. 162, *g*).

5. Lumbosacral cord.

6. Sacral plexus (p. 399, and Fig. 162). Note the nerves entering into its formation and identify and trace the following branches from it:

a. Superior gluteal (Fig. 162, *i*).

b. Inferior gluteal (Fig. 162, *j*).

c. Great sciatic (Fig. 162, *h*).

d. Pudendal (Fig. 162, *l*).

e. Posterior femoral cutaneous (p. 162, *k*).

f. Inferior hemorrhoidal (Fig. 162, *m*).

Trace the sympathetic trunk from the diaphragm caudad throughout the remainder of its course. Note the ganglia, connections with the spinal nerves, and review the branches to the viscera (pp. 411–413).

THE HIND LIMB

Use the appendage which was not disturbed during the dissection of the urogenital organs, and proceed with the following study:

A. Hip and Thigh.

Remove the integument from the hip and the entire appendage to the tips of the toes. Note the nature of the integument and of the superficial fascia in the different portions of the appendage. Study the superficial vessels of the extremity:

1. The formation of the veins in the foot which unite in the formation of the greater saphenous vein (p. 329, and Fig. 127, *f*). Follow this to its union with the femoral. Accompanying this vein on the medial side of the leg are the saphenous artery (p. 311, and Fig. 127, *f*) and the saphenous nerve (p. 397, and Fig. 127, *g*).

2. Lesser saphenous vein (p. 330, and Fig. 163, *k*).

Review the lumbar and sacral plexuses (pp. 395, 399, and 450), and note the nerves which pass to the thigh. Study the external iliac artery (p. 309) and its branches and trace the femoral branch (p. 310, and Fig. 127, *a*) into the thigh.

Note the iliopectineal fossa, or Scarpa's triangle (p. 310), and its contents:

1. Boundaries of triangle.

2. In the medial portion of the triangle note the femoral vein. Its tributaries correspond to the branches of the femoral artery and have the same course. The greater saphenous vein enters the femoral in the triangle.

3. Immediately laterad of the femoral vein note the femoral artery (p. 310, and Fig. 127) and trace it through the thigh to its entrance into the adductor canal. Branches:

a. Lateral femoral circumflex (Fig. 127, *d*).

b. Muscular branches (Fig. 127, *e*).

c. Superior articular branch (Fig. 127, *h*). Trace to the region of the knee.

d. Saphenous (Fig. 127, *f*).

4. Laterad of the artery is the femoral nerve (p. 397, and Fig. 162, *f*). Branches from this nerve will be observed during the dissection of the thigh muscles.

Work under the cranial and caudal borders of the biceps femoris muscle (p. 194) and find the tenuissimus muscle (p. 195). Transect the biceps. Note its nerve supply from the great sciatic nerve (p. 400). After the biceps has been transected, the entire course of the sciatic nerve through the thigh may be observed. Study its course and branches. Note its distal division into the tibial and common peroneal nerves. Note at this time the fine branch from this nerve to the tenuissimus muscle.

The remainder of the work on the hip and thigh is to be completed by the dissection of the muscles. Each muscle is to be carefully separated from all surrounding structures, cleaned, and studied for origin, insertion, relations, nerve supply, and action.

1. Caudofemoralis (p. 195, and Fig. 68, *s*). Transect near its origin. Its nerve supply may be noted entering near its origin.

2. Gluteus maximus (p. 187). Transect near its insertion and reflect.

3. Sartorius (p. 197, and Fig. 91, *a*; Fig. 68, *q*). Transect near its middle and reflect.

4. Tensor fasciæ latæ (p. 187, and Fig. 68, *r*; Fig. 92, *a*). Cut the fascia along the distal end of the muscle and reflect the muscle fibers. The nerve to this muscle may be seen emerging from beneath the

cranial border of the gluteus medius muscle accompanied by the superior gluteal artery (p. 308, and Fig. 126, *p*; Fig. 163, *j*).

5. Gluteus medius (p. 188, and Fig. 90, *b*). Carefully separate from the underlying muscles, cut close to its insertion, and reflect.

6. Pyriformis (p. 188, and Fig. 163, 7). The great sciatic nerve will be observed passing from the greater sciatic notch between this muscle and the gemellus superior.

7. Gemellus superior (p. 189, and Fig. 163, 6). Transect.

8. Gluteus minimus (p. 189, and Fig. 163, 5). Transect.

9. Obturator internus (p. 192, and Fig. 90, *e*). Cut at the dorsal border of the ischium.

10. Gemellus inferior (p. 190). This will be seen beneath the obturator internus.

11. Gracilis (p. 198, and Fig. 91, *b*). Transect.

12. Semitendinosus (p. 196, and Fig. 90, *j*). Transect.

13. Semimembranosus (p. 196, and Fig. 91, *i*). Transect.

14. Adductor femoris (p. 198, and Fig. 92, *g*; Fig. 90, *h*). This includes the adductor magnus and brevis of man.

15. Quadratus femoris (p. 191, and Fig. 90, *f*). Transect.

16. Obturator externus (p. 191).

17. Adductor longus (p. 199, and Fig. 91, *g*; Fig. 92, *f*). This may be united with the pectineus.

18. Pectineus (p. 200, and Fig. 92, *e*).

19. Iliopsoas (pp. 138 and 193, and Fig. 162, 8; Fig. 91, *c*). The origin of this muscle has been studied, and its insertion is to be noted at this time. Note that the femoral nerve passes through the substance of this muscle to reach the thigh.

20. Quadriceps femoris (p. 201). Isolate the rectus femoris (Fig. 92, *b*; Fig. 90, *c*) and cut it at its junction with the vastus lateralis. This will expose the other divisions of the muscle which need not be cut. Note beneath the rectus femoris, the femoral nerve and lateral femoral circumflex artery, divisions of which pass to the various heads of this muscle.

B. Lower Leg.

Note the division of the sciatic nerve within the popliteal fossa into the tibial and common peroneal divisions (p. 400). Trace these as far as possible at present.

Study the superficial muscles on the ventral surface of the leg.

1. Gastrocnemius (p. 203, and Fig. 90, *m*; Fig. 91, *k*). Divide

near the middle and reflect, being careful not to injure the plantaris muscle. This will expose the tibial nerve (p. 402, and Fig. 163, *e*) in its course through the leg. Trace it into the foot and note its division there into the medial and lateral plantar nerves (p. 403). Trace branches from the tibial nerve to the divisions of the triceps suræ muscle.

2. Plantaris (p. 205, and Fig. 90, *l*; Fig. 91, *l*). Transect.
3. Soleus (p. 205, and Fig. 90, *o*). Cut and reflect.

Separate the deep muscles of the ventral surface of the leg, and study each separately.

1. Popliteus (p. 206, and Fig. 92, *k*).
2. Flexor longus digitorum (p. 207, and Fig. 91, *m* and *n*). Before the tendons of this muscle can be traced to their insertion it will be necessary to study and then carefully remove the quadratus plantæ muscle (p. 213). This muscle corresponds to two muscles found in man, the flexor hallucis longus and the flexor longus digitorum.
3. Tibialis posterior (p. 208, and Fig. 91, *o*).

Carefully separate the muscles on the dorsal and lateral surfaces of the leg, and study each:

1. Peroneus brevis (p. 210, and Fig. 90, *s*).
2. Peroneus longus (p. 209, and Fig. 90, *q*).
3. Peroneus tertius (p. 210, and Fig. 90, *r*).
4. Extensor digitorum longus (p. 210, and Fig. 90, *p*).
5. Tibialis anterior (p. 211, and Fig. 90, *n*).

Trace the course of the tibial (p. 402, and Fig. 163, *e*) and peroneal (p. 400, and Fig. 163, *d*) nerves and their branches in the lower leg. Trace the popliteal artery (p. 312) through the popliteal fossa and its branches through the lower leg. Trace the femoral vein and its tributaries.

The intrinsic muscles of the foot are difficult to dissect, and their study should usually be omitted. If the student wishes to do them, he should proceed as follows:

1. Extensor brevis digitorum (p. 212, and Fig. 90, *u*).
2. The quadratus plantæ was removed during the dissection of the flexor longus digitorum.
3. Lumbricales (p. 213).
4. Interossei (p. 214).
5. Muscles of the fifth digit as listed on page 215.

6. Remove the overlying ligaments and dissect the tarsal muscles (p. 215).

Preserve the appendage that has just been dissected. It will be used later for review and for comparison with the upper extremity. Remove the muscles from the appendage which has not been dissected, and study the joints associated with it:

1. Hip-joint (p. 87).
2. Knee-joint (p. 87, and Fig. 60; Fig. 61).
3. Articulations between the tibia and fibula (p. 90).
4. Ankle-joint (p. 91).
5. Intertarsal joints (p. 91).
6. Tarsometatarsal, metatarsophalangeal, and interphalangeal joints (p. 92).

THE FORE LIMB

A. Shoulder and Upper Arm.

Remove the integument from the entire anterior extremity, being careful not to destroy the tendons in the hand. Study the subcutaneous fascia of the arm and forearm. That of the forearm will be noted to consist of a superficial and a deep layer (p. 172). Note the transverse carpal ligaments, the vaginal and the annular ligaments (p. 173). Remove this fascia so as to expose the underlying structures.

Study the superficial veins of the extremity (p. 318). Trace the vena cephalica humeri (p. 319, and Fig. 130, *a*) and the vena mediana cubiti (Fig. 130, *b*). Note the formation of the superficial veins in the hand.

Review the muscles attached to the scapula which have been dissected. Review the vessels of the axilla (Fig. 122) and trace the brachial artery (p. 296, and Fig. 122, *g′*) and vein (p. 318) into the forearm. Review the formation of the brachial plexus (p. 386, and Fig. 159) and, by separating the muscles without cutting any structures, trace the nerves that originate from the plexus:

1. Musculocutaneous (p. 388, and Fig. 160, *d*). Trace along the biceps brachii muscle and near its distal end note that it passes dorsal to the muscle to reach its lateral side, becoming superficial between the clavobrachial and pectoantibrachialis muscle.

2. Median (p. 390, and Fig. 160, *e*). This may be traced with the

brachial artery (p. 296) to where the two enter the supracondyloid foramen. Note that this nerve gives no branches in the upper arm.

3. Axillary (p. 388, and Fig. 159, *d*). Trace with the posterior humeral circumflex artery (p. 296) between the subscapular and teres major muscles.

4. Radial (p. 392). Trace the nerve with the profunda brachii artery (p. 296) around the caudal surface of the humerus and through the substance of the medial head of the triceps brachii muscle.

5. Ulnar (p. 393, and Fig. 160, *n*). Trace with the brachial artery and median nerve through the upper arm. Note that it does not enter the supracondyloid foramen with the structures which it accompanies, but passes within the medial head of the triceps brachii over the medial epicondyle to reach the dorsal border of the forearm.

After identifying the nerves and vessels of the axilla, study the muscles listed below for origin, insertion, relations, actions, and nerve supply:

1. Clavobrachial (p. 157, and Fig. 65, *k*; Fig. 68, *e*). Dissect to its insertion, but do not transect.

2. Coracobrachialis (p. 164, and Fig. 77, *f*; Fig. 79, *c*). Cut in the middle and reflect.

3. Subscapularis (p. 161, and Fig. 77, *a*). Clean and study, but do not reflect.

4. Supraspinatus (p. 159, and Fig. 75, *a*). Transect near its insertion and reflect. Note relation of suprascapular nerve (p. 388) and artery (p. 293) to this muscle.

5. Spinodeltoideus (p. 156, and Fig. 75, *e*; Fig. 68, *i*). Transect and reflect.

6. Acromiodeltoideus (p. 157, and Fig. 75, *f*; Fig. 68, *g*). Transect and reflect.

7. Infraspinatus (p. 160, and Fig. 75, *c*). Transect at the great scapular notch and reflect.

8. Teres major (p. 163, and Fig. 75, *d*; Fig. 77, *o*). Cut at its junction with the latissimus dorsi.

9. Teres minor (p. 161, and Fig. 80, *c*). Do not cut.

10. Epitrochlearis (p. 164, and Fig. 65, *r*).

11. Triceps brachii (p. 166). Separate into its divisions.

a. Long head (Fig. 75, *g*; Fig. 68, *k*; Fig. 77, *i*).

b. Lateral head (Fig. 75, *h*; Fig. 68, *l*).

c. Medial head (Fig. 77, *g*, *h*, and *j*).

12. Anconeus (p. 170, and Fig. 80, *l*).

13. Brachioradialis (p. 173, and Fig. 75, *k*; Fig. 77, *n*). This muscle is accompanied by the vena cephalica and the radial nerve.

14. Biceps brachii (p. 165, and Fig. 77, *g*; Fig. 65, *t*). The capsule of the shoulder joint should be opened to observe the origin of this muscle. Its insertion will be better noted during the dissection of the forearm.

15. Brachialis (p. 166, and Fig. 79, *i*; Fig. 75, *i*).

B. FOREARM.

The dorsal interosseous division of the radial nerve (p. 392) is to be noted in its course between the brachialis muscle and the proximal end of the extensor carpi radialis longus to pass deep to the extensor muscles. Branches may be seen passing to the muscles of this region.

The muscles of the ulnar and dorsal side of the forearm are to be separated from one another and studied for origins, insertions (trace the tendons of the muscles completely to their insertions in the hand), relations, actions, and nerve supply. Do not disturb the relations or cut any of the muscles:

1. Brachioradialis (p. 173, and Fig. 75, *k*; Fig. 77, *n*).
2. Extensor carpi radialis longus (p. 173, and Fig. 75, *l*; Fig. 77, *o*).
3. Extensor carpi radialis brevis (p. 174, and Fig. 77, *p*).
4. Extensor digitorum communis (p. 174, and Fig. 77, *m*).
5. Extensor digitorum lateralis (p. 175, and Fig. 75, *n*).
6. Extensor carpi ulnaris (p. 176, and Fig. 75, *o*).
7. Extensor indicis (p. 176, and Fig. 85, *c*; Fig. 75, *p*).
8. Extensor pollicis brevis (p. 178, and Fig. 85, *a*).
9. Supinator (p. 177, and Fig. 85, *b*).

Separate the muscles on the radial and ventral side of the forearm, trace the median (p. 390) and ulnar (p. 393) nerves through the entire forearm, and note the distribution of each in the hand. Trace the radial artery (p. 297, and Fig. 123) and vein and the ulnar artery (p. 300) and vein through the forearm.

Study the following muscles of the radial and ventral side, but do not cut:

1. Pronator teres (p. 179, and Fig. 77, *q*).
2. Flexor carpi radialis (p. 179, and Fig. 77, *r*).
3. Palmaris longus (p. 179, and Fig. 77, *s*).
4. Flexor carpi ulnaris (p. 180, and Fig. 77, *t* and *t'*).

5. Flexor sublimis digitorum (p. 181).
6. Flexor profundus digitorum (p. 181).
7. Pronator quadratus (p. 183, and Fig. 87, *a*).

If desired, the small intrinsic muscles of the palm of the hand may be dissected, but this usually should not be done:

1. Lumbricales (p. 184, and Fig. 88, *f*).
2. Flexor brevis pollicis (p. 184, and Fig. 89, *a*).
3. Adductor pollicis (p. 185, and Fig. 89, *b*).
4. Abductor digiti quinti (p. 185, and Fig. 89, *i*).
5. Flexor brevis digiti quinti (p. 186, and Fig. 89, *h*).
6. Opponens digiti quinti (p. 186, and Fig. 89, *g*).
7. Interossei (p. 185, and Fig. 89).

Preserve the appendage which has just been dissected. It will be used for review and for comparison with the hind limb. Remove the muscles from the appendage which has not been dissected, and study the joints associated with it:

1. Shoulder-joint (p. 73).
2. Elbow-joint (p. 74, and Fig. 52; Fig. 53).
3. Articulations of radius and ulna (p. 75).
4. Wrist-joint (p. 75).
5. Intercarpal articulations (p. 75).
6. Carpo-metacarpal articulations (p. 75).
7. Metacarpophalangeal joints (p. 76).
8. Interphalangeal joints (p. 76).